GLEIM®

6-1
EDITION

PRIVATE PILOT

Flight Maneuvers
and Practical Test Prep

by
Irvin N. Gleim, Ph.D., CFII
and
Garrett W. Gleim, CFII

Gleim Publications, Inc.
P.O. Box 12848
University Station
Gainesville, Florida 32604
(800) 874-5346
(352) 375-0772
Fax: (352) 375-6940

Internet: www.GleimAviation.com
Email: admin@gleim.com

For updates to the first printing of the sixth edition of
Private Pilot Flight Maneuvers and Practical Test Prep

Go To: www.gleim.com/updates

Or: Email update@gleim.com with **PPFM 6-1** in the subject line. You will receive our current update as a reply.

Updates are available until the next edition is published.

ISSN 1084-4333

ISBN 978-1-61854-050-8

First Printing: August 2016

CAUTION: This book is an academic presentation for training purposes only. Under NO circumstances can it be used as a substitute for your Pilot's Operating Handbook or FAA-approved Airplane Flight Manual. **You must fly and operate your airplane in accordance with your Pilot's Operating Handbook or FAA-approved Airplane Flight Manual.**

YOU CAN HELP

This is the Sixth Edition, designed specifically for potential pilots, student pilots, and private pilots.

Please send any corrections and suggestions for subsequent editions to the authors, c/o Gleim Publications, Inc. Please share your feedback with us at www.gleim.com/AviationQuestions.

Also, please bring this book to the attention of flight instructors, fixed-base operators, and others interested in flying. Wide distribution of these books and increased interest in flying depend on your assistance and good word. Thank you.

Visit our website or email update@gleim.com as described at the top right of this page for the latest updates and information on all of our products. Updates to this edition will be available until the next edition is published. To continue providing our customers with first-rate service, we request that technical questions about our materials be sent to us via www.gleim.com/AviationQuestions. We will give each question thorough consideration and a prompt response. Questions concerning orders, prices, shipments, or payments will be handled via telephone by our competent and courteous customer service staff.

ABOUT THE AUTHORS

Irvin N. Gleim earned his private pilot certificate in 1965 from the Institute of Aviation at the University of Illinois, where he subsequently received his Ph.D. He is a commercial pilot and flight instructor (instrument) with multi-engine and seaplane ratings and is a member of the Aircraft Owners and Pilots Association, American Bonanza Society, Civil Air Patrol, Experimental Aircraft Association, National Association of Flight Instructors, and Seaplane Pilots Association. He is the author of flight maneuvers and practical test prep books for the sport, private, instrument, commercial, and flight instructor certificates/ratings and the author of study guides for the sport, private/recreational, instrument, commercial, flight/ground instructor, fundamentals of instructing, airline transport pilot, and flight engineer FAA knowledge tests. Three additional pilot training books are *Pilot Handbook*, *Aviation Weather and Weather Services*, and *FAR/AIM*.

Dr. Gleim has also written articles for professional accounting and business law journals and is the author of widely used review manuals for the CIA (Certified Internal Auditor) exam, the CMA (Certified Management Accountant) exam, the CPA (Certified Public Accountant) exam, and the EA (IRS Enrolled Agent) exam. He is Professor Emeritus, Fisher School of Accounting, University of Florida, and is a CFM, CIA, CMA, and CPA.

Garrett W. Gleim earned his private pilot certificate in 1997 in a Piper Super Cub. He is a commercial pilot (single- and multi-engine), ground instructor (advanced and instrument), and flight instructor (instrument and multi-engine), and he is a member of the Aircraft Owners and Pilots Association and the National Association of Flight Instructors. He is the author of study guides for the sport, private/recreational, instrument, commercial, flight/ground instructor, fundamentals of instructing, and airline transport pilot FAA knowledge tests. He received a Bachelor of Science in Economics from The Wharton School, University of Pennsylvania. Mr. Gleim is also a CPA (not in public practice).

REVIEWERS AND CONTRIBUTORS

Paul Duty, CFII, MEI, AGI, is a graduate of Embry-Riddle Aeronautical University with a Master of Business Administration-Aviation degree. He is one of our aviation editors and an aviation marketing specialist. Mr. Duty researched questions, wrote and edited answer explanations, and incorporated revisions into the text.

Char Marissa Gregg, CFII, LTA, Glider, ASES, ATP, is the Gleim 141 Chief Flight Instructor and one of our aviation editors. Ms. Gregg researched questions, wrote and edited answer explanations, and incorporated revisions into the text.

W. Rhett Lawton, CFI, CFII, MEI, ATP, Type Rating DA-50, B.S., Brigham Young University, M.B.A., Henderson State University, is one of our aviation editors. Mr. Lawton researched questions, wrote and edited answer explanations, and incorporated revisions into the text.

Erik T. Vrooman, Commercial Pilot, A&P Mechanic, is a graduate of the maintenance program at Embry-Riddle Aeronautical University. In addition to working with Gleim, he is on staff with the College of Missionary Aviation. Mr. Vrooman researched material and incorporated revisions into the text.

The CFIs who have worked with us throughout the years to develop and improve our pilot training materials.

The many FAA and NWS employees who helped, in person or by telephone, primarily in Gainesville, Orlando, Oklahoma City, and Washington, DC.

The many pilots who have provided comments and suggestions during the past several decades.

A PERSONAL THANKS

This manual would not have been possible without the extraordinary effort and dedication of Julie Cutlip, Blaine Hatton, Kelsey Olson, Breanna Rodriguez, Teresa Soard, Justin Stephenson, Joanne Strong, and Elmer Tucker, who typed the entire manuscript and all revisions and drafted and laid out the diagrams, illustrations, and cover for this book.

The authors also appreciate the production and editorial assistance of Jacob Bennett, Melody Dalton, Jessica Felkins, Jim Harvin, Kristen Hennen, Katie Larson, Diana León, Jake Pettifor, Shane Rapp, and Drew Sheppard.

Finally, we appreciate the encouragement, support, and tolerance of our families throughout this project.

ACKNOWLEDGMENTS

Image on the cover of a Cirrus SR22-G3 aircraft reproduced with the permission of Cirrus, Copyright 2016 Cirrus Aircraft or its Affiliates. All rights reserved. Inclusion of Cirrus Aircraft copyrighted material in the Publications does not imply any endorsement by Cirrus or its Affiliates of the Publications.

TABLE OF CONTENTS

PREFACE

This book will facilitate your pilot flight training and prepare you to pass your PRIVATE PILOT AIRPLANE FAA PRACTICAL TEST. In addition, this book will assist you and your flight instructor in planning and organizing your flight training.

The private pilot practical test is a rigorous test of concept knowledge, risk management, and motor skills. This book explains all of the knowledge that your instructor and FAA inspector/examiner will expect you to demonstrate and discuss with him or her. Previously, private pilot candidates had only the FAA testing standards "reprints" to study. Now you have the Airman Certification Standards (ACS) followed by a thorough explanation of each task and a step-by-step description of each flight maneuver. Thus, through careful organization and presentation, we will decrease your preparation time, effort, and frustration, **and** increase your knowledge and understanding.

As an additional feature of this book, we have listed some of the common errors made by pilots in executing each flight maneuver or operation. You will be aware of *what not to do*. We all learn by our mistakes, but our *common error* explanations provide you with an opportunity to learn from the mistakes of others.

Most books create additional work for the user. In contrast, *Private Pilot Flight Maneuvers and Practical Test Prep* facilitates your effort; i.e., it is easy to use. The outline format, numerous illustrations and diagrams, type styles, indentations, and line spacing are designed to improve readability. Concepts are often presented as phrases rather than complete sentences.

Relatedly, our outline format frequently has an "a" without a "b" or a "1" without a "2." While this violates some journalistic rules of style, it is consistent with your cognitive processes. This book was designed, written, and formatted to facilitate your learning and understanding. Another similar counterproductive "rule" is *to not write in your books*. We urge you to mark up this book to assist you in learning and understanding.

We are confident this book will allow for speedy completion of your flight training and success on your practical test. In addition, please use our *Private Pilot ACS and Oral Exam Guide* to prepare for the oral portion of your practical exam. This book has over 900 practice oral questions that help solidify your knowledge of the material. We also wish you the very best in subsequent flying and in obtaining additional ratings and certificates.

If you have *not* passed your private pilot FAA knowledge test and do *not* have *Private Pilot FAA Knowledge Test* (another book with a red cover), FAA Test Prep Online, Audio Review, and/or Online Ground School, please order today. Almost everything you need to pass the FAA's knowledge and practical tests for the private pilot certificate, minus a CFI and an airplane, is available from Gleim in our Private Pilot Kit and our Online Ground School. If your FBO, flight school, or aviation bookstore is out of stock, visit www.GleimAviation.com or call (800) 874-5346.

We encourage your suggestions, comments, and corrections for future printings and editions. Please contact us at www.gleim.com/AviationQuestions. Thank you.

Enjoy Flying -- Safely!

Irvin N. Gleim
Garrett W. Gleim

August 2016

PART I
GENERAL CERTIFICATE INFORMATION

Private Pilot Flight Maneuvers and Practical Test Prep is one book in a series of six books for obtaining your private pilot certificate. The other five books are

1. *Private Pilot FAA Knowledge Test*
2. *Private Pilot ACS and Oral Exam Guide*
3. *Private Pilot Syllabus*
4. *Pilot Handbook*
5. *FAR/AIM*

This book assumes that you have these five companion books available. You will be referring to them as appropriate. This approach precludes the need for duplicate explanations in each of the six related books.

Part I (Study Units 1 and 2) of this book provides general information to assist you in obtaining your private pilot certificate.

Part II consists of Study Units 3 through 9, which contain basic and common information necessary for various ACS tasks. Think of this material as core knowledge a private pilot is expected to have. Many of the study units in Part III refer back to this information.

Part III consists of Study Units 10 through 54, which provide an extensive explanation of each of the 45 tasks required of those taking the private pilot FAA practical test in a single-engine airplane.

OTHER BOOKS IN SERIES

Private Pilot FAA Knowledge Test contains over 800 airplane-related questions and organizes them into logical topics called subunits. Those subunits are grouped into 11 study units. Each study unit begins with a brief, user-friendly outline of what you need to know, and answer explanations are provided next to each question. This book will transfer knowledge to you and give you the confidence to do well on the FAA private pilot knowledge test.

Private Pilot Syllabus is a step-by-step syllabus of ground and flight training lesson plans for your private pilot training. This book, which is appropriate for both 14 CFR Parts 61 and 141 training, prepares you, in advance, with precisely what will be covered in each ground or flight training lesson.

Pilot Handbook is a complete text and reference for all pilots. Aerodynamics, airplane systems and instruments, aviation weather, navigation systems, and aeronautical decision making are among the topics explained.

The Gleim *FAR/AIM* is an easy-to-read reference book containing all of the Federal Aviation Regulations ("FARs" or "14 CFRs") applicable to general aviation flying, plus the full text of the FAA's *Aeronautical Information Manual (AIM)*.

If you are planning on purchasing the FAA's books on aviation weather, the Gleim *Aviation Weather and Weather Services* book combines all of the information from the FAA's *Aviation Weather* (AC 00-6), *Aviation Weather Services* (AC 00-45), and numerous other FAA publications into one easy-to-understand book. It will help you study all aspects of aviation weather and provide you with a single reference book.

The Gleim *Private Pilot ACS and Oral Exam Guide* is a convenient, easy-to-use book that combines a reprint of the FAA Private Pilot ACS with an oral exam guide containing over 900 questions designed to prepare you for the assortment of oral exam questions you may encounter during your practical test.

2

Update
Service

Visit the **GLEIM**® website for free updates,
which are available until the next edition is published.

gleim.com/updates

STUDY UNIT ONE
OPTIMIZING YOUR FLIGHT
AND GROUND TRAINING

The purpose of this study unit is to help you get the most out of your ground and flight training. They should support each other: Ground training should facilitate your flight training and vice versa. While your immediate objective is to pass your practical test, your long-range goal is to become a safe and proficient pilot. Thus, you have to work hard to be able to **do your best.** No one can ask for more!

1.1 GROUND TRAINING

A.   First and foremost: Ground training is extremely important to facilitate flight training. Each preflight and postflight discussion is as important as the actual flight training of each flight lesson!

    1.   Unfortunately, most students and some CFIs incorrectly overemphasize the in-airplane portion of a flight lesson.

        a.   The airplane, all of its operating systems, ATC, other traffic, etc., are major distractions from the actual flight maneuver and the aerodynamic theory/factors underlying the maneuver.

        b.   This is not to diminish the importance of dealing with operating systems, ATC, other traffic, etc.

    2.   Note that the effort and results are those of the student. Instructors are responsible for directing student effort so that optimal results are achieved.

B.   Again, **the effort and results are dependent upon you.** Prepare for each flight lesson so you know exactly what is going to happen and why. The more you prepare, the better you will do, both in execution of maneuvers and in acquisition of knowledge.

    1.   At the end of each flight lesson, find out exactly what is planned for the next flight lesson.

    2.   At home, begin by reviewing everything that occurred during the last flight lesson -- preflight briefing, flight, and postflight briefing. Make notes on follow-up questions and discussion to be pursued with your CFI at the beginning of the next preflight briefing.

    3.   Study all new flight maneuvers scheduled for the next flight lesson and review flight maneuvers that warrant additional practice (refer to the appropriate study units in Part III of this book). Make notes on follow-up questions and discussion to be pursued with your CFI at the beginning of the next preflight briefing.

    4.   Before each flight, sit down with your CFI for a preflight briefing. Begin with a review of the last flight lesson. Then focus on the current flight lesson. Go over each maneuver to be executed, including maneuvers to be reviewed from previous flight lessons.

    5.   During each flight lesson, be diligent about safety (continuously check traffic and say so as you do it). During maneuvers, compare your actual experience with your expectations.

    6.   Your postflight briefing should begin with a self-critique, followed by evaluation by your CFI. Ask questions until you are satisfied that you have expert knowledge. Finally, develop a clear understanding of the time and the maneuvers to be covered in your next flight lesson.

1.2 USE OF SIMULATORS, X-PLANE

A.   One method of efficient ground training is use of a simulator. By practicing each lesson on the ground, your time in the airplane will be more effective.

B.   A flight simulator can be a valuable tool during your training, but like any tool, it must be used properly. It is important to know what to expect from the simulation environment.

C.   Flight simulators effectively remove many of the airborne distractions and anxiety often experienced during actual flight training.

   1.   Flight maneuvers can be performed in a simulator with a high degree of realism; however, not all types of simulators will represent the same degrees of motion, if any, that are experienced in the actual aircraft.

   2.   Many types of scenarios can be practiced in a simulator that are not feasible in the actual aircraft, e.g., emergency procedures, including actual engine failures, or adverse weather conditions.

D.   Types of Simulators

   1.   There are different types of flight simulators available to supplement your ground and flight training.

      a.   Flight Simulation Training Device (FSTD)

         1)   FSTDs include both Full Flight Simulators (FFS) and Flight Training Devices (FTD).

         2)   These devices must be qualified and approved by the FAA for specific types of training, testing, maneuvers, functions, and aircraft or instrument representations.

         3)   Use of an FSTD for the completion of the private pilot airplane practical test is permitted only when accomplished in accordance with an FAA approved curriculum or training program.

      b.   Aviation Training Device (ATD)

         1)   ATDs include Basic Aviation Training Devices (BATD) and Advanced Aviation Training Devices (AATD).

         2)   These devices must have a letter of authorization from the FAA including the amount of credit a pilot may take for training and experience.

         3)   Use of an ATD for the private pilot airplane rating practical test is not permitted.

         4)   Check with your local flight school to inquire about use of an FSTD or ATD and any approvals they may have.

      c.   Home Computer Flight Simulators

         1)   Off-the-shelf flight simulator software for use at home may not be approved for official flight training. However, structured practice can enhance your training by providing additional understanding and familiarization with maneuvers and procedures.

E.   The **Gleim X-Plane Flight Training Course** is an affordable software program that fully integrates flight lessons from the Gleim syllabus, enabling you to learn and practice all flight maneuvers at home. This software provides training videos, step-by-step guidance, real time corrective feedback, and performance evaluations. Although the flight time may not count toward your training, you will still gain valuable experience to build proficiency and confidence. This can ultimately save you a significant amount of expensive aircraft rental time.

1.3 GLEIM ONLINE GROUND SCHOOL

A. Gleim **Online Ground School** (OGS) course content is based on the Gleim Knowledge Test books, **FAA Test Prep Online**, FAA publications, and Gleim reference books.

1. The Private Pilot OGS contains study outlines that automatically reference current FAA publications, the appropriate knowledge test questions, FAA figures, and Gleim answer explanations.

2. OGS is always up to date.

3. OGS users have access to expert assistance from our team of instructors through their online personal classroom.

4. Users achieve very high knowledge test scores and a near-100% pass rate.

5. **Gleim Online Ground School is the most flexible course available!** Access your OGS personal classroom from any computer or mobile device with Internet access 24 hours a day, 7 days a week. Your virtual classroom is never closed!

6. **Save time and study only the material you need to know!** Gleim **Online Ground School** Certificate Selection will provide you with a customized study plan. You save time because unnecessary questions will be automatically eliminated.

7. **We are truly interactive. We help you focus on any weaker areas.** Answer explanations for wrong choices help you learn from your mistakes.

8. Register for the Gleim Private Pilot OGS at www.GleimAviation.com/OGS.

1.4 AIRCRAFT INFORMATION

A. The Aircraft Information on the following page should be copied and reproduced or printed from www.gleim.com/aviation/general_resources, so you can handwrite your aircraft's performance information. This page helps you put this information into your long-term memory.

1. Make- and model-specific information

   a. Weight
   b. Airspeeds
   c. Center of gravity
   d. Fuel
   e. Performance data

B. The bottom portion of the page helps you get organized and know whether your aircraft is airworthy. If you are renting aircraft from a flight school, wait to fill in this information until you know which aircraft you will use in your practical test.

AIRCRAFT INFORMATION

AIRPLANE MAKE/MODEL _____

WEIGHT		AIRSPEEDS		FUEL		
Gross	_____	V_{SO}	_____	Capacity	L ___ gal	R ___ gal
Empty	_____	V_{S1}	_____	Current Estimate	L ___ gal	R ___ gal
Pilot/Pasngrs	_____	V_X	_____	Endurance (Hr.)	_____	
Baggage	_____	V_Y	_____	Fuel-Flow -- Cruise (GPH)	_____	
Fuel (gal × 6)	_____	V_A	_____			
		V_{NO}	_____			
CENTER OF GRAVITY		V_{NE}	_____			
Fore Limit	_____	V_{FE}	_____			
Aft Limit	_____	V_{LO}	_____			
Current CG	_____	V_R	_____			

PERFORMANCE DATA	Airspeed	Power*	
		MP	RPM
Takeoff Rotation	_____	_____	_____
Climbout	_____	_____	_____
Cruise Climb	_____	_____	_____
Cruise Level	_____	_____	_____
Cruise Descent	_____	_____	_____
Approach to Land (Visual)	_____	_____	_____
Landing Flare	_____	_____	_____

* If you do not have a constant-speed propeller, ignore manifold pressure (MP).

AIRCRAFT MAINTENANCE RECORDS

Date of Most Recent Annual Inspection [91.409(a)] _____

Date of Most Recent 100-Hour Inspection [91.409(b)] _____

Tachometer Time at Most Recent 100-Hour Inspection _____

Current Tachometer Time _____ Date _____

Date of Most Recent ATC Transponder Tests and Inspections (91.413) _____

Date of Most Recent ELT Inspection [91.207(d)] _____

STUDY UNIT TWO
YOUR FAA PRACTICAL (FLIGHT) TEST

After all the training, studying, and preparing, the final step to receive your private pilot certificate is the FAA practical test. It requires that you exhibit your previously gained knowledge to your evaluator and demonstrate that you are a proficient and safe private pilot who can manage the risks of flight.

Your practical test requires more than repeating familiar flight maneuvers to an evaluator. While you will be well practiced with honed stick and rudder skills, the evaluator needs to assess your ability to fly safely within the complex National Airspace System (NAS) and ensure you can adequately assess and mitigate risks.

Do not let this overwhelm you. The FAA (or a designated FAA evaluator) is testing you at the expected proficiency level of a private pilot, not a NASA astronaut. Most applicants pass the private pilot practical test on the first attempt. The vast majority of those having trouble will succeed on the second attempt.

Airman Certification Standards

The FAA's Private Pilot Airman Certification Standards (ACS) are reprinted in Study Units 10 through 54 of Part III. Read these study units carefully so that you know exactly what will be expected of you.

Your goal is to exceed each requirement. For instance, you should try to maintain altitudes within +/– 50 ft. instead of the 100 ft. threshold. This goal will ensure that even a slight mistake will fall within the tolerances allowed. If you recognize an issue with an allowable threshold, it's important to explain your error to your evaluator and immediately fix it because you may still fall within the expected abilities of a private pilot. For example, if you are getting close to the 100-ft. tolerance of a prescribed altitude when encountering a thermal, explain the situation to the evaluator and try your best to return to your prescribed altitude. The FAA wants to make sure you know how to safely fly and control your aircraft, but the FAA also realizes you are human and nature can cause you to inadvertently exceed tolerances. The evaluator wants to make sure you are aware of altitudes and you make a concerted effort at maintaining them.

Also keep in mind that your flight instructor does not send applicants to an evaluator until the applicant can pass the practical test on an average day; an exceptional flight will not be needed. You should feel confident that you will be successful. However, your ability to assess risks and make sound decisions is crucial to a successful checkride.

Finding Your Evaluator and Scheduling Your Practical Test

As you proceed with your flight training, you and your instructor should plan ahead and schedule your practical test. Several weeks before your practical test is scheduled, contact one or two individuals who took the private pilot practical test with your evaluator.

Ask each person to explain the routine, length, emphasis, maneuvers, and any peculiarities (e.g., surprises). This step is very important because, like all people, evaluators are unique. One particular facet of the practical test may be tremendously important to one evaluator, while another evaluator may emphasize an entirely different area. By gaining this information beforehand, you can focus on the areas of apparent concern to the evaluator. Also, knowing what to expect will relieve some of the apprehension and tension about your practical test.

When you schedule your practical test, ask your evaluator for the cross-country flight you should plan for on the day of your test. The Private Pilot ACS Task I.D., Cross-Country Flight Planning (beginning on page 151), states that you are to present to your evaluator a preplanned cross-country flight that was previously assigned. However, some evaluators may want to wait until the day of your test to assign you a cross-country flight.

Oral versus Flight Portions

Through the oral and flight portions of the practical test, the FAA expects evaluators to assess the applicant's mastery of the topics in accordance with the level of learning most appropriate for the specified task. For some topics, you will be asked to describe or explain. For other items, the evaluator will assess your understanding by providing a scenario requiring you to appropriately apply and/or correlate knowledge, experience, and information to the circumstances of the given scenario.

The flight portion of the practical test requires the applicant to demonstrate knowledge, risk management, flight proficiency, and operational skill in accordance with the Airmen Certification Standards.

In addition, you can expect evaluators to place emphasis on areas you were deficient on the knowledge exam. Be sure to review these areas thoroughly with your CFI.

2.1 AIRMAN CERTIFICATION STANDARDS CONCEPT

A.   The goal of the airman certification process is to ensure the applicant possesses the knowledge and skill consistent with the privileges of the certificate or rating being exercised, as well as the ability to manage the risks of flight in order to act as pilot in command.

B.   The ACS consists of **Areas of Operation** arranged in a logical sequence, beginning with Preflight Preparation and ending with Postflight Procedures. Each Area of Operation includes tasks appropriate to that Area of Operation. Each task begins with an **Objective** stating what the applicant should know, consider, and/or do. The ACS then lists the aeronautical knowledge, risk management, and skill elements relevant to the specific task, along with the conditions and standards for acceptable performance.

C.　The 45 tasks for the private pilot certificate (airplane single-engine land) are listed below in the areas of operation as organized by the FAA.

Area of Operation X. Multiengine Operations is deleted as it is not relevant to ASEL (airplane single-engine land)

Tasks for seaplanes and multiengine are deleted as they are not relevant to ASEL (airplane single-engine land)

*Page number on which discussion begins in Study Units 10 through 54

D.　This book is based on the FAA's Private Pilot ACS (FAA-ACS-8081-6). We will revise this edition to reflect new ACS when they become available. Email update@gleim.com with "PPFM 6-1" in the subject line or go to www.gleim.com/updates to determine if new ACSs have been released or if there are any other updates to this book. See page ii.

2.2 FORMAT OF ACS TASKS

A.   Each of the FAA's 45 private pilot tasks listed on the previous page is presented at the beginning of Study Units 10 through 54 of Part III, similar to the excerpt from Task I.A. reproduced below.

Task	*Task A. Pilot Qualifications*
References	14 CFR parts 61, 91; FAA-H-8083-2, FAA-H-8083-25
Objective	To determine that the applicant exhibits satisfactory knowledge, risk management, and skills associated with airman and medical certificates including privileges, limitations, currency, and operating as Pilot-in-Command (PIC) as a private pilot.
Knowledge	The applicant demonstrates understanding of:
PA.I.A.K1	1. Currency, regulatory compliance, privileges, and limitations.
PA.I.A.K2	2. Location of airman documents and identification required when exercising private pilot privileges.
PA.I.A.K3	3. The required documents to provide upon inspection.
Risk Management	The applicant demonstrates the ability to identify, assess and mitigate risks, encompassing:
PA.I.A.R1	1. Distinguishing proficiency versus currency.
PA.I.A.R2	2. Setting personal minimums.
PA.I.A.R3	3. Maintaining fitness to fly.
Skills	The applicant demonstrates the ability to apply requirements to:
PA.I.A.S1	1. Act as PIC under VFR in a scenario given by the evaluator.

1.   The task letter is followed by the title.

2.   The reference list identifies the FAA publication(s) that describe the task.

   a.   Our discussion of each task is based on the FAA reference list. Note, however, that we will refer you to *Pilot Handbook* for further discussion of specific topics.

   b.   A listing of the FAA references used in the ACS is on page 90.

3.   Next, the task has "**Objective.** To determine that the applicant . . . ," followed by a number of "exhibits knowledge, risk management, and skills associated with" various aviation concepts and maneuvers.

B.   Each task in this book is outlined and explained by the following general format:

> 1.   General information
>
>   a.   The FAA's objective and/or rationale for this task
>
>   b.   A list of the Gleim *Pilot Handbook* study units and/or subunits that provide additional discussion of the task, as appropriate
>
>   c.   Any general discussion relevant to the task
>
> 2.   Comprehensive discussion of each concept or item listed in the FAA's task
>
> 3.   Common errors for each of the flight maneuvers, i.e., tasks appearing in Study Units XX through XX and Study Unit XX relative to knowledge, risk management, and skill tasks

2.3 AIRPLANE AND EQUIPMENT REQUIREMENTS

A.   You are required to provide an appropriate and airworthy airplane for the practical test. The airplane must be equipped for, and its operating limitations must not prohibit, the pilot operations required on the practical test.

2.4 WHAT TO TAKE TO YOUR PRACTICAL TEST

A. You should ensure that you are completely prepared to begin your practical test before you meet your evaluator. If you are unprepared, the test will become time-consuming and awkward for you and the evaluator as you search for items that should have been located beforehand.

B. The following checklist from the FAA's Private Pilot Airman Certification Standards should be reviewed with your instructor both 1 week and 1 day before your scheduled practical test:

Acceptable Aircraft

- ☐ Aircraft Documents:
    - ☐ Airworthiness Certificate
    - ☐ Registration Certificate
    - ☐ Operating Limitations
- ☐ Aircraft Maintenance Records:
    - ☐ Logbook Record of Airworthiness Inspections and AD Compliance
- ☐ Pilot's Operating Handbook, FAA-Approved Aircraft Flight Manual

Personal Equipment

- ☐ View-Limiting Device
- ☐ Current Aeronautical Charts (Printed or Electronic)
- ☐ Computer and Plotter
- ☐ Flight Plan Form
- ☐ Flight Plan Form and Flight Logs (printed or electronic)
- ☐ Chart Supplements U.S., Airport Diagrams and appropriate Publications
- ☐ Current *AIM*

Personal Records

- ☐ Identification--Photo/Signature ID
- ☐ Pilot Certificate
- ☐ Current Medical Certificate
- ☐ Completed FAA Form 8710-1, *Airman Certificate and/or Rating Application with Instructor's Signature*
- ☐ Original Knowledge Test Report
- ☐ Pilot Logbook with appropriate Instructor Endorsements
- ☐ FAA Form 8060-5, *Notice of Disapproval* (if applicable)
- ☐ Letter of Discontinuance (if applicable)
- ☐ Approved School Graduation Certificate (if applicable)
- ☐ Evaluator's Fee (if applicable)

2.5 PRACTICAL TEST APPLICATION FORM AND IACRA

A.   Prior to your practical test, your instructor may have you complete a paper version of an FAA Form 8710-1 before filling out the 8710-1 on IACRA.

    1.   Your CFI should explain to you how to complete the form.

        a.   The form is not largely self-explanatory.

        b.   For example, the FAA wants dates shown as 02/14/16, **not** 2-14-16.

    2.   Do not go to your practical test without completing the IACRA application process; remind your CFI about it as you schedule your practical test.

        a.   Information on how to complete your IACRA can be found at www.gleim.com/aviation/ general_resources.

B.   If you are enrolled in a Part 141 flight school, the IACRA Air Agency Recommendation block of information may be completed by the chief instructor of your Part 141 flight school. (S)he, rather than a designated evaluator or FAA inspector, will administer the practical test if examining authority has been granted to your flight school.

C.   After review and approval, your permanent private pilot certificate will be issued and mailed to you.

    1.   However, you will be issued a temporary certificate when you successfully complete the practical test (see Subunit 2.9, "Your Temporary Pilot Certificate," on page 14).

2.6 AUTHORIZATION TO TAKE THE PRACTICAL TEST

A.   Before taking your practical test, your CFI will endorse your logbook to certify that you have received and logged ground and flight training in the required areas of operation, have logged the required flight experience, and that you are prepared to take the practical test.

> *I certify that (First name, MI, Last name) has received the required training in accordance with Sec. 61.107 and 61.109. I have determined he/she is prepared for the (name the practical test).*
>
> _Date_ _____   _Name/Signature_ _____   _CFI No._ _____   _Expiration Date_

B.   Your logbook must contain the following endorsement from your flight instructor certifying that you have received the logged training time within the 2 calendar months preceding the month of application in preparation for the practical test and that (s)he has found that you are prepared to take the practical test.

> *I certify that (First name, MI, Last name) has received and logged the training time within 2 calendar months preceding the month of application in preparation for the practical test and he/she is prepared for the required practical test for the issuance of (applicable) certificate.*
>
> _Date_ _____   _Name/Signature_ _____   _CFI No._ _____   _Expiration Date_

C.   In addition, your logbook must contain the following endorsement that states (s)he has reviewed the deficiencies identified on your airman knowledge test.

> *I certify that (First name, MI, Last name) has demonstrated satisfactory knowledge of the subject areas in which he/she was deficient on the (applicable) airman knowledge test.*
>
> _Date_ _____   _Name/Signature_ _____   _CFI No._ _____   _Expiration Date_

2.7 ORAL EXAMINATION DURING THE PRACTICAL TEST

A. Your practical test will probably begin in your evaluator's office.

     1. You should have with you

         a. This book

         b. Your Pilot's Operating Handbook (POH) or Airplane Flight Manual (AFM) for your airplane (including weight and balance data)

         c. Your current edition of Gleim *FAR/AIM*

         d. All of the items listed on page 11

     2. Your evaluator will probably begin by reviewing your paperwork (FAA Form 8710-1, *Airman Computer Test Report*, logbook signoff, etc.) and receiving payment for his or her services.

     3. Typically, your evaluator will then question you about your preplanned VFR cross-country flight with discussion of weather, charts, 14 CFRs, etc. When you schedule your practical test, your evaluator will probably assign a cross-country flight for you to plan and bring to your practical test.

     4. As your evaluator asks you questions, follow the guidelines listed below:

         a. Attempt to position yourself in a discussion mode with the evaluator rather than being interrogated by him or her.

         b. Be respectful but do not be intimidated. Both you and your evaluator are professionals.

         c. Draw on your knowledge from this book and other books, your CFI, and your prior experience.

         d. Ask for amplification of any points your CFI may have appeared uncertain about.

         e. If you do not know an answer, try to explain how you would research the answer.

     5. Be confident that you will do well. You are a good pilot. You have thoroughly prepared for this discussion by studying the subsequent pages and have worked diligently with your CFI.

     6. Make use of the Gleim Airmen Certification Standards (ACS) and Oral Exam Guide book to prepare for the assortment of oral exam questions they may face during their practical test.

         a. Unlike most publishers, Gleim combines a reprint of the ACS and an Oral Exam Guide into one convenient, easy-to-use book, the *Private Pilot ACS and Oral Exam Guide*.

         b. The ACS portion is a reprint of the most current version of the FAA Private Pilot ACS at the time of print (minus references to seaplanes and multi-engine).

         c. The Oral Exam Guide contains over 900 questions and is easily navigated via the detailed Table of Contents and the comprehensive index. The depth and breadth of these questions will give you a significant advantage as you prepare for your test.

B. While your practical test will begin with dedicated time for oral examination and discussion, the evaluator will continue to evaluate your ability to make sound decisions throughout the entire practical test. The practical test will segue from strictly oral examination to the flight portion as the tasks covered transition from the preflight preparation to the preflight procedures area of operation.

     1. If possible and appropriate in the circumstances, thoroughly preflight your airplane just before you go to your evaluator's office.

     2. As you and your evaluator approach your airplane, explain that you have already preflighted the airplane (explain any possible problems and how you resolved them).

     3. Volunteer to answer any questions.

     4. Make sure you walk around the airplane to observe any possible damage by ramp vehicles or other aircraft while you were in your evaluator's office.

     5. As you enter the airplane, make sure that your cockpit is organized and you feel in control of your charts, clock, navigation logs, etc.

     6. Conduct an appropriate passenger briefing for your evaluator just as you would for any other occupants.

2.8 FLIGHT PORTION OF THE PRACTICAL TEST

A.   As you begin the flight portion of your practical test, your evaluator will have you depart on the VFR cross-country flight you previously planned.

    1.   You will taxi out, depart, and proceed on course to your destination.

    2.   Your departure procedures usually permit demonstration/testing of many of the tasks in Areas of Operation III, IV, V, and IX. After you complete these tasks, your evaluator will probably have you discontinue your cross-country flight so you can demonstrate additional flight maneuvers. Be prepared to demonstrate diversion and lost procedures.

B.   Note that you are required to perform all 45 tasks during your practical test.

C.   Remember that at all times you are the pilot in command of this flight. Take polite but firm charge of your airplane and instill in your evaluator confidence in you as a safe and proficient pilot.

D.   To evaluate your ability to utilize proper control technique while dividing attention both inside and/ or outside the cockpit, your evaluator will cause realistic distractions during the flight portion of your practical test to evaluate your ability to divide attention while maintaining safe flight.

E.   Use your evaluator as a resource. They can assist with scanning for traffic and reading checklists as appropriate. Do not solely rely on them for these tasks though.

2.9 YOUR TEMPORARY PILOT CERTIFICATE

A.   When you successfully complete your practical test, your evaluator will prepare a temporary pilot certificate.

    1.   The temporary certificate is valid for 120 days.

B.   Your permanent certificate will be sent to you directly from the FAA Aeronautical Center in Oklahoma City in about 60 to 90 days.

    1.   If you do not receive your permanent certificate within 120 days, your evaluator can arrange an extension of your temporary certificate.

2.10 FAILURE ON THE PRACTICAL TEST

A.   About 90% of applicants pass their private pilot practical test the first time, and virtually all who experienced difficulty on their first attempt pass the second time.

B.   If you do not meet the standards for any of the 45 tasks, you will fail the practical test.

    1.   When on the ground, your evaluator will complete the FAA Form 8060-5, *Notice of Disapproval of Application*, and will indicate the areas necessary for reexamination.

    2.   Your evaluator will give you credit for the areas of operation you successfully completed, if you pass the practical test within 60 days.

C.   You should do the following:

    1.   Indicate your intent to work with your instructor on your deficiencies.

    2.   Inquire about rescheduling the next practical test within the next 60 days.

        a.   Many evaluators have a reduced fee for a retake (FAA inspectors do not charge for their services).

    3.   Inquire about having your flight instructor discuss your proficiencies and deficiencies with the evaluator.

PART II
COMMON ELEMENTS TO
FLIGHT TASKS

The following part consists of 7 study units. These study units contain basic and common information that is pervasive throughout your flight training. You must understand the following sections of material to be able to successfully complete the ACS tasks in Part III.

Moreover, in Part III, we will refer back to information written in Part II to avoid duplicating a significant amount of material. As you continue your flight training and further develop your flight skills and knowledge, we presume you will be referencing Part II often, as this information begins to transition from your short-term memory to long-term memory until you have the ability to correlate all of the information provided and successfully complete your practical test.

STUDY UNIT THREE
YOUR PILOT'S OPERATING HANDBOOK/
AIRPLANE FLIGHT MANUAL

3.1 PILOT'S OPERATING HANDBOOK (POH)/AIRPLANE FLIGHT MANUAL (AFM)

A. The FAA requires an official Pilot's Operating Handbook (POH) and/or Airplane Flight Manual (AFM) to be on board your airplane and easily accessible during all flight operations.

   1. The POH contains most of the relevant information about a particular make and model of airplane.

      a. The format and content of the POH was standardized in 1975 to make it easier for pilots to use and allow for easier transitions between different makes and models of airplanes.

   2. Since March 1, 1979, the FAA has required all airplanes to be equipped with an FAA-approved AFM that is specifically assigned to each individual airplane.

      a. To satisfy this requirement, aircraft with a POH designated that as the AFM.

   3. Because the POH/AFM normally remains in the airplane and is not easily accessible for review, many manufacturers also publish a Pilot's Information Manual (PIM) that you can purchase.

      a. The PIM contains the same information as the POH/AFM except for the exact weight and balance data and optional equipment specific to a particular aircraft.

   4. The POH/AFM and PIM typically have nine sections:

1. General	Description of the airplane
2. Limitations	Description of operating limits
3. Emergency Procedures	What to do in each situation
4. Normal Procedures	Checklists and operating procedures
5. Performance	Graphs and tables of airplane capabilities
6. Weight and Balance	Equipment list, airplane empty weight
7. Airplane and Systems Description	Description of the airplane's systems
8. Servicing and Maintenance	Explanation of what and when
9. Supplements	Description of optional equipment

B. You must rely completely on your POH/AFM for your airplane's specific operating procedures and limitations.

   1. Your POH/AFM is also critical for emergency operations.

      a. Your POH/AFM must be easily accessible to you during flight.

   2. Also be aware that some POH/AFMs have two parts to each section:

      a. Abbreviated procedures (which are checklists)
      b. Amplified procedures (which consist of discussion of the checklists)

3. As a practical matter, after you study your POH/AFM and gain some experience in your airplane, you may wish to retype some of the standard checklists on heavy (and possibly laminate) paper.

    a. Having the checklists available is more convenient than trying to find checklists in your POH/AFM while engaged in other cockpit activities.

    b. Also, electronic checklists are available which provide checklist items one at a time.

C. Call or visit your flight school in advance of your private pilot training to see if a POH/AFM for the aircraft that you intend to fly is available for review.

    1. Often, flight schools have digital copies of the POH/AFMs for their aircraft available online for their students to reference and study.

    2. Alternatively, you should purchase the same model PIM for study.

        a. You will need to get specific weight and balance and optional equipment information from the actual POH/AFM because the PIM is for general purposes only.

    3. Read the POH/AFM or PIM from cover to cover and study the normal operating checklists, standard airspeeds, and emergency procedures.

    4. Familiarize yourself with the cockpit by taking pictures of the control panel and cockpit from the back seat of the airplane.

    5. Some online vendors sell POH/AFM reprints, e.g., www.esscoaircraft.com.

3.2 COCKPIT FAMILIARITY

A. Before getting ready to start the engine on your first flights and whenever preparing to fly an unfamiliar airplane, take a few minutes to acquaint yourself with the cockpit, i.e., the flight controls, radios, and instruments.

    1. Your POH/AFM should have a control panel diagram similar to that of the Piper Tomahawk illustrated below or the glass cockpit illustrated on the next page.

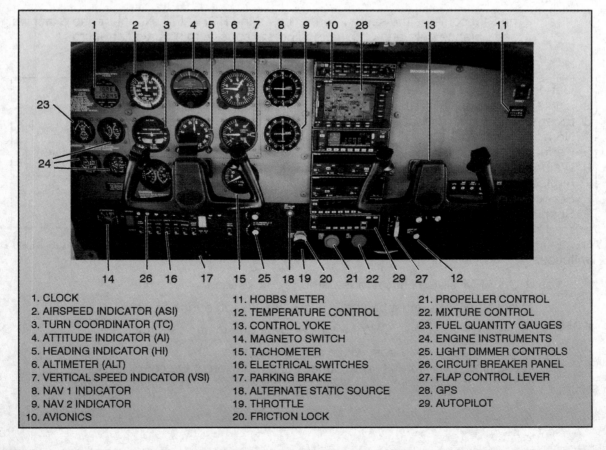

1. CLOCK	11. HOBBS METER	21. PROPELLER CONTROL
2. AIRSPEED INDICATOR (ASI)	12. TEMPERATURE CONTROL	22. MIXTURE CONTROL
3. TURN COORDINATOR (TC)	13. CONTROL YOKE	23. FUEL QUANTITY GAUGES
4. ATTITUDE INDICATOR (AI)	14. MAGNETO SWITCH	24. ENGINE INSTRUMENTS
5. HEADING INDICATOR (HI)	15. TACHOMETER	25. LIGHT DIMMER CONTROLS
6. ALTIMETER (ALT)	16. ELECTRICAL SWITCHES	26. CIRCUIT BREAKER PANEL
7. VERTICAL SPEED INDICATOR (VSI)	17. PARKING BRAKE	27. FLAP CONTROL LEVER
8. NAV 1 INDICATOR	18. ALTERNATE STATIC SOURCE	28. GPS
9. NAV 2 INDICATOR	19. THROTTLE	29. AUTOPILOT
10. AVIONICS	20. FRICTION LOCK	

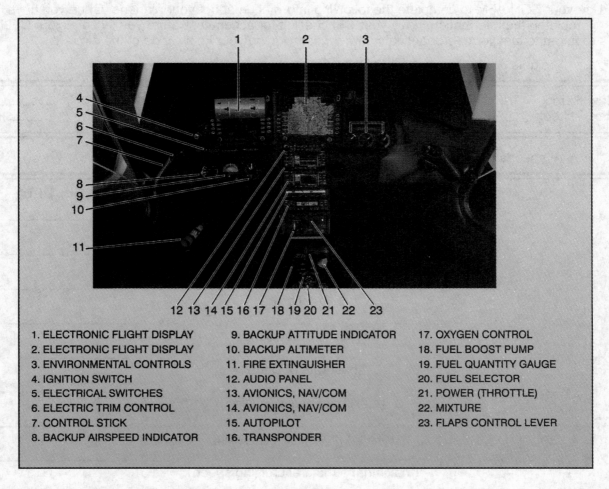

1. ELECTRONIC FLIGHT DISPLAY	9. BACKUP ATTITUDE INDICATOR	17. OXYGEN CONTROL
2. ELECTRONIC FLIGHT DISPLAY	10. BACKUP ALTIMETER	18. FUEL BOOST PUMP
3. ENVIRONMENTAL CONTROLS	11. FIRE EXTINGUISHER	19. FUEL QUANTITY GAUGE
4. IGNITION SWITCH	12. AUDIO PANEL	20. FUEL SELECTOR
5. ELECTRICAL SWITCHES	13. AVIONICS, NAV/COM	21. POWER (THROTTLE)
6. ELECTRIC TRIM CONTROL	14. AVIONICS, NAV/COM	22. MIXTURE
7. CONTROL STICK	15. AUTOPILOT	23. FLAPS CONTROL LEVER
8. BACKUP AIRSPEED INDICATOR	16. TRANSPONDER	

B. After your first flights and debriefing with your flight instructor, return to the airplane, sit in the pilot's seat, and study the location of all instruments, radios, and control devices.

1. Mentally review their location, operation, and use. Then mentally review your flight and ways it could have been improved.

2. After subsequent flight lessons, you may find this procedure continues to be constructive if the airplane is available.

3. Next, take a blank sheet of paper and, without the aid of a diagram or photo, sketch your control panel and review normal control positions and normal gauge indications.

3.3 LEARNING YOUR AIRPLANE

A. Your CFI will supplement the POH/AFM information about your airplane. Such instruction ensures that you have studied your airplane's POH/AFM to learn and understand the information in each of its nine sections.

1. By the end of your flight training, you will be thoroughly familiar with your airplane and its operating systems and limitations.

a. During your practical test, your evaluator is required to test you on your knowledge of your airplane.

2. Before your first lesson, you should read Section 4, Normal Procedures, and Section 7, Airplane and Systems Description, in your POH/AFM.

B.   Use your POH/AFM to complete the following information about your airplane. Once you have completed the information, have your CFI check it for accuracy. Before you fly solo, your CFI is required to test your aeronautical knowledge, including your knowledge of the aircraft.

   1.   Weights

| Max. Ramp | _____ | Max. Landing | _____ |
| Max. Takeoff | _____ | Max. Baggage Compartment | _____ |

   2.   Airspeeds

	KT or MPH*
V_{SO} (stall speed in landing configuration)	_____
V_{S1} (stall speed in a specified configuration)	_____
V_R (rotation)	_____
V_X (best angle of climb)	_____
V_Y (best rate of climb)	_____
V_{FE} (maximum flap extension)	_____
V_A (design maneuvering speed)	_____
V_{NO} (maximum structural cruising speed)	_____
V_{NE} (never exceed speed)	_____
$V_{Best\ Glide}$ (best glide speed)	_____

*Circle one.

   3.   Additional information

Fuel
   Type/Grade Used _____
   Capacity of Each Tank:
       Left _____
       Right _____

Oil
   Type/Weight _____
   Capacity _____
   Minimum Level _____
   Suggested Level _____

Brake Fluid Reservoirs
   Location _____
   Type of Fluid _____
   Capacity _____

Tire Pressure
   Mains _____
   Nose _____

4.   Performance data

	Airspeed	Power (RPM/MP)
Rotation (V_R)	_____	_____
Climbout	_____	_____
Cruise climb	_____	_____
Cruise level	_____	_____
Cruise descent	_____	_____
Traffic pattern	_____	_____
Final approach	_____	_____
Landing flare	_____	_____

3.4 CHECKLISTS

A.   The use of checklists is vital to the safety of each flight. Airplanes have many controls, switches, instruments, and indicators. Failure to correctly position or check any of these could have serious results.

B.   Each item on the checklist requires evaluation and possible action:

1.   Is the situation safe?
2.   If not, what action is required?
3.   Is the overall airplane/environment safe when you take all factors into account?

C.   There are different types of checklists:

1.   "Read and do," e.g., pretakeoff checklist.

2.   "Do and read," e.g., in reacting to emergencies. Do everything you learned (memorized), and then confirm that all appropriate actions were taken by using the appropriate checklist.

D.   In other words, checklists are not an end in and of themselves. Checklists are a means of flying safely. Generally, they are to be used as specified in your POH/AFM to accomplish safe flight.

1.   Emergency checklists are found in Section 3, Emergency Procedures, of your POH/AFM.
2.   Normal operation checklists are found in Section 4, Normal Procedures, of your POH/AFM.

E.   Electronic checklists are available for a number of airplanes (make- and model-specific) and may be hand-held or mounted in an airplane.

1.   An advantage of an electronic checklist is that it forces you to respond (i.e., by pressing a button) to each item before the next item is displayed.

a.   The requirement to respond reduces the chances of missing an item due to a distraction or skipping a line on a printed checklist.

F.   For more information on using checklists, see Study Unit 6, Subunit 4.

3.5 WEIGHT AND BALANCE

A. Section 6, Weight and Balance, in your POH/AFM presents all the information required to compute weight and balance.

    1. The equipment list in this section lists all of the equipment installed in your airplane.

B. More important is your Weight and Balance Record, which consists of an ongoing record of weight and balance changes in your airplane.

    1. Every time a component (e.g., a new radio) is added or deleted that changes the weight and/or balance of the airplane, the Weight and Balance Record is updated.

        a. Thus, this record is the source of the airplane's basic empty weight and its moment. See the illustration below.

    2. The last entries at the right should be your airplane's basic empty weight and moment.

        a. Some airplane manufacturers divide moments by 1,000, as shown below, while others divide by 100, and some do not divide moments at all.

C. For a detailed discussion of weight and balance, see Study Unit 5, "Airplane Performance and Weight and Balance," in *Pilot Handbook*.

WEIGHT AND BALANCE RECORD
CONTINUOUS HISTORY OF CHANGES IN STRUCTURE OR EQUIPMENT
AFFECTING WEIGHT AND BALANCE

DATE	ITEM NO.		DESCRIPTION OF ARTICLE OR MODIFICATION	WEIGHT CHANGE						RUNNING BASIC EMPTY WEIGHT	
	In	Out		ADDED (+)			REMOVED (-)				
				Wt. (lb.)	Arm (In.)	Moment /1000	Wt. (lb.)	Arm (In.)	Moment /1000	Wt. (lb.)	Moment /1000

For academic illustration/training purposes only!
For flight: **Use your Pilot's Operating Handbook or FAA-approved Airplane Flight Manual.**

3.6 PERFORMANCE DATA

A. Section 5, Performance, of your POH/AFM contains charts, tables, and/or graphs for you to use to determine airplane performance (e.g., takeoff/landing distance, climb, cruise, etc.).

1. Additionally, Section 4, Normal Procedures, of your POH/AFM contains takeoff, climb, cruise, and landing power settings and airspeeds.

B. The performance data table in Subunit 3.3 provides for normal power settings and airspeeds for various phases of flight. Obtain the information from your POH/AFM and confirm it with your CFI.

C. As your CFI introduces you to the use of performance charts, you may want to fill out the table below before each flight to develop your proficiency.

1. During your practical test, your evaluator will test you on your ability to determine airplane performance.

---

1. Airplane weight and balance .... _____
     Takeoff weight .... _____
        CG .... _____
     Landing weight .... _____
        CG .... _____
2. Runway length (at all airports of intended use) .... _____
3. Headwind component .... _____
4. Temperature .... _____
5. Field elevation .... _____
6. Pressure altitude .... _____
7. Runway conditions, obstructions, etc. .... _____
8. Rotation airspeed .... _____
9. Takeoff distance .... _____
     Ground roll .... _____
     50-ft. obstacle .... _____
10. Landing distance .... _____
     Ground roll .... _____
     50-ft. obstacle .... _____

---

24   *Notes*

STUDY UNIT FOUR
BASIC FLIGHT MANEUVERS

During your first few flight lessons, your instructor will introduce you to the basic flight maneuvers, i.e., straight-and-level flight, turns, climbs, and descents. While these maneuvers are not specifically listed as tasks in the FAA's Practical Test Standards, they are the fundamentals of flying. Every maneuver you will do is either one or a combination of the basic flight maneuvers.

Always look for other aircraft. See Study Unit 3, "Airports, Air Traffic Control, and Airspace," in *Pilot Handbook* for a discussion on collision avoidance procedures. Clearing turns are usually two 90° turns in opposite directions (e.g., a 90° turn to the left, then a 90° turn to the right) or a 180° turn with the purpose of complete and careful vigilance for other traffic.

In subsequent study units, we present a list of common errors for each flight maneuver. Now, while you are just getting started, you should focus on how to do these basic flight maneuvers. We do not want to confuse or burden you with what might go wrong. Your flight instructor will diagnose any improper technique.

4.1 INTEGRATED FLIGHT TRAINING

A.   The FAA recommends integrated flight training, which means that each flight maneuver (except those requiring ground references) should be learned first by outside visual references and then by instrument references only (i.e., flight instruments).

    1.   Thus, instruction in the control of the airplane by outside visual references is **integrated** with instruction in the use of flight instrument indications for the same operations.

    2.   Integrated instruction will assist you in developing a habit of monitoring your flight and engine instruments.

        a.   You should be able to hold desired altitudes, control airspeed during various phases of flight, and maintain headings.

4.2 AERODYNAMIC FACTORS

A.   Among the aerodynamic forces acting on an airplane during flight, four are considered to be basic because they act upon the airplane during all maneuvers. These basic forces in relation to straight-and-level, unaccelerated flight are

    1.   **Lift** -- the upward-acting force that opposes weight. Lift is produced by the dynamic effect of the air acting on the wing and acts perpendicular to the flight path through the wing's center of lift.

    2.   **Weight** -- the combined load of the airplane itself, the crew, the fuel, and the cargo or baggage. Weight pulls the airplane downward toward the center of the Earth because of the force of gravity. It opposes lift and acts vertically downward through the airplane's center of gravity.

3. **Thrust** -- the forward force produced by the engine/propeller. Thrust opposes or overcomes the force of drag. As a general rule, it is said to act parallel to the longitudinal axis.

4. **Drag** -- the rearward, retarding force that is caused by disruption of airflow by the wing, fuselage, and other protruding objects. Drag opposes thrust and acts rearward and parallel to the relative wind.

B. While in steady (unaccelerated) flight, the attitude, direction, and speed of the airplane will remain constant until one or more of the basic forces change in magnitude.

1. In steady flight, the opposing forces are in equilibrium.

    a. That is, the sum of all upward forces (not just lift) equals the sum of all downward forces (not just weight), and the sum of all forward forces (not just thrust) equals the sum of all rearward forces (not just drag).

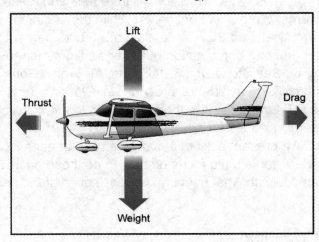

4.3 STRAIGHT-AND-LEVEL FLIGHT

A. Straight-and-level flight simply means that a constant heading and altitude are maintained.

1. It is accomplished by making corrections for deviations in direction and altitude from unintentional turns, descents, and climbs.

B. The pitch attitude for **level flight** (i.e., constant altitude) is obtained by selecting some portion of the airplane's nose or instrument glare shield as a reference point and then keeping that point in a fixed position relative to the horizon.

1. That position should be cross-checked occasionally against the altimeter to determine whether or not the pitch attitude is correct for the power setting being used.

    a. If altitude is being lost or gained, the pitch attitude should be readjusted in relation to the horizon, and then the altimeter should be checked to determine if altitude is being maintained.

2. The application of forward or back elevator pressure is used to control this attitude.

    a. The term "increasing the pitch attitude" implies raising the nose in relation to the horizon by pulling back on the control yoke.

    b. The term "decreasing the pitch" means lowering the nose by pushing forward on the control yoke.

3. The pitch information obtained from the attitude indicator will also show the position of the nose relative to the horizon.

C. To achieve **straight flight** (i.e., constant heading), you should select two or more outside visual reference points directly ahead of the airplane (e.g., roads, section lines, towns, lakes, etc.) to form an imaginary line and then keep the airplane headed along that line.

1. While using these references, you should occasionally check the heading indicator (HI) to determine that the airplane is maintaining a constant heading.

2. Both wingtips should be equidistant above or below the horizon (depending on whether your airplane is a high-wing or low-wing type). Any necessary adjustment should be made with the ailerons to return to a wings level flight attitude.

   a. Observing the wingtips helps to divert your attention from the airplane's nose and expands the radius of your visual scan, which assists you in collision avoidance.

3. The attitude indicator (AI) should be checked for small bank angles, and the heading indicator (HI) should be checked to note deviations from the desired direction.

D. Straight-and-level flight requires almost no application of control pressure if the airplane is properly trimmed and the air is smooth.

1. Trim the airplane so it will fly straight and level without constant assistance.

   a. This is called "hands-off flight."
   b. The trim controls, when correctly used, are aids to smooth and precise flying.
   c. Improper trim technique usually results in flying that is physically tiring, particularly in prolonged straight-and-level flight.

2. The airplane should be trimmed by first applying control pressure to establish the desired attitude, and then adjusting the trim so that the airplane will maintain that attitude without control pressure in hands-off flight.

E. The airspeed will remain constant in straight-and-level flight with a constant power setting.

1. Significant changes in airspeed (e.g., power changes) will, of course, require considerable changes in pitch attitude to maintain altitude.

2. Pronounced changes in pitch attitude will also be necessary as the flaps and landing gear (if retractable) are operated.

4.4 TURNS

A. A turn is a basic flight maneuver used to change from, or return to, a desired heading. This maneuver involves the coordinated use of the ailerons, rudder, and elevator.

1. Your CFI will use the terms shallow, medium, or steep turns to indicate the approximate bank angle to use.

   a. EXAMPLE: A shallow turn uses 20° of bank, a medium turn uses 30° of bank, and a steep turn uses 45° of bank.

2. You will begin your training by using shallow to medium banked turns.

B. To enter a turn, you should simultaneously turn the control wheel (i.e., apply aileron control pressure) and rudder pressure in the desired direction.

1. The speed (or rate) at which your airplane rolls into a bank depends on the rate and amount of control pressure you apply.

   a. The amount of bank depends on how long you keep the ailerons deflected.

2. Rudder pressure must be enough to keep the ball of the inclinometer (part of the turn coordinator) centered.

   a. If the ball is not centered, step on the ball to recenter.
   b. EXAMPLE: If the ball is to the right, apply right rudder pressure (i.e., step on the ball) to recenter.

3.   The best outside reference for establishing the degree of bank is the angle made by the top of the engine cowling or the instrument panel with respect to the horizon.

    a.   Since the engine cowling is fairly flat on most light airplanes, its horizontal angle to the horizon will give some indication of the approximate degree of bank.

    b.   Your posture while seated in the airplane is very important in all maneuvers, particularly during turns, since that will affect the alignment of outside visual references.

        1)   At first, you may want to lean away from the turn in an attempt to remain upright in relation to the ground instead of rolling with the airplane.

        2)   You must overcome this tendency and learn to ride with your airplane.

    c.   In an airplane with side-by-side seating, you will be seated in the left seat. Since your seat is to the left of the centerline of the airplane, you will notice that to maintain altitude the nose position will be different on turns to the left than to the right.

        1)   In a turn to the left, the nose may appear level or slightly high.

        2)   In a turn to the right, the nose will appear to be low.

4.   Information obtained from the attitude indicator (AI) will show the angle of the wings in relation to the horizon. This information will help you learn to judge the degree of bank based on outside references.

C.   The lift produced by the wings is used to turn the airplane. When you bank the airplane, the lift is separated into two components known as the vertical and the horizontal components of lift, as shown below.

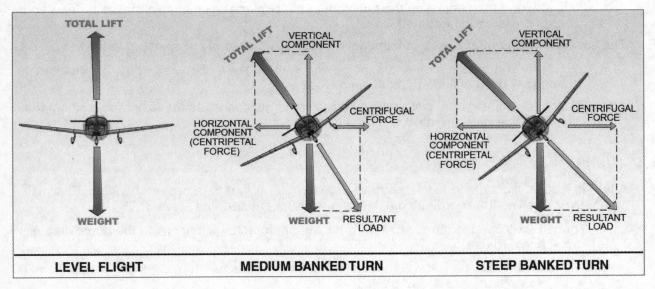

1.   The horizontal component of lift creates a force that is directed inward toward the center of the airplane's rotation. This force, known as centripetal force, causes the airplane to turn.

    a.   The steeper the bank, the sharper the turn due to the increase in the horizontal lift.

2.   In a bank, the total lift consists of both horizontal lift (to turn the airplane) and vertical lift (counteracting weight/gravity).

    a.   Given the same amount of total lift, there is less vertical lift in a bank than in straight-and-level flight.

    b.   To maintain altitude, the vertical lift must remain equal to weight. Thus, total lift must be increased.

        1)   Total lift is increased by applying enough back elevator pressure (i.e., increasing the angle of attack) to maintain altitude.

        2)   This increase in pitch will cause a slight decrease in airspeed. In a medium banked turn, this slight decrease in airspeed is acceptable and will be regained once the wings are level, so no increase in power is required.

D.   As the desired angle of bank is established, aileron and rudder pressures should be released. The bank will not continue to increase since the aileron control surfaces will be neutral in their streamlined position.

    1.   The back elevator pressure should not be released but should be held constant or sometimes increased to maintain a constant altitude.

    2.   Throughout the turn, you should cross-check the references and occasionally include the altimeter to determine whether the pitch attitude is correct.

    3.   If gaining or losing altitude, adjust the pitch attitude in relation to the horizon, and then recheck the altimeter and vertical speed indicator to determine if altitude is now being maintained.

E.   The rollout from a turn is similar to the roll-in except that control pressures are used in the opposite direction. Aileron and rudder pressures are applied in the direction of the rollout or toward the high wing.

    1.   Since the airplane will continue turning as long as there is any bank, the rollout must be started before reaching the desired heading.

        a.   The time to begin rollout in order to lead the heading will depend on the rate of turn and the rate at which the rollout will be made.

        b.   Lead your rollout by an amount equal to one-half your bank angle.

            1)   If you are using a 30° bank, begin your rollout approximately 15° before your desired heading.

    2.   As the angle of bank decreases, the elevator pressure should be released smoothly as necessary to maintain altitude. Remember, when the airplane is no longer banking, the vertical component of lift increases.

    3.   As the wings become level, the control pressures should be gradually and smoothly released so that the controls are neutralized as the airplane resumes straight-and-level flight.

    4.   As the rollout is completed, attention should be given to outside visual references as well as to the attitude indicator and heading indicator to determine that the wings are leveled precisely and the turn stopped.

4.5 CLIMBS

A.   Climbs and climbing turns are basic flight maneuvers in which the pitch attitude and power result in a gain in altitude. In a straight climb, the airplane gains altitude while traveling straight ahead. In climbing turns, the airplane gains altitude while turning.

B.   Your CFI will introduce you to various climb airspeeds early in your flight training.

    1.   **Best rate of climb (V_Y)** provides the greatest gain in altitude in the least amount of time.

    2.   **Best angle of climb (V_X)** provides the greatest gain in altitude in a given distance.

    3.   **Cruise climb** is used to climb to your desired altitude. This speed provides better engine cooling and forward visibility.

    4.   These airspeeds are listed in your Pilot's Operating Handbook (POH) and/or Airplane Flight Manual (AFM).

C. To enter the climb, simultaneously advance the throttle and apply back elevator pressure.

    1. As the power is increased to the climb setting, the airplane's nose will tend to rise to the climb attitude.

        a. In most trainer-type airplanes, the climb setting will be full power. Check your POH/ AFM for information.

    2. While the pitch attitude increases and airspeed decreases, progressively more right-rudder pressure must be used to compensate for torque effects and to maintain direction.

        a. Since the angle of attack is relatively high, the airspeed is relatively slow, and the power setting is high, the airplane will have a tendency to roll and yaw to the left.

            1) While right-rudder pressure will correct for the yaw, some aileron pressure may be required to keep the wings level.

        b. See Study Unit 1, "Airplanes and Aerodynamics," in *Pilot Handbook* for a discussion on torque (left-turning tendency).

D. When the climb is established, back elevator pressure must be maintained to keep the pitch attitude constant.

    1. As the airspeed decreases, the elevators may try to return to their streamline or neutral position, which will cause the nose to lower.

        a. Nose-up trim will be required.

    2. Since you want to climb at a specific airspeed, you will need to cross-check the airspeed indicator (ASI), which will also provide you with an indirect indication of pitch attitude.

        a. If the airspeed is higher than desired, you need to use the outside references and attitude indicator to raise the nose.

        b. If the airspeed is lower than desired, you need to use the outside references and attitude indicator to lower the nose.

    3. After the climbing attitude, power setting, and airspeed have been established, trim the airplane to relieve all pressures from the controls.

        a. If further adjustments are made in pitch, power, and/or airspeed, you must retrim the airplane.

    4. If a straight climb is being performed, you need to maintain a constant heading with the wings level.

        a. If a climbing turn is being performed, maintain a constant angle of bank.

E. To return to straight-and-level flight from a climbing attitude, you should lead the level-off before reaching the desired altitude.

    1. Start to level off a distance below the desired altitude equal to about 10% of the airplane's rate of climb as indicated on the vertical speed indicator.

        a. EXAMPLE: If you are climbing at 500 fpm, start to level off 50 ft. below your desired altitude.

    2. To level off, the wings should be leveled and the nose lowered.

    3. The nose must be lowered gradually, however, because a loss of altitude will result if the pitch attitude is decreased too abruptly before allowing the airspeed to increase adequately.

        a. As the nose is lowered and the wings are leveled, retrim the airplane.

        b. When the airspeed reaches the desired cruise speed, reduce the throttle setting to appropriate cruise power setting, adjust the mixture control to the manufacturer's recommended setting, and trim the airplane.

F. **Climbing turns.** The following factors should be considered:

1. With a constant power setting, the same pitch attitude and airspeed cannot be maintained in a bank as in a straight climb due to the decrease in the vertical lift and airspeed during a turn.

   a. The loss of vertical lift becomes greater as the angle of bank is increased, so shallow turns may be used to maintain an efficient rate of climb. If a medium- or steep-banked turn is used, the airplane's rate of climb will be reduced.

   b. The airplane will have a greater tendency towards nose heaviness than in a straight climb, due to the decrease in the vertical lift.

2. As in all maneuvers, attention should be diverted from the airplane's nose and divided among all references equally.

3. There are two ways to establish a climbing turn: Either establish a straight climb and then turn or establish the pitch and bank attitudes simultaneously from straight-and-level flight.

   a. The second method is usually preferred because you can more effectively check the area for other aircraft while the climb is being established.

4.6 DESCENTS

A. A descent is a basic maneuver in which the airplane loses altitude in a controlled manner. Descents can be made

1. With partial power, as used during an approach to a landing
2. Without power, i.e., as a glide
3. At cruise airspeeds, during en route descents

B. To enter a descent, you should first apply carburetor heat (if recommended in the POH/AFM) and then reduce power to the desired setting or to idle.

1. Maintain a constant altitude by applying back elevator pressure as required until the airspeed decreases to the desired descent airspeed.

2. Once the descent airspeed has been reached, lower the nose attitude to maintain that airspeed and adjust the trim.

C. When the descent is established, cross-check the airspeed indicator (ASI) to ensure that you are descending at the desired airspeed.

1. If the airspeed is higher than desired, slightly raise the nose. Allow the airspeed to stabilize to confirm the adjustment.

2. If the airspeed is lower than desired, slightly lower the nose. Allow the airspeed to stabilize to confirm the adjustment.

3. Once you are descending at the desired airspeed, note the position of the airplane's nose to the horizon and the position on the attitude indicator (AI).

   a. Trim the airplane to relieve all control pressures.

4. Maintain either straight or turning flight, as desired.

D.   The level-off from a descent must be started before reaching the desired altitude.

    1.   Begin the level-off at a distance equal to about 10% of the airplane's rate of descent as indicated on the vertical speed indicator (VSI).

        a.   EXAMPLE: If you are descending at 500 fpm, start the level-off 50 ft. above your desired altitude.

    2.   At the lead point, you should simultaneously raise the nose to a level attitude and increase power to the desired cruise setting.

        a.   The addition of power and the increase in airspeed will tend to raise the nose. You will need to apply appropriate elevator control pressure and make a trim adjustment to relieve some of the control pressures.

E.   **Turning Descents**

    1.   As with climbing turns, you can either enter the turn after the descent has been established or simultaneously adjust the bank and pitch attitudes.

    2.   At a desired power setting during a descending turn, maintain airspeed with pitch as you would in a straight descent.

4.7 ATTITUDE FLYING

A.   As a practical matter, your initial experience (i.e., introductory flight) with the flight controls will be based on outside visual references. As your flight instructor works with you on perfecting the basic flight maneuvers, you should be prepared to fly the airplane based on the six flight instruments:

    • Airspeed indicator (ASI)   • Attitude indicator (AI)   • Altimeter (ALT)
    • Turn coordinator (TC)   • Heading indicator (HI)   • Vertical speed indicator (VSI)

    1.   Turn to Study Unit 43 and invest 15 minutes in Subunit 3, item 2., so you learn and understand what each of the above six flight instruments looks like, what each tells you, and how you "scan" and interpret the instruments.

    2.   View-limiting devices. In order to learn how to fly by instrument reference only, you will use an easily removable device (e.g., a hood, an extended visor cap, or foggles) that will limit your vision to the instrument panel. There are numerous sizes and shapes available. Some of these are illustrated below.

        a.   These view-limiting devices require acclimation. You should spend a few minutes in "your" airplane with "your" device on before you meet your CFI for your first flight lesson that prescribes flying by instrument reference only. This added familiarity with (1) the view-limiting device and (2) the location of the instruments and their appearance will make it easier to concentrate on flight maneuvers once in the air.

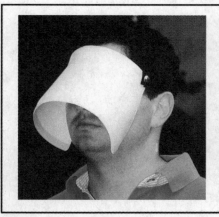 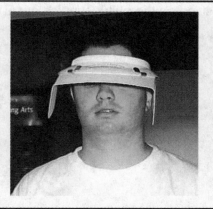 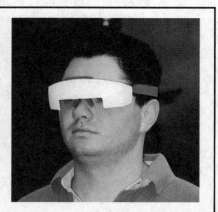

3.   As you practice your flight maneuvers, your instructor will have you perform them under the hood as well as by visual reference.

B.   Airplane control is composed of four components: pitch control, bank control, power control, and trim.

1.   **Pitch control** is the control of the airplane about its lateral axis (i.e., wingtip to wingtip) by applying elevator pressure to raise or lower the nose, usually in relation to the horizon.

2.   **Bank control** is the control of the airplane about its longitudinal axis (i.e., nose to tail) by use of the ailerons to attain the desired angle of bank in relation to the horizon.

3.   **Power control** is the control of power or thrust by use of the throttle to establish or maintain a desired airspeed, climb rate, or descent rate in coordination with the attitude changes.

4.   **Trim** is used to relieve all possible control pressures held after a desired attitude has been attained.

5.   For additional information on the flight controls and control surfaces, refer to the discussion/ illustration in Study Unit 1, "Airplanes and Aerodynamics," in *Pilot Handbook*.

C.   The outside references used in controlling the airplane include the airplane's nose and wingtips to show both the airplane's pitch attitude and flight direction, and the wings and frame of the windshield to show the angle of bank.

1.   The instrument references will be the six basic flight instruments: attitude indicator, heading indicator, altimeter, airspeed indicator, turn coordinator, and vertical speed indicator, all typically laid out as shown below:

- ASI
- AI
- ALT
- TC
- HI
- VSI

2. If your airplane features an electronic flight information system (EFIS), you will obtain the same information in a digital display. See the following labeled example:

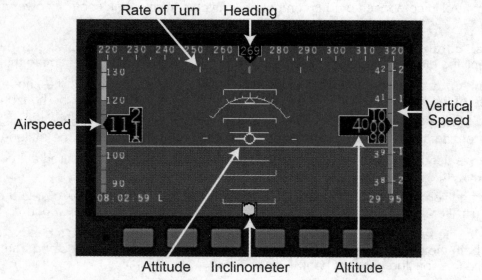

a. The remainder of this text will refer to standard cockpit instrumentation. Because the same information is presented on an EFIS, you will have no problem determining what instrumentation is being referred to.

b. Additionally, completing the Aircraft Information sheet on page 6 and following the cockpit familiarization guidance on page 18 will ensure that you become comfortable interpreting flight information early in your training.

D. The objectives of these basic flight maneuvers are

1. To learn the proper use of the flight controls for maneuvering the airplane

2. To attain the proper attitude in relation to the horizon by use of visual and instrument references

3. To emphasize the importance of dividing your attention and constantly checking all reference points while looking for other traffic

4. Being able to safely fly an airplane if you ever inadvertently lose reference to the horizon

STUDY UNIT FIVE
RISK MANAGEMENT OVERVIEW

This study unit contains various items that are tested in multiple tasks and areas of operation. Instead of duplicating the material in each related study unit, we provide it once in this study unit. These items in the study units will refer you back to this study unit for information.

It is impossible to cover every possible scenario when discussing risk management. This text expands on FAA guidance by correlating sound decision making with proper use of available resources and providing common-sense solutions to the many types of considerations you may face as a pilot. Being well prepared for the checkride is only the first step. Take this information seriously, and you too will become a safer, more competent pilot.

The first subunit of this study unit contains an overview of risk management and aeronautical decision making and applies to all tasks.

5.1 OVERVIEW OF RISK MANAGEMENT AND AERONAUTICAL DECISION MAKING

A. Every area of operation in the Airmen Certification Standards (ACS) includes elements pertaining to risk management.

   1. Risk management task items specific to a unique area of operation will be discussed in detail within the text for the respective study unit.

B. **Risk Management Definitions**

   1. **Risk management** – A formalized way of dealing with hazards, which is the logical process of weighing the potential costs of risks against the possible benefits of allowing those risks to stand uncontrolled. In order to better understand risk management, the terms "hazard" and "risk" need to be understood.

   2. **Hazard** – A real or potential condition, event, or circumstance that could lead to or contribute to an unplanned or undesired event. A hazard exists in the present.

      a. A thunderstorm along your route of flight is a hazard.

   3. **Risk** – The future impact of a hazard that is not controlled or eliminated. It can be viewed as future uncertainty created by the hazard.

      a. Failing to properly plan to avoid the thunderstorm creates risk.

C. **Risk management** is the part of the decision-making process that relies on situational awareness, problem recognition, and good judgment to reduce risks associated with flight. The goal of risk management is to proactively identify safety-related hazards and mitigate the associated risks.

   1. There are four **risk elements** involved in decisions made during a flight: the pilot in command, the airplane, the environment, and the operation. In decision making, each risk element is evaluated to attain an accurate perception of circumstances.

      a. **Pilot.** Consider factors such as competency, condition of health, mental and emotional state, level of fatigue, and many other variables.

      b. **Airplane.** Assess performance, equipment, and airworthiness.

      c. **Environment.** Consider a range of factors not related to pilot or airplane: weather, air traffic control, NAVAIDs, terrain, takeoff and landing areas, and surrounding obstacles.

d.   **External pressures.** Assessing factors relating to pilot, airplane, and environment is largely influenced by the purpose of the operation. Decisions should be made in the context of why the flight is being made, how critical it is to maintain the schedule, and whether or not the trip is worth the risks.

e.   The formal risk management decision-making process involves six steps.

2.   Accept no unnecessary risk. Flying is not possible without risk, but unnecessary risk comes without a corresponding return. If you are flying a new airplane for the first time, you might determine that the risk of making that flight in low visibility conditions is unnecessary.

3.   Make risk decisions at the appropriate level. Risk decisions should be made by the person who can develop and implement risk controls. Remember that you are pilot in command, so never let anyone else—not ATC and not your passengers—make risk decisions for you.

4.   Accept risk when benefits outweigh dangers (costs). In any flying activity, it is necessary to accept some degree of risk. A day with good weather, for example, is a much better time to fly an unfamiliar airplane for the first time than a day with low IFR conditions.

5.   Integrate risk management into planning at all levels. Because risk is an unavoidable part of every flight, safety requires the use of appropriate and effective risk management not just in the preflight planning stage, but in all stages of the flight.

6.   You must carefully process each risk you perceive when analyzing the four risk elements to determine the likelihood of it occurring and the severity of the results of such an occurrence. Use the simple table on the next page to quantify the impact of risks encountered during risk management.

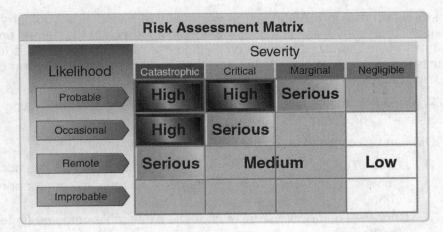

7. The final step in risk management is reducing, eliminating, or accepting the risks associated with a flight or decision. The goal is to choose the best, safest course of action for a given situation.

    a. Experience, training, and personal minimum standards will aid you in determining alternative courses of action to reduce and/or eliminate risks.

D. Make use of the FAA's *Risk Management Handbook* (available electronically on the FAA website) for additional background reading on this subject.

    1. Portions of this book refer to content contained in that text.

E. Common Errors Associated with Risk Management

    1. **Lack of familiarity with risk management processes, including perceiving, processing, and mitigating risks**

        a. Many pilots and instructors assume that risk management is unnecessarily academic and "common sense."

            1) General aviation (GA) accident data shows that risk management is not common sense.

            2) As far as the academic nature of the material goes, your evaluator is not looking to hear you explain the 3P or 5P models and the rationale behind each. The evaluator needs to see that you can use a logical, efficient risk assessment process to mitigate and/or eliminate risks.

        b. Like any problem, you have to be able to recognize risks, analyze them, and then (most importantly) decide what to do about them.

            1) The evaluator will be looking for your ability to spot hazards and rectify any risks associated with them.

    2. **Improper risk management due to flawed risk assessment**

        a. Ego, pride, and lack of knowledge can all affect how effective your risk assessment is.

        b. In risk assessment, you must be objective and open to the possibility that the only safe solution might be canceling or terminating the flight.

        c. The evaluator will be monitoring how your decisions impact the safety of the flight and how you evaluate your decisions after you have made them.

            1) Remember, making a mistake is human. Disapproval comes from "consistently exceeding the tolerances."

            2) If you make a mistake, correct it and explain the situation to the evaluator.

        d. Be proactive.

F. **Aeronautical decision making (ADM)** is how you make decisions, how you carry them out, and how you evaluate their effectiveness. It is a systematic approach to the mental process used by aircraft pilots to consistently determine the best course of action in response to a given set of circumstances. Your evaluator needs to know that, once certificated, you can be a decisive, effective pilot in command.

   1. The evaluator wants to see you make competent, confident decisions using a logical decision-making process.

       a. ADM can be practiced using the DECIDE model.

           1) **D**etect. The decision maker detects the fact that change has occurred.
           2) **E**stimate. The decision maker estimates the need to counter or react to the change.
           3) **C**hoose. The decision maker chooses a desirable outcome (in terms of success) for the flight.
           4) **I**dentify. The decision maker identifies actions that could successfully control the change.
           5) **D**o. The decision maker takes the necessary action.
           6) **E**valuate. The decision maker evaluates the effect(s) of his or her action countering the change.

           The six elements of the DECIDE model should be treated as a continuous loop. If a pilot practices the DECIDE model in all decision making, its use can become very natural and result in better decisions being made under all types of situations.

       b. The **3P model** focuses on decision making as well as risk assessment and management.

           1) **P**erceive the given set of circumstances.
           2) **P**rocess by evaluating their impact on flight safety.
           3) **P**erform by implementing the best course of action.

       c. You must be able to react to situations and logically determine the best solution.

           1) In addition, you should be ready to explain what alternatives you considered and why you chose the solution you did.

   2. Your analysis of why you determined to act in a certain way is a critical step in both the decision-making process and your ability to display satisfactory competence in this task.

G. The following Gleim resources can also offer assistance:

   1. *Pilot Handbook*, Study Unit 6, "Aeromedical Factors and Aeronautical Decision Making (ADM)" – Covers decision making, including weather-related decision making, and risk management techniques.

   2. *Aviation Weather and Weather Services*, Part III, "Aviation Weather Services" – Covers many FAA weather reports and forecasts in common use, explaining interpretation and common errors associated with each.

H.   Be able to decide and execute an appropriate course of action to properly handle any situation that arises that may cause a change in the original flight plan in such a way that leads to a safe and successful conclusion of the flight.

   1.   The evaluator will be testing your adaptability to unforeseen circumstances. (S)he will want to see that you can safely and effectively alter your plans when the situation demands it.

      a.   EXAMPLE: While inbound to land at an airport, the evaluator tells you to suppose that ATC advised you that an emergency aircraft was 15 min. out and inbound to land at your airport. You have 2 hr. of fuel remaining, and the nearest airport with a suitable runway is 20 mi. away. The evaluator asks what action you would take.

         1)   The two most obvious alternatives are to ask to circle at your destination or divert to another airport.

            a)   Since you have 2 hr. of fuel remaining, you could plan to circle for 30 min. and then divert if the emergency situation had not been resolved. That allows you a safe margin of fuel when you arrive at your alternate airport.

            b)   You could elect to divert immediately, in case of unforeseen circumstances at your alternate airport.

            c)   Either option is a safe choice. The key is being able to explain why you choose to follow a particular course of action.

   2.   Notice the terminology used – "an appropriate course of action." There is rarely one way to solve a problem. As long as your solution maintains the safety of the flight, you need not worry about choosing the solution that the evaluator may select.

      a.   There is no one right answer in this situation except for maintaining safety.

I.   Be able to explain how the elements of risk management, CFIT awareness, overall situational awareness, use of automation, and task management influenced the decisions made and the resulting course of action.

   1.   Be aware that all elements of SRM work together toward the common goal of producing better pilot reactions and decisions in flight.

      a.   Assessing the risks associated with a course of action gives you a better idea of the potential outcomes of your decisions.

      b.   CFIT awareness and situational awareness in general provide a framework for where you are and what is going on around you, which are two important factors in choosing or eliminating potential action steps.

      c.   In some situations, using automation to assist you can actually get you behind the airplane and cause you to miss important transmissions or course changes. You must choose effectively when to use automation.

      d.   Task management is critical because some phases of flight require more action on your part than others. You must know what the demands of flight are and whether you have the ability to address them all within the time allotted. If not, you must select an alternative course of action.

   2.   The course of action you pursue should be based on your overall assessment of the situation and your determination that you have chosen the best alternative. Every element of SRM should be employed because making a good decision directly relates to how effectively you have used the resources available to you.

J.   Common Errors Associated with ADM

1.   **Making knee-jerk reactions rather than following a logical decision-making process**

a.   Snap judgments in the cockpit are usually unnecessary. Reactionary measures are necessary in some emergency situations, but even those decisions are the product of a practiced, logical decision-making process.

b.   Practice explaining in-flight decisions with your CFI early in your training. This will get you in the habit of thinking through the choices you make as well as explaining your motivations.

c.   Practice using a decision-making model in your day-to-day activities so that the process can become more familiar and practiced.

2.   **Lack of familiarity with ADM concepts and how they interrelate**

a.   Despite the fact that ADM principles are regarded by many as unnecessarily academic, a lack of these skills is the cause of most accidents. You will do well to take these concepts seriously, study them, and understand how they interrelate with one another.

1)   EXAMPLE: Understanding the avionics in your airplane but not understanding task and automation management techniques can present risks to you because you have a valuable resource you cannot effectively use. In trying to use your advanced equipment, you may become distracted and lose control of the airplane. Alternatively, in failing to use it, you may miss out on critical assistance that could make the difference between a safe landing and an accident.

b.   Almost all of these concepts have mnemonic memory aids that can help you remember them. Practice listing various ADM concepts and writing explanations of what role they play and how they connect with other concepts

1)   You will not have time to do this in the cockpit. It is no place to try to remember how to make a good decision. Your decision-making and ADM skills will only be acceptable if you spend time practicing them on the ground.

5.2   PILOT-RELATED, AIRCRAFT-RELATED, AND ENVIRONMENTAL FACTORS AND EXTERNAL PRESSURES

A.   **Be aware of the four fundamental risk elements associated with flight.**

1.   The four risk elements in any flight are the pilot, aircraft, environment, and external pressures of any given aviation situation.

a.   Each of these items is discussed in Subunit 5.1.

2.   You must explain to the evaluator what risks are associated with each element in a given scenario and how you evaluated those risks.

a.   EXAMPLE: Your evaluator asks what weather minimums exist for operating in Class G surface airspace.

1)   As a student pilot, you explain that you will set personal minimums for yourself in regard to ceilings and visibilities that must exist for you to conduct flight operations.

2)   Even though Class G weather minimums allow you to operate with 1 mi. of visibility while you remain clear of clouds, you determine that you will not attempt flight operations unless you have a 1,000-ft. or higher ceiling and at least 3 mi. visibility. As your experience and comfort levels grow, you will re-evaluate these minimums.

        3) In this example, you have explained that, due to pilot-related risk factors, you will not conduct operations in certain inherently risky environmental conditions due to lack of experience personally and with the aircraft in such circumstances. You elect to set personal minimums so that no external pressures (such as a sick relative, business need, etc.) can force you into unsafe situations.

B. **Create personal minimums to ensure a safe decision is made every time.**

  1. Personal minimums define your self-imposed limitations on a variety of flight factors, including weather.

  2. Personal minimums should be constructed from a variety of sources, including Federal Aviation Regulations, personal experience, and pilot comfort levels.

    a. Begin by determining what is legal (i.e., look to the regulations).

    b. From there, consider personal experience and comfort levels to further restrict yourself to minimums more in line with what is safe.

  3. Personal minimums should be reviewed and updated over time.

    a. As your experience grows, your personal minimums will grow as well.

    b. Review your personal minimums every 6 months and consider revisions carefully.

  4. Personal minimums must not be altered for a given flight. Stick with the plan you have established.

    a. Giving in to the pressure to take a flight that contradicts your personal minimums is inviting trouble; it is a breakdown in the risk management process.

C. **Use a tool, such as the PAVE checklist, to help assess the four risk elements.**

  1. Such tools help you identify risk before departure and assist you in the decision-making process.

  2. The PAVE checklist (**P**ilot, **A**ircraft, en**V**ironment, **E**xternal pressures) can help you remember the four risk elements associated with a flight to remind you to examine each area.

    a. The PAVE checklist is discussed in more detail in Study Unit 6 of the Gleim *Pilot Handbook*.

  3. Whatever tool or memory aid you use, the important thing is that you understand what risks exist for a given flight condition.

    a. This should be done before every flight, even familiar trips, to ensure you are seeing the big picture.

D. **Use a personal checklist, such as the I'M SAFE checklist, to determine personal risks.**

  1. The I'M SAFE checklist is a familiar personal risk assessment tool. Each item is listed below.

    a. **I - Illness:** Am I suffering from any illness or symptoms?

    b. **M - Medication:** Am I currently taking any drugs (prescription or over-the-counter)?

    c. **S - Stress:** Am I worried about other factors in life? Are any psychological pressures of everyday living a distraction that will affect my performance?

    d. **A - Alcohol:** Have I consumed alcohol in the past 8 hr.? In the past 24 hr.? Even if I am legal, I must be sure there is zero chance of impairment.

    e. **F - Fatigue:** Am I well rested?

    f. **E - Emotion/Eating:** Am I emotionally upset about anything? Have I eaten enough of the proper foods to keep adequately nourished during the entire flight?

  2. Creating and using a risk assessment matrix is also an effective way to ensure that all risk elements are considered and evaluated.

    a. You can find an example matrix created by Gleim on the next page. Make use of this tool as a guide for considering all risk elements prior to a flight.

Gleim Preflight Risk Assessment Matrix

During each preflight planning session, use this form to gauge your overall risk. This form is based on the PAVE checklist and will help you determine if your intended flight is riskier than normal based on the factors listed. Making good decisions in the airplane starts on the ground. Grade yourself in each of these categories in an honest, self-evaluative manner. Further note that this list is not exclusive. If any other factors will affect your flight, you must consider those factors. The go/no-go decision could be entirely based on factors not listed here. **Remember, as the pilot in command, you have the ultimate responsibility for the safety of your flight.**

Before each flight, fill in the appropriate element score in the Rating column and total these numbers to assess your overall flight risk.

	1	2	3	4	5	Rating
Pilot						
Experience	>1500 hours	500-1500 hours	300-500 hours	100-300 hours	<100 hours	
Recency (last 90 days)	>20 hours	15-20 hours	10-14 hours	5-9 hours	<5 hours	
Currency	VFR and IFR		VFR not IFR		Not VFR or IFR	
Emotional Condition	Excellent	Good	Average	Poor	Unacceptable	
Aircraft						
Fuel Reserves	Exceeds requirement		Meets requirement		None	
Time in Type	>400 hours	300-400 hours	200-300 hours	100-200 hours	<100 hours	
Performance	Well within limits		At limits		Outside limits	
Equipment	GPS, weather display	Hand-held GPS	VOR	Minimum required	Does not meet 14 CFR 91.205	
enVironment						
Airport	Adequate, familiar		Barely adequate		Unfamiliar, inadequate	
Weather (IFR/VFR)	VFR		MVFR	IFR	LIFR	
Runways	Dry, hard, long	Dry, hard, short	Dry, soft, short	Wet, hard, short	Wet, soft, short	
Lighting (Day VFR=1)	Runway, taxiway		Runway only		None	
Terrain	Flat, populated		Flat, unpopulated		Mountainous	
External pressures						
Delays/Diversions	No pressure exists		Inconvenient		Not possible	
Alternate Plans	No pressure exists		Inconvenient		Not possible	
Personal Equipment	Emergency kit		Cell phone only		None available	
Additional Factors						
					Total Risk Rating →	

Risk within normal parameters. Flying is inherently risky. Do not take any unnecessary risks and examine your personal minimums to ensure compliance.	16-33
Elevated risk. Plan for extra time for flight planning. Review your personal minimums to ensure that all your self-determined standards are being met. Carefully analyze any risks near or on the boundaries of your personal minimums. Delay any flight that exceeds your personal minimums until conditions improve.	34-55 Or a 5 in any row
High risk. Plan for extra time for flight planning and consider requesting assistance from a more experienced pilot, if one is available. Carefully examine your personal minimums to ensure none are being violated. Examine methods of reducing the risk to the extent possible. Consider delaying or canceling the flight if risks cannot be reduced to an acceptable level.	56-80 Or a 5 in any two rows

E. **Use weather reports and forecasts to determine weather risks associated with the flight.**

    1. There is so much weather information available to today's pilots that, at times, we can become overloaded and fail to understand what we should be looking for.

        a. You must be able to access pertinent weather information, decipher it, and interpret what impact that information will have on your flight.

        b. Do not attempt to use weather products you do not fully understand. Your evaluator will spot that immediately.

    2. For basic guidance on weather products specifically tested during your practical test, see Study Unit 12, "Weather Information," beginning on page 119.

    3. Use the table below or a similar tool to quantify weather risks associated with a flight.

Baseline Personal Minimums

Weather Condition		VFR	MVFR	IFR	LIFR
Ceiling					
	Day				
	Night				
Visibility					
	Day				
	Night				

Turbulence		SE	ME	Make/Model	
	Surface Wind Speed				
	Surface Wind Gust				
	Crosswind Component				

Performance		SE	ME	Make/Model	
	Shortest runway				
	Highest terrain				
	Highest density altitude				

	If you are facing:		Adjust baseline personal minimums to:
Pilot	Illness, medication, stress, or fatigue; lack of currency (e.g., haven't flown for several weeks)	A d d	*At least* 500 feet to ceiling
			At least ½ mi. to visibility
Aircraft	An unfamiliar airplane, or an aircraft with unfamiliar avionics/ equipment		*At least* 500 ft. to runway length
enVironment	Airports and airspace with different terrain or unfamiliar characteristics	S u b t r a c t	*At least* 5 kt. from winds
External Pressures	"Must meet" deadlines, passenger pressures, etc.		

F.   **Explain how to recognize risks and how to mitigate those risks throughout the flight.**

    1.   The ultimate goal of risk management is to mitigate (reduce) or eliminate risks.

    2.   You will need to demonstrate to the evaluator that you can use the techniques discussed previously to recognize risks and mitigate them during the entire course of your practical test.

G.   **Use the 5P model to assess the risks associated with each of the five factors of single-pilot resource management (SRM).**

    1.   The **5P model** of SRM is another way to look at risk assessment. Each item is explained below and on the next two pages.

        a.   **Plan**

            1)   The plan can also be called the mission or the task. It contains the basic elements of cross-country planning: weather, route, fuel, current publications, etc.

            2)   The plan should be reviewed and updated several times during the course of the flight.

                a)   A delayed takeoff due to maintenance, fast-moving weather, and a short-notice temporary flight restriction (TFR) may all radically alter the plan.

                b)   The plan is always being updated and modified and is especially responsive to changes in the other four remaining Ps.

            3)   Obviously, weather is a huge part of any plan.

                a)   The addition of real-time data link weather information provided by advanced avionics gives the pilot a real advantage in inclement weather, but only if the pilot is trained to retrieve and evaluate the weather in real time without sacrificing situational awareness.

                b)   Pilots of aircraft without datalink weather or without the ability to effectively interpret it should get updated weather in flight through an FSS.

        b.   **Plane**

            1)   The plane consists of the usual array of mechanical and cosmetic issues that every aircraft pilot, owner, or operator can identify.

            2)   With the advent of advanced avionics, the plane has expanded to include database currency, automation status, and emergency backup systems that were unknown a few years ago.

        c.   **Pilot**

            1)   Flying, especially when used for business transportation, can expose the pilot to high-altitude flying, long distance and endurance, and more challenging weather.

                a)   An advanced avionics aircraft, simply due to its advanced capabilities, can expose a pilot to even more of these stresses.

            2)   The traditional "I'M SAFE" checklist (covered previously) is a good start for pilot risk assessment.

                a)   The combination of late night, pilot fatigue, and the effects of sustained flight at high altitudes may cause pilots to become less discerning, less critical of information, less decisive, and more compliant and accepting.

                b)   Just as the most critical portion of the flight arises (e.g., a night instrument approach in inclement weather after a 4-hour flight), the pilot's guard is down the most.

   3) The 5P process helps a pilot to recognize the physiological situation before takeoff, during flight, and at the end of the flight.

   a) Once risks are identified, the pilot is better equipped to make alternate plans that lessen the effects of these factors and provide a safer solution.

d. **Passengers**

   1) Passengers present a unique situation because, depending on the circumstances of the flight, these individuals can be co-pilots.

   a) Passengers can re-read and help you verify checklist items, keep your navigation materials organized and accessible, and assist with many other tasks.

   b) Obviously, in some circumstances, it would not be appropriate to utilize passengers in such a manner.

   c) Be careful to consider what roles your passengers could play in reducing your workload.

   2) Passengers can also create additional pressures on the pilot to complete a flight as planned or take unnecessary risks.

   a) You should plan for passenger pressures any time they will be on board. Planning for this in advance allows you to be ready to handle these situations with a programmed response.

e. **Programming**

   1) The advanced avionics in modern aircraft add an entirely new dimension to the way GA aircraft are flown.

   a) The electronic instrument displays, GPS, and autopilot reduce pilot workload and increase pilot situational awareness.

   b) The pilot must be trained to properly use these avionics for them to be effective.

   2) While programming and operation of these devices are fairly simple and straightforward (unlike the analog instruments they replace), they tend to capture the pilot's attention and hold it for long periods of time.

   a) To avoid this phenomenon, the pilot should plan in advance when and where the programming for approaches, route changes, and airport information gathering should be accomplished, as well as times it should not.

   b) Pilot familiarity with the equipment, the route, the local air traffic control environment, and personal capabilities in using the automation should dictate when, where, and how the automation is programmed and used.

H.   **More on External Pressures**

1.   External pressures are influences external to the flight that create a sense of pressure to complete a flight–often at the expense of safety.

2.   Meeting deadlines, pleasing people, and accomplishing secondary tasks can push a pilot to take risks that are unnecessary and may be to the detriment of the safety of the flight.

3.   Factors that can be external pressures include the following:

   a.   Someone waiting at the airport for the flight's arrival.

   b.   A passenger the pilot does not want to disappoint.

   c.   The desire to demonstrate pilot qualifications.

   d.   The desire to impress someone (Probably the two most dangerous words in aviation are "Watch this!").

   e.   Desire to satisfy a specific personal goal ("get-home-itis," "get-there-itis," and "let's-go-itis").

   f.   A pilot's general goal-completion orientation.

   g.   The emotional pressure associated with acknowledging that skill and experience levels may be lower than a pilot would like them to be. Pride can be a powerful external factor.

5.3   HAZARDOUS ATTITUDES

A.   Pilots, particularly those with considerable experience, as a rule always try to complete a flight as planned, please passengers, meet schedules, and generally demonstrate that they have the "right stuff."

1.   The basic drive to demonstrate the "right stuff" can have an adverse effect on safety and can impose an unrealistic assessment of piloting skills under stressful conditions.

2.   These tendencies ultimately may lead to dangerous and often illegal practices that could cause a mishap.

B.   In addition to understanding how to make good decisions, you need to understand some of the obstacles to doing so. Below is a list of hazardous attitudes and corresponding antidotes.

1.   Recognize and correct these behaviors in your aeronautical decision-making (ADM) processes.

C.   **Hazardous Attitudes**

1.   **Antiauthority (*Don't tell me!*).** This attitude is found in people who do not like anyone telling them what to do. In a sense, they are saying, "No one can tell me what to do." They may be resentful of having someone tell them what to do or may regard rules, regulations, and procedures as silly or unnecessary. Of course, it is always your prerogative to question authority if you feel it is in error.

2.   **Impulsivity (*Do something quickly!*).** This is the attitude of people who frequently feel the need to do something -- anything -- immediately. They do not stop to think about what they are about to do, they do not determine the best alternative, and they do the first thing that comes to mind.

3.   **Invulnerability (*It won't happen to me.*).** Many people feel that accidents happen to others but never to them. They know accidents can happen, and they know that anyone can be affected. However, they never really feel or believe that they will be personally involved. Pilots who think this way are more likely to take chances and increase risk.

4. **Macho (*I can do it.*).** Pilots who are always trying to prove that they are better than anyone else are thinking *I can do it -- I'll show them.* Pilots with this type of attitude will try to prove themselves by taking risks in order to impress others. While this pattern is often thought of as a male characteristic, women are equally susceptible.

5. **Resignation (*What's the use?*).** Pilots who think *What's the use?* do not see themselves as being able to make a great deal of difference in what happens to them. The pilot is apt to think that things go well due to good luck. When things go badly, the pilot may feel that someone is out to get him or her or may attribute the situation to bad luck. The pilot will leave the action to others, for better or worse. Sometimes, such pilots will even go along with unreasonable requests just to be nice.

D. **Antidotes for Hazardous Attitudes**

1. Hazardous attitudes, which contribute to poor pilot judgment, can be effectively counteracted by redirecting each hazardous attitude so that appropriate action can be taken.

    a. Recognition of hazardous thoughts is the first step in neutralizing them in the ADM process.

2. After recognizing and labeling a thought as hazardous, the pilot should correct the hazardous thought by stating the corresponding antidote.

    a. Antidotes should be memorized for each of the hazardous attitudes so that they automatically come to mind when needed.

3. The hazardous attitude antidotes shown below should be learned thoroughly and practiced.

Hazardous Attitude	Antidote
Antiauthority: *Don't tell me!*	Follow the rules. They are usually right.
Impulsivity: *Do something quickly!*	Not so fast. Think first.
Invulnerability: *It won't happen to me.*	It could happen to me.
Macho: *I can do it.*	Taking chances is foolish.
Resignation: *What's the use?*	I'm not helpless. I can make a difference.

5.4 CONTINUING VFR FLIGHT INTO IMC OR ANY CONDITIONS OUTSIDE OF PERSONAL MINIMUMS

A. The goal is not to fly VFR into IMC.

1. The pilot must manage the risk by checking the weather before the flight. The pilot must make sure to have adequate weather information before the flight, which helps reduce the chance of the pilot inadvertently flying into IMC conditions.

B. Weather is the single largest cause of aviation fatalities. Most of these fatalities are general aviation pilots that encounter IMC conditions while operating under VFR. The importance of complete weather information, understanding the significance of the weather information, and being able to correlate the pilot's skills and training, aircraft capabilities, and operating environment with an accurate forecast cannot be emphasized enough.

1. The ultimate goal of risk management is to mitigate (reduce) or eliminate this risk. You must be open to the possibility that the only safe solution might be canceling or terminating the flight.

C. Continuing VFR into IMC often leads to spatial disorientation or collision with ground/obstacles. It is even more dangerous when the pilot is not instrument rated or current. The FAA and NTSB have studied the problem extensively with the goal of reducing this type of accident. Weather-related accidents, particularly those associated with VFR flight into IMC, continue to be a threat to GA safety because 80% of the VFR-IMC accidents resulted in a fatality.

    1. Research offers no single explanation to account for this type of accident. Is it the end result of poor situational awareness, hazardous risk perception, motivational factors, or simply improper decision making? Or is it that adequate weather information is unavailable, simply not used, or perhaps not understood? Extracting critical facts from multiple sources of weather information can be challenging for even the experienced aviator. And once the pilot is in the air, en route weather information is available only to the extent that (s)he seeks it out if the aircraft is not equipped with operational weather displays.

D. No one has yet determined why a pilot would fly into IMC when limited by training to fly under VFR. In many cases, the pilot does not understand the risk. Without education, we have a fuzzy perception of hazards. It should be noted that pilots are taught to be confident when flying.

E. The pilot needs to be able to recognize risks, analyze them, and then (most importantly) decide what to do about them. Analysis done by the FAA on VFR flight into IMC conditions has yielded some considerations for pilots to mitigate or eliminate this risk. Items to consider include

    1. Understanding that weather presents a hazard that can become an unmanageable risk

    2. Obtaining a thorough and official weather briefing during your preflight preparation

    3. Being aware of self-induced pressure to conduct your flight (identify your motivation)

    4. Exercising good judgment and decision making

    5. Maintaining good situational awareness before, during, and after the flight

    6. Updating weather en route with FSS and confirming weather information from operational displays that need clarification

    7. Always having an alternate flight plan filed and being flexible to change the alternate en route

    8. Doing a risk assessment during your preflight preparation and continuing to evaluate these factors en route

    9. Establishing personal minimums and operating within those minimums

    10. Being aware that overconfidence and ability can conflict with good decision-making

    11. Having an objective standard to make go-no go decisions for launching

    12. Determining an alternate course of action immediately if you do find yourself in a deteriorating weather situation (do not continue into the deteriorating circumstance)

    13. Seeking assistance from FSS or ATC to avoid flight into IMC or any conditions outside of your personal minimums

    14. Always being aware of where VMC conditions exist along the route of your flight

F. For more information on assessing personal minimums, including the Gleim Preflight Risk Assessment Matrix and the Baseline Personal Minimums table for weather, see Subunit 5.2.

G. **Improper risk assessment due to poor weather report/forecast interpretation**

    1. Whether presented on paper, a computer screen, or avionics in the cockpit, you must understand how to read and interpret the weather product you are referencing in order to gain any useful information from it.

    2. Take notes during your preflight weather briefing to discuss with your evaluator.

    3. Make use of stability and significant weather charts to get the big picture on weather conditions. Don't just focus on your planned route of flight.

    4. Be organized and develop a weather avoidance plan that has planned update points and opportunities to re-evaluate the continuation of the flight.

STUDY UNIT SIX
COMPLETING PROCEDURES

6.1 TASK MANAGEMENT

A.   Certain phases of flight (e.g., taking off) are more task-intensive than others. In times of high workload, the evaluator will be monitoring how well you organize your thoughts and prioritize the required tasks.

   1.   EXAMPLE: You should plan for your departure from the airport before taking off. By having all necessary frequencies on standby and a fresh concept of the departure plan and operational considerations, you can focus on proper airspeed and configuration changes required, as well as collision avoidance and any necessary radio communications, as you depart the airport.

B.   Task management is critical because some phases of flight require more action on your part than others. You must know what the demands of flight are and whether you have the ability to address them all within the time allotted. If not, you must select an alternative course of action.

C.   Complete all tasks in a timely manner considering the phase of flight without causing a distraction from flying.

   1.   Plan ahead so you can focus on proper airspeed and configuration changes, as well as collision avoidance.

   2.   Planning ahead prevents situations where more tasks are necessary than you have the capability to complete.

D.   The focus of task management is completing all required tasks in the most efficient manner possible while also minimizing distractions from flying the airplane.

   1.   With experience, a pilot learns to recognize future workload requirements and to prepare for high workload periods during times of low workload.

   2.   Use resources, such as ATIS and UNICOM, to know what to expect and be better prepared.

   3.   Review charts, plates, and performance checklists in advance whenever possible to allow time to focus on other tasks during high workload periods.

   4.   Recognize work overload situations, then slow down, think, and prioritize. "Aviate, navigate, communicate."

E.   **Explain how to prioritize tasks in such a way to minimize distractions from flying the aircraft.**

   1.   It is easy to lose focus in certain phases of flight if you are not thinking ahead.

   2.   You should explain to the evaluator your standard operating procedures when it comes to taxi procedures, takeoff and departure, cruise, and approach.

      a.   EXAMPLE: You could explain that you only perform checklist items when stopped on the ground, rather than when moving. Additionally, you might explain that you brief the airport diagram for unfamiliar airports 20 miles out from the destination and again before arriving in the traffic pattern.

F. **Complete all tasks in a timely manner considering the phase of flight without causing a distraction from flying.**

    1.   Certain phases of flight (e.g., approach and landing) are more task-intensive than others. In times of high workload, the evaluator will be monitoring how well you organize your thoughts and prioritize the required tasks.

        a.   EXAMPLE: You should plan for your arrival at the airport long before arriving in the airport area. By having all necessary frequencies on standby and a fresh concept of the airport layout and operational considerations, you can focus on proper airspeed and configuration changes, as well as collision avoidance and any necessary radio communications, required as you approach the airport.

    2.   Planning ahead prevents situations where more tasks are necessary than you have the capability to complete.

G. **Execute all checklists and procedures in a manner that does not increase workload at critical times.**

    1.   Effective task management reduces pilot workload and cockpit stress.

    2.   During critical phases of flight, all supplementary work should be complete and your focus should be on maintaining positive control of the airplane.

    3.   Remember, if you realize you have missed an important step (e.g., checklist, not extending the landing gear, etc.), you should do whatever is necessary to accomplish that step, including breaking off a landing approach and executing a go-around.

        a.   Do not try to rush through such items, because it will show the evaluator that you have poor task management skills.

H. Common Errors Associated with Task Management

    1.   **Failure to accomplish efficient task management leading to high workload that exceeds the pilot's capabilities**

        a.   In the absence of effective task management, especially during times of high workload, the pilot's capabilities may be exceeded, creating an unsafe situation.

            1)   If warranted, the evaluator may have to take control of the airplane, resulting in immediate failure of the test.

        b.   Think and plan ahead. Know what is coming next and be ready for it.

            1)   Review the content of your airplane checklist and consider expanding it to cover your standard operating procedures regarding traffic pattern entry/exit, power and configuration changes, and automation programming requirements.

    2.   **Failure to take prompt corrective action if tasks are missed or require repetition**

        a.   If you realize that your workload level is quickly becoming too high to maintain safety, it is your responsibility to alter the situation.

            1)   Depending on the phase of flight you are in, you may have time to correct missed tasks, or you may need to remove yourself from your current task, including a landing approach.

            2)   Do not add to your workload by trying to squeeze in a missed checklist item or airport layout review.

3. **Failure to utilize all resources available to the pilot to expedite and/or streamline task management**

    a. Use the internal and external resources available to you to help you accomplish required tasks.

    b. GPS waypoint information, navigational charts, passengers, ATC, Flight Service, and many other resources are at your disposal.

        1) You need to be able to identify the available resources and choose the one(s) that can reduce your workload given the conditions of flight.

6.2 STERILE COCKPIT

A. The Sterile Cockpit Rule is a 14 CFR Part 121 and Part 135 rule, but it is considered a best-practice for 14 CFR Part 91. Your evaluator will expect you to follow it.

B. During critical phases of flight (e.g., takeoff and landing), pilots should refrain from nonessential activities, including personal conversations.

    1. For the purposes of this section, critical phases of flight includes all ground operations involving taxi, takeoff and landing, and all other flight operations conducted from the time of departure to the first intermediate altitude and clearance from the local airspace.

    2. No flight crew member may engage in, nor may any pilot in command permit, any activity during a critical phase of flight that could interfere in any way with the proper conduct of those duties.

C. You must be vigilant during takeoff and climb due to reasons that have already been identified and discussed.

D. The evaluator will expect to see that you can accomplish all required tasks while filtering out the non-essential tasks, such as unnecessary conversation or cell phone use.

E. Focus on the task at hand and do not allow yourself to be distracted.

    1. Be aware that the evaluator may try to distract you with questions. Politely ask the evaluator to standby while you accomplish safe procedures.

F. Bear in mind though that maintaining a sterile cockpit free of distractions is not merely limited to takeoff and climb.

    1. The evaluator will expect you to minimize distractions throughout the entire course of your flight.

6.3 AUTOMATION MANAGEMENT

A. Determine how to use cockpit automation to effectively manage your workload, including how well you handle unanticipated unit operation.

    1. Advanced avionics offer multiple levels of automation from strictly manual flight to highly automated flight.

        a. No one level of automation is appropriate for all flight situations, but in order to avoid potentially dangerous distractions when flying with advanced avionics, the pilot must know how to manage the course deviation indicator (CDI), navigation source, autopilot, and any version of flight management system (FMS) installed in the airplane.

        b. It is important for a pilot to know the peculiarities of the particular automated system being used. This ensures that the pilot knows what to expect, how to monitor for proper operation, and how to promptly take appropriate action if the system does not perform as expected.

    2. In advanced avionics aircraft, proper automation management requires a thorough understanding of how the autopilot interacts with the other systems.

B.   **Recognize the current mode of operation of the autopilot/FMS.**

   1.   Every autopilot installation will offer some form of status indication to the pilot, whether as part of a digital display or a lighted status panel.

      a.   Consult your unit's user guide and your CFI for specific operational considerations.

   2.   You must be able to explain to the evaluator how, at a glance, you can recognize and interpret the mode of operation, for example, NAV hold mode, altitude armed mode, etc.

C.   **Recognize anticipated and unanticipated mode or status changes of the autopilot/FMS.**

   1.   You should be able to explain automatic and manual mode changes that are necessary for your autopilot to function correctly in various phases of flight.

      a.   When switching between VOR and GPS NAV sources while in NAV hold mode, some autopilots revert to wing leveler mode and require the pilot to re-enter NAV hold mode.

   2.   You should be able to explain and demonstrate how altitude changes are made with your autopilot.

      a.   You will likely have to select a vertical speed or airspeed setting for the autopilot to climb to the armed altitude.

      b.   The autopilot should automatically capture the armed altitude and switch to altitude hold mode.

      c.   If for any reason something unexpected happens, you should demonstrate adequate systems knowledge by getting the autopilot into the desired flight condition or taking manual control of the airplane, if necessary.

   3.   Pilots need to identify, assess, and mitigate the risks involved in ineffective monitoring of automation.

      a.   When using full automation, pilots should monitor the aircraft to ensure the aircraft is turning at appropriate lead times and descending once established on-course.

      b.   When pilots do not monitor the automation on the aircraft effectively, it leads to a loss of situational awareness.

D.   **Be able to state at any time during the flight the current mode or status and what the next anticipated mode or status will be.**

   1.   The evaluator may ask you during any phase of flight to report on the current mode or status of cockpit automation as well as to explain what the next mode or status will be.

   2.   You should demonstrate adequate system knowledge by being able to answer without becoming distracted from your other tasks.

      a.   If the evaluator asks you to report on the automation status during a particularly demanding phase of flight, you should politely ask the evaluator to stand by until you have accomplished all necessary tasks.

   3.   At the most basic level, managing the autopilot means knowing at all times which modes are engaged and which modes are armed to engage.

E.   **Use the autopilot/FMS to reduce workload as appropriate for the phase of flight, during emergency or abnormal operations.**

   1.   Automation should be used to reduce your workload, especially during abnormal or emergency operations.

   2.   The evaluator will be monitoring your performance to see how you utilize the available automation resources to manage your workload during all phases of flight, including emergencies.

   3.   If the evaluator does not want you to use the autopilot at any time, (s)he will let you know, usually by telling you to suppose the autopilot has failed.

4. Most of the aviation community believes automation has made flying safer, but there is a fear that pilots fail to see that automation is a double-edged sword. Pilots need to understand the advantages of automation while being aware of its limitations. Experience has shown that automated systems can make some errors more evident while sometimes hiding other errors or making them less obvious.

F. **Recognize unanticipated mode changes in a timely manner and promptly return the automation to the correct mode.**

1. If any abnormal mode changes should occur or anticipated mode change not occur, you should recognize it quickly, report it to the evaluator, and resolve the situation.

2. If you are unable to effectively correct the error without undue distraction, you must revert to manual flight control and reinstate automation when your workload allows.

3. It is important for pilots to know that automation does not replace basic flying skills.

    a. In some situations, using automation to assist you can actually get you behind the airplane and cause you to miss important transmissions or course changes. You must choose effectively when to use automation.

        1) EXAMPLE: Understanding the avionics in your airplane but not understanding task and automation management techniques can present risks to you because you have a valuable resource you cannot effectively use. In trying to use your advanced equipment, you may become distracted and lose control of the airplane. Alternatively, in failing to use it, you may miss out on critical assistance that could make the difference between a safe landing and an accident.

G. Understand the advantages of automation while being aware of its limitations.

1. It is recommended that pilots use their best judgment to choose what level of automation will most efficiently do the task considering the workload and situational awareness.

2. Pilot familiarity with all equipment is critical in optimizing both safety and efficiency. Unfamiliarity with any aircraft system will add to workload and may contribute to a loss of situational awareness.

H. When using automation, you should maintain flight skills and ability to maneuver the aircraft manually within the standards set forth in by the FAA.

1. It is recommended that pilots of automated aircraft occasionally disengage the automation and manually fly the aircraft to maintain stick-and-rudder proficiency.

2. When using automation, it is a good time to practice callouts.

I. Transitioning to Automated Systems

1. For the GA pilot transitioning to automated systems, it is helpful to note that all human activity involving technical devices entails some element of risk.

    a. Knowledge, experience, and flight requirements tilt the odds in favor of safe and successful flights.

    b. Advanced avionics aircraft offer many new capabilities and simplify the basic flying tasks, but only if the pilot is properly trained and all the equipment is working properly.

2. Humans are characteristically poor monitors of automated systems.

    a. When passively monitoring an automated system for faults, abnormalities, or other infrequent events, humans perform poorly. The more reliable the system is, the worse human performance becomes.

        1) For example, when a pilot monitors only a backup alert system rather than the situation that the alert system is designed to safeguard.

    b. It is a paradox of automation that technically advanced avionics can both increase and decrease pilot awareness.

J. Common Errors Associated with Automation Management

    1. **Failure to properly program cockpit automation**

        a. This error could be caused by lack of familiarity with the equipment or lack of attention to follow the correct procedures.

        b. Create standard operating procedures for when and how to use the autopilot in all phases of flight.

            1) Entering data into an FMS or autopilot system should be done systematically each time.

            2) Conducting operations in this way better equips you to spot potential problems and errors.

    2. **Improper automation use resulting in distractions and/or loss of situational awareness**

        a. You must program automation at times when workload allows.

            1) Trying to set up the autopilot while maintaining the final approach course is inappropriate and unsafe.

            2) Likewise, trying to program the flight plan into an FMS during climbout shows poor task management and automation management.

        b. Overloading yourself puts you in danger of exceeding your capabilities and losing situational awareness.

    3. **Failure to make effective use of automation resources to reduce workload in critical situations**

        a. In an emergency situation or if you feel you are being overloaded with tasks, cockpit automation should be used to help maintain safety.

        b. You should select the correct resources and, in turn, use them correctly. It is as much about effective resource use as it is about effective resource choice.

6.4 UTILIZE/COMPLETE CHECKLISTS

A. The purpose of a checklist is for operational safety.

    1. A checklist is a tool to aid memory and help ensure that critical items necessary for the safe operation of aircraft are not overlooked or forgotten.

    2. Without discipline and dedication to using the checklist at the appropriate times, the odds are on the side of error.

    3. Pilots who fail to take the checklist seriously become complacent and the only thing they can rely on is memory.

B. You should use the appropriate checklist for a specific phase of your flight while on the ground or in the air (e.g., before starting engine, during climb, before landing, etc.).

C. We emphasize the appropriate use of checklists throughout this book.

    1. A checklist provides a listing of actions and/or confirmations. For example, you either "turn on the fuel pump" or "confirm that the fuel pump is on."

    2. If the desired condition is not available, you have to decide whether to accept the situation or take action. For example, if your engine oil temperature is indicating a higher-than-normal temperature while en route, you may continue your flight or attempt to divert for a landing, depending upon the level of overheating and relative changes in the temperature.

3.   Each item on the checklist requires evaluation and possible action:

    a.   Is the situation safe?

    b.   If not, what action is required?

    c.   Is the overall airplane/environment safe when you take all factors into account?

4.   There are different types of checklists:

    a.   "Read and do," e.g., before-takeoff checklist.

    b.   "Do and read," e.g., in reacting to emergencies. Do everything that comes to mind and then confirm or research in your POH/AFM.

5.   Ensure that the checklist is a **tool**, not a crutch.

    a.   You should be able to function without the checklist.

6.   The checklist is designed to "back you up," not remind you how to do things.

    a.   In other words, checklists are not an end in and of themselves. Checklists are a means of flying safely. Generally, they are to be used as specified in the POH/AFM and to accomplish safe flight.

D.   All checklists should be read aloud at all times.

1.   Call out each item on the checklist as you undertake the action or make the necessary observation.

E.   When using a checklist, you must consider proper scanning vigilance and division of attention at all times.

STUDY UNIT SEVEN
SITUATIONAL AWARENESS

7.1 SITUATIONAL AWARENESS

A. **Situational awareness**, by definition, is the accurate perception and understanding of all the factors and conditions within the four fundamental risk elements (pilot, aircraft, environment, and external pressures) that affect safety before, during, and after the flight.

    1.   It includes pilot knowledge of where the aircraft is in regard to location, air traffic control, weather, terrain, regulations, aircraft status (including fuel), and other factors that may affect flight.

    2.   Being situationally aware means that you have an overview of the total operation and are not fixated on one perceived significant factor.

B. Maintaining situational awareness requires an understanding of the relative significance of all flight related factors and their future impact on the flight.

    1.   When a pilot understands what is going on and has an overview of the total operation, (s)he is not fixated on one perceived significant factor. It important to know the aircraft's geographical location, and also just as important to understand what is happening.

    2.   Monitoring radio communications for traffic, weather discussion, and ATC communication can enhance situational awareness by helping the pilot develop a mental picture of what is happening.

C. In extreme cases, when a pilot gets behind the aircraft, a loss of positional or situational awareness may result.

    1.   The pilot may not know the aircraft's geographical location, or may be unable to recognize deteriorating circumstances.

D. Fatigue, stress, and work overload can cause a pilot to **fixate** on a single perceived important item and reduce an overall situational awareness of the flight.

    1.   A contributing factor in many accidents is a distraction that diverts the pilot's attention from monitoring the instruments or scanning outside the aircraft.

    2.   Many flight deck distractions begin as a minor problem, such as a gauge that is not reading correctly, but result in accidents as the pilot diverts attention to the perceived problem and neglects to properly control the aircraft.

    3.   Just like instrument fixation can lead to disorientation, situational fixation can lead to missed cues of hazards in flight that could impact safety.

E. You should be able to state the current situation at any time during the flight in such a way that displays an accurate assessment of the current and future status of the flight, including weather, terrain, traffic, ATC situation, fuel status, and aircraft status.

    1.   Make it a habit to regularly scan your engine instruments as well as weather, terrain, and traffic displays (if equipped).

        a.   Also listen to and store ATC/traffic communications to determine what is going on around you.

F. Situational awareness is not limited to airborne operations.

   1. The pilot must be aware of the potential risks of losing situational awareness during low visibility and/or instrument conditions. According to National Transportation Safety Board (NTSB) and FAA data, one of the leading causes of GA accidents is continued VFR flight into IMC.

      a. Most of these accidents occur to a GA operator, usually flying a light single- or twin-engine aircraft, who encounters IMC conditions while operating under VFR.

      b. The pilot must always know where he or she is, be able to recognize deteriorating circumstances, and judge the rate of the deterioration.

      c. When VFR pilots continue to fly into low visibility and/or instrument conditions, the possibility of a loss of situational awareness resulting in a loss of control is greatly increased.

G. The pilot should devote maximum possible attention to maintaining situational awareness during all phases of flight.

   1. The risk of losing situational awareness is greatest in conditions of darkness or reduced visibility and during times of high workload.

   2. Without a clearly discernible horizon, even large deviations from a desired heading, attitude, altitude, or course may not be immediately obvious.

   3. Continued flight in reduced visual conditions or instrument conditions is further compounded by night operations and/or overwater flight.

H. VFR pilots are trained in the basics of attitude instrument flying to allow them the opportunity to successfully get out of deteriorating VFR or IFR conditions.

   1. An inadvertent encounter into IFR conditions is an emergency situation that will require proficiency in basic instrument maneuvers for successful exiting.

I. Understand taxi operation planning procedures, such as recording taxi instructions, reading back taxi clearances, and reviewing taxi routes on the airport diagram.

   1. Your taxi route, including where to hold short, should be determined and firmly established in your mind before you leave the ramp.

      a. Make use of airport diagrams to review runway incursion hotspots (if any).

      b. If you are operating at a non-towered airport, be sure that you fit into the flow of ground traffic and choose the most appropriate taxi route to and from the active runway.

   2. Whether you are operating at a tower-controlled airport or not, make it a habit early in your training to write down your taxi route to your intended takeoff runway or to the ramp after landing.

      a. Consider drawing your taxi route on an airport diagram to aid your situational awareness during your taxi.

      b. Make note of ATC taxi instructions, especially when they involve multiple turns, so that you do not get lost, take a wrong turn, and/or cause a ground traffic incident.

   3. Whenever you are assigned taxi instructions by ATC, read back the instructions in a clear tone of voice so the controller is sure you know what is expected of you.

      a. Avoid rushing through your radio transmissions. The controller is much more interested in the fact that you understood and acknowledge the correct taxi route than in your speed of delivery.

      b. Be sure to clearly announce your acknowledgment of holding instructions in a timely manner.

   4. Always make use of airport diagrams for unfamiliar airports, especially large, complex ones, so that you are well aware of your position on the airport and the location of your destination when operating on the ground.

J. Pilots have many resources to help with situational awareness in the traffic pattern. These include

    1. Advanced avionics, such as GPS moving maps, traffic systems, and weather display systems

    2. The use of autopilot systems to allow more time for scanning

    3. Radio communication with ATC and other aircraft

K. Other factors that contribute to situational awareness relate to "Staying ahead of the airplane" by proper planning.

    1. Conduct a proper approach briefing, which includes studying the airport diagram.
    2. Program frequencies ahead of time when possible.
    3. Be familiar with the aircraft you are flying.

L. **Explain procedures for steering, maneuvering, maintaining taxi, runway position, and situational awareness.**

    1. The evaluator wants to see that you have thought ahead and know how you will accomplish your ground operations at the airport.

        a. You should expect scenario-based questioning on busy airport operations whether or not you are operating out of a complex airport.

    2. You should explain, based on real or scenario ATC instructions, how you will maneuver the aircraft either from the ramp to the runway or the runway to the ramp while simultaneously ensuring that you comply with ATC requirements and taxi in a manner that promotes ground safety (e.g., considering crosswinds, other aircraft or vehicles, and appropriate speeds).

    3. Again, consider highlighting your route on an airport diagram printout so you can visually comprehend your taxi route, thus encouraging positive situational awareness.

M. **Keeping your workload to a minimum during taxi operations should increase your awareness during taxiing.**

    1. Avoid programming cockpit automation or completing checklists while the aircraft is moving on the ground.

        a. Ideally, all programming and all checklist items that can be completed prior to taxi should be accomplished prior to leaving the ramp area.

        b. Head-down time during taxi operations is a very serious distraction that can result in missing a routing assignment, bumping into an airplane, or just getting behind and forgetting something important prior to takeoff/shutdown.

    2. Repeat all ATC instructions and ask clarification for any instructions that you do not understand.

    3. Focus on the task at hand and do not allow yourself to be distracted.

        a. Be aware that the evaluator may try to distract you with questions during taxi. Politely ask the evaluator to standby while you accomplish safe taxi procedures.

N. **Explain ATC communications and pilot operations before takeoff, before landing, and after landing at controlled and uncontrolled airports.**

    1. Always use standard terminology/phraseology when communicating with ATC, especially in high-volume traffic environments.

    2. Make all appropriate position reports whenever you are arriving to or departing from an airport, regardless of whether or not the airport is tower-controlled.

O. **Use the navigation displays, traffic displays, terrain displays, weather displays, and other features of the aircraft to maintain a complete and accurate awareness of the current situation and any reasonably anticipated changes that may occur.**

    1.   Effective resource management is critical to maintaining situational awareness.

    2.   Consider the following recommendations for helping you maintain situational awareness while in flight.

        a.   Perform verification checks of all programming. Before departure, check all information programmed while on the ground.

            1)   Incorrect keystrokes could lead to loss of situational awareness because the pilot may not recognize errors made during a high workload period.

        b.   Check the flight routing. Before departure, ensure all routing matches the planned flight route.

            1)   Enter the planned route and legs, including headings and leg length, on a paper log.

            2)   Use this log to evaluate what has been programmed. If the two do not match, do not assume the computer data is correct; double-check the computer entry.

        c.   Verify that waypoints and vectors issued by ATC are reasonable.

            1)   Make use of moving map displays to ensure your routing is logical and ordered correctly.

        d.   Make use of all onboard navigation equipment. For example, use VOR to back up GPS and vice versa.

        e.   Match the use of the automated system with pilot proficiency. Stay within personal limitations.

        f.   Plan a realistic flight route to maintain situational awareness.

            1)   Planning a direct flight across the country is unreasonable. Make use of ATC preferred routing in the Chart Supplement, and ask Flight Service for flow delays and routing issues when filing your flight plan, especially if you are flying into a busy airport or busy airspace.

P.   Common Errors Associated with Situational Awareness

    1.   **Fixation on individual flight situations rather than on the flight environment as a whole**

        a.   Refer to the explanation of items A. and C. to better understand and be able to better explain what situational awareness is as well as the dangers inherent in not maintaining that awareness.

    2.   **Failure to accomplish all relevant pre-taxi tasks before leaving the ramp area and/or performing distracting tasks while attempting to taxi to or from the runway**

        a.   Accomplish all checklist items from the ramp area or at appropriate times when the aircraft is in a designated area for stopping on the airport, such as a run-up area.

        b.   Program and set all cockpit avionics and instruments before leaving the ramp area to avoid distractions while taxiing and delays when waiting for takeoff.

    3.   **Failure to make use of available resources to maintain situational awareness throughout the flight**

        a.   Refer to the explanation in item O. to better understand the value and necessity of effective resource use in maintaining situational awareness.

7.2 RUNWAY INCURSION AVOIDANCE

A. A runway incursion is any occurrence in the airport runway environment involving an aircraft, vehicle, person, or object on the ground that creates a collision hazard or results in a loss of required separation with an aircraft taking off, intending to take off, landing or intending to land.

B. A pilot should be aware of the aircraft's position at all times and be aware of the other aircraft's position.

C. As it applies to traffic patterns, the following practices can help prevent runway incursions:

1. Read back all runway landing and take off clearances, including runway number.
2. Review airport layouts as part of preflight planning and before descending to land.
3. Know airport signage and markings.
4. Review NOTAM information.
5. Fly the correct traffic pattern for the runway in use.
6. Confirm runway number with heading indicator during all traffic pattern legs.
7. Request progressive taxi from ATC when unsure of taxi route.
8. Check for traffic before crossing or entering any runway or taxiway.
9. When landing, clear the active runway in a timely fashion.
10. Use proper phraseology and good radio discipline at all times.
11. Write down complex taxi instructions.

D. The potential for runway incidents and accidents can be reduced through adequate planning, coordination, and communication.

E. The following guidelines will help you cope with current airport conditions during taxi operations:

1. Plan for airport surface movement as you would for other phases of flight.

    a. Review airport diagrams, NOTAMs, hot spots, runway hold short lines, ILS critical areas, and determine the best location to complete checklists.

    b. Brief the following at the appropriate time (e.g., before taxi and prior to initial descent for landing)

        1) The expected taxi route to include any hold short lines and runways to cross, hot spots as well as any potential conflicts.

        2) Complete the after-landing checklist after the entire aircraft has crossed the runway hold short line.

2. Pilot/Passenger communications: advise passengers of sterile cockpit and to refrain from any unnecessary conversation.

    a. Advise occupants of sterile cockpit, but to speak up if anyone sees a potential conflict.

    b. Do not allow any cell phone use by anyone during taxi or flight operations.

3. Situational awareness: Use a "continuous loop" process to actively monitor and update their progress and location during taxi.

    a. This includes knowing the aircraft's present location and mentally calculating the next location on the route.

        1) Have current airport diagram readily available.

        2) Monitor the taxi clearance and read back all hold short instructions.

        3) Know and use all of the visual aids available at the airport.

        4) Prior to crossing any runway, be positive that ATC has cleared you and scan the full length of the runway and for aircraft on final approach.

        5) Comply with hold short instructions when approaching a runway.

        6) Be vigilant if another aircraft has a similar call sign.

        7) If you become disoriented, never stop on a runway and initiate communications.

        8) Be especially vigilant when instructed to taxi and "Line Up and Wait."

4. Write down taxi instructions.

5. ATC/Pilot communication:

    a. Use standard phraseology.
    b. Do not perform other nonessential tasks during communications.
    c. Read back all clearances.
    d. Actively monitor the assigned tower frequency or CTAF for potential conflicts.

6. Taxiing: use good operating practices regarding cockpit activities during taxi.

7. Use of exterior aircraft lights to make aircraft more visible:

    a. Engine running – Rotating beacon
    b. Taxiing – Navigation, position, anti-collision, and logo lights, if available

        1) Taxi light on during taxi movement, and off when stopped or yielding

        2) Strobe lights off if they will adversely affect the vision of other pilots or ground personnel

    c. Crossing a runway – all exterior lights on
    d. Takeoff – landing light on when takeoff clearance is received

7.3 TERRAIN AVOIDANCE, INCLUDING CONTROLLED FLIGHT INTO TERRAIN (CFIT)

A. Do not become so fixated you neglect to scan the area and understand your altitude versus terrain.

B. Controlled flight into terrain (CFIT) can be defined as an event in which a normally functioning aircraft is inadvertently flown into terrain, water, or obstacles, often without prior knowledge by the pilot/crew.

1. Due to the physical forces involved, the vast majority of CFIT accidents are fatal to one or more of the aircraft's occupants.

2. The element of surprise is also a factor in the lethality of CFIT accidents because it prevents the pilot/crew from taking actions (such as reducing airspeed or modifying the flight path) to minimize the impact forces.

3. Accordingly, you must aggressively emphasize **avoidance** of the scenarios that lead to CFIT accidents.

C. While CFIT accidents are typically associated with IFR operations in mountainous areas, they can happen to aircraft operating under IFR or VFR, over all kinds of terrain, and at any time of day or night.

   1. While many factors can contribute to a CFIT accident, one causal factor common to most such accidents is **the loss of situational awareness**.

   2. Devote maximum possible attention to maintaining situational awareness during all phases of flight.

       a. The risk of losing situational awareness is greatest in conditions of darkness or reduced visibility and during times of high workload.

       b. Without a clearly discernible horizon, even large deviations from a desired heading, attitude, altitude, or course may not be immediately obvious.

   3. Under high-workload conditions, a pilot's instrument scan can break down, allowing such changes to go unnoticed and setting the stage for a CFIT event.

   4. Times of low workload can also be hazardous because they can lead to boredom and complacency at a time when the pilot should be monitoring the progress of the flight and preparing for the upcoming phases.

D. CFIT is an issue of concern to all pilots, whether operating visually or under instrument conditions.

   1. CFIT involves any accident where a pilot or crew has control of the airplane (meaning normal flight operations) and flies into terrain or obstacles with little or no warning.

   2. CFIT normally results from a combination of factors including

       a. Weather
       b. Unfamiliar environment
       c. Nonstandard procedures
       d. Breakdown or loss of communications
       e. Loss of situational awareness
       f. Lack of perception of hazards
       g. Lack of sound risk management techniques

E. **Use current charts and procedures during the planning of the flight to ensure the intended flight path avoids terrain and obstacles.**

   1. Have current aeronautical charts available for the practical test.

   2. Understand altitude figures printed on charts, and be ready to explain the meanings of those figures to the evaluator.

   3. The evaluator will want to see that you have selected altitudes and courses that avoid terrain and obstacles.

       a. You must also be able to explain the "why" behind your planning.

       b. Recall that the evaluator is not just looking for decisions. (S)he is also looking for a sound decision-making process that analyzes and mitigates risk.

F. **Be aware of potential terrain and obstacle hazards along the intended route.**

   1. If you do not have high terrain in your area, you can expect the evaluator to have you plan a route that at least involves obstacle awareness and avoidance.

   2. Be familiar with charts from mountainous areas, as your evaluator could present one to you and ask for your analysis of a particular route.

       a. Make use of online resources to review these charts.

G. **Explain the terrain display, Terrain Awareness and Warning System (TAWS), and/or Ground Proximity Warning System (GPWS) as installed in the aircraft.**

    1. If you operate a modern aircraft equipped with advanced avionics, you will need to explain what equipment you have installed as well as how you can use that equipment to avoid terrain and obstacles.

    2. A terrain display is usually associated with a GPS unit or multi-function display (MFD).

        a. Colors are used to alert the pilot to his or her proximity to terrain features.

            1) Red generally indicates the airplane is within 100 ft. of the terrain.
            2) Yellow generally indicates the airplane is within 1,000 ft. of the terrain.

        b. Towers and other obstructions are usually depicted with reference to the airplane's current heading.

        c. Many systems also include pop-up messages and/or aural warnings when immediate hazards are present.

        d. Refer to your unit's user guide for specific indications, and be ready to explain these indications to the evaluator along with what you would do if you encountered them.

    3. TAWS and GPWS are essentially the same thing. TAWS is merely a broader category within which GPWS fits.

        a. These systems provide aural warnings to the pilot/crew to provide alerts for immediate hazards caused by terrain or obstacles.

        b. Using a digital database, these systems make predictions of potential terrain hazards using the current flight path of the airplane.

        c. In addition to giving impact warnings, these systems are also capable of warning pilots of excessive descent rates, lack of altitude gain during takeoff, excessive ground closure rate, proximity to the ground during descent, and other useful items.

        d. These systems are generally more advanced technology than that found in GA cockpits. However, you should still exhibit knowledge of the technology and how it is different than what your airplane is equipped with.

H. **Use the terrain display, TAWS, and/or GPWS of the navigation displays as appropriate to maintain awareness and to avoid terrain and obstacles.**

    1. This task objective is the next logical step following the one above. In addition to explaining your equipment and its use, the evaluator will want to see you using it to positively maintain situational awareness in the avoidance of terrain and obstacles during all pertinent phases of flight.

    2. Again, if you do not operate in a mountainous area, expect scenario-based questioning on that topic as well as emphasis on obstacle awareness and avoidance near your route of flight.

    3. Your use of automation in the cockpit must aid in task management by reducing your workload.

        a. Do not attempt to use this equipment to show off for the evaluator at the expense of missing critical tasks and losing situational awareness.

I. **Plan departures and arrivals to avoid terrain and obstacles.**

    1. You must consider the performance capabilities of your airplane, and plan your departure and arrival procedures accordingly.

        a. Be aware of where obstacles are located near your departure and destination airports, and plan to use runways that provide maximum obstacle clearance.

        b. Be sure to consider atmospheric factors, such as high density altitude, when planning for obstacle clearance.

J. **Alter flight as necessary to avoid terrain.**

    1. After you determine a terrain hazard exists, whether during preflight planning or while in flight, you must act accordingly to avoid that hazard.

    2. Be sure to explain to your evaluator your thought process for making course/altitude changes, especially before doing so in flight.

        a. Make sure you consider all applicable factors when making a diversion decision, including but not limited to fuel use, requirements relating to ATC communication, and weather and additional terrain avoidance.

K. **Plan any course diversion, for whatever reason, in such a way to ensure proper terrain and obstruction clearance to the new destination.**

    1. When you make a diversion decision due to terrain hazards, be sure that you have allowed yourself proper terrain clearance for the remainder of the flight.

        a. This directly relates to not making snap judgments, but rather using a logical, practiced decision-making process.

    2. Making diversion after diversion increases your workload, creates many distractions, and can cause a significant reduction in your situational awareness.

L. **Explain and understand aircraft performance limitations associated with CFIT accidents.**

    1. Consider the performance of the specific aircraft intended to be used for the flight. Ask yourself the following questions to consider whether the aircraft has any limitations that could cause a CFIT accident.

        a. Are you familiar with the aircraft and its unique performance characteristics? Different variations of the same model handle and perform differently.

        b. Are the runways of adequate length to allow for a sufficient margin of safety under the conditions of flight and aircraft loading?

        c. Can the aircraft operate at the altitudes required for obstacle and terrain clearance for the entire flight?

        d. Does the aircraft have sufficient fuel capacity and reserves for the planned legs and conditions of flight?

M. Common Errors Associated with CFIT

    1. **Improper knowledge and use of installed aircraft equipment**

        a. There is an old adage regarding technology in aircraft – "If you don't understand it, don't use it."

        b. While that might seem to be sound logic, it does not fly during the practical test.

            1) The evaluator will expect you to be proficient at using the equipment installed in the airplane.

            2) If your airplane is equipped with terrain monitoring/avoidance resources, you need to be able to use those resources and explain your interpretation of and reaction to the information you receive.

    c.   There is an attitude in many pilots that they are required to demonstrate their single-handed control of the airplane without using cockpit resources. This is absolutely false.

        1)   If your airplane is equipped with an autopilot, not only should you use it to reduce your workload, but the evaluator will expect and in some cases require you to use the autopilot during the practical test.

        2)   Likewise, there is no need to fumble around with a sectional chart in the cockpit when you have a current terrain database capable of providing you with terrain and obstacle references based on your current position and flight path.

        3)   Such resources reduce distractions and allow you to maintain positive control of the airplane, especially in emergency situations where terrain avoidance becomes critical to the safety of the flight.

2.   **Poor task management during terrain-related diversion leading to loss of situational awareness**

    a.   Again, make use of the available resources in the cockpit to reduce your workload and maintain or increase your situation awareness.

    b.   With most terrain-related situations, there is not a lot of time for you to consult charts or query ATC. Because of this, it is critical that you minimize your workload and act deliberately and efficiently.

    c.   Head-down time is your enemy in the cockpit. In addition to creating a distraction from flying the airplane, it can also lead to potential collisions and spatial disorientation in reduced visibility conditions.

3.   **Failure to ensure terrain and obstacle avoidance during and after a diversion is initiated**

    a.   Successfully avoiding terrain and obstacles by planning and executing a diversion is important, but more important is your ability to ensure that your diversion fixes the terrain-related problem without creating another one.

    b.   Terrain and obstacles must be thought of in the big picture sense.

        1)   The only way to do this is to maintain situational awareness of your environment.

        2)   You rarely have the ability to slightly alter your course to avoid terrain without creating other terrain issues in the process.

    c.   Use a programmed decision-making process to ensure that the outcome of your actions is a desired and safe outcome.

7.4 COLLISION AND OBSTACLE AVOIDANCE AND SCANNING

A.   Check the area to ensure to ensure that no obstructions or other aircraft are in the immediate vicinity.

B.   Conduct two clearing turns while scanning for traffic and obstacles.

C.   For enhanced collision avoidance and better visibility when landing or taking off, landing lights are strongly encouraged even in airplanes that are not operated for compensation or hire.

D.   Obstacles may be difficult to discern until it is too late, especially in lower visibility conditions. Provide adequate margin of safety and engage passengers to assist with scanning.

E.   Also, keep a good visual look-out and encourage passengers to look for traffic and point it out to you.

F.   Monitor the radio for calls from other aircraft that would give you an indication of where they are and what their intentions might be.

G. **Scanning** the sky for other aircraft is a key factor in **collision avoidance**. You should scan continuously to cover all areas of the sky visible from the cockpit. Most midair collisions and reported near midair collisions occur during good VFR weather conditions and during the hours of daylight.

1. You must develop an effective scanning technique that maximizes your visual capabilities.

2. Effective scanning is accomplished with a series of short, regularly-spaced eye movements that bring successive areas of the sky into the central visual field.

    a. Each eye movement should not exceed 10°.
    b. Each area should be observed for at least 1 second to enable detection.

3. Visual tasks inside the cabin should represent no more than 1/4 to 1/3 of the scan time outside or no more than 4 to 5 seconds on the instrument panel for every 16 seconds outside.

H. Specific techniques to avoid collisions with traffic:

1. Determining relative altitude -- Use the horizon as a reference point. If you see another aircraft above the horizon, it is probably on a higher flight path. If it appears to be below the horizon, it is probably flying at a lower altitude.

2. Taking appropriate action -- You must be familiar with the rules of right-of-way so that, if an aircraft is on an obvious collision course, you can take the appropriate evasive action.

3. Considering multiple threats -- The decision to climb, descend, or turn is a matter of personal judgment, but you should anticipate that the other pilot also may be making a quick maneuver. Watch the other aircraft during the maneuver, but begin your scanning again immediately. There may be even more aircraft in the area!

4. Observing collision course targets -- Any aircraft that appears to have no relative motion and stays in one scan quadrant is likely to be on a collision course. Also, if a target shows no lateral or vertical motion, but it increases in size, take evasive action.

5. Recognizing high-hazard areas

    a. Airways, VORs, and airport traffic areas are places where aircraft tend to cluster.
    b. Remember that most collisions occur on days when the weather is good.

6. Practicing cockpit management -- Study maps, checklists, and manuals BEFORE flight, along with other proper preflight planning (e.g., noting necessary radio frequencies). Also, organizing cockpit materials can reduce the time you need to look at them during flight, permitting more scan time.

7. Improving windshield conditions -- Dirty or bug-smeared windshields can greatly reduce your ability to see other aircraft. Keep a clean windshield.

8. Considering visibility conditions -- Smoke, haze, dust, rain, and flying toward the sun can also greatly reduce the ability to detect other aircraft.

9. Being aware of visual obstructions in the cockpit.

    a. You may need to move your head to see around blind spots caused by fixed aircraft structures, such as door posts, wings, etc. It may even be occasionally necessary to maneuver your airplane (e.g., lift a wing) to facilitate seeing.
    b. Check that curtains and other cockpit objects (e.g., maps that glare on the windshield) are removed and stowed during flight.

10. Using lights.

    a. Day or night, exterior lights can greatly increase the visibility of any aircraft.
    b. Keep interior lights low at night so that you can see out in the dark.

11. Requesting ATC support -- ATC facilities often provide radar traffic advisories (e.g., flight following) on a workload-permitting basis. Use this support whenever possible or when required.

a. Nevertheless, being in a radar environment (i.e., where traffic is separated by radar) still requires vigilance to avoid collisions. Radar does not relieve you of the responsibility to see and avoid other aircraft.

7.5 COMMUNICATION AND EXPECTATION BIAS

A. When issued instructions by ATC, focus on listening and repeat to yourself exactly what is said in your head and then apply that information actively.

1. Does the clearance make sense? If something does not make sense (incorrect call sign, runway assignment, altitude, etc.), then query the controller about it.

B. When issued instructions by ATC – focus on listening and repeat to yourself exactly what is said in your head – and then apply that information actively.

1. Does the clearance make sense? If something does not make sense (incorrect call sign, runway assignment, altitude, etc.) – then query the controller about it.

2. Don't let your expectations lead to a pilot deviation. Listen carefully – and fly safe!

C. Expectation bias: what we hear

1. The Air Traffic Control System is heavily dependent upon verbal communication to exchange information between controllers and pilots.

2. Hearing what we expect to hear is frequently listed as a causal factor for pilot deviations that occur both on the ground and in the air.

3. ATC expectation bias is defined as "Having a strong belief or mindset towards a particular outcome."

a. An analysis of runway incursion data shows that expectation bias is one of the most common causal factors for pilot deviations.

b. Data from the Air Traffic Safety Action Program confirms this fact.

4. Understand that expectation bias often affects the verbal transmission of information.

7.6 WIRE STRIKE AVOIDANCE

A. While low-level flying is dangerous by nature, the possibility of wire strike makes it even riskier.

1. The advent of cellular towers and other technologies has led to the regular construction of many new towers.

2. Some towers are held in place by guide wires attached to the surface.

B. Proper planning can help pilots avoid wire strike. This planning should include the use of

1. Applicable sectional and terminal area charts
2. Chart Supplements
3. Minimum en route and/or approach altitudes
4. Notices to Airmen (NOTAMs)

a. NOTAMs are especially important because they contain timely information about new construction that may not be included in printed publications.

C. Be cognizant of wire strikes when choosing areas for emergency landings/ditching.

1. Power lines are often found along roads and on the edges of fields.

D. Be cognizant of wire strikes at the end of runways.

    1. Power lines are often found along roads and on the edges of fields. Roads are often found perpendicular to the ends of runways.

    2. Power lines adjacent to runways are usually marked with orange markers.

E. A mistake with a wire strike is one where you never have a chance to make the mistake a second time.

F. Pay close attention to antennas, powerlines, and roads.

    1. You should assume any road has powerlines and, therefore, try to not use a road as an emergency landing strip unless it is your last resort.

7.7 WAKE TURBULENCE

A. Wake turbulence is a phenomenon resulting from the passage of an aircraft through the atmosphere. The term includes thrust stream turbulence, jet blast, jet wash, propeller wash, and rotor wash, both on the ground and in the air, but wake turbulence mostly refers to wingtip vortices.

B. You should memorize and practice the following wake turbulence avoidance procedures:

    1. **Landing behind a larger aircraft that is landing on the same runway** -- Stay at or above the larger aircraft's final approach flight path. Note the aircraft's touchdown point and land beyond it.

    2. **Landing behind a larger aircraft that is landing on a parallel runway closer than 2,500 ft. to your runway** -- Consider possible vortex drift to your runway. Stay at or above the larger aircraft's final approach path and note its touchdown point.

    3. **Landing behind a larger aircraft that is landing on a crossing runway** -- Cross above the larger aircraft's flight path.

    4. **Landing behind a larger aircraft departing on the same runway** -- Note the larger aircraft's rotation point. Land well prior to the rotation point.

    5. **Landing behind a larger aircraft departing on a crossing runway** -- Note the larger aircraft's rotation point.

        a. If the larger aircraft rotates past the intersection, continue your approach and land prior to the intersection.

        b. If the larger aircraft rotates prior to the intersection, avoid flight below the larger aircraft's flight path.

            1) Unless your landing is assured well before reaching the intersection, abandon the approach.

    6. **Departing behind a larger aircraft taking off** -- Note the larger aircraft's rotation point. You should rotate prior to the larger aircraft's rotation point. Continue to climb above and stay upwind of the larger aircraft's climb path until turning clear of its wake.

        a. Avoid subsequent headings that will cross below and behind a larger aircraft.

        b. Be alert for any critical takeoff situation that could lead to a vortex encounter.

    7. **Intersection takeoffs on the same runway** -- Be alert to adjacent larger aircraft operations, particularly upwind of your runway. If intersection takeoff clearance is received, avoid a subsequent heading that will cross below a larger aircraft's path.

    8. **Departing or landing after a larger aircraft has executed a low approach, a missed approach, or a touch-and-go landing** -- Vortices settle and move laterally near the ground, so the vortex hazard may exist along the runway and in your flight path.

        a. Ensure that an interval of at least 2 min. has elapsed before your takeoff or landing.

9. **En route VFR** -- Avoid flight below and behind a larger aircraft's path. If you observe a larger aircraft above and on the same track as your airplane (meeting or overtaking), adjust your position laterally, preferably upwind.

10. Operational Problem Areas

    a. While serious, even fatal, accidents can be caused by wake encounters, not all wake encounters are hazardous.

        1) A wake encounter can be one or more jolts with varying severity depending upon

            a) The direction of the wake encounter
            b) The weight of the generating aircraft
            c) The size of your airplane
            d) The distance from the generating aircraft
            e) The point of vortex encounter

        2) The probability of an induced roll increases when your airplane's heading is generally aligned or parallel with the flight path of the generating aircraft.

    b. You must avoid the area below and behind the generating aircraft, especially at low altitudes where even a momentary wake encounter could be hazardous.

        1) Avoiding a wake encounter is not always easy to do; some accidents have occurred even though the pilot of the trailing aircraft had carefully noted that the aircraft in front was at a considerably lower altitude.

            a) Unfortunately, the flight path of the lead aircraft does not always remain below the flight path of the trailing aircraft.

    c. You should be particularly alert in calm wind conditions and situations in which the vortices could

        1) Remain in the touchdown area
        2) Drift from aircraft operating on a nearby runway
        3) Sink into the takeoff or landing path from a crossing runway
        4) Sink into the traffic pattern from other airport operations

STUDY UNIT EIGHT
EMERGENCIES

8.1 ENERGY MANAGEMENT

A. Energy management refers to managing the energy state of the airplane. The energy state of an airplane is the balance between airspeed, altitude, drag, and thrust and represents how efficiently the airfoil is operating.

    1. In other words, it is the ability to manage the kinetic and potential energy of the aircraft.

B. The more efficiently the airfoil operates, the larger the stall margin present.

    1. Increasing a pilot's situational awareness of the energy condition of the airplane can provide him or her with information that (s)he needs to prevent a loss of control (LOC) scenario resulting from a stall/spin.

    2. Additionally, the less energy that is utilized to maintain flight, the greater the overall efficiency of the airplane, which is typically realized in fuel savings. This equates to a lower operating cost to the pilot.

C. A pilot should be aware of the aircraft's energy condition during all phases of flight (e.g., taxi, takeoff, climb, level off, descent, maneuvers, approach, landing, and parking). A pilot should strive to perfect the art of energy management.

    1. There are four basic forces always acting on an airplane: lift, weight, thrust, and drag.

    2. Airspeed, along with trending airspeed, power settings, drag, altitude, and environmental conditions all factor into an aircraft's energy.

        a. How the pilot controls the variables of aircraft energy is the making of the artistic balance of flight.

        b. A poorly performed action or lack of action can fundamentally "snowball" into another maneuver or phase of flight, causing disastrous effects.

D. To understand energy management, the pilot must understand basic aerodynamics.

    1. In steady (or constant) flight, the four basic forces are in equilibrium.

        a. When pressure is applied to one or more of the airplane controls, one or more of the basic forces change in magnitude and become greater than the opposing force, causing the airplane to move in the direction of the applied force(s).

            1) EXAMPLE: If power is applied (increasing thrust) and altitude is maintained, the airplane will accelerate. As speed increases, drag increases until a point is reached at which drag again equals thrust. Then the airplane will continue in steady flight at a higher speed.

        b. The amount of lift that a given wing generates at a given altitude is directly related to its angle of attack and airspeed.

    2. The amount of drag present at a given airspeed is equal to the amount of thrust required to maintain level flight at that airspeed and angle of attack.

        a. If thrust is increased beyond that required for level flight, the airplane will climb unless it is retrimmed for a lower angle of attack and a higher airspeed.

        b. If thrust is reduced, the airplane will descend.

E. Energy management requires an understanding of the relationship between pitch and power. In many situations, pilots must appropriately manage the energy available to them.

   1. Adjusting the angle of attack varies the amounts of lift and drag produced by the wing.

   2. Adjusting the airplane's power allows the airplane to change airspeed, altitude, or both.

   3. Thus, the pilot can achieve a desired performance from the airplane (in terms of airspeed and altitude) through a variety of pitch and power combinations.

      a. A climb may be initiated by raising the nose to increase the angle of attack, or by increasing power, or by using both.

      b. A descent may be initiated by lowering the nose to reduce the angle of attack, or by decreasing power, or by using both.

      c. To increase airspeed in level flight, power must be increased and angle of attack reduced to maintain level flight.

      d. To decrease airspeed in level flight, power must be reduced and angle of attack increased to maintain level flight.

   4. You need to get in the habit of having either pitch or power control (adjust) airspeed. The same goes for altitude, which can be controlled by either pitch or power.

   5. Depending on the aircraft configuration, a combination of pitch and power adjustments are necessary to change altitude and airspeed.

F. In critical situations, such as when airplanes are at a high angle of attack (e.g., take off and initial climb) or when airplanes are without power (e.g., a power-off approach or engine out situation), energy management is paramount because pilots cannot rely on thrust to gain airspeed.

   1. Unfortunately, in these scenarios, the only force a pilot can control is pitch because no additional (or any) thrust is available.

   2. To keep from stalling the airplane, a pilot's only choice is to decrease the pitch (i.e., lower the nose of the airplane).

   3. When flying the **backside of the power curve** or **region of reversed command**, you should avoid the natural tendency to pull back on the control yoke in order to climb because increasing the angle of attack will increase drag and may cause the airplane to descend or stall (if the critical angle of attack is exceeded).

   4. In essence, by decreasing the pitch, gravity is providing the energy by turning the airplane's potential energy (i.e., altitude) into kinetic energy. In other words, the airplane will gain airspeed at a cost of altitude.

      a. In power-off or engine out situations, it is imperative for pilots to try to maintain their best glide speed.

         1) By pitching for the best glide speed, pilots can use the least amount of "energy" to keep them airborne, so they can make the runway or emergency landing area.

   5. In practice, this is why your instructor, during a stall, tells you to lower the nose to decrease your angle of attack.

G. Energy management is necessary to achieve safe landings.

   1. During approach and landing, there may be situations in which a deficit of energy (low/slow) or excess (high/fast) regularly occur. These situations can result in landing short/long, overshooting the runway, a go-around/missed approach, or even a loss of control.

H. Energy management is helpful in other situations.

1. Pilots can continually ensure they manage the energy of their aircraft by keeping the airspeed at or near the maximum endurance speed (V_{ME}).

   a. This is the airspeed that requires the least amount of thrust to obtain the highest airspeed. An example can found found in *Pilot Handbook*, Study Unit 1, Subunit 7.

   b. For example, a descent in a high performance aircraft at altitude with the aircraft in a clean configuration and flight idle power settings may result in an "over speed" condition.

      1) The pilot with proper situational awareness in energy management should notice the tailwind, adjust the speed or path accordingly and if necessary apply the proper drag (i.e., speed brakes) to control the situation.

I. In summary, pilots must monitor and adjust artificially and appropriately the energy of the aircraft in all phases of flight.

1. Pilots accomplish this with the coordination of power, drag, flight path, and altitude by the manipulation of the controls available.

2. The FAA and the General Aviation Joint Steering Committee (GAJSC) promote the use of an angle of attack indicator to show the amount of reserve lift available. This helps prevent LOC accidents.

8.2 EMERGENCY PROCEDURES (INCLUDING ENGINE FAILURE)

A. Checklists describing the recommended procedures and airspeeds for coping with various types of emergencies or critical situations are located in the Section 3, Emergency Procedures, of your POH/AFM.

1. Some of the emergencies covered include engine failure, fire, and system failure. The procedures for inflight engine restarting and ditching may also be included. Manufacturers may first show an emergency checklist in an abbreviated form, with the order of items reflecting the sequence of action. Amplified checklists that provide additional information on the procedures follow the abbreviated checklist.

2. To be prepared for emergency situations, memorize the immediate action items and, after completion, refer to the appropriate checklist.

B. In any case, pilots must follow the applicable emergency procedures outlined in the POH/AFM. Generally, these procedures contain recommendations concerning altitude and airspeed where the airstart is most likely to be successful.

C. **Emergency Procedures**

1. Remember that an emergency situation exists (e.g., loss of pressurization, cockpit smoke, and/or fire), and you have decided that the best course of action is an emergency descent.

   a. EXAMPLE: If you are in a pressurized airplane at 18,000 ft. MSL and you lose pressurization, you must descend to a lower altitude at the fastest rate practicable before the effects of hypoxia overcome you and your passengers.

2. As with any emergency, you must understand and recognize the urgency of the situation.

3. Always follow the phrase: Aviate, Navigate, Communicate.

   a. If your airplane is experiencing an emergency such as loss of power, if you become doubtful about any condition that could adversely affect flight safety, or if you become apprehensive about your safety for any reason, use the emergency frequency 121.5 MHz.

      1) When you broadcast on the emergency frequency, you will receive immediate attention at the FSSs and towers monitoring 121.5.

2) All towers, FSSs, and radar facilities monitor the emergency frequency, but normally only one FAA facility at a given location monitors the frequency.

3) If you are already on an ATC control frequency, e.g., a control tower or approach control, you should declare an emergency with that facility because its controllers are already conversant with your call sign, location, etc.

4. Emergency approaches and landings can be the result of a complete engine failure, a partial power loss, or a system and/or equipment malfunction that requires an emergency landing.

   a. During actual forced landings, it is recommended that you maneuver your airplane to conform to a normal traffic pattern as closely as possible.

   b. Continuing straight ahead or making only a slight turn allows you more time to establish a safe landing attitude, and the landing can be made as slowly as possible.

      a) Importantly, the airplane can be landed while under control.

   c. The main objective when a forced landing is imminent is to complete a safe landing in the largest and best field available.

      1) Completing a safe landing involves getting the airplane on the ground in as near a normal landing attitude as possible without hitting obstructions.

      2) Your airplane may suffer damage, but as long as you keep the airplane under control, you and your passengers should survive.

D. **Emergency Procedures relating to the Takeoff Sequence**

1. Before taxiing onto the runway, review the critical airspeeds used for takeoff, the takeoff distance required, and takeoff emergency procedures.

   a. You will then be thinking about this review during the takeoff roll. It helps prepare you for any type of emergency that may occur.

2. Review the V_R, V_X, V_Y, and other takeoff performance airspeeds for your airplane.

   a. As you reach these airspeeds, plan to call them out loud.

3. From your preflight planning, you have already determined the expected takeoff distance for the conditions.

   a. Confirm that the runway and wind conditions are adequate to meet performance expectations.

4. Takeoff emergency procedures are set forth in Section 3, Emergency Procedures, of your POH/AFM. Prepare ahead for all contingencies. Be prepared at all times to execute an emergency landing if you lose an engine. Remember, **maintain airspeed** so you control your situation rather than enter a stall/spin.

   a. The most common emergency on takeoff is the loss of engine power during the takeoff roll or during the takeoff climb.

      1) If engine power is lost during the takeoff roll, pull the throttle to idle, apply the brakes, and slow the airplane to a stop.

      2) If you are just lifting off the runway and lose your engine power, try to land the airplane on the remaining runway. Leave it in the flair attitude that it is already in. It will settle back down to the ground; i.e., land it like a normal landing.

         a) It is very important not to lower the nose because you do not want to come down on the nosewheel.

      3) If you cannot land on remaining runway, maintain your heading. Turning the airplane will result in a drastic loss of altitude. It is safest to maintain your heading and find the most suitable landing area in front of you.

E. **Engine Failure during Takeoff and Climb**

1. The first step is to maintain positive control of your airplane. DO NOT PANIC.

2. The second step in any emergency is deciding an appropriate course of action.

    a. The action will depend on how critical a situation is.

    b. An engine failure on takeoff is a very critical situation that will not allow time for emergency checklists or a restart, in most cases. However, an engine failure at altitude will allow some time to attempt a restart and go through the appropriate emergency checklists.

3. After you decide the appropriate course of action, immediately implement your decision.

4. If engine power is lost during the takeoff roll, pull the throttle to idle, apply the brakes, and slow the airplane to a stop.

    a. If you are just lifting off the runway and you lose your engine power, land the airplane straight ahead.

5. If an actual engine failure should occur immediately after takeoff and before a safe maneuvering altitude (at least 500 ft. AGL) is attained, it is usually inadvisable to attempt to turn back to the runway from which the takeoff was made.

    a. Instead, it is generally safer to establish the proper glide attitude immediately and select a field directly ahead or slightly to either side of the takeoff path.

    b. The decision to continue straight ahead is often a difficult one to make unless you consider the problems involved in turning back.

        1) First, the takeoff was in all probability made into the wind. To get back to the runway, you must make a downwind turn, which will increase your groundspeed and rush you even more in the performance of emergency procedures and in planning the approach.

        2) Next, your airplane will lose considerable altitude during the turn and might still be in a bank when the ground is contacted, thus resulting in the airplane cartwheeling.

        3) Last, but not least, after you turn downwind, the apparent increase in groundspeed could mislead you into attempting to slow down your airplane prematurely, thus causing it to stall.

6. Even though your performance calculations may show the runway length is adequate, consider creating personal minimums that allow for an additional margin of safety in case a failure occurs immediately after takeoff.

F. **Engine Failure after Takeoff**

1. A power loss or engine failure occurring after lift off requires immediate action while maintaining aircraft control.

    a. In most instances, the pilot has only a few seconds after an engine failure to decide what course of action to take and to execute it.

    b. Unless prepared in advance to make the proper decision, the pilot is more likely to make a poor decision or make no decision at all and allow events to rule.

2. In the event of an engine failure on initial climbout, the pilot's first responsibility is to maintain aircraft control.

    a. At a climb pitch attitude without power, the airplane will be at or near a stalling angle of attack.

    b. At the same time, the pilot may still be holding right rudder.

    c. It is essential the pilot immediately lower the pitch attitude to prevent a stall and possible spin.

3. The pilot should establish a controlled glide toward a plausible landing area (preferably straight ahead on the remaining runway).

4.   Remember not to panic and to take appropriate action based on your training. Be mentally prepared for the possibility of engine failure.

   a.   Review the manufacturer's recommended procedures for engine failure after takeoff ahead of time.

   b.   There is little time available to search for a suitable field for landing in the event the need arises, so research available emergency landing sites in advance.

   c.   Check the area to ensure that no obstructions or other aircraft are in the immediate vicinity.

5.   Establish and maintain best glide speed while keeping turns to a minimum. Do not attempt to turn back to the runway as this could result in a low altitude stall/spin that could be unrecoverable.

6.   The altitude available is, in many ways, the controlling factor in the successful accomplishment of an emergency landing. If an actual engine failure should occur immediately after takeoff and before a safe maneuvering altitude is attained, it is usually inadvisable to attempt to turn back to the field from where the takeoff was made. Rather, establish the proper glide attitude and select a field directly ahead or slightly to the side of the takeoff path.

7.   Pilots should be aware of the minimum altitude to turn back to the airport.

   a.   Experimentation at a safe altitude should give the pilot an approximation of height lost in a descending 180° turn at idle power.

   b.   By adding a safety factor of about 25%, the pilot should arrive at a practical decision height. The ability to make a 180° turn does not necessarily mean that the departure runway can be reached in a power-off glide; this depends on the wind, the distance traveled during the climb, the height reached, and the glide distance of the airplane without power.

   c.   The pilot should also remember that a turn back to the departure runway may in fact require more than a 180° change in direction.

8.   EXAMPLE: Engine failure at 300 feet AGL:

   a.   Using a standard rate (3° change in direction per second) turn, it will take 1 min. to turn 180°.

   b.   At a glide speed of 65 kt., the radius of the turn is 2,100 ft., so at the completion of the turn, the airplane will be 4,200 ft. to one side of the runway. The pilot must turn another 45° to head the airplane toward the runway. By this time, the total change in direction is 225°, equating to 75 sec. plus 4 sec. initial reaction time for the pilot to make a decision.

   c.   If the airplane in a power-off glide descends at approximately 1,000 fpm, it will have descended 1,316 ft., placing it 1,016 ft. below the runway.

G.   **Emergency Procedures during Approach and Landing**

1.   Checklists describing the recommended procedures and airspeeds for coping with various types of emergencies or critical situations are located in the Section 3, Emergency Procedures, of your POH/AFM.

   a.   Some of the emergencies covered include engine failure, fire, and system failure. The procedures for inflight engine restarting and ditching may also be included. Manufacturers may first show an emergency checklist in an abbreviated form, with the order of items reflecting the sequence of action. Amplified checklists that provide additional information on the procedures follow the abbreviated checklist. To be prepared for emergency situations, memorize the immediate action items and, after completion, refer to the appropriate checklist.

2.   In any case, pilots must follow the applicable emergency procedures outlined in the POH/AFM. Generally, these procedures contain recommendations concerning altitude and airspeed where the airstart is most likely to be successful.

STUDY UNIT NINE
WEATHER

9.1 ATMOSPHERIC CONDITIONS AND EFFECTS ON AIRCRAFT

A. **Air density** has significant effects on the aircraft's performance. The general rule is that, as air density decreases, airplane performance decreases.

   1. Temperature, altitude, barometric pressure, and humidity all affect air density. The density of the air DECREASES as

      a. Air temperature INCREASES
      b. Altitude INCREASES
      c. Barometric pressure DECREASES
      d. Humidity INCREASES

   2. The engine produces power in proportion to the density of the air.

      a. As air density decreases, the power output of the engine decreases.

         1) This decrease in power is true of all engines not equipped with a supercharger or turbocharger.

   3. The propeller produces thrust in proportion to the mass of air being accelerated through the rotating blades.

      a. As air density decreases, propeller efficiency decreases.

   4. The wings produce lift as a result of the air passing over and under them.

      a. As air density decreases, the lift efficiency of the wing decreases.

   5. At power settings of less than 75%, or at density altitudes above 5,000 ft., it is essential that normally aspirated engines be leaned for maximum power on takeoff, unless equipped with an automatic altitude mixture control.

      a. The excessively rich mixture adds another detriment to overall performance.

      b. Turbocharged engines need not be leaned for takeoff in high density altitude conditions because they are capable of producing manifold pressure equal to or higher than sea-level pressure.

      c. At airports of higher elevations, such as those in the western U.S., high temperatures sometimes have such an effect on density altitude that safe operations may be impossible.

         1) Even at lower elevations with excessively high temperature or humidity, airplane performance can become marginal, and it may be necessary to reduce the airplane's weight for safe operations.

B. As the PIC, you must know and understand your aircraft's performance limits. Specifically, you must know whether, under a given set of atmospheric conditions, your aircraft is capable of clearing terrain and obstacles near the airport on departure or during a go-around.

C. Takeoff performance data can normally be found in Section 5, Performance, in the airplane's POH/AFM. These data may be presented in either a graph or a chart.

   1. Takeoff performance graphs are presented either in terms of density altitude or in terms of pressure altitude and temperature.

D. An increase in density altitude has the following effects on takeoff performance:

    1. Decreased thrust and thus reduced accelerating force.

        a. Non-turbocharged engines have less available power.
        b. Propeller efficiency is decreased.

    2. Greater takeoff speed.

        a. A higher true airspeed is required to provide sufficient lift for takeoff.
        b. However, indicated airspeed will remain the same regardless of density altitude.

    3. Accurate determination of pressure altitude (not field elevation) and temperature is essential for predicting takeoff performance.

E. The most critical conditions of takeoff performance are the result of some combination of high gross weight, high airport elevation, high temperature, and unfavorable wind.

9.2 WIND DIRECTION INDICATORS

A. It is important for you to know the wind direction when landing or taking off at an airport.

    1. At airports without an operating control tower, wind direction may be obtained by

        a. Listening to an automated weather system, such as ASOS or AWOS
        b. Contacting ground personnel on a UNICOM frequency
        c. Wind sock, tetrahedron, or other wind indicators

            1) Where wind or landing direction indicators do not exist, observe the flow of traffic or use natural indicators, such as smoke or wind over a lake.

    2. At towered airports,

        a. ATC provides wind direction information
        b. Listen to Automated Terminal Information System (ATIS)
        c. Monitor tower frequency for traffic flow indications

    3. At an airport with an operating control tower, ATC provides this information.

        a. At an airport with a flight service station (FSS) and without an operating control tower, the FSS can provide you with the wind information.

    4. At an airport without an operating control tower, you may be able to receive wind information from an FBO at the airport.

    5. You may also be able to obtain wind information from automated weather systems located at some airports.

B. Virtually all airports have a wind indicator of one of the following types:

    1. Wind socks (or cones) are fabric "socks" through which wind blows.

        a. The large end of the wind sock points into the wind; the wind blows through the sock from the large end to the small end.
        b. The vertical angle out from the pole indicates the strength of the wind.

            1) A limp sock means no wind.
            2) A horizontal sock means strong wind.
            3) A sock that is moving back and forth may indicate a variable or a gusty wind.

    2. Wind (landing) tees have the stem (bottom) of the "T" pointing in the direction the wind is GOING (indicating that landings should be in the opposite direction). Think of the wind tee as a small airplane (with the wings represented by the crossbar or top of the "T") landing into the wind.

        a. The landing tee indicates the direction of the wind but not the wind velocity.

3. Tetrahedrons point to the direction from which the wind is COMING (indicating that landings should be in that direction).

    a. A tetrahedron will indicate the direction of the wind but not the wind velocity.

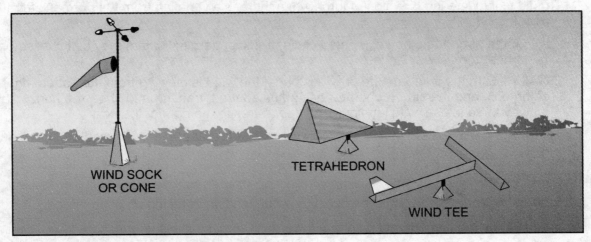

WIND SOCK OR CONE

TETRAHEDRON

WIND TEE

C. Some airports have a landing direction indicator (tetrahedron or landing tee) that is manually set by the airport operator to show the direction of landings and takeoffs.

    1. Think of the tetrahedron as a delta-wing jet fighter landing into the wind.

    2. Pilots are cautioned against using the tetrahedron as a wind indicator.

    3. When making a runway selection by use of a tetrahedron in very light or calm wind conditions, you should use extreme caution when selecting a runway because the tetrahedron may not be aligned with the designated calm-wind runway.

D. Where wind or landing direction indicators do not exist, observe the flow of traffic or use natural indicators.

    1. Smoke from ground fires, power plants, etc., shows wind direction.

    2. The water on the windward side of lakes and ponds tends to be calm, leaving a glassy surface that can be easily identified when airborne.

    3. The term windward refers to the side of the lake or pond that the wind is coming from.

E. The segmented circle system, if installed, provides traffic pattern information at airports without operating control towers. It consists of the following:

    1. The **segmented circle** is located in a position affording maximum visibility to pilots in the air and on the ground. A wind and/or landing direction indicator is usually in the center.

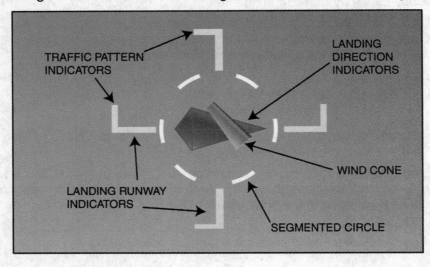

TRAFFIC PATTERN INDICATORS

LANDING DIRECTION INDICATORS

WIND CONE

LANDING RUNWAY INDICATORS

SEGMENTED CIRCLE

2. **Landing runway (strip) indicators** are installed in pairs as shown in the segmented circle on the previous page and are used to show the alignment of runways.

3. **Traffic pattern indicators** are arranged in pairs with the landing runway indicators and are used to indicate the direction of turns when there is a variation from the normal left traffic pattern.

    a. If the airport has no segmented circle, traffic pattern indicators may be installed on or near the runway ends.

4. EXAMPLE: In the figure on the previous page, the wind is blowing from the bottom right of the box, and the airport operator has adjusted the tetrahedron to show the horizontal runway to be in use, with landings and departures to the right of the box.

    a. The traffic pattern indicators show the left traffic pattern is to be used on this runway.

9.3 WIND CONDITIONS

A. It is important for you to know the wind direction when landing or taking off at an airport.

1. At an airport with an operating control tower, ATC provides this information.

2. At an airport without an operating control tower, you may be able to receive wind information from an FBO at the airport.

B. Wind direction and velocity will have a significant effect on the takeoff roll, as well as approach and landing performance.

1. A headwind will reduce the overall takeoff distance because the airplane will reach its takeoff airspeed at a lower groundspeed, thus becoming airborne sooner than in calm wind.

2. A tailwind will increase the takeoff distance because the airplane must achieve a greater groundspeed to attain the takeoff speed, thus becoming airborne later than in calm wind.

3. The effects of a crosswind on takeoff performance will vary depending on the wind direction. A 90° crosswind will have very little effect on takeoff distance.

4. A gusting wind situation will require that the airplane's takeoff speed be increased slightly, thus keeping the airplane on the ground longer and increasing the overall takeoff roll.

5. Thus, you must be aware of wind direction and velocity both for the desired landing direction and for their effect on glide distance.

C. Other factors may dictate a crosswind or downwind landing.

1. Insufficient altitude may make it inadvisable or impossible to attempt to maneuver into the wind.

2. Ground obstacles may make landing into the wind impractical or inadvisable because they shorten the effective length of the available field.

3. The distance from a suitable field upwind from the present position may make it impossible to reach the field from the altitude at which the engine failure occurs.

4. The best available field may be on a hill and at such an angle to the wind that a downwind landing uphill would be preferable and safer.

D. Crosswind

1. A crosswind takeoff and climb is one in which your airplane is NOT headed directly into the wind.

2. Takeoffs and landings in certain crosswind conditions are inadvisable or even dangerous. If the crosswind is strong enough that the airplane is incapable of preventing a sideways drift, a hazardous landing condition may result.

    a. Always consider the takeoff or landing capabilities with respect to the reported surface wind conditions and the available landing directions.

　　　b.　The airplane's POH/AFM indicates the maximum crosswind component capability of the airplane.

　　　c.　Some POH/AFMs have a chart so the pilot can determine the crosswind component.

3.　Many airplanes have an upper limit to the amount of direct crosswind in which they can land (usually about 20% of stall speed). Crosswinds of less than 90° are converted into a 90° component on graphs.

4.　Consider that your aircraft may need to decrease the wind components further than the suggested POH/AFM.

　　　a.　Do you have an STC for your airplane, such as tip tanks or vortices?

　　　b.　Are you comfortable with crosswind landings when the airplane is half full of fuel?

　　　　　1)　Landing on minimum fuel reserves mans the airplane is light and more susceptible to crosswinds than when the airplane is heavier.

5.　When encountering a crosswind on takeoff, have your ailerons positioned into the wind, with the aileron up as the roll begins. With the aileron up, this action prevents the wind from getting under the wing and lifting it prematurely. As your speed builds, gradually neutralize the ailerons to prevent a sudden roll to the side with an aileron up as the ailerons gain control authority. At the point of lift off, the ailerons will be neutralized, and then shift to a crab that is sufficient to maintain a straight ground track as you climb out.

9.4 WIND SHEAR

A.　Wind shear is the unexpected change in wind direction and/or wind speed. During an approach, it can cause severe turbulence and a possible decrease in your airspeed (when a headwind changes to a tailwind), causing your airplane to stall and possibly crash.

1.　Wind shear generates eddies between two wind currents of differing velocities.

　　　a.　The differences may be in speed and/or direction (both horizontal and vertical) and may occur at any altitude.

2.　Three conditions are of special interest:

　　　a.　Wind shear with a low-level temperature inversion,

　　　b.　Wind shear in a frontal zone, and

　　　c.　Clear air turbulence (CAT) at high levels associated with a jet stream or strong circulation.

　　　　　1)　High-level CAT is discussed in detail in Study Unit 13, "High Altitude Weather," in *Aviation Weather and Weather Services*.

3.　Wind shear with a low-level temperature inversion.

　　　a.　A temperature inversion forms near the surface on a clear night with calm or light surface wind. Wind above the inversion may be relatively strong.

　　　　　1)　A wind shear zone develops between the calm winds and the stronger winds above.

　　　b.　When taking off or landing in calm wind under clear skies within a few hours before or after sunrise, be prepared for a temperature inversion.

　　　　　1)　A shear zone in the inversion is relatively certain if the wind at 2,000 to 4,000 ft. is 25 kt. or greater.

4.　Wind shear in a frontal zone.

　　　a.　Wind changes abruptly in the frontal zone and can induce wind shear turbulence.

　　　b.　The degree of turbulence depends on the magnitude of the wind shear.

5. Microburst.

    a. A microburst is a strong downdraft of up to 6,000 feet per minute that can produce a hazardous change in wind direction of 45 kt. or more.

        1) Microbursts normally occur over horizontal distances of 1 NM and vertical distances of less than 1,000 ft.

6. Wind shear reports.

    a. Wind shear is the unexpected change in wind direction and/or windspeed.

        1) During an approach to landing, it can cause severe turbulence and a possible decrease to your airspeed (when a headwind changes to a tailwind), causing your airplane to stall (and possibly crash).

    b. The best method of dealing with wind shear is avoidance.

        1) You should never conduct landing approaches through, or in close proximity to, an active thunderstorm.

        2) Thunderstorms provide visible signs of possible wind shear activity.

    c. Many airports that are served by the air carriers employ one of the following systems for wind shear detection:

        1) **Terminal Doppler weather radar (TDWR)** is designed to advise the controller of wind shear and microburst events impacting all runways and the areas 1/2 mi. on either side of the extended centerline of the runways out to 3 mi. on final approach and 2 mi. on departure.

        2) The **weather systems processor (WSP)** provides the same products as the TDWR but uses the weather channel capabilities of the existing airport surveillance radar.

        3) The **low-level wind shear alert system (LLWAS)** employs wind sensors around the airport to warn ATC of the presence of hazardous wind shear and microbursts in the vicinity of the airport.

    d. If you are conducting a landing approach with possible wind shear or a thunderstorm nearby, you should consider

        1) Using more power during the approach

        2) Flying the approach at a faster airspeed (general rule: adding half the gust factor to your airspeed)

            a) EXAMPLE: Normal approach speed is 70 kt. and wind is 12 kt., gusting to 20 kt. The gust factor is 8 kt. (20 kt. – 12 kt.). Add half the gust factor (4 kt.) to your approach speed, to equal 74 kt. (70 kt. + 4 kt.).

        3) Staying as high as feasible on the approach until it is necessary to descend for a safe landing (unless a lower altitude is necessary due to low ceilings)

        4) Initiating a go-around at the first sign of a change in airspeed or an unexpected pitch change

            a) The most important factor is to use the maximum power available to get the airplane climbing.

            b) Many accidents caused by wind shear are due to a severe downdraft (or a rapid change from headwind to tailwind) that pushes the aircraft into the ground. In extreme cases, even the power of an airliner is unable to counteract the descent.

7. The best method of dealing with wind shear is avoidance. You should never conduct traffic pattern operations in close proximity to an active thunderstorm. Thunderstorms provide visible signs of possible wind-shear activity.

9.5 METARS, TAFS, AND AREA FORECASTS

A. A METAR is a statement of a weather observer's interpretation of the weather conditions at a given site and time.

    1. The weather observation can be made by a trained human observer or a machine (e.g., an AWOS or ASOS station).

    2. Elements. A METAR report contains the following sequence of elements in the following order:

        a. Type of report
        b. ICAO station identifier
        c. Date and time of report
        d. Modifier (as required)
        e. Wind
        f. Visibility
        g. Runway visual range (RVR)
        h. Weather
        i. Sky condition
        j. Temperature/dew point
        k. Altimeter
        l. Remarks (RMK)

> NOTE: The elements in the body of a METAR report are separated by a space, except temperature and dew point, which are separated by a solidus (/). When an element does not occur or cannot be observed, that element is omitted from that particular report.

    3. Example of a METAR Report

METAR KGNV 201953Z 24015KT 3/4SM R28/2400FT + TSRA BKN008 OVC015CB 26/25 A2985 RMK TSB32RAB32

To aid in the discussion, we have divided the report into the 12 elements:

METAR	KGNV	201953Z	____	24015KT	3/4SM	R28/2400FT	+TSRA
1.	2.	3.	4.	5.	6.	7.	8.

BKN008 OVC015CB	26/25	A2985	RMK TSB32RAB32
9.	10.	11.	12.

    1. Aviation routine weather report
    2. Gainesville, FL
    3. Observation taken on the 20th day at 1953 UTC (or Zulu)
    4. Modifier omitted; i.e., not required for this report
    5. Wind 240° true at 15 kt.
    6. Visibility 3/4 statute miles
    7. Runway 28, runway visual range 2,400 ft.
    8. Thunderstorm with heavy rain
    9. Ceiling 800 ft. broken, 1,500 ft. overcast, cumulonimbus clouds
    10. Temperature 26°C, dew point 25°C
    11. Altimeter 29.85
    12. Remarks: Thunderstorm began at 32 min. past the hour; rain began at 32 min. past the hour.

---

    4. You can find more information on METARs in Study Unit 8 of *Pilot Handbook*.

B. Terminal Aerodrome Forecast (TAF)

    1. The terminal aerodrome forecast (TAF) is a concise statement of the expected weather at a specific airport during a 24- or 30-hr. period.

        a. The TAF covers an area within a 5-SM radius of the center of the airport and is prepared four times daily at 0000Z, 0600Z, 1200Z, and 1800Z.

        b. Many of the weather codes used in the METAR are also used in the TAF.

        c. The 32 largest airports in the U.S. offer 30-hr. forecasts. Every other site provides a 24-hr. forecast.

2.   Elements. A TAF contains the following sequence of elements in the following order (items a-i). Forecast change indicators (items j-l) and probability forecast (item m) are used as appropriate.

<table>
<tr><td colspan="3">Forecast of</td></tr>
<tr><td>Communications Header</td><td>Meteorological Conditions</td><td>Time Elements</td></tr>
<tr><td>a. Type of report</td><td>e. Wind</td><td>j. Temporary (TEMPO)</td></tr>
<tr><td>b. ICAO station identifier</td><td>f. Visibility</td><td>k. From (FM)</td></tr>
<tr><td>c. Date and time of origin</td><td>g. Weather</td><td>l. Becoming (BECMG)</td></tr>
<tr><td>d. Valid period date and time</td><td>h. Sky condition</td><td>m. Probability (PROB)</td></tr>
<tr><td></td><td>i. Wind shear (optional)</td><td></td></tr>
</table>

3.   Example of a TAF:

```
TAF
KOKC 051130Z 0512/0612 14008KT 5SM BR BKN030 WS018/32030KT
    TEMPO 0513/0516 1SM BR
    FM051600 16010KT P6SM SKC
    BECMG 0522/0624 20013G20KT 4SM SHRA OVC020
    PROB40 0600/0606 2SM TSRA OVC008CB=
```

To aid in the discussion, we have divided the TAF above into elements 1. – 13. as follows:

TAF	KOKC	051130Z	0512/0612	14008KT	5SM	BR	BKN030
1.	2.	3.	4.	5.	6.	7.	8.

WS018/32030KT	TEMPO 0513/0516 1SM BR	FM051600 16010KT P6SM SKC
9.	10.	11.

BECMG 0522/0624 20013G20KT 4SM SHRA OVC020
12.

PROB40 0600/0606 2SM TSRA OVC008CB=
13.

1.   Routine terminal aerodrome forecast

2.   Oklahoma City, OK

3.   Forecast prepared on the 5th day at 1130 UTC (or Z)

4.   Forecast valid from the 5th day at 1200 UTC until 1200 UTC on the 6th day

5.   Wind 140° true at 8 kt.

6.   Visibility 5 SM

7.   Visibility obscured by mist

8.   Ceiling 3,000 ft. broken

a.   A vertical visibility (VV) may also be forecast as a sky condition when the sky is expected to be obscured by a surface-based phenomena.

9.   Low-level wind shear at 1,800 ft., wind 320° true at 30 kt.

10.   Temporary (spoken as occasional) visibility 1 SM in mist between 1300 UTC and 1600 UTC of the 5th day

11.   From (or after) 1600 UTC on the 5th day, wind 160° true at 10 kt., visibility more than 6SM, sky clear

12.   Becoming (gradual change) wind 200° true at 13 kt., gusts to 20 kt., visibility 4 SM in moderate rain showers, ceiling 2,000 ft. overcast between 2200 UTC and 2400 UTC on the 5th and beginning the 6th day

13.   Probability (40% chance) between 0000 UTC and 0600 UTC of the 6th day of visibility 2 SM, thunderstorm, moderate rain, ceiling 800 ft. overcast, cumulonimbus clouds (The = sign indicates end of forecast.)

C.   Aviation Area Forecast (FA)

  1.   An aviation area forecast (FA) is a forecast of VFR weather, clouds, and general weather conditions over an area the size of several states. It is used to determine forecast en route weather and to interpolate conditions at airports that do not have TAFs issued.

    a.   FAs for the continental U.S. describe, in abbreviated language, specified en route weather phenomena below FL450.

    b.   To understand the complete weather picture, the FA must be used in conjunction with the current AIRMETs and SIGMETs.

    c.   FAs are issued three times a day by the Aviation Weather Center (AWC) for each of the six areas in the contiguous 48 states and the Gulf of Mexico.

    d.   The FA is comprised of four sections:

      1)   Communication and product header section
      2)   A precautionary statement section
      3)   SYNOPSIS section
      4)   VFR CLOUDS/WX section

2.   EXAMPLE: A portion of an FA is presented below.

Section 1

```
MIAC FA 221745
SYNOPSIS AND VFR CLDS/WX
SYNOPSIS VALID UNTIL 231200
CLDS/WX VALID UNTIL 230600...OTLK VALID 230600-231200
NC SC GA FL AND CSTL WTRS
.
```

Section 2

```
SEE AIRMET SIERRA FOR IFR CONDS AND MTN OBSCN.
TS IMPLY SEV OR GTR TURB SEV ICE LLWS AND IFR CONDS.
NON MSL HGTS DENOTED BY AGL OR CIG.
.
```

Section 3

```
SYNOPSIS...SLO MOVG CDFNT XTRM NRN FL FCST BECM NRLY STNR BY 06Z.
HI PRES FCST BLD SEWD FROM GREAT LAKE RGN THRU 12Z WITH RIDGE
AXIS SWD OVR CNTRL CAROLINAS BY 12Z. ..SMITH..
.
```

Section 4

```
FL
PNHDL...SCT-BKN030 SCT-BKN100. TOPS FL250. SCT TSRA. CB TOPS ABV 450. 02Z
      SCT030 SCT100..BKN CI. ISOL-TSRA. CB TOPS FL350. OTKL...MVFR BR.
NRN PEN...SCT-BKN030 BKN100. SCT TSRA. CB TOPS ABV FL450. 02Z SCT030 BKN100.
      TOPS FL250. ISOL-TSRA. CB TOPS FL 350. OTLK...MVFR BR.
CNTRL/SRN PEN/KEYS...SCT035 SCT100. WDLY SCT TSRA. CB TOPS FL450. 02Z
      SCT030 SCT120. OTLK...VFR.
.
CSTL WTRS
NS SC WTRS...SCT040. OTLK...VFR.
GA-NRN FL ATLC WTRS...SCT-BKN040 BKN100. SCT TSRA. CB TOPS FL400. OTLK...VFR.
NRN FL GULF WTRS...SCT030 SCT100. SCT TSRA. CB TOPS FL350. OTLK...VFR.
CNTRL/SRN FL WTRS...SCT030 SCT100. WDLY SCT TSRA. CB TOPS FL400. OTLK...VFR.
...
```

9.6 SEASONAL WEATHER PHENOMENA

A.   Earth has seasonal variations in weather. Because the axis of the Earth tilts to the plane of orbit, the sun is more nearly overhead in one hemisphere than in the other, depending upon the season.

  1.   The Northern Hemisphere is warmer in June, July, and August because it receives more solar energy than does the Southern Hemisphere.

  2.   The Southern Hemisphere receives more solar radiation and is warmer during December, January, and February.

B.   Because pressure differences cause wind, seasonal pressure variations determine to a great extent the areas of large masses of cold air breaking south from the arctic and sub-arctic towards the tropics.

  1.   This causes cold air outbreaks and mid-latitude storms.

  2.   Large mid-latitude storms develop between cold outbreaks and carry warm air northwind.

  3.   The result is a mid-latitude band of migratory storms with ever-changing weather.

C.   Cold outbreaks are strongest in the winter and are predominantly from the colder continental areas.

  1.   Outbreaks are weaker in the summer, and more likely to originate from the cooler water surfaces.

  2.   Because these outbreaks are masses of cool, dense air, they characteristically are high-pressure areas.

D. Seasonal weather phenomena include the unique weather associated with the transition from one season to the next and the weather associated with a particular season in your area. Be knowledgeable about the flying season weather in your local area. Some seasonal weather characteristics for local areas can include

1. High summer heat (combined with altitude) in the Southwest
2. Summertime afternoon thunderstorms in the Southeast
3. IFR conditions in the Northwest during Autumn
4. Winter icing conditions in the Midwest
5. Crosswinds during the winter months in the Southeast

E. Be aware of the weather systems and weather trends that come with the change of season in your particular area. Prepare yourself for the weather this flying season by doing the following:

1. Review – Are you proficient or just current for the expected weather this season? Consider the weather possibilities for your area (see item D. above for examples)

2. Practice – Enlist the services of an authorized instructor or proficient safety pilot to better prepare you for the flying season.

3. Educate – Review how you get weather information and pay special attention to those items appropriate to the season in which you are flying (e.g., forecast icing potential in the winter months and radar imaging products during the summertime).

4. Plan – Write down your personal minimums considering the type of weather you will expect to encounter this flying season.

5. Share – Talk to fellow pilots, family, and friends about weather decision making: on the ramp or even at the airport restaurant.

This is the end of Part II. Part III consists of Study Units 10 through 54. Each study unit covers one Task in the Private Pilot Airman Certification Standards.

PART III
FLIGHT MANEUVERS AND
FAA AIRMAN CERTIFICATION STANDARDS:
DISCUSSED AND EXPLAINED

Part III of this book (Study Units 10 through 54) provides an in-depth discussion of flight maneuvers and the Private Pilot Airman Certification Standards (ACS). Each of the eleven areas of operation is presented in a separate section, with each of its related task(s) in a separate study unit.

		No. of Tasks	No. of Pages
I.	Preflight Preparation	8	118*
II.	Preflight Procedures	5	48
II.	Airport Operations	2	22
IV.	Takeoffs, Landings, and Go-Arounds	8	110*
V.	Performance Maneuvers	2	28
VI.	Navigation	4	56
VII.	Slow Flight and Stalls	4	38
VIII.	Basic Instrument Maneuvers	6	56
IX.	Emergency Operations	4	38
XI.	Night Operations	1	14
XII.	Postflight Procedures	1	12
		45	540

*Larger sections because they have more tasks.

Each task, reproduced verbatim from the ACS, appears at the beginning each study unit. The FAA's objective and/or rationale for the task and any other general discussion is presented under "A. General Information." This is followed by "Knowledge," "Risk Management," and "Skills" subunits that cover each item of the FAA's task. Additionally, for each flight maneuver, common errors are listed and briefly discussed in a "Common Errors" subunit. We want you to understand what can go wrong so you can prevent it from happening to you.

Each objective of a task lists, in sequence, the important elements that must be satisfactorily performed. The objective includes

1. Specific abilities that are needed
2. The conditions under which the task is to be performed
3. The acceptable standards of performance

Be confident. You have prepared diligently and are better prepared and more skilled than the average private pilot applicant. Satisfactory performance to meet the requirements for certification is based on your ability to safely

1. Perform the tasks specified in the areas of operation for the certificate or rating sought within the approved standards

2. Demonstrate mastery of the airplane with the successful outcome of each task performed never seriously in doubt

3. Demonstrate satisfactory proficiency and competency within the approved standards

4. Demonstrate sound judgment and risk management abilities

Each task has an FAA reference list that identifies the publication(s) that describe(s) the task. Our discussion is based on the current issue of these references. Make sure you use the most current published version of each of these references. For example, the most current version of AC 00-45 is AC 00-45G. The current edition of all FAA publications can be found at www.faa.gov. The following FAA references are used in the Private Pilot ACS:

14 CFR part 39	Airworthiness Directives
14 CFR part 43	Maintenance, Preventive Maintenance, Rebuilding and Alteration
14 CFR part 61	Certification: Pilots, Flight Instructors, and Ground Instructors
14 CFR part 71	Designation of Class A, B, C, D and E Airspace Areas; Air Traffic Service Routes; and Reporting Points
14 CFR part 91	General Operating and Flight Rules
14 CFR part 93	Special Air Traffic Rules
AC 00-6	Aviation Weather
AC 00-45	Aviation Weather Services
AC 60-28	English Language Skill Standards Required by 14 CFR parts 61, 63, and 65
AC 61-67	Stall and Spin Awareness Training
AC 91-73	Parts 91 and 135 Single Pilot, Flight School Procedures During Taxi Operations
AIM	Aeronautical Information Manual
Chart Supplements U.S.	Chart Supplements U.S. (previously Airport/Facility Directory or A/FD)
FAA-H-8083-1	Aircraft Weight and Balance Handbook
FAA-H-8083-2	Risk Management Handbook
FAA-H-8083-3	Airplane Flying Handbook
FAA-H-8083-6	Advanced Avionics Handbook
FAA-H-8083-15	Instrument Flying Handbook
FAA-H-8083-25	Pilot's Handbook of Aeronautical Knowledge
FAA-P-8740-19	Flying Light Twins Safely
POH/AFM	Pilot's Operating Handbook/FAA-Approved Airplane Flight Manual
Other	Navigation Charts
	Navigation Equipment Manual
	NOTAMs

In each task, as appropriate, we will provide you with the study unit and/or subunit from the Gleim *Pilot Handbook* for additional discussion of an element (or concept) of the task.

NOTE: For many decades, the FAA referred to its regulations as FARs (Federal Aviation Regulations). The FAA now refers to these regulations as "14 CFRs" rather than "FARs." CFR stands for Code of Federal Regulations, and the Federal Aviation Regulations are in Title 14. For example, FAR Part 1 and FAR 61.109 are now referred to as 14 CFR Part 1 and 14 CFR 61.109, respectively. Due to CFIs' and pilots' widespread use of the acronym FAR, we use FAR and 14 CFR interchangeably to familiarize you with both.

PART III
SECTION I:
PREFLIGHT PREPARATION

Study Units 10 through 17 of Section I explain the eight FAA ACS tasks (A-H) of Preflight Preparation. These tasks include knowledge, risk management, and skill. Your evaluator is required to test you on all eight of these tasks. Further, your evaluator may develop a scenario based on real-time weather to test Tasks C and D.

The tasks in this section have several common items, listed and explained here instead of repeated throughout the text.

The following common task item topics are included in this section introduction:

KNOWLEDGE   Page

A. **The applicant demonstrates understanding of the types of airspace/airspace classes and basic VFR weather minimums.**   92

B. **The applicant demonstrates understanding of symbology found on VFR charts including airspace, obstructions, and terrain features.**   93

KNOWLEDGE

A.   **The applicant demonstrates understanding of the types of airspace/airspace classes and basic VFR weather minimums.**

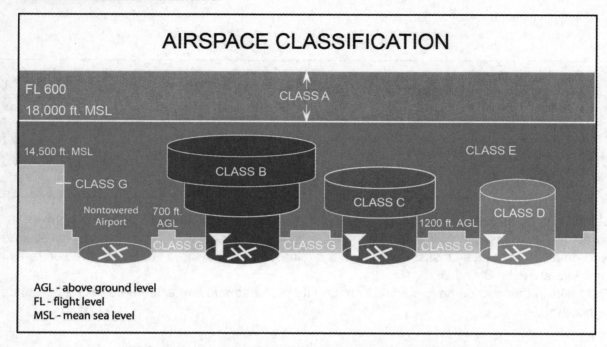

Cloud Clearance and Visibility Required for VFR

Airspace	Flight Visibility	Distance from Clouds
Class A	Not Applicable	Not applicable
Class B	3 SM	Clear of Clouds
Class C	3 SM	500 ft. below 1,000 ft. above 2,000 ft. horiz.
Class D	3 SM	500 ft. below 1,000 ft. above 2,000 ft. horiz.
Class E:		
Less than 10,000 ft. MSL	3 SM	500 ft. below 1,000 ft. above 2,000 ft. horiz.
At or above 10,000 ft. MSL*	5 SM	1,000 ft. below 1,000 ft. above 1 SM horiz.

Airspace	Flight Visibility	Distance from Clouds
Class G:		
1,200 ft. or less above the surface (regardless of MSL altitude)		
Day	1 SM**	Clear of clouds
Night*	3 SM	500 ft. below 1,000 ft. above 2,000 ft. horiz.
More than 1,200 ft. above the surface but less than 10,000 ft. MSL		
Day	1 SM**	500 ft. below 1,000 ft. above 2,000 ft. horiz.
Night*	3 SM	500 ft. below 1,000 ft. above 2,000 ft. horiz.
More than 1,200 ft. above the surface and at or above 10,000 ft. MSL*	5 SM	1,000 ft. below 1,000 ft. above 1 SM horiz.

 * Not applicable to sport pilots
 ** Minimum visibility for sport pilots is 3 SM

1. An airplane may be operated clear of clouds in Class G airspace at night below 1,200 ft. AGL when the visibility is less than 3 SM but not less than 1 SM in an airport traffic pattern and within 1/2 mi. of the runway.

2. Except when operating under a special VFR clearance, you may not operate your airplane beneath the ceiling under VFR within the lateral boundaries of the surface areas of Class B, Class C, Class D, or Class E airspace designated for an airport when the ceiling is less than 1,000 ft.

   a. You may not take off, land, or enter the traffic pattern of an airport unless ground visibility is at least 3 SM. If ground visibility is not reported, flight visibility must be at least 3 SM.

B. **The applicant demonstrates understanding of symbology found on VFR charts including airspace, obstructions, and terrain features.**

1. Sectional charts have legends that define many of the depictions. You can and should refer to these during your practical test if you have doubts concerning depictions.

2. **Airspace** is denoted by the following:

   a. Class A airspace is not depicted because it is all airspace from 18,000 to 60,000 ft. MSL.

   b. Class B airspace is depicted with solid blue radials and arcs. The name by which the Class B airspace is identified is shown in blue block letters, all capitalized.

      1) The MSL ceiling and floor altitudes of each sector are shown in solid blue figures with the last two zeros omitted. $\frac{90}{20}$

         a) Floors extending "upward from above" a certain altitude are preceded by a (+).

      2) Operations at and below these altitudes are outside of Class B airspace.

   c. Class C airspace is depicted with solid magenta radials and arcs. The name by which the Class C airspace is identified is shown in magenta block letters, all capitalized.

      1) The MSL ceiling and floor altitudes of each sector are shown in solid magenta figures with the last two zeros eliminated. $\frac{70}{15}$

         a) The figure at right identifies a sector that extends from the surface to the base of the Class B airspace. $\frac{T}{SFC}$

      2) Separate notes, enclosed in magenta boxes, give the approach control frequencies to be used by arriving VFR aircraft to establish two-way radio communication before entering Class C (generally within 20 NM).   `CTC BURBANK APP WITHIN 20 NM ON 124.6 395.9`

   d. Class D airspace is identified with a blue dashed line.

      1) Ceilings of Class D airspace are shown as follows: `⌐30⌐`

         a) A minus in front of the figure is used to indicate "from surface to, but not including . . ."

   e. Class E airspace exists at 1,200 ft. AGL unless designated otherwise.

      1) Class E is symbolized with a magenta dashed line if the floor is the surface.

      2) The lateral and vertical limits of all Class E airspace (up to but not including 18,000 ft.) are shown by narrow bands of vignette on Sectionals and TACs.

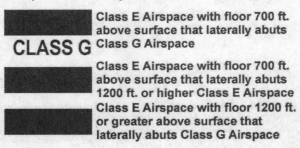

CLASS G — Class E Airspace with floor 700 ft. above surface that laterally abuts Class G Airspace

Class E Airspace with floor 700 ft. above surface that laterally abuts 1200 ft. or higher Class E Airspace

Class E Airspace with floor 1200 ft. or greater above surface that laterally abuts Class G Airspace

3)   Controlled airspace floors of 700' above the ground are defined by a magenta vignette; floors other than 700' that laterally abut uncontrolled airspace (Class G) are defined by a blue vignette; differing floors greater than 700' above the ground are annotated by a symbol and a number indicating the floor.

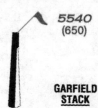

2400 AGL

4500 MSL

f.   Class G airspace within the United States extends up to 14,500' MSL. At and above this altitude is Class E, excluding the airspace less than 1,500' above the terrain and certain special use airspace areas.

3.   **Obstruction** symbols show manmade vertical features that could affect safe navigation. Obstructions are denoted by the following:

a.   Sectional Charts and Terminal Area Charts (TACs) typically show manmade obstacles extending more than 200' AGL.

b.   The elevation of the top of the obstacle above MSL and the height of the structure (AGL) is also indicated (when known or able to be reliably determined by a Specialist).

1)   The AGL height is in parentheses below the MSL elevation. In extremely congested areas, the FAA typically omits the AGL values to avoid confusion.

c.   Man-made features used by FAA Air Traffic Control as checkpoints use a graphic symbol shown in black with the required elevation data in blue as shown at the right.

5540
(650)

d.   Obstacles with high-intensity strobe lighting systems may operate part-time or by proximity activation. As in the example below, guy wires may extend from obstacles.

GARFIELD STACK

4.   **Terrain** elevation is denoted by color, as shown to the right.

a.   Different color tints show bands of elevation relative to sea level. These colors range from light green for the lower elevations to dark brown for the higher elevations.

5.   The maximum elevation figure (MEF) represents the highest elevation within a quadrant, including terrain and other vertical obstacles (towers, trees, etc.). A quadrant on Sectionals is the area bounded by ticked lines dividing each 30" of latitude and each 30" of longitude. MEF figures are rounded up to the nearest 100' value and the last two digits of the number are not shown. In the example below, the MEF represents 12,500'.

12^5

19633

GLACIER

12000

9000

7000

5000

3000

2000

1000

Sea Level

-228

STUDY UNIT TEN
PILOT QUALIFICATIONS

Task	*Task A. Pilot Qualifications*
References	14 CFR parts 61, 91; FAA-H-8083-2, FAA-H-8083-25
Objective	To determine that the applicant exhibits satisfactory knowledge, risk management, and skills associated with airman and medical certificates including privileges, limitations, currency, and operating as Pilot-in-Command (PIC) as a private pilot.
Knowledge	The applicant demonstrates understanding of:
PA.I.A.K1	1. Currency, regulatory compliance, privileges, and limitations.
PA.I.A.K2	2. Location of airman documents and identification required when exercising private pilot privileges.
PA.I.A.K3	3. The required documents to provide upon inspection.
PA.I.A.K4	4. Pilot logbook/record keeping.
PA.I.A.K5	5. Compensation.
PA.I.A.K6	6. Towing.
PA.I.A.K7	7. Category and class.
PA.I.A.K8	8. Endorsements.
PA.I.A.K9	9. Medical certificates: class, expiration, privileges, temporary disqualifications.
PA.I.A.K10	10. Drugs, alcohol regulatory restrictions that affect the pilot's ability to operate safely.
Risk Management	The applicant demonstrates the ability to identify, assess and mitigate risks, encompassing:
PA.I.A.R1	1. Distinguishing proficiency versus currency.
PA.I.A.R2	2. Setting personal minimums.
PA.I.A.R3	3. Maintaining fitness to fly.
PA.I.A.R4	4. Flying unfamiliar aircraft.
PA.I.A.R5	5. Operating with unfamiliar flight display systems or unfamiliar avionics.
Skills	The applicant demonstrates the ability to apply requirements to:
PA.I.A.S1	1. Act as PIC under VFR in a scenario given by the evaluator.

A. General Information

    1. The objective of this task is for you to demonstrate your knowledge, risk management, and skills related to airman and medical certificates, including privileges, limitations, currency, and operating as pilot-in-command (PIC) as a private pilot.

10.1 KNOWLEDGE

A.   Task Objectives

1.   **The applicant demonstrates understanding of currency, regulatory compliance, privileges, and limitations.**

   a.   Currency and recent flight experience.

      1)   Exercise the privileges of an airman certificate, rating, endorsement, or authorization issued under 14 CFR Part 61 unless that person meets the appropriate airman and medical recency requirements of this part, specific to the operation or activity.

      2)   To act as pilot in command (PIC) of an aircraft carrying passengers, you must have completed three takeoffs and landings within the preceding 90 days as sole manipulator of the flight controls in an aircraft of the same category, class, and type (if a type rating is required).

      3)   If made in a tailwheel aircraft, the landings must be to a full stop.

      4)   Category means airplane, rotorcraft, glider, or lighter than air. Class means single-engine land, multi-engine land, single-engine sea, or multi-engine sea.

   b.   Night experience.

      1)   Night officially begins (for the logging of night experience under 14 CFR 61.57) 1 hr. after sunset and ends 1 hr. before sunrise.

      2)   To act as PIC of an aircraft carrying passengers at night, you must have made, within the preceding 90 days, three takeoffs and landings to a full stop during night flight in an aircraft of the same category, class, and type (if a type rating is required).

   c.   You may not act as PIC unless you have completed a flight review (commonly referred to as a biennial flight review or BFR) within the preceding 24 months.

      1)   To act as PIC of an aircraft, you must have

         a)   Satisfactorily accomplished a flight review or completed a proficiency check or a practical test for a new certificate/rating within the preceding 24 calendar months, or

         b)   Satisfactorily completed at least the basic phase of the FAA Pilot Proficiency Program (WINGS).

   d.   Regulatory compliance.

      1)   General aviation (GA) pilots enjoy a level of responsibility and freedom unique in aviation. Unlike the air carrier, corporate, and military communities, most GA pilots are free to fly when and where they choose.

      2)   Pilots should not be lulled into a false sense of security simply because they are in compliance with the regulations. Judgment and aeronautical decision making serve as the bridge between regulatory compliance and safety.

         a)   EXAMPLE: Deciding if or when to undertake any flight lies solely with the PIC. GA pilots should remember that FAA regulations designed to prevent accidents and incidents come out **after** the accident or incident.

3) Validity. No person may

    a) Exercise the privileges of a certificate, rating, endorsement, or authorization issued under 14 CFR Part 61 if the certificate, rating, or authorization is surrendered, suspended, revoked, or expired.

    b) Exercise privileges of a medical certificate issued under 14 CFR Part 67 to meet any requirements of 14 CFR Part 61 if the medical certificate is surrendered, suspended, revoked, or expired according to the duration standards set forth in 14 CFR 61.23(d).

    c) Use an official government-issued driver's license to meet any requirements of Part 61 related to holding that driver's license if the driver's license is surrendered, suspended, revoked, or expired.

e. Privileges and limitations.

1) According to 14 CFR 61.113, as a private pilot, you may not act as PIC of an aircraft that is carrying passengers or property for compensation or hire, nor may you be paid to act as PIC **except**

    a) You may act as PIC of an aircraft, for compensation or hire, in connection with any business or employment if the flight is only incidental to that business or employment and the aircraft does not carry passengers or property for compensation or hire.

    b) You may not pay less than the equal share of the operating expenses of a flight with your passengers, provided the expenses involve only fuel, oil, airport expenditures, or rental fees.

    c) If you are an aircraft salesperson and have at least 200 hr. of logged flight time, you may demonstrate an aircraft to a prospective buyer.

    d) You may act as PIC of an aircraft used in a passenger-carrying airlift sponsored by a charitable organization for which passengers make a donation if all of the following apply:

        i) The sponsor of the airlift notifies the Flight Standards District Office (FSDO) at least 7 days before the flight and provides the FSDO with specific information.

        ii) The flight is conducted from a public airport or an airport approved by an FAA inspector.

        iii) You have logged at least 200 hr. of flight time.

        iv) No aerobatic or formation flights are conducted.

        v) Each aircraft used is certificated in the standard category and complies with the 100-hr. inspection requirement.

        vi) The flight is made under VFR during the day.

2. **The applicant demonstrates understanding of the location of airman documents and identification required when exercising private pilot privileges.**

a. Although you are required to carry your medical and pilot certificates, you are not required to have your logbook with you at all times (unless you are a student pilot).

b. According to 14 CFR 61.3, no person may serve as a required pilot flight crewmember of a civil aircraft of the U.S. unless that person has

1) In the person's physical possession or readily accessible in the aircraft when exercising the privileges of that pilot certificate or authorization.

    a) A pilot certificate issued under 14 CFR Part 61 and in accordance with 14 CFR 61.19.

2) A photo identification that is in that person's physical possession or readily accessible in the aircraft when exercising the privileges of that pilot certificate or authorization. The photo identification must be a

    a) Driver's license issued by a state, the District of Columbia, or territory or possession of the U.S.;

    b) Government identification card issued by the federal government, a state, the District of Columbia, or a territory or possession of the U.S.;

    c) U.S. armed forces' identification card;

    d) Official passport;

    e) Credential that authorizes unescorted access to a security identification display area at an airport regulated under 49 CFR Part 1542; or

    f) Other form of identification that the FAA Administrator finds acceptable.

3. **The applicant demonstrates understanding of the required documents to provide upon inspection.**

    a. Each person who holds an airman certificate, medical certificate, authorization, or license required by 14 CFR Part 61 must present it and photo identification as described above for inspection upon a request from

        1) The FAA Administrator;
        2) An authorized representative of the National Transportation Safety Board;
        3) Any federal, state, or local law enforcement officer;
        4) An authorized representative of the Transportation Security Administration.

4. **The applicant demonstrates understanding of pilot logbook/record keeping.**

    a. According to 14 CFR 61.51, all the training and aeronautical experience used to meet the requirements for a certificate, rating, or flight review must be shown by a reliable record, e.g., a pilot logbook.

        1) All flight time used to meet the recent flight requirements must also be logged (e.g., three takeoffs and landings within the preceding 90 days). All other time need only be logged at your discretion.

        2) Each logbook entry shall include

            a) General information

                i) Date
                ii) Total flight time or lesson time
                iii) Location where the aircraft departed and arrived or, for lessons in a flight simulator or a flight training device, location where the lesson occurred
                iv) Type and identification of aircraft, flight simulator, or flight training device, as appropriate
                v) Name of the safety pilot, if required by 14 CFR 91.109

            b) Type of pilot experience or training

                i) Pilot in command
                ii) Solo
                iii) Second in command
                iv) Flight and ground training received from an authorized instructor
                v) Training received in a flight simulator or flight training device from an authorized instructor

        c)   Conditions of flight

           i)   Day or night

           ii)   Actual instrument

           iii) Simulated instrument conditions in flight, a flight simulator, or a flight training device

3)   **Solo** time means that a pilot is the sole occupant of the airplane. This time is logged as pilot-in-command time.

4)   **Pilot in Command (PIC)**

     a)   A student pilot may log PIC time only when the student pilot

        i)   Is the sole occupant of the airplane (solo)

        ii)   Has a current solo flight endorsement

        iii) Is undergoing training for a pilot certificate or rating

     b)   A sport, recreational, private, commercial, or ATP pilot may log as PIC time only the time during which that person

        i)   Is the sole manipulator of the controls of an aircraft for which the pilot is rated

        ii)   Is the sole occupant of the airplane

        iii) Except for a sport or recreational pilot, is acting as PIC of an airplane that requires more than one pilot under the airplane's type certificate or the 14 CFRs under which the flight is conducted

5)   **Training time** is logged when you receive training from an authorized instructor in an airplane, flight simulator, or flight training device.

     a)   Your logbook must be endorsed in a legible manner by the authorized instructor and include a description of the training given, the length of the lesson, and the authorized instructor's signature, certificate number, and certificate expiration date.

5.   **The applicant demonstrates understanding of compensation.**

    a.   According to 14 CFR 61.113, as a private pilot, you may not act as PIC of an aircraft that is carrying passengers or property for compensation or hire, nor may you be paid to act as PIC **except**

       1)   See other exceptions in item A.1.e., Privileges and Limitations, on page 97.

6.   **The applicant demonstrates understanding of towing.**

    a.   According to 14 CFR 61.113, a private pilot who meets the requirements of 14 CFR 61.69 may act as PIC of an aircraft towing a glider or unpowered ultralight vehicle. These requirements include

       1)   100 hr. of PIC time in the category and class and type of aircraft being used for towing

       2)   Ground and flight instruction on towing

       3)   An endorsement for towing

7.   **The applicant demonstrates understanding of category and class.**

    a.   Each pilot certificate is issued based on category and class of aircraft.

       1)   The FAA defines an airman category as a broad classification of aircraft.

          a)   Examples include airplane, rotorcraft, glider, and lighter than air.

       2)   The FAA defines an airman class as a classification of aircraft within a category having similar operating characteristics.

          a)   Examples include single-engine land, multi-engine land, single-engine sea, multi-engine sea, airship, and helicopter.

b.   Aircraft are also certified based upon category and class.

  1)   The FAA defines aircraft category as a grouping of aircraft based upon intended use or operating limitations.

  a)   Examples include transport, normal, utility, acrobatic, limited, restricted, and provisional.

  2)   The FAA defines aircraft class as a broad grouping of aircraft having similar characteristics of propulsion, flight, or landing.

  a)   Examples include airplane, rotorcraft, glider, balloon, landplane, and seaplane.

8.   **The applicant demonstrates understanding of endorsements.**

a.   During your private pilot training, you need to receive numerous endorsements, for example

  1)   Presolo test
  2)   Ability to fly solo
  3)   Solo cross-country flights
  4)   Operation in Class B airspace

b.   After you become a private pilot, there are other endorsements you need before being a PIC under certain circumstances.

  1)   To act as PIC of a complex airplane (an airplane that has a retractable landing gear, flaps, and a controllable pitch propeller), you must receive and log ground and flight training from an authorized instructor in a complex airplane and receive a one-time logbook endorsement that you are proficient to operate a complex airplane.

  2)   To act as PIC of a high-performance airplane (an airplane with an engine of more than 200 horsepower), you must receive and log ground and flight training from an authorized instructor in a high-performance airplane and receive a one-time logbook endorsement that you are proficient to operate a high-performance airplane.

  3)   To act as PIC of a pressurized airplane that has a service ceiling or maximum operating altitude, whichever is lower, above 25,000 ft. MSL, you must have both ground and flight instruction in such an airplane and obtain a logbook endorsement.

  4)   To act as PIC of a tailwheel airplane, you must receive flight instruction in such an airplane and obtain a logbook endorsement of competence. Training must include

  a)   Normal and crosswind takeoffs and landings
  b)   Wheel landings, unless the manufacturer does not recommend them
  c)   Go-around procedures

c.   All private pilots need a flight review, which culminates in a logbook endorsement.

9.   **The applicant demonstrates understanding of medical certificates: class, expiration, privileges, temporary disqualifications.**

a.   All airplane pilots must possess valid and appropriate medical certificates to exercise the privileges of their pilot certificates.

  1)   The periodic medical examinations required for the medical certificate are conducted by FAA-designated aviation medical examiners (AMEs).

  2)   Although a history of certain medical conditions may disqualify a pilot from flying, most pilots who do not meet medical standards may still be qualified under certain conditions.

b. Obtain at least a third-class FAA medical certificate.

   1) You must undergo a routine medical examination that may be administered only by FAA-designated AMEs.

      a) For operations requiring a private, recreational, or student pilot certificate, a first-, second-, or third-class medical certificate expires at the end of the last day of the month either

         i) 5 years (60 months) after the date of examination shown on the certificate, if you have not reached your 40th birthday on or before the date of examination or

         ii) 2 years (24 months) after the date of examination shown on the certificate, if you have reached your 40th birthday on or before the date of examination.

   2) Even if you have a physical handicap, medical certificates can be issued in many cases. Operating limitations may be imposed depending upon the nature of the disability.

      a) The process of granting medical certification to person with an otherwise disqualifying condition is known as a Statement of Demonstrated Ability (SODA).

         i) For more information, contact an AME.

c. Requirement and Duration of Medical Certificates

   1) A person must hold

      a) A first-class medical certificate when exercising the privileges of an ATP certificate

      b) At least a second-class medical certificate when exercising the privileges of a commercial pilot certificate

      c) At least a third-class medical certificate

         i) When exercising the privileges of a private, recreational, or student pilot certificate

         ii) When exercising the privileges of a flight instructor certificate if the CFI is acting as PIC or as a required pilot flight crewmember

         iii) Prior to taking a practical test that is performed in an airplane for a certificate or rating at a recreational, private, commercial, or ATP certificate level

   2) A person is not required to hold a medical certificate when

      a) Exercising the privileges of a flight instructor certificate if the person is not acting as PIC or serving as a required pilot flight crewmember

      b) Exercising the privileges of a ground instructor certificate

      c) Taking a test or check for a certificate, rating, or authorization conducted in a flight simulator or flight training device

      3) Duration of a medical certificate

          a) A first-class medical certificate expires at the end of the last day of

             i) The 12th month after the date of the examination for operations requiring an airline transport certificate if under age 40

             ii) The 6th month after the date of examination for operations requiring an airline transport certificate if age 40 or older

             iii) The 12th month after the date of examination for operations requiring only a commercial pilot certificate

             iv) The period specified in item c) below, for operations requiring only a private, recreational, flight instructor (when acting as PIC), or student pilot certificate

          b) A second-class medical certificate expires at the end of the last day of

             i) The 12th month after the date of examination for operations requiring a commercial pilot certificate

             ii) The period specified in item c) below, for operations requiring only a private, recreational, flight instructor (when acting as PIC), or student pilot certificate

          c) A third-class medical certificate for operations requiring a private, recreational, flight instructor (when acting as PIC), or student pilot certificate expires at the end of the last day of

             i) The 60th month after the date of examination if the person has not reached his or her 40th birthday on or before the date of the examination.

             ii) The 24th month after the date of examination if the person has reached his or her 40th birthday on or before the date of examination.

   d. Replacement of Medical Certificate

      1) A request for the replacement of a lost or destroyed medical certificate must be made by a signed letter to the Department of Transportation · FAA · Aerospace Medical Certification Division · P.O. Box 26200 · Oklahoma City, OK 73125. Letter must be accompanied by a check or money order payable to the FAA.

          a) Allow 4-6 weeks for processing your request.

      2) A fax from the FAA showing that the medical certificate was issued may be used for a period not to exceed 60 days pending the arrival of the replacement certificate.

          a) To receive a temporary medical certificate, call (866) 878-2498.

   e. Prohibition on Operations during Medical Deficiency

      1) You may not act as a PIC or required pilot flight crewmember while you have a known medical problem that would make you unable to meet the requirements of your current medical certificate (i.e., Class I, II, or III).

10. The applicant demonstrates understanding of drugs and alcohol regulatory restrictions that affect the pilot's ability to operate safely.

   a. According to 14 CFR 91.17, Alcohol or Drugs, you may not act, or attempt to act, as a crewmember of a civil aircraft

      1) While under the influence of drugs or alcohol
      2) Within 8 hr. after the consumption of any alcoholic beverage
      3) While having .04% by weight or more alcohol in your blood
      4) While using any drug that affects your faculties in any way contrary to safety

b. Except in any emergency, no person who appears to be under the influence of drugs or alcohol (except those under medical care) may be carried aboard an aircraft.

c. Upon request of a law enforcement officer or an FAA employee, you must submit to a test to determine alcohol concentration in the blood or breath.

d. You may not operate an aircraft within the U.S. with knowledge that narcotic drugs, marijuana, or depressant or stimulant drugs or substances are aboard.

e. Conviction for a violation of any law relating to drugs or alcohol is the basis for

   1) The denial of an application for a certificate or rating for up to 1 yr. after the final conviction

   2) The suspension or revocation of any existing certificates or ratings

f. If you refuse to submit test results for drugs or alcohol when requested by the FAA, you may not receive a certificate or rating for a period of 1 yr.

   1) Your refusal is also grounds for suspension or revocation of existing certificates or ratings.

g. Keep in mind that legal drugs can affect your flying abilities.

   1) Pilot performance can be seriously impaired by both prescribed and over-the-counter medications.

      a) Many medications, such as tranquilizers, sedatives, strong pain relievers, and cough-suppressant preparations, have primary effects that may impair judgment, memory, alertness, coordination, vision, and the ability to make calculations.

      b) Others, such as antihistamines, blood pressure drugs, muscle relaxants, and agents to control diarrhea and motion sickness, have side effects that may impair the same critical functions.

      c) Any medication that depresses the nervous system, such as sedatives, tranquilizers, or antihistamines, can make you more susceptible to hypoxia.

   2) The safest rule is not to fly while taking any medication, unless approved by the FAA.

END OF KNOWLEDGE ELEMENT

10.2 RISK MANAGEMENT

A.   Task Objectives

1.   **The applicant demonstrates the ability to identify, assess, and mitigate risks encompassing distinguishing proficiency vs. currency.**

   a.   Competency may be described in two different levels: current and proficient.

      1)   A pilot who is current is compliant with all regulations and may legally exercise the privileges for which (s)he is certificated.

      2)   A pilot who is proficient is a fully competent professional who carries out each flight with expert accuracy. Such a pilot commits to putting safety first in each flight, no matter the circumstances.

   b.   Currency merely covers being legal to fly. Proficiency means being an expert in safe flying, and is a level of competency every pilot should commit to achieving.

   c.   Therefore, the requirements specified in 14 CFR 61.57 should be regarded as minimums that need to be adjusted for various factors, such as overall pilot experience, different operating environments, complexity of the facilities used, and variations in makes and models of aircraft within specific categories and classes.

2.   **The applicant demonstrates the ability to identify, assess, and mitigate risks encompassing the setting of personal minimums.**

   a.   For information on setting personal minimums, see Study Unit 5, Subunits 1-2.

   b.   *Pilot Handbook*, Study Unit 6, Subunits 12-14, have more information on PAVE and personal minimums.

3.   **The applicant demonstrates the ability to identify, assess, and mitigate risks encompassing maintaining fitness to fly.**

   a.   When using the PAVE checklist, the first element, **P**ilot, reminds you to consider such factors as competency, condition of health, mental and emotional state, level of fatigue, and many other variables.

      1)   See Study Unit 5, Subunit 2, for more information on the PAVE Checklist.

   b.   A recommended tool for pilots to use to assess their fitness to fly is the I'M SAFE checklist.

      1)   See Study Unit 5, Subunit 2, for information on the I'M SAFE Checklist.

   c.   Whatever tool or memory aid you use, it is important to understand what risks exist for a given flight condition. Evaluate your fitness before every flight, even familiar trips, to ensure you are seeing the big picture.

4.   **The applicant demonstrates the ability to identify, assess, and mitigate risks encompassing flying unfamiliar aircraft.**

   a.   All airplanes are different and each one you fly requires learning its systems and handling.

   b.   Flying unfamiliar aircraft can increase your stress level.

      1)   Complex or unfamiliar tasks require higher levels of performance than do simple or overlearned tasks.

         a)   Thus, complex or unfamiliar tasks are also more subject to the adverse effects of increasing stress than are tasks that are simple or familiar.

      2)   Accidents are more likely to occur when flying task requirements exceed pilot capability.

         a)   The difference between pilot capabilities and task requirements is the margin of safety.

    c.   Before flying unfamiliar aircraft, consider the following:

        1)   Make sure you read the POH/AFM of any unfamiliar aircraft before flying.

        2)   Know the airspeeds (gear down, rotation, stall, flap extension, etc.) before flying.

        3)   It is advisable to fly with a flight instructor before flying unfamiliar aircraft solo.

        4)   Airways practice landing solo before taking passengers in an unfamiliar aircraft.

5.   **The applicant demonstrates the ability to identify, assess, and mitigate risks encompassing operating with unfamiliar flight display systems or unfamiliar avionics.**

    a.   New advanced avionics (regardless of being new to aviation or the pilot) can increase a pilot's stress level.

        1)   Pilots need to understand the advantages of automation while being aware of its limitations.

        2)   Experience has shown that automated systems can make some errors more evident while sometimes hiding other errors or making them less obvious.

    b.   Nevertheless, the advanced avionics in modern aircraft add an entirely new dimension to the way GA aircraft are flown.

        1)   The electronic instrument displays, GPS, and autopilot reduce pilot workload and increase pilot situational awareness.

        2)   The pilot must be trained to properly use advanced avionics systems in order to become proficient in the operation of all functions applicable to each phase of flight.

END OF RISK MANAGEMENT ELEMENT

10.3 SKILLS

A. Task Objectives

    1. **The applicant demonstrates the ability to apply requirements to act as PIC under VFR in a scenario given by the evaluator.**

        a. The evaluator will provide a scenario. After thinking through currency, types of flight (e.g., for hire), endorsements, and medical issues, provide the best response.

        b. Remember, you can always refer to the Gleim *FAR/AIM* if you have any doubts about the rules regulations promulgated by the FAA.

        c. If in doubt, do not guess the correct answer. Know where to find relevant information in official sources and offer to look it up.

END OF SKILLS ELEMENT

STUDY UNIT ELEVEN
AIRWORTHINESS REQUIREMENTS

Task	Task B. Airworthiness Requirements
References	14 CFR parts 39, 43, 91; FAA-H-8083-2, FAA-H-8083-25
Objective	To determine that the applicant exhibits satisfactory knowledge, risk management, and skills associated with airworthiness requirements, including aircraft certificates.
Knowledge	The applicant demonstrates understanding of:
PA.I.B.K1	1. General airworthiness requirements and compliance for airplanes.
PA.I.B.K1a	a. Certificate location and expiration dates
PA.I.B.K1b	b. Required inspections
PA.I.B.K1c	c. Inspection requirements
PA.I.B.K2	2. Individuals who can perform maintenance on the aircraft, including A&P and IA roles in aircraft maintenance and inspections.
PA.I.B.K3	3. Pilot-performed preventive maintenance.
PA.I.B.K4	4. Equipment requirements for day and night flight for example: flying with inoperative equipment (approved Minimum Equipment List (MEL), Kinds of Operation Equipment List (KOEL), VFR and placards).
PA.I.B.K5	5. Proving airworthiness (specifics of the aircraft–compliance with Airworthiness Directives or applicability of Safety Bulletins).
PA.I.B.K6	6. Obtaining a special flight permit.
PA.I.B.K7	7. Experimental aircraft airworthiness.
PA.I.B.K6	8. Equipment malfunctions.
Risk Management	The applicant demonstrates the ability to identify, assess and mitigate risks, encompassing:
PA.I.B.R1	1. Inoperative equipment.
PA.I.B.R2	2. Equipment failure during flight.
PA.I.B.R3	3. Discrepancy records or placards.
Skills	The applicant demonstrates the ability to:
PA.I.B.S1	1. Locate aircraft airworthiness and registration information.
PA.I.B.S2	2. Determine the aircraft is airworthy in a scenario given by the evaluator.
PA.I.B.S3	3. Explain conditions where flight can be made with inoperative equipment.
PA.I.B.S4	4. Explain requirements for obtaining and flying with a Special Flight Permit.
PA.I.B.S5	5. Locate and explain operating limitations, placards, instrument markings, POH/AFM, weight and balance data, and equipment list.

A. General Information

   1. The objective of this task is for you to demonstrate your knowledge, risk management, and skills related to airworthiness requirements, including aircraft certificates.

11.1 KNOWLEDGE

A.   Task Objectives

1.   **The applicant demonstrates understanding of general airworthiness requirements and compliance for airplanes.**

a.   **Certificate location and expiration dates**

1)   Your airplane must have both an airworthiness certificate and a certificate of aircraft registration.

a)   An airworthiness certificate is issued to an aircraft by the FAA at the time of manufacture. It remains valid as long as all maintenance, airworthiness/ safety directives, and equipment 14 CFRs are complied with.

b)   A registration certificate is issued to the current owner of an aircraft as registered with the FAA. It expires every 3 yr. from the expiration date of the previous certificate and must be renewed.

c)   The location varies, but the registration, airworthiness certificate, and radio license (if required) are typically found in a plastic-covered pocket on the sidewall of the cockpit area.

b.   **Required inspections**

1)   Aircraft inspections are performed to ensure the aircraft has been maintained in an airworthy condition.

2)   The maintenance requirements on aircraft that are used in commercial operations (i.e., flight training, charter, etc.) are more stringent than on noncommercial Part 91, which requires a maintenance inspection only on an annual basis.

a)   Annual inspections must be completed prior to the last day of the 12th calendar month after the previous annual inspection.

EXAMPLE: An aircraft has its annual inspection on March 22, 2016. The next inspection is due March 31, 2017.

b)   Airplanes that are used to carry people for hire or to provide flight instruction for hire must undergo an annual or 100-hr. inspection within the preceding 100 hr. of flight time.

i)   The 100 hr. may not be exceeded by more than 10 hr. if necessary to reach a place at which an inspection can be performed.

ii)   The next inspection, however, is due 200 hr. from the prior inspection; e.g., if the inspection is done at 105 hr., the next inspection is due in 95 hr.

          iii)   If you have an inspection done prior to 100 hr., you cannot add the time remaining to 100 hr. to the next inspection.

      c)   The only difference between a 100-hr. inspection and an annual inspection is the requirement for who makes the logbook endorsement.

      d)   Based on the specific make and model aircraft, further checks beyond the 100-hr. check may be necessary to comply with the 14 CFRs or ASTM standards. This additional maintenance may be required at the 50-, 150-, or 250-hr. point, and so on.

   3)   You may not use an ATC transponder unless it has been tested and inspected within the preceding 24 calendar months.

   4)   The emergency locator transmitter (ELT) battery must be replaced after half its useful life has expired (as established by the transmitter manufacturer) or after 1 hr. of cumulative use.

      a)   The ELT must be inspected every 12 calendar months for

          i)   Proper installation
          ii)   Battery corrosion
          iii)   Operation of the controls and crash sensor
          iv)   Sufficient signal radiated from its antenna
          v)   Pitot/Static

   5)   The pitot/static system, altimeter, and encoder are required to be inspected every 24 calendar months if the aircraft is operated under IFR.

2.   **The applicant demonstrates understanding of individuals who can perform maintenance on the aircraft, including A&P and IA roles in aircraft maintenance and inspections.**

   a.   An annual inspection must be performed by a certificated mechanic (A&P) who also has an inspection authorization (IA).

   b.   An A&P can perform 100-hr. inspections as well as ELT checks.

   c.   An appropriately rated avionics technician must perform the transponder inspection.

3.   **The applicant demonstrates understanding of pilot-performed preventive maintenance.**

   a.   A person who holds a pilot certificate (e.g., private pilot) may perform preventive maintenance on any airplane owned or operated by that pilot that is not used in air carrier services.

   b.   After preventive maintenance has been performed, the signature, certificate number, the type of certificate held by the person approving the work, the date the work was performed, and a description of the work must be entered into the aircraft maintenance records.

   c.   A complete list of operations that are classified as preventive maintenance is included in Part 43. Some common examples include

      1)   Removal, installation, and repair of landing gear tires,
      2)   Replenishing hydraulic fluid,
      3)   Replenishing or changing the oil,
      4)   Servicing landing gear struts, and
      5)   Replacing landing light bulbs.

4. **The applicant demonstrates understanding of equipment requirements for day and night flight, for example: flying with inoperative equipment [approved Minimum Equipment List (MEL), Kinds of Operation Equipment List (KOEL), VFR, and placards].**

    a. Make sure your airplane has the required equipment for the flight you are about to take, e.g., Mode C transponder for an operation in Class B or Class C airspace.

        1) The operating limitations of any optional equipment installed in your airplane (e.g., an autopilot) will be found in Section 9, Supplements, of the POH/AFM.

        2) Section 6, Weight and Balance/Equipment List, in your POH/AFM presents all the equipment installed in your airplane.

    b. You may not operate a powered civil aircraft with a standard category U.S. airworthiness certificate without the specified operable instruments and equipment.

        1) Except as provided in 14 CFR 91.213, you may not take off in an airplane with any inoperative instruments or equipment installed, i.e., in an airplane that is not airworthy.

        2) Required equipment: VFR - day

            a) <u>T</u>achometer for each engine

            b) <u>O</u>il pressure gauge for each engine using a pressure system

            c) <u>M</u>anifold pressure gauge for each altitude engine

            d) <u>A</u>ltimeter

            e) <u>T</u>emperature gauge for each liquid-cooled engine

            f) <u>O</u>il temperature gauge for each air-cooled engine

            g) <u>F</u>uel gauge indicating the quantity of fuel in each tank

            h) <u>L</u>anding gear position indicator, if the aircraft has a retractable landing gear

            i) <u>A</u>irspeed indicator

            j) <u>M</u>agnetic direction indicator (compass)

            k) An <u>E</u>mergency locator transmitter (ELT), if required by 14 CFR 91.207

            l) Approved <u>S</u>afety belt with approved metal-to-metal latching device for each occupant who is 2 yr. of age or older

            m) For small civil airplanes manufactured after July 18, 1978, an approved shoulder harness for each front seat

            n) For normal, utility, and acrobatic category airplanes with a seating configuration, excluding pilot seats, of nine or less, manufactured after December 12, 1986, a shoulder harness for each seat in the airplane

            o) For small airplanes certificated after March 11, 1996, an approved anticollision light system

            p) Approved flotation gear for each occupant and one pyrotechnic signaling device if the aircraft is operated for hire over water beyond power-off gliding distance from shore

        3) Required equipment: VFR - night

            a) All equipment listed in item 2) above

            b) A set of spare <u>F</u>uses or three spare fuses for each kind required which are accessible to the pilot in flight

            c) If the aircraft is operated for hire, one electric <u>L</u>anding light

            d) Approved aviation red or white <u>A</u>nticollision light system on all U.S.-registered civil aircraft

            e) Approved <u>P</u>osition (navigation) lights

            f) An adequate <u>S</u>ource of electricity for all electrical and radio equipment

c. 14 CFR 91.213 describes the acceptable methods for the operation of an airplane with certain inoperative instruments and equipment that are not essential for safe flight. These acceptable methods of operation are

1) Operation with an approved MEL

a) An MEL is a specific inoperative equipment document for a particular make and model aircraft by serial and registration number.

b) An MEL is designed to provide owners/operators with the authority to operate an aircraft with certain items or components inoperative, provided the FAA finds an acceptable level of safety maintained by

i) Appropriate operations limitations

ii) A transfer of the function to another operating component

iii) Reference to other instruments or components providing the required information

2) Operation without an MEL (probably the way your airplane is operated)

a) You may take off in an aircraft with inoperative instruments and equipment without an approved MEL provided the inoperative instruments and equipment are not

i) Part of the VFR-day type certification instruments and equipment under which the aircraft was type certificated

ii) Indicated as required on the aircraft's equipment list or on the Kinds of Operations Equipment List for the kind of flight operation being conducted

iii) Required by any 14 CFR

iv) Required by an airworthiness directive

b) The inoperative instruments or equipment must be

i) Removed from the airplane with the cockpit control placarded and the maintenance properly recorded or

ii) Deactivated and placarded "inoperative."

c) A determination must be made by a certificated and appropriately rated pilot or an appropriately certificated mechanic that the inoperative instrument or equipment does not constitute a hazard to the aircraft.

d) By following these procedures, the aircraft is considered to be in a properly altered condition acceptable to the FAA.

d. For information on operating limitations, placards, instrument markings, and POH/AFM, see Study Unit 3.

5. **The applicant demonstrates understanding of proving airworthiness (specifics of the aircraft–compliance with Airworthiness Directives or applicability of Safety Bulletins).**

a. Airworthiness directives (ADs) are issued by the FAA to require correction of unsafe conditions found in an airplane, an airplane engine, a propeller, or an appliance when such conditions exist and are likely to exist or develop in other products of the same design. The actions specified in an AD are intended to detect, prevent, resolve, or eliminate the unsafe condition.

1) ADs may be divided into two categories:

a) Those of an emergency nature requiring immediate compliance

b) Those of a less urgent nature requiring compliance within a relatively longer period of time

2) ADs are regulatory (i.e., issued under 14 CFR Part 39, Airworthiness Directives) and must be complied with unless a specific exemption is granted.

    b.   An FAA inspector is very likely to ask you if the aircraft complies with all ADs.

        1)   You should verify with your evaluator ahead of time if you should bring maintenance records or copies to your practical test.

        2)   14 CFR 91.417, Maintenance Records, requires that a record be maintained that shows the current status of applicable ADs, including the method of compliance, the AD number, the revision date, and the signature and certificate number of the repair station or mechanic who performed the work.

            a)   If the AD involves recurring action (e.g., an inspection every 50 hr.), a record must be kept of the time and date when the next action is required.

    c.   A Service Bulletin (S.B.) is a notice to an aircraft operator from a manufacturer informing him or her of a product improvement. An alert service bulletin is issued when an unsafe condition shows up that the manufacturer believes to be a safety related as opposed to a mere improvement of a product.

        1)   Although a service bulletin may be categorized as mandatory by the manufacturer, it is crucial to know that compliance with service bulletins isn't necessarily required under the 14 CFRs unless the service bulletin includes or is accompanied by an airworthiness directive.

        2)   Service bulletins are often a prelude to the issuance of ADs by the FAA.

6.   **The applicant demonstrates understanding of obtaining a special flight permit.**

    a.   When a special flight permit is required

        1)   A special flight permit may be issued to an airplane with inoperable instruments or equipment under 14 CFR Part 21, Certification Procedures for Products and Parts.

            a)   This can be done despite any provisions listed in 14 CFR 91.213.

        2)   Special flight permits may be issued for an airplane that does not currently meet applicable airworthiness requirements but is capable of safe flight in order for the pilot to fly the airplane to a base where repairs, alterations, or maintenance can be performed or to a point of storage (14 CFR 21.197).

7.   **The applicant demonstrates understanding of experimental aircraft airworthiness.**

    a.   Experimental certificates are issued for kit planes, built from plans, or amateur-built aircraft that do not have type certificates or for some reason do not conform to their type certificates. They are commonly referred to as homebuilts.

    b.   The duration of the experimental certificate is unlimited unless the FAA established an expiration date.

    c.   A person who builds an aircraft from a kit and wants to be issued an experimental certificate [thus certifying the aircraft as an experimental light-sport aircraft (ELSA)] must provide the following:

        1)   Evidence that an aircraft of the same make and model was manufactured and assembled by the aircraft kit manufacturer and issued a special airworthiness certificate in the light-sport category.

        2)   The aircraft's operating instructions.

        3)   The aircraft's maintenance and inspection procedures.

        4)   The manufacturer's statement of compliance for the aircraft kit and assembly instructions that meet the consensus standard.

        5)   The aircraft's flight training supplement.

        6)   For an aircraft kit manufactured outside of the U.S., evidence that the aircraft kit was manufactured in a country with which the U.S. has some type of an Airworthiness Agreement.

    (All of the items in c. are supplied by the kit manufacturer.)

8. **The applicant demonstrates understanding of equipment malfunctions.**

    a. You can continue to fly an airplane with inoperative equipment, even without an MEL, provided the equipment that is inoperative is not included on the required VFR instrument and equipment list or the aircraft's equipment list and provided it is not required by any 14 CFR or by an AD.

    b. If the airplane has inoperable instruments or equipment and it needs to be moved to a location where the repair work can be performed, a special flight permit would be required.

        1) The implication is that the airplane does not meet the current airworthiness requirements but that it can be flown safely in order to get it to an airport where repairs can be made.

        2) Contact the FSDO to obtain a special flight permit.

    c. For more information, see Study Unit 51, "Systems and Equipment Malfunction."

END OF KNOWLEDGE ELEMENT

11.2 RISK MANAGEMENT

A. Task Objectives

1. **The applicant demonstrates the ability to identify, assess, and mitigate risks encompassing inoperative equipment.**

    a. The airplane consists of the usual array of mechanical and cosmetic issues that every aircraft pilot, owner, or operator can identify.

    b. With the advent of advanced avionics, the airplane has expanded to include database currency, automation status, and emergency backup systems that were unknown a few years ago.

    c. You should be able to explain to the evaluator what equipment is required and what to do if equipment is inoperative before your flight.

    d. The evaluator will want to see that you can make a competent go/no-go decision based on regulatory requirements and personal minimums, including experience and proficiency with the equipment.

    e. Refer to item A.4. in Subunit 11.1 for details on equipment requirements.

2. **The applicant demonstrates the ability to identify, assess, and mitigate risks encompassing equipment failure during flight.**

    a. The evaluator may discuss hypothetical scenarios encompassing various types of equipment failures in flight.

    b. When equipment has failed in flight, the decision to continue the flight to the intended destination or divert to an alternate airport must be made.

    c. You should be able to explain your decision-making process.

        1) In case of an emergency, your number one priority as PIC is maintaining control of the aircraft.

            a) Know the checklists for the areas requiring immediate attention.

            b) Some emergencies may not allow enough time to "read, then do." However, if you are able to "do then verify," this will mitigate the act of using a checklist from becoming a distraction from maintaining control of the aircraft.

        2) For non-emergency failures, knowing the systems on your airplane is imperative to completing this task. In some situations, redundancy may allow you to continue while mitigating risks.

            a) EXAMPLE: If the vacuum pump fails, you may lose your heading indicator and attitude indicator. Explain how other instruments could be used to determine pitch, bank, and heading information.

                i) Or, your airplane may have an alternate or standby vacuum system. If so, explain any limitations or operating procedures.

            b) Explain that you would consult the POH/AFM to review system descriptions and limitations for any areas you are unsure about.

            c) Explain that you should not fixate on minor problems, which could become a distraction from flying the plane.

    d. Whenever in doubt, land and assess whether you can continue your trip given the malfunctioning equipment.

    e. For more information, see Study Unit 51, "Systems and Equipment Malfunction."

3. **The applicant demonstrates the ability to identify, assess, and mitigate risks encompassing discrepancy records or placards.**

   a. As PIC, you must be certain the aircraft is airworthy.

   b. A record of maintenance discrepancies should be easily accessible by anyone operating the aircraft.

   c. This record may be a formal tracking system or less-formal method to verify the status of outstanding discrepancies.

      1) The methods used should work for all the operators of the aircraft.

         a) If you are the owner and sole operator, a less-formal system may work.

         b) If you share the aircraft with a club or are renting from an FBO, a discrepancy list, sometimes called a squawk sheet, should be checked to help determine whether the aircraft has been maintained in an airworthy condition.

      2) If you are in doubt of the status of any discrepancy, do not fly.

   d. For information on placards, see Study Unit 3.

END OF RISK MANAGEMENT ELEMENT

11.3 SKILLS

A.   Task Objectives

1.   **The applicant demonstrates the ability to locate aircraft airworthiness and registration information.**

   a.   The aircraft worthiness and registration certificates should be in a conspicuous place within the aircraft. Your CFI can point out their location to you.

2.   **The applicant demonstrates the ability to determine the aircraft is airworthy in a scenario given by the evaluator.**

   a.   Use your knowledge to answer the evaluator's questions. When in doubt with a scenario, it is okay to say you would ask your A&P or your FSDO before flying in the given scenario.

3.   **The applicant demonstrates the ability to explain conditions where flight can be made with inoperative equipment.**

   a.   You will need to recite your knowledge of items A.4. and 8. in Subunit 11.1.

4.   **The applicant demonstrates the ability to explain requirements for obtaining and flying with a Special Flight Permit.**

   a.   To obtain a special flight permit, you must submit a written request to the nearest FSDO indicating

      1)   The purpose of the flight
      2)   The proposed itinerary
      3)   The crew required to operate the airplane (e.g., pilot, co-pilot)
      4)   The ways, if any, the airplane does not comply with the applicable airworthiness requirements
      5)   Any restriction that you consider is necessary for safe operation of your airplane
      6)   Any other information considered necessary by the FAA for the purpose of prescribing operating limitations

5.   **The applicant demonstrates the ability to locate and explain operating limitations, placards, instrument markings, POH/AFM, weight and balance data, and equipment list.**

   a.   You may not operate an airplane unless the operating limitations (i.e., airspeed, powerplant, weight, CG, load factor, etc.) are in the airplane and are accessible to you during flight.

   b.   These operating limitations will be found in the POH/AFM, placards, and/or instrument markings.

      1)   See Section 2, Limitations, of your POH/AFM.

         a)   The operating limitations of any optional equipment installed in your airplane (e.g., an autopilot) will be found in Section 9, Supplements, of the POH/AFM.

      2)   You need to be able to know the location and the importance of the placards in your aircraft.

   c.   Weight and balance data are very important and are presented and explained in the POH/AFM or included with that type of information. It is important that you understand the weight and balance calculations for the airplane in which you will be training and that you work through several examples to verify that you will be in the proper weight and balance, given one or two persons aboard the airplane and various fuel loads.

      1)   Obtain a weight and balance form for your airplane from your POH/AFM or CFI.

d.   The equipment list is in Section 6, Weight and Balance, of the airplane's POH/AFM. It shows the weight and moment of each accessory added to the basic airframe. After each modification or equipment addition, the repair facility will recompute the airplane's empty weight and center of gravity. These figures are used in your weight and balance computations.

END OF SKILLS ELEMENT

STUDY UNIT TWELVE
WEATHER INFORMATION

Task	Task C. Weather Information
References	14 CFR part 91; FAA-H-8083-25; AC 00-6, AC 00-45; AIM
Objective	To determine that the applicant exhibits satisfactory knowledge, risk management, and skills associated with weather information for a flight under VFR.
Knowledge	The applicant demonstrates understanding of:
PA.I.C.K1	1. Acceptable sources of weather data for flight planning purposes.
PA.I.C.K2	2. Weather products required for preflight planning and en route operations.
PA.I.C.K3	3. Current and forecast weather for departure, en route, and arrival phases of flight.
PA.I.C.K4	4. Meteorology applicable to the airport, local area, departure, en route, alternate, and destination of a VFR flight in Visual Meteorological Conditions (VMC) to include expected climate and hazardous conditions such as:
PA.I.C.K4a	a. Atmospheric composition and stability
PA.I.C.K4b	b. Wind (e.g., crosswind, tailwind, wind shear, etc.)
PA.I.C.K4c	c. Temperature
PA.I.C.K4d	d. Moisture/precipitation
PA.I.C.K4e	e. Weather system formation, including air masses and fronts
PA.I.C.K4f	f. Clouds
PA.I.C.K4g	g. Turbulence
PA.I.C.K4h	h. Thunderstorms
PA.I.C.K4i	i. Icing and freezing level information
PA.I.C.K4j	j. Fog
PA.I.C.K4k	k. Frost
PA.I.C.K4l	l. METARs and TAFs
PA.I.C.K4m	m. Weather related charts
PA.I.C.K4n	n. Weather advisories
PA.I.C.K4o	o. PIREPs
PA.I.C.K5	5. En route weather resources.
PA.I.C.K6	6. Cockpit displays of digital weather and aeronautical information.
PA.I.C.K7	7. Seasonal weather phenomena.
Risk Management	The applicant demonstrates the ability to identify, assess and mitigate risks, encompassing:
PA.I.C.R1	1. Factors involved in determining a valid go/no-go decision.
PA.I.C.R2	2. Dynamic weather affecting flight.
PA.I.C.R3	3. The limitations of weather equipment.
PA.I.C.R4	4. The limitations of aviation weather reports and forecasts.
PA.I.C.R5	5. The limitations of inflight aviation weather resources.
PA.I.C.R6	6. Identification of alternate airports along the intended route of flight and circumstances that would make diversion prudent.
PA.I.C.R7	7. Identification of weather conditions that may increase or reduce risk for the planned flight.
PA.I.C.R8	8. Establishing personal weather minimums based on the parameters of the flight (e.g., ceilings, visibility, crosswind component, etc.), and determining when existing and/or forecast weather conditions exceed these minimums.
Skills	The applicant demonstrates the ability to:
PA.I.C.S1	1. Use available aviation weather resources to obtain an adequate weather briefing.
PA.I.C.S2	2. Correlate weather information to determine alternate requirements.
PA.I.C.S3	3. Correlate available weather information to make a competent go/no-go or diversion decision.
PA.I.C.S4	4. Update/interpret weather in flight.
PA.I.C.S5	5. Evaluate environmental conditions using valid and reliable information sources to be able to make a competent go/no-go or diversion decision.
PA.I.C.S6	6. Given a scenario based on real-time weather, where it would be appropriate, divert.
PA.I.C.S7	7. Use cockpit displays of digital weather and aeronautical information, as applicable.

A.   General Information

1.   The objective of this task is to demonstrate your knowledge, risk management, and skills related to weather information for a flight under VFR.

12.1 KNOWLEDGE

A.   Task Objectives

1.   **The applicant demonstrates understanding of acceptable sources of weather data for flight planning purposes.**

a.   The regulations pertaining to aviation weather reflect that, historically, the federal government was the only source of aviation weather information. Thus, the term "approved source(s)" referred exclusively to the federal government.

1)   Due to the growing sophistication of aviation operations and scientific and technological advances, the federal government is no longer the only source of weather information.

b.   The FAA and National Weather Service (NWS) collect weather observations.

1)   The NWS analyzes the observations, and produces forecasts, including inflight aviation weather advisories (e.g., SIGMETs).

2)   The FAA and NWS disseminate meteorological observations, analyses, and forecast products through a variety of systems.

3)   Pilots and operators should be cautious when using unfamiliar products or products not supported by FAA/NWS technical specifications.

4)   Commercially-available proprietary weather products that substantially alter NWS-produced weather products, or information, may only be approved for use by Part 121 or Part 135 operators (among other limitations).

2.   **The applicant demonstrates understanding of weather products required for preflight planning and en route operations.**

a.   A **standard briefing** should be obtained before every flight because it provides all the necessary information.

b.   An **abbreviated briefing** should be requested when you need information to supplement mass disseminated information or update a previous briefing, or when you need only one or two specific items.

1)   Inform the briefer of the time and source of the previously received information so that necessary information will not be omitted inadvertently.

c.   An **outlook briefing** should be requested whenever your proposed departure time is 6 or more hours from the time of your briefing.

d.   An **in-flight briefing** provides updates on weather conditions affecting your flight. As the name implies, this is received in-flight.

e.   Request a standard briefing any time you are planning a flight and have not received a previous briefing. The briefer will provide the following information in sequence:

1)   Adverse conditions -- significant weather and aeronautical information that might influence you to alter the proposed flight, e.g., hazardous weather conditions, runway closures, NAVAID outages, etc.

2)   VFR flight not recommended (VNR) -- an announcement made by the briefer when conditions are present or forecast, surface or aloft, that in the briefer's judgment would make proposed VFR flight doubtful. The briefer will describe the conditions and affected locations and will announce, "VFR flight is not recommended."

a)   This announcement is advisory in nature. You are responsible for making a final decision as to whether the flight can be conducted safely.

3) Synopsis -- a brief statement describing the types, locations, and movement of weather systems and/or air masses that may affect the proposed flight.

4) Current conditions -- reported weather conditions applicable to the flight summarized from all available sources.

5) En route forecast -- conditions for the proposed route summarized in logical order, i.e., departure/climbout, en route, and descent.

6) Destination forecast -- at the planned ETA, any significant changes within 1 hr. before and after the planned arrival.

7) Winds aloft -- forecast winds aloft summarized for the proposed route and altitude.

8) NOTAMs.

9) ATC delays.

10) Request for PIREPs, if appropriate.

3. **The applicant demonstrates understanding of current and forecast weather for departure, en route, and arrival phases of flight.**

   a. METAR, TAF, and FA are explained in detail in Study Unit 9, Subunit 5, beginning on page 83.

   b. **AWOS, ASOS, and ATIS reports**

      1) Definitions:

         a) **AWOS** – Automated Weather Observing System: This is an older automated reporting system that may provide only basic observed weather information for an airport (e.g., an altimeter setting), or it may be capable of generating a complete automated METAR. AWOS capabilities vary from location to location.

         b) **ASOS** – Automated Surface Observing System: This automated weather reporting system is more advanced than AWOS and is gradually replacing the older system.

         c) **ATIS** – Automatic Terminal Information Service: ATIS is a continuous broadcast of recorded information in selected terminal areas. In addition to providing current observed weather information, ATIS broadcasts also reduce controller workload by including recorded airport information such as runways/approaches in use or local NOTAMs.

      2) You should listen to the appropriate AWOS, ASOS, or ATIS broadcast prior to entering the pattern at any airport at which you intend to make a landing, if one is available.

         a) This will help you to anticipate the weather conditions you can expect, as well as which runway is in use.

         b) In addition, when flying cross-country under VFR, you can periodically update your altimeter setting using broadcasts from airports along your route.

      3) Be aware that the information contained in AWOS, ASOS, and especially ATIS reports may be up to 1 hr. old, so conditions at the airport may differ from those reported.

      4) Additional reading: For a more detailed discussion of AWOS and ASOS, refer to Part III, Study Unit 3, "Aviation Routine Weather Reports (METAR)," in *Aviation Weather and Weather Services.*

4.   **The applicant demonstrates understanding of meteorology applicable to the airport, local area, departure, en route, alternate, and destination of a VFR flight in Visual Meteorological Conditions (VMC) to include expected climate and hazardous conditions such as:**

a.   **Atmospheric composition and stability**

    1)   Air is a mixture of several gases.

        a)   When completely dry, it is about 78% nitrogen and 21% oxygen.

        b)   The remaining 1% is other gases.

        c)   However, air is never completely dry. It always contains some water vapor in amounts varying from almost zero to about 5% by volume.

    2)   Our restless atmosphere is almost constantly in motion as it strives to reach equilibrium.

    3)   Because the sun heats the atmosphere unequally, differences in pressure result, which cause a series of never-ending air movements.

    4)   These air movements set up chain reactions which culminate in a continuing variety of weather.

    5)   Virtually all of our activities are affected by weather, but aviation is affected most of all.

    6)   The atmosphere is classified into layers, or spheres, by the characteristics exhibited in these layers. See below.

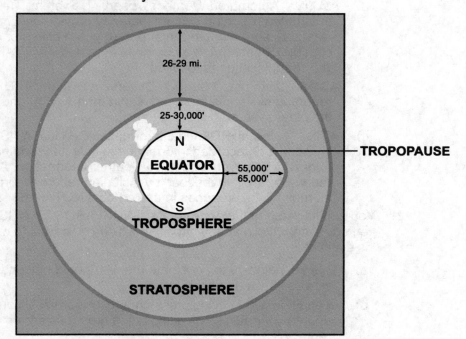

Earth's Atmosphere to 29 Miles High.

        a)   The **troposphere** is the layer from the surface to an average altitude of about 7 mi.

            i)   It is characterized by an overall decrease of temperature with increasing altitude.

            ii)   The height of the troposphere varies with latitude and seasons.

            iii)   It slopes from about 20,000 ft. over the poles to about 65,000 ft. over the Equator (4-12 mi.).

            iv)   It is higher in summer than in winter.

7) A stable atmosphere resists any upward or downward displacement. An unstable atmosphere allows upward and downward disturbances to grow into vertical (convective) currents.

   a) Any time air moves upward, it expands because of decreasing atmospheric pressure. Conversely, downward-moving air is compressed by increasing pressure.

      i) When air expands, it cools, and when compressed, it warms.

      ii) These changes are adiabatic, meaning that no heat is removed from, or added to, the air.

   b) **Adiabatic lapse rate.** Unsaturated (dry) air moving upward and downward cools and warms at about 3.0°C (5.4°F) per 1,000 ft.

   c) **Adiabatic moist lapse rate.** Saturated (moist) air moving upward and downward cools and warms at a rate varying between 1.1°C and 2.8°C (2°F and 5°F) per 1,000 ft.

      i) Recall that the standard temperature lapse rate of 2°C per 1,000 ft. of altitude gained or lost is only an average lapse rate.

   d) The difference between the existing lapse rate of a given air mass and the adiabatic lapse rate determines whether the air is stable or unstable.

8) The stability of an air mass determines its typical weather characteristics. When one air mass overlies another, conditions change with height. The following are typical characteristics of stable and unstable air:

   a) Stable air -- stratiform clouds and fog, continuous precipitation, smooth air, and fair-to-poor visibility in haze and smoke.

   b) Unstable air -- cumuliform clouds, showery precipitation, turbulence, and good visibility, except in blowing obstructions, e.g., dust, sand, snow, etc.

b. **Wind (e.g., crosswind, tailwind, wind shear, etc.)**

1) Differences in temperature create differences in pressure. These pressure differences cause the movement of air masses.

   a) The horizontal movement of air is called wind, and the vertical movement of air is called convection.

   b) A cooler surface area would create a high-pressure area, while a warmer surface area would create a low-pressure area. (Recall the effect of temperature on air pressure.)

2) Since the Earth rotates, the air does not flow directly from high- to low-pressure areas. In the Northern Hemisphere, it is deflected to the right by what is called the **Coriolis Force**.

   a) In the Northern Hemisphere, the wind blows clockwise around a high and counterclockwise around a low due to the Coriolis Force.

   b) The strength of the Coriolis Force is directly proportional to wind speed. The faster the wind, the stronger the Coriolis Force.

3) At approximately 3,000 ft. AGL and below, friction between the wind and the Earth's surface slows the wind. This reduces the Coriolis Force but does not affect the pressure gradient force.

4) Types of Wind

   a) A **jet stream** is a narrow band of strong winds (50 kt. or more) moving generally from west to east at a level near the tropopause.

   b) A **valley wind** occurs when colder, denser air in the surroundings settles downward and forces the warmer air near the ground up the mountain slope.

   c) A **mountain wind** occurs at night when the air near the mountain slope is cooled by terrestrial radiation, becomes heavier than the surrounding air, and sinks along the slope.

   d) A **katabatic wind** is a wind blowing down an incline, where the incline itself has been a factor in causing the wind. A mountain wind is a good example of a katabatic wind.

   e) **Sea and land breezes**

      i) During the day, the land is warmer than the sea.

- Sea breezes are caused by cooler and denser air moving inland off the water.
- Once over the warmer land, the air heats up and rises.
- Currents push the air out over the water where it cools and descends, starting the process over again.

      ii) At night, the wind reverses from the cool land to the warmer water.

- This is called a land breeze.

5) For information on crosswind and tailwind, see Study Unit 9, Subunit 3, beginning on page 80.

6) For information on wind shear, see Study Unit 9, Subunit 4, beginning on page 81.

c. **Temperature**

1) **Temperature scales.** Two commonly used temperature scales are Celsius (C) and Fahrenheit (F).

   a) The Celsius scale is used in most aviation weather reports, forecasts, and charts.

   b) Two common temperature references are the melting point of pure ice and the boiling point of pure water at sea level.

      i) The boiling point of water is 100°C or 212°F.
      ii) The melting point of ice is 0°C or 32°F.

   c) Most flight computers provide for direct conversion of temperature from one scale to the other.

2) Heat is a form of energy. When a substance contains heat, it exhibits the property we measure as temperature, which is the degree of a substance's warmth or coldness.

3) Temperature variations. Five main types of temperature variations affect weather:

   a) **Diurnal variation.** This change in temperature from day to night and night to day is brought about by the rotation of the Earth.

   b) **Seasonal variation.** Since the Earth's axis is tilted with respect to its orbit, the angle at which a particular spot or region receives solar radiation varies throughout the year. This phenomenon accounts for the temperature variations of the four seasons.

   c) **Variation with latitude.** The sun is nearly overhead in the equatorial regions. Since the Earth is spherical, the sun's rays reach the higher latitudes at an angle. For this reason, the equatorial regions receive the most radiant energy and are the warmest.

   d) **Variations with topography.** Since land heats and cools at a faster rate than water, air temperatures over land vary more widely than those over large bodies of water, which tend to have more minimal temperature changes. Wet soil, swamps, and thick vegetation also help to control temperature fluctuations.

e)   **Temperature variation with altitude.** The amount of temperature decrease with increases in altitude is defined as the lapse rate.

   i)   Standard sea level temperature is 15°C.

   ii) The average standard lapse rate in the troposphere is 2°C per 1,000 ft.

   iii) An increase in temperature with an increase in altitude is called an inversion because the lapse rate is inverted.

   • An inversion may occur when the ground cools faster than the air over it. Air in contact with the ground becomes cold, while only a few hundred feet higher, the temperature has changed very little. Thus, the temperature increases with altitude.

   • Inversions may occur at any altitude.

d.   **Moisture/Precipitation**

1)   Water vapor is invisible like the other atmospheric gases, but its quantity in the air can still be measured. It is generally expressed as

   a)   Relative humidity -- a ratio of how much actual water vapor is present to the amount that could be present. At 100% relative humidity, the air is saturated.

   b)   Dew point -- the temperature to which air must be cooled to become saturated by the water vapor that is already present in that air.

      i)   Dew point is compared to air temperature to determine how close the air is to saturation. This difference is referred to as the temperature-dew point spread.

      ii) As the temperature and dew point converge, fog, clouds, or rain should be anticipated.

2)   The six possible transformations of water are designated by the following terms:

   a)   **Condensation** -- the change of water vapor to liquid water
   b)   **Evaporation** -- the change of liquid water to water vapor
   c)   **Freezing** -- the change of liquid water to ice
   d)   **Melting** -- the change of ice to liquid water
   e)   **Sublimation** -- the change of ice to water vapor
   f)   **Deposition** -- the change of water vapor to ice

3)   Supercooled water consists of water droplets existing at temperatures below freezing.

   a)   Supercooled water is dangerous because it immediately forms into heavy, clear ice when it strikes an airplane's surface.

4)   Dew forms when the Earth's surface cools to below the dew point of adjacent air as a result of heat radiation. Moisture forms (condenses) on leaves, grass, and exposed objects. This is the same process that causes a cold glass of water to "sweat" in warm, humid weather.

5)   Frost forms in much the same way as dew. The difference is that the dew point of surrounding air must be colder than freezing. Water vapor sublimates directly as ice crystals or frost rather than condensing as dew.

e.   **Weather system formation, including air masses and fronts**

1)   **Air masses.** When a body of air comes to rest or moves slowly over an extensive area having uniform properties of temperature and moisture, the body of air takes on the same properties.

a)   The area over which the air mass acquires its properties of temperature and moisture is its source region. There are many source regions, the best examples being large polar regions, cold northern and warm tropical oceans, and large desert areas.

2)   **Fronts.** The zone between two different air masses is a frontal zone or front. Across this zone, temperature, humidity, and wind often change rapidly over short distances.

a)   Discontinuities. When you pass through a frontal zone, these changes may be abrupt, indicating a narrow front. A more subtle change indicates a broad and diffused front.

i)   Wind **always** changes across a front. Direction, speed, or both will change.

ii)   The most easily recognizable indication that you are passing through a front will be a temperature change.

iii)   Temperature-dew point spread usually differs across a front.

iv)   Pressure may change abruptly as you move from one air mass to another. It is important to keep a current altimeter setting when in the vicinity of a front.

b)   Types of fronts. There are four principal types of fronts:

i)   Cold front -- the leading edge of an advancing cold air mass. At the surface, cold air overtakes and replaces warm air. Cold fronts tend to precede high pressure systems.

ii)   Warm front -- the leading edge of an advancing mass of warm air. Since cold air is more dense, it hugs the ground. Warm air slides up and over the cold mass. This elongates the frontal zone making it more diffuse. Warm fronts generally move about one-half as fast as cold fronts under the same wind conditions. Warm fronts tend to precede low pressure systems.

iii)   Stationary front -- occurs when neither air mass is replacing the other and there is little or no movement. Surface winds tend to blow parallel to the front.

iv)   Occluded front -- occurs when a fast-moving cold front catches up with a slow-moving warm front. The difference in temperature within each frontal system is a major factor in determining whether a cold or warm front occlusion (i.e., which will be dominant) occurs.

c)   Weather occurring with a front depends on the

i)   Amount of moisture available
ii)   Degree of stability of the air that is forced upward
iii)   Slope of the front
iv)   Speed of the frontal movement
v)   Upper wind flow

d)   In fronts, flying weather varies from virtually clear skies to extremely hazardous conditions.

i)   Surface weather charts pictorially portray fronts and, in conjunction with other forecast charts and special analyses, help you in determining expected weather conditions along your proposed route.

ii) Frontal weather may change rapidly.

iii) A mental picture of what is happening and what is forecast should greatly help you in avoiding adverse weather conditions.

e) Additional reading: For more information, refer to Part I, Study Unit 8, "Air Masses and Fronts," in *Aviation Weather and Weather Services*.

f. **Clouds**

1) Clouds are a visible collection of minute water or ice particles suspended in air. A cloud may be composed entirely of liquid water, ice crystals, or a mixture of the two.

a) Cloud formation. Normally, air must become saturated for condensation to occur. Saturation may result from cooling the temperature, increasing the dew point, or both. Cooling is far more predominant.

b) If the cloud is on the ground, it is fog.

c) When entire layers of air cool to the point of saturation, fog or sheet-like stratus clouds result.

2) Precipitation is an all-inclusive term denoting drizzle, rain, snow, ice pellets, hail, and ice crystals. Precipitation occurs when any of these particles grow in size and weight until the atmosphere can no longer suspend them, and they fall.

a) Precipitation can change its state as the temperature of its environment changes.

i) Falling snow may melt to form rain in warmer layers of air at lower altitudes.

ii) Rain falling through colder air may become supercooled, freezing on impact as freezing rain.

- Freezing rain always indicates warmer air at higher altitudes.
- It may freeze during its descent, falling as ice pellets.

    ■ Ice pellets always indicate freezing rain at higher altitudes.

iii) Hailstones form when water droplets are lifted above the freezing level by updrafts of a thunderstorm, where they freeze solid. They may be circulated up and down within the storm, increasing in size and weight until they become too heavy to remain aloft and fall to the surface or are ejected through the anvil.

- Hail may be encountered up to 20 mi. from a strong thunderstorm cell.

b) There are four major classifications or families of clouds:

i) High clouds -- composed almost entirely of ice crystals. The height of the bases of these clouds usually range from about 16,500 ft. to 45,000 ft. in middle latitudes. The high cloud family is cirriform.

ii) Middle clouds -- composed primarily of water, much of which may be supercooled. Cloud bases range from 6,500 ft. to 23,000 ft. in middle latitudes.

iii) Low clouds -- composed almost entirely of water, but at times the water may be supercooled. Cloud bases range from the surface to about 6,500 ft. in middle latitudes.

iv) Clouds with extensive vertical development -- usually composed of supercooled water above the freezing level. Bases range from 1,000 ft. or less to above 10,000 ft.

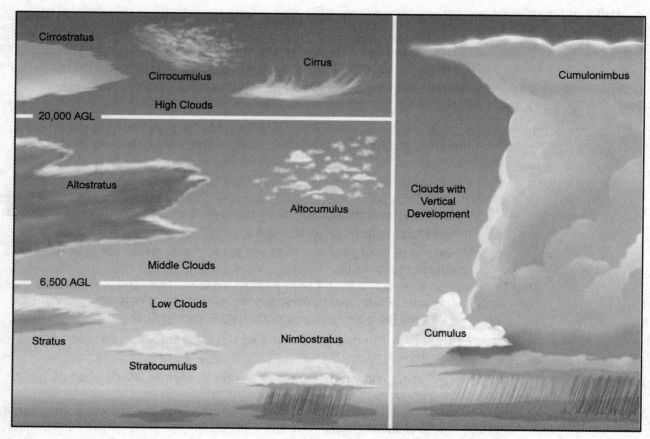

g.   **Turbulence**

1)   A turbulent atmosphere is one in which air currents vary greatly over short distances.

a)   As an airplane moves through these currents, it undergoes changing accelerations that jostle it from its smooth flight path. This jostling is called turbulence.

i)   An airplane's reaction to turbulence varies with the difference in wind speed in adjacent currents, the size of the airplane, wing loading, airspeed, and altitude.

b)   The main causes of turbulence are

i)   Convective currents
ii)   Obstructions to wind flow
iii) Wind shear

2)   Turbulence also occurs in the wake of moving aircraft whenever the airfoils are producing lift. It is called wake turbulence.

a)   You need to avoid flying through these wingtip vortices.

3)   Although general forecasts of turbulence are quite good, forecasting precise locations is, at present, impossible.

4)   Generally, when you receive a forecast of turbulence, you should plan your flight to avoid areas of most probable turbulence. Thus, large areas are often forecasted.

a)   Since no instruments are currently available for directly observing turbulence, the weather briefer can only confirm its existence or absence via pilot reports.

b)   Help your fellow pilots and the weather service -- send pilot reports.

5) To make reports and forecasts meaningful, turbulence is classified into intensities based on the effects it has on the aircraft and passengers.

   a) These intensities are listed and described in Part III, Study Unit 4, "Pilot Weather Reports (PIREP)," in *Aviation Weather and Weather Services*. Use this guide in reporting your turbulence encounters.

h. **Thunderstorms**

   1) For a thunderstorm to form, the air must have

      a) Sufficient water vapor
      b) An unstable lapse rate
      c) An initial upward boost (lifting) to start the storm process in motion

         i) Surface heating, converging winds, sloping terrain, a frontal surface, or any combination of these can provide the necessary lifting.

   2) A thunderstorm cell progresses through three stages during its life cycle:

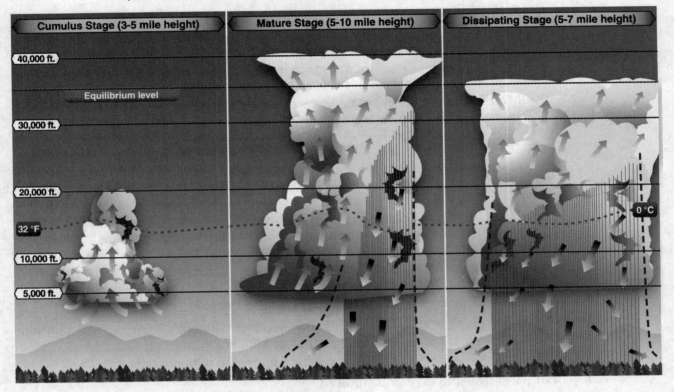

   a) **Cumulus stage.** Although most cumulus clouds do not grow into thunderstorms, every thunderstorm begins as a cumulus. The key feature in the cumulus stage is the updraft.

      i) Early during the cumulus stage, water droplets are quite small but grow to raindrop size as the cloud grows.

   b) **Mature stage.** Precipitation beginning to fall from the cloud base is the sign that a downdraft has developed and a cell has entered the mature stage.

      i) Downdrafts spread outward at the surface, producing strong gusty surface winds, a sharp temperature drop, and a rapid rise in pressure.

      ii) Updrafts and downdrafts in close proximity create strong vertical shear and a very turbulent environment.

iii)   All thunderstorm hazards reach their greatest intensity during the mature stage.

- Hazards include tornadoes, turbulence, icing, hail, lightning, low visibility and ceiling, and effects on an airplane's altimeter.

c)   **Dissipating stage.** Downdrafts characterize the dissipating stage of the thunderstorm cell, and the storm dies.

3)   **Types of Thunderstorms**

a)   Air mass thunderstorms most often result from surface heating and last only about 20 to 90 min.

b)   Steady state thunderstorms are usually associated with weather systems.

i)   Fronts, converging winds, and troughs aloft force air upwards to initiate the storms.

ii)   They may last for several hours.

4)   A squall line is a nonfrontal narrow band of steady state thunderstorms.

a)   Squall lines often form in front of cold fronts in moist unstable air, but they may also develop in unstable air far removed from any fronts.

b)   Squall lines generally produce the most severe thunderstorm conditions (e.g., heavy hail, destructive winds, tornadoes, etc.).

5)   Microbursts are small-scale, intense downdrafts that, on reaching the surface, spread outward in all directions from the downdraft center. This causes the presence of both vertical and horizontal wind shears that can be extremely hazardous to all types and categories of aircraft, especially at low altitudes.

6)   Microburst wind shear may create a severe hazard for aircraft within 1,000 ft. of the ground, particularly during the approach to landing and landing and takeoff phases.

a)   The aircraft may encounter a headwind (performance increasing) followed by a downdraft and tailwind (both performance decreasing), possibly resulting in terrain impact.

b)   Flight in the vicinity of suspected or reported microburst activity should always be avoided.

7)   Do NOT fly in or near thunderstorms for any reason.

a)   You can safely fly around scattered thunderstorms if you provide sufficient spacing between your aircraft and the storm.

b)   Never attempt to fly through or underneath a thunderstorm.

i.   **Icing and freezing level information**

1)   **Icing**

a)   Icing is a cumulative hazard to airplanes. When ice builds up on the surface of an airplane, it increases weight and drag while reducing lift and thrust. These factors tend to slow the airplane and/or force it to descend. Icing can also seriously impair engine performance and flight instruments.

b)   Structural icing will occur if two conditions are met:

i)   The airplane is flying through visible moisture, such as rain or cloud droplets.

ii)   The air temperature where the moisture strikes the aircraft is 0°C or cooler.

- Aerodynamic cooling can lower the temperature of an airfoil to 0°C even though ambient temperature is slightly higher.

c)   Structural icing can occur as clear ice, rime ice, or a mixture of the two.

d) Induction system icing, e.g., carburetor icing, lowers engine performance by reducing the intake of air necessary to support combustion.

e) Instrument icing affects the airspeed and vertical speed indicators and the altimeter. Also, ice forming on the radio antenna may result in failure of the communication and/or radio navigation systems.

f) Forecasters can identify regions in which icing is possible.

   i) However, they cannot define the precise small pockets in which it occurs.

   ii) Icing is where you find it. Icing may be local in extent and transient in character.

g) Plan your flight to avoid those areas where icing is occurring or is forecast to occur.

   i) Also, you must be prepared to avoid or to escape the hazard when it is encountered en route.

   ii) Aircraft certified for known icing can pick up icing. It is best to avoid, but if your aircraft accidentally encounters icing, your deicing equipment is available to use.

h) Here are a few specific points to remember:

   i) Before takeoff, check weather for possible icing areas along your planned route.

      • Check for pilot reports and, if possible, talk to other pilots who have flown along your proposed route.

   ii) If your aircraft is not equipped with deicing or anti-icing equipment, avoid areas of icing.

2) **Freezing Level**

   a) The freezing level panel of the composite moisture stability chart provides information about the observed freezing-level data from upper-air observations. This provides an idea of where icing could occur.

      i) The contour analysis shows an overall view of the lowest observed freezing level.

   b) AIRMET ZULU (for icing and freezing level) will state the forecast areas of expected icing.

   c) The low-level significant weather prog will depict the forecast highest freezing level.

   d) Additional reading: For a more detailed discussion of freezing level information, refer to the following sections of *Aviation Weather and Weather Services*:

      i) Part III, Study Unit 10, "Freezing-Level Graphics"
      ii) Part III, Study Unit 33, "Forecast Icing Potential (FIP)"

j. **Fog**

1) Fog is a surface-based cloud composed of either water droplets or ice crystals.

   a) It is the most frequent cause of IFR conditions and is one of the most persistent weather hazards encountered in aviation.

   b) A small temperature-dew point spread is essential for fog to form.

      i) Abundant condensation nuclei, such as may be found in industrial areas, enhance the formation of fog.

   c) Fog is classified by the way it forms.

2) **Radiation fog**, or ground fog, is relatively shallow. It forms almost exclusively at night or near daybreak under a clear sky, with little or no wind, and with a small temperature-dew point spread.

3) **Advection fog** forms when moist air moves over colder ground or water. At sea, it is called sea fog.

   a) Advection fog deepens in wind speeds up to 15 kt.
   b) Wind much stronger than 15 kt. lifts the fog into a layer of low clouds.
   c) Advection fog is more persistent and extensive than radiation fog and can appear during day or night.

4) **Upslope fog** forms as a result of moist, stable air being cooled adiabatically as it moves up sloping terrain.

5) **Precipitation-induced fog** forms when relatively warm rain falls through cool air; evaporation from the precipitation saturates the cool air and forms fog.

6) **Steam fog** forms in winter when cold, dry air passes from land areas over comparatively warm ocean waters.

7) Be especially alert for development of fog when

   a) The following morning when at dusk temperature-dew point spread is 10°C (15°F) or less, skies are clear, and winds are light
   b) When moist air is flowing from a relatively warm surface to a colder surface
   c) When temperature-dew point spread is 3°C (5°F) or less and decreasing
   d) When a moderate or stronger moist wind is blowing over an extended upslope

      i) Temperature and dew point converge at about 2°C (4°F) for every 1,000 ft. the air is lifted.

   e) When air is blowing from a cold surface (either land or water) over warmer water

      i) This would produce steam fog.

   f) When rain or drizzle falls through cool air

      i) This is especially prevalent during winter ahead of a warm front and behind a stationary front or stagnating cold front.

k. **Frost**

1) Frost forms in much the same way as dew. The difference is that the dew point of surrounding air must be colder than freezing.

   a) Water vapor then sublimates directly as ice crystals or frost rather than condensing as dew.

2) Frost on wings disrupts the smooth airflow over the airfoil by causing early airflow separation from the wing. This

   a) Decreases lift
   b) Causes friction and increases drag

3) Frost may make it difficult or impossible for an airplane to take off. Frost should be removed before attempting takeoff.

4) Thin metal airfoils are especially vulnerable surfaces on which frost will form.

5) Test data have shown that frost, ice, or snow formations having thickness and surface roughness similar to medium or course sandpaper on the leading edge and upper surfaces of a wing can reduce lift by as much as 30% and increase drag by 40%.

    a) Changes in lift and drag can significantly increase stall speed, reduce controllability, and alter the airplane's flight characteristics.

    b) These adverse effects on the aerodynamic properties of an airfoil may result in sudden departure from the desired flight path without any prior indications or aerodynamic warning to the pilot.

        i) Even a small amount of frost on airfoils may prevent an aircraft from becoming airborne at normal takeoff speed.

        ii) Also possible is that, once airborne, an aircraft could have insufficient margin of airspeed above stall so that moderate gusts or turning flight could produce incipient or complete stalling.

l. **METARs and TAFs**

1) These forecasts are described in detail in Study Unit 9, Subunit 5, beginning on page 83.

m. **Weather related charts**

1) **Surface Analysis Chart**

    a) The surface analysis chart is a computer-generated chart that depicts the observed weather conditions that existed at the valid time shown on the chart.

        i) The surface analysis chart displays the following weather information for specific locations in the form of multiple "station circles" (i.e., a group of symbols representing the observed weather at a specific location):

- Surface wind direction and speed
- Surface temperature and dew point
- Total sky cover
- Obstructions to vision
- Precipitation type
- Predominant type of low, middle, and high clouds
- Sea level pressure
- Pressure change during the past 3 hr.
- Precipitation recorded during the past 6 hr.

        ii) The chart also displays the following large-scale weather phenomena:

- Position and type of fronts
- Position of highs and lows
- Position of ridges and troughs
- Isobars (lines of constant pressure)

    b) Additional reading: For a more detailed discussion of surface analysis charts, refer to Part III, Study Unit 8, "Surface Analysis Charts," in *Aviation Weather and Weather Services.*

2) **Winds and Temperatures Aloft Chart**

    a) There are two types of computer-generated winds and temperatures aloft charts:

        i) Forecast winds and temperatures aloft charts are prepared for eight levels ranging from 6,000 ft. MSL to 39,000 ft. MSL on eight separate panels.

- Each station that prepares a winds and temperatures aloft forecast is represented on the panel by a station circle.

  - This station circle indicates wind speed and direction in the form of an arrow that is aligned with the wind direction. Barbs and pennants on the upwind end of the arrow indicate speed.
  - Temperature is shown in degrees Celsius above and to the right of the station circle.
  - A calm or light and variable wind is shown by "99" entered to the lower left of the station circle.

- There is also a textual version of the forecast winds and temperatures aloft chart called a winds and temperatures aloft forecast (FB).

        ii) Observed winds and temperatures aloft charts are prepared for four levels ranging from approximately 2,000 ft. AGL to 34,000 ft. MSL

- Information collected at each reporting station is shown by a station circle using symbols that are similar to the forecast winds and temperatures aloft chart.

    b) Additional reading: For a more detailed discussion of winds and temperatures aloft charts, refer to Part III, Study Unit 25, "Wind and Temperature Aloft Forecasts (FB)," in *Aviation Weather and Weather Services*.

3) **Surface Prognostic and Significant Weather Charts**

    a) Short-Range Surface Prognostic (PROG) Charts provide a forecast of surface pressure systems, fronts, and precipitation for a 2-day period.

        i) The forecast area covers the 48-contiguous states, the coastal waters, and portions of Canada and Mexico.

        ii) The forecasted conditions are divided into four forecast periods: 12, 24, 36, and 48 hr.

- Each chart depicts a "snapshot" of weather elements expected at the specified valid time.

        iii) PROGs plot pressure systems, frontal boundaries, and precipitation.

    b) PROGs are very similar to surface analysis charts.

        i) All of the symbols depicted on both charts are the same.

        ii) The primary difference between the two charts is that PROGs are forecast charts, whereas the surface analysis chart is a "current conditions" chart.

    c) For more information about PROG charts, refer to Part III, Study Unit 26, "Short-Range Surface Prognostic (PROG) Charts," in *Aviation Weather and Weather Services*.

    d)   Significant weather (SIGWX) charts exist for three altitude ranges.

        i)   Low-Level SIGWX Charts range from the surface to FL240.

        ii)   Mid-Level SIGWX Charts range from 10,000 feet MSL to FL450.

        iii)   High-Level SIGWX Charts range from FL250 to FL630.

        iv)   This overview will focus primarily on the Low-Level SIGWX Charts because these are most likely to be used by pilots of piston-engine airplanes.

    e)   Low-Level SIGWX Charts are updated four times per day.

        i)   Two charts are issued: a 12-hr. and a 24-hr. chart.

        ii)   Charts become valid at 0000Z, 0600Z, 1200Z, and 1800Z.

    f)   Low-Level SIGWX Charts depict weather flying categories, turbulence, and freezing levels. **Icing is not specifically forecast.**

        i)   **Flying Categories**

- Visual Flight Rules (VFR) areas are not depicted but are assumed to be located wherever other areas are not depicted.
- Marginal Visual Flight Rules (MVFR) areas are outlined with a scalloped, blue line.
- Instrument Flight Rules (IFR) areas are outlined with a solid, red line.

        ii)   **Turbulence**

- Areas of moderate or greater turbulence are enclosed by bold, dashed, yellow lines.
- Turbulence intensity is depicted using chevron-shaped symbols. One chevron represents moderate turbulence, two represent severe, and three represents extreme.
- Turbulence height is depicted by two numbers separated by a solidus (/).
- Turbulence associated with thunderstorms is not depicted on the chart.

        iii)   **Freezing Levels**

- If the freezing level is at the surface, it is depicted by a blue, sawtoothed symbol.
- Freezing levels above the surface are depicted by fine, green, dashed lines labeled in hundreds of feet MSL beginning at 4,000 feet using 4,000-ft. intervals.
- If multiple freezing levels exist, these lines are drawn to the highest freezing level.
- The lines are discontinued where they intersect the surface.
- The freezing level for locations between lines is determined by interpolation.

    g)   For a more detailed discussion of significant weather charts, refer to the following sections of *Aviation Weather and Weather Services*:

        i)   Part III, Study Unit 27, "Low-Level Significant Weather (SIGWX) Charts"

        ii)   Part III, Study Unit 28, "Mid-Level Significant Weather (SIGWX) Charts"

        iii)   Part III, Study Unit 29, "High-Level Significant Weather (SIGWX) Charts"

    4) Convective Outlooks

       a) A Convective Outlook (AC) is a forecast containing the area(s) of expected thunderstorm occurrence and expected severity over the contiguous United States. The terms listed in the report (slight risk, moderate risk, and high risk) are used to describe severe thunderstorm potential.

          i) The AC is a textual translation of the images provided in the Convective Outlook Chart.

          ii) The Convective Outlook and the Convective Outlook Chart are usually presented as a single unit, with the chart available to be used as a reference to the text and vice-versa.

       b) Narrative and graphical convective outlooks provide information concerning the potential for severe and non-severe convection and specific severe weather threats during the following 8 days.

          i) **Severe** is defined as the expected occurrence of

             • A tornado,
             • Wind gusts 50 kt. or greater, or
             • Hail of 3/4 in. diameter size or greater.

          ii) The Day 1, Day 2, and Day 3 outlooks are considered to be the most accurate, given that the predictability of severe weather decreases the further into the future a forecaster looks.

       c) The Convective Outlook defines areas of slight risk **(SLGT)**, moderate risk **(MDT)**, or high risk **(HIGH)** of severe thunderstorms for a 24-hr. period beginning at 1200 UTC.

       d) For a more detailed discussion of convective outlooks, refer to Part III, Study Unit 19, "Additional Products for Convection," in *Aviation Weather and Weather Services*.

  n. Weather advisories

    1) Convective SIGMET (WST)

       a) Convective SIGMETs are issued in the contiguous 48 states (i.e., none for Alaska and Hawaii) for any of the following:

          i) Severe thunderstorm due to

             • Surface winds greater than or equal to 50 kt.
             • Hail at the surface greater than or equal to 3/4 in. in diameter
             • Tornadoes

          ii) Embedded thunderstorms

          iii) A line of thunderstorms

          iv) Thunderstorms producing precipitation greater than or equal to heavy precipitation affecting 40% or more of an area of at least 3,000 sq. mi.

       b) Any convective SIGMET implies severe or greater turbulence, severe icing, and low-level wind shear.

          i) A convective SIGMET may be issued for any convective situation that the forecaster feels is hazardous to all categories of aircraft.

       c) Convective SIGMET bulletins are issued for the eastern (E), central (C), and western (W) United States.

2) **SIGMET (WS)**

    a) A SIGMET advises of nonconvective weather that is potentially hazardous to all aircraft.

        i) In the conterminous U.S., SIGMETs are issued when the following phenomena occur or are expected to occur:

- Severe icing not associated with thunderstorms
- Severe or extreme turbulence or clear air turbulence (CAT) not associated with thunderstorms
- Duststorms, sandstorms, or volcanic ash lowering surface or in-flight visibilities to below 3 SM
- Volcanic eruption

        ii) In Alaska and Hawaii, SIGMETs are also issued for

- Tornadoes
- Lines of thunderstorms
- Embedded thunderstorms
- Hail greater than or equal to 3/4 in. in diameter

    b) SIGMETs are unscheduled products that are valid for 4 hr. unless conditions are associated with a hurricane. Then the SIGMETs are valid for 6 hr.

    c) A SIGMET is identified by an alphabetic designator from NOVEMBER through YANKEE, excluding SIERRA and TANGO.

3) **AIRMET (WA)**

    a) AIRMETs are advisories of significant weather phenomena but describe conditions at intensities lower than those requiring SIGMETs to be issued. AIRMETs are intended for dissemination to all pilots in the preflight and en route phase of flight to enhance safety.

        i) AIRMET bulletins are issued on a scheduled basis every 6 hr.

    b) Each AIRMET bulletin contains

        i) Any current AIRMETs in effect
        ii) An outlook for conditions expected after the AIRMET valid period

    c) There are three AIRMETs:

        i) AIRMET Sierra describes

- IFR weather conditions -- ceilings less than 1,000 ft. and/or visibility less than 3 SM affecting over 50% of the area at one time
- Extensive mountain obscuration

NOTE: AIRMET Sierra is referenced in the area forecast.

        ii) AIRMET Tango describes

- Moderate turbulence
- Sustained surface winds of 30 kt. or greater
- Low-level wind shear

        iii) AIRMET Zulu describes

- Moderate icing
- Freezing-level heights

    d) After the first issuance each day, scheduled or unscheduled bulletins are numbered sequentially for easier identification.

4) Additional reading: For a more detailed discussion of SIGMETs and AIRMETs, refer to the following sections of *Aviation Weather and Weather Services* and *Pilot Handbook*:

    a) Part III, Study Unit 16, "Significant Meteorological Information (SIGMET)," in *Aviation Weather and Weather Services*,

    b) Part III, Study Unit 17, "Airmen's Meteorological Information (AIRMET)," in *Aviation Weather and Weather Services*, or

    c) Study Unit 8, "Aviation Weather Services," Subunit 6, "In-Flight Aviation Weather Advisories," in *Pilot Handbook*.

o. **PIREPs**

1) No more timely or helpful weather observations fill the gaps between reporting stations than those observations and reports made by fellow pilots during flight. Aircraft in flight are the only source of direct observations of cloud tops, icing, and turbulence.

    a) Pilots are also urged to volunteer reports when encountering any unforecasted condition.

2) A PIREP is usually transmitted as one of a group of PIREPs collected by a state or as a remark appended to the surface aviation weather report.

3) PIREPs can be obtained through FSS and ATC.

4) A PIREP is transmitted in the format shown below. Items 1 through 6 are included in all transmitted PIREPs along with one or more of items 7 through 13.

    a) All altitude references are MSL unless otherwise noted.

    b) Distances are in nautical miles (NM), and time is in UTC (or Z).

	PIREP Element	PIREP Code	Contents
	PIREP ELEMENT CODE CHART		
1.	Station identifier	XXX	Nearest weather reporting location to the reported phenomenon
2.	Report type	UA or UUA	Routine or Urgent PIREP
3.	Location	/OV	In relation to a VOR
4.	Time	/TM	Coordinated Universal Time
5.	Altitude	/FL	Essential for turbulence and icing reports
6.	Type aircraft	/TP	Essential for turbulence and icing reports
7.	Sky cover	/SK	Cloud height and coverage (sky clear, few, scattered, broken, or overcast)
8.	Weather	/WX	Flight visibility, precipitation, restrictions to visibility, etc.
9.	Temperature	/TA	Degrees Celsius
10.	Wind	/WV	Direction in degrees true north and speed in knots
11.	Turbulence	/TB	Intensity
12.	Icing	/IC	Type and Intensity
13.	Remarks	/RM	For reporting elements not included or to clarify previously reported items

5) EXAMPLE: OKC UA /OV OKC 063064/TM 1522/FL080/TP C172/TA M04/WV 245040
/TB LGT/RM IN CLR

    a) The PIREP decodes as follows: Pilot report, 64 NM on the 063-degree radial from the Oklahoma City VOR at 1522 UTC. Flight level is 8,000 ft. Type of aircraft is a Cessna 172. Outside air temperature is –4° C, wind is 245° true at 40 kt., light turbulence, and the aircraft is in clear skies.

6) Additional reading: For a more detailed discussion of PIREPs, refer to the following sections of *Aviation Weather and Weather Services* and *Pilot Handbook*:

    a) Part III, Study Unit 4, "Pilot Weather Reports (PIREP)," in *Aviation Weather and Weather Services*, or

    b) Study Unit 8, "Aviation Weather Services," Subunit 3, "Pilot Weather Report (PIREP)," in *Pilot Handbook*.

5. **The applicant demonstrates understanding of en route weather resources.**

  a. If you are already in flight and you need weather information and assistance, the following services are provided by flight service stations (FSSs). They can be accessed over the proper radio frequencies listed on aeronautical charts and the Chart Supplement.

    1) Hazardous Inflight Weather Advisory Service (HIWAS) is a continuous broadcast service over selected VORs of in-flight aviation weather advisories, i.e., AIRMETs, SIGMETs, convective SIGMETs, severe weather forecast alerts (AWW), center weather advisories (CWA), and urgent pilot reports (PIREPs).

    2) **In-flight weather briefings.** An FSS may be contacted in flight using the universal frequency of 122.2 MHz or the frequencies listed on aeronautical charts and the Chart Supplement for the purposes listed below. To use this service, call the local FSS by its locality name and "radio." For example, "(Gainesville) Radio, this is . . . "

      a) Receiving timely and meaningful weather information tailored to the type of flight intended, route of flight, and altitude

      b) Opening and closing flight plans, position reporting, and disseminating pilot reports

      c) Receiving updates on NOTAMs and temporary flight restrictions (TFRs)

6. **The applicant demonstrates understanding of cockpit displays of digital weather and aeronautical information.**

  a. Advanced avionics cockpit weather systems provide many of the same weather products available on the ground and have a variety of uses that can enhance awareness of weather that may be encountered during almost any phase of flight.

  b. Examples include radar images, satellite weather pictures, aviation routine weather reports (METARs), terminal weather forecasts (TAFs), significant meteorological information (SIGMETs), airmen's meteorological information (AIRMETs), and other products are now readily accessible at any time during flight.

  c. The increased availability of weather information is changing the way pilots think about weather briefing and the weather decision-making process. You are no longer limited to obtaining weather forecast products prior to a flight, only to discover different actual flight conditions in the air.

  d. Broadcast weather services can also provide graphical wind data, SIGMETs and AIRMETs, freezing levels, temporary flight restrictions, surface analyses, and hurricane tracks.

e.   Weather products provided by cockpit weather systems are typically presented on a multi-functional display (MFD). Some installations allow the overlay of this data in the primary flight display (PFD).

f.   You must learn the procedures required to show each kind of weather product on the MFD and/or PFD, and how to interpret each type of weather product.

    1)   Know the limitations of each type of product, and the ways in which cockpit weather systems can be used to gather information and remain clear of weather hazards throughout the flight.

g.   In the advanced avionics cockpit, radar data can come from one of two sources: an onboard weather radar system or a ground weather surveillance radar system, such as the Next Generation Radar (NEXRAD) system.

h.   Ground weather surveillance system data is transmitted to the cockpit via a broadcast (or datalink) weather service.

    1)   Many downloaded radar images and other reports are delayed for some time period for various reasons.

    2)   Given the nature of thunderstorms and other weather hazards, this delay could prove hazardous. You must know the true quality and age of the data.

i.   Advanced weather technology does have drawbacks that pilots must be aware of:

    1)   Weather radar does not detect most other kinds of hazardous weather such as fog, icing, and turbulence. The absence of radar return on a radar display does not in any way mean "clear skies." Skillful users of weather radar are able to recover clues of other weather phenomena, such as hail and turbulence, from radar data.

    2)   The earliest (cumulus) stage of a thunderstorm is usually free of precipitation and may not be detected by radar. Convective wind shear, severe turbulence, and icing are characteristic of thunderstorms during the cumulus stage.

    3)   Pilots must be aware of areas that offer no radar coverage. In many cases, these areas appear blank on a weather display. The absence of weather hazards as shown on a screen does not imply the actual absence of weather hazards.

7.   **The applicant demonstrates understanding of seasonal weather phenomena.**

a.   For information on seasonal weather phenomena, see Study Unit 9, Subunit 6, beginning on page 86.

END OF KNOWLEDGE ELEMENT

12.2 RISK MANAGEMENT

A.   Task Objectives

   1.   **The applicant demonstrates the ability to identify, assess, and mitigate risks encompassing factors involved in determining a valid go/no-go decision.**

   a.   Make a competent "go/no-go" decision based on available weather information.

   1)   Every planned flight requires a go/no-go decision. To be able to make a decision based on weather conditions, you must first understand the overall weather situation and the dangers associated with the flight environment.

   2)   The best way to ensure a safe decision is made every time is to create personal minimums.

   a)   For information on creating your personal minimums, see Study Unit 5, Subunit 2.

   3)   Your evaluator will want to see how you make the go/no-go decision.

   a)   You may be given a specific scenario that will require you to make that decision.

   b)   Coming in to the practical test with a set of personal minimums will show the evaluator that you are prepared and safety conscious.

   b.   One approach to practical weather analysis is to review weather data in terms of how current and forecast conditions will affect visibility, turbulence, and aircraft performance for your specific flight.

   c.   The 3P model of aeronautical decision making can be applied to making a go/no-go decision.

   1)   **Perceive.** Your first major preflight task is to perceive the flight environment by collecting information about current and forecast conditions along the route you intend to take, and then using the information to develop a good mental picture of the situation you can expect to encounter during the flight.

   2)   **Process.** The critical next step is to study and evaluate the information to understand what it means for your circumstances.

   a)   First, look at the weather data elements that report ceiling and visibility.

   b)   Next, carefully review current and forecast temperatures–departure, en route, and destination–for possible adverse impact on aircraft performance.

   c)   Review wind conditions for departure airport, enroute, and destination airport. You will also need a mental picture of vertical wind profiles, so as to select the best altitude(s) for cruise flight, and to determine whether wind shear is present.

   3)   **Perform.** The third step in practical preflight weather planning is to perform an honest evaluation of whether your skill and/or aircraft capability are up to the challenge posed by this particular set of weather conditions.

   d.   Always plan an alternative or escape route in case your flight cannot be completed as planned.

   e.   A decision to fly on days other than when it is clear and calm should be based on competence, the type of equipment you would be flying with (including the aircraft), and the weather conditions. Over time, expect your increased experience to enhance your abilities and judgment when making weather-related decisions.

   f.   Three weather conditions that would absolutely make you cancel or postpone a cross-country flight would be an area with a fast-moving cold front, embedded thunderstorms, or fog at the destination airport.

g. If the ceiling is high enough to allow for adequate cloud clearance and the visibility is above VFR minimums, a light rain forecast would not automatically cause you to cancel the flight.

h. If you were at an airport with only one runway and you calculated a crosswind component of 15 kt., make your go/no-go decision based on the maximum crosswind component listed for your aircraft in the POH/AFM or your airman abilities, whichever is less.

    1) If the crosswind is above that maximum crosswind component, do not fly.

    2) If the crosswind is below the maximum crosswind component, base your decision on your level of experience, the terrain, and the existence of obstacles in the area that might cause a safety issue.

    3) If in doubt, do not fly.

i. If your destination airport reports visibility below VFR minimums due to fog, but your navigation log suggests the flight would take 74 min., you should probably wait.

    1) If you have sufficient fuel, you can legally make the flight and opt not to land if the fog has not cleared. But the fog could also lift in a low layer of clouds. Until you have a better indication that the conditions will be above VFR minimums at your arrival time, you should delay your takeoff.

2. **The applicant demonstrates the ability to identify, assess, and mitigate risks encompassing dynamic weather affecting flight.**

a. Pilots will often encounter new weather phenomena as they fly on cross-country flights. It is imperative that you maintain constant vigilance in determining it is safe to continue your flight to your destination.

b. Remember that you are the pilot-in-command and if the weather is visually different than predicted, take action to ensure you do not fly into deteriorating conditions.

    1) If there are differences, you need to get an update weather briefing in flight, or if conditions are getting progressively worse, land before flight conditions deteriorate to below VFR weather minimums.

       a) You should also file a PIREP to alert other pilots and ATC to the conditions you are witnessing.

3. **The applicant demonstrates the ability to identify, assess, and mitigate risks encompassing the limitations of weather equipment.**

a. On-board weather radar is real-time weather information.

    1) Although the tilt of a radar antenna can be adjusted upward and downward, the weather phenomena that the weather radar can detect are limited in both direction and range, so it is possible for the system to fail to detect cells that lie below and beyond the radar beam.

    2) False ground clutter from radar echo returns from trees, building, or other objects on the ground is another limitation of onboard radar.

    3) Diffused echos in apparently clear air caused by a "cloud" of point targets, such as insects, or by refraction returns of the radar beam in truly clear air is another limitation to be aware of.

    4) Weather radar does not detect most other kinds of hazardous weather, such as fog, icing, and turbulence. The absence of radar return on a radar display does not in any way mean "clear skies."

    5) Weather associated with the earliest (cumulus) stage of a thunderstorm is usually free of precipitation and may not be detected by radar. Convective wind shear, severe turbulence, and icing are characteristic of thunderstorms during the cumulus stage.

b. Weather data received from a ground weather surveillance radar system is not real-time information.

1) Using a broadcast weather product to attempt to find a hole in a line of thunderstorms is inappropriate, because you cannot know if the current location of the thunderstorm cells is the same as when the broadcast weather product was generated.

c. Lightning detectors or spheric receivers, such as Stormscope® and Strikefinder®, have been known to indicate areas of static consistent with turbulence even where there was no rain associated with the turbulence.

4. **The applicant demonstrates the ability to identify, assess, and mitigate risks encompassing the limitations of aviation weather reports and forecasts.**

a. In-flight weather information obtained from ATIS and ASOS/AWOS broadcasts can contribute useful pieces to the en route weather picture, but it is important to understand that this information is only a weather "snapshot" of a limited area.

1) ATIS and ASOS/AWOS broadcasts are primarily intended to provide information on conditions in the airport vicinity.

2) The further in the future from the report, the less accurate the report will be.

b. The FAA places limitations on some weather reports and forecasts.

1) Aviation weather products produced by the federal government (NWS) are primary products unless designated as a supplementary product by the FAA. In addition, the FAA may choose to restrict certain weather products to specific types of usage or classes of users.

a) Any limitations imposed by the FAA on the use of a product will appear in the product label.

c. The weather depiction chart is computer-prepared (with the frontal analysis from a forecaster) from aviation routine weather reports (METARs).

1) Some stations are not plotted due to space limitations, particularly on the chart that covers the entire state of Alaska.

d. **SIGMET** and **AIRMET** items are considered to be widespread because they must be affecting or be forecast to affect an area of at least 3,000 sq. mi. at any one time. However, if the total area to be affected during the forecast period is very large, it could be that only a small portion of this total area would be affected at any time.

5. **The applicant demonstrates the ability to identify, assess, and mitigate risks encompassing the limitations of inflight aviation weather resources.**

a. Advanced cockpit automation requires the pilot to

1) Properly manage the amount of weather information and properly display the specific information

2) Be familiar with where to find the pertinent weather information

3) Understand that data-link weather information, including ADS-B and subscription satellite weather services, is delayed information as opposed to real-time weather

b. Pilots need knowledge and proficiency in the use of on-board weather equipment, such as radar and lightening detection equipment.

6. **The applicant demonstrates the ability to identify, assess, and mitigate risks encompassing identification of alternate airports along the intended route of flight and circumstances that would make diversion prudent.**

    a.   You should continuously monitor your position on your sectional chart and the proximity of useful alternative airports.

        1)   Determine that your alternate airport will meet the needs of the situation.

            a)   Ensure your alternative is in an area of good weather; otherwise, you may be forced into the same situation again.

        2)   Determine that the intended route does not penetrate adverse weather or special-use airspace.

    b.   Any weather that is below the forecast has a potential to become an adverse weather condition.

    c.   If there are any doubts about the weather, get an update from the nearest FSS.

    d.   Adverse weather conditions are those that decrease visibility and/or cloud ceiling height.

        1)   Understanding your preflight weather forecasts will enable you to look for signs of adverse weather (e.g., clouds, wind changes, precipitation).

        2)   Contact the nearest FSS for updated weather information.

    e.   At the first sign of deteriorating weather, you should divert to an alternate. Attempting to remain VFR while the ceiling and visibility are getting below VFR minimums is a dangerous practice.

    f.   In order to remain VFR, you may be forced to lower altitudes and possibly marginal visibility. Under these conditions, visibility relates to time as much as distance.

        1)   At 100 kt., your airplane is traveling at approximately 170 ft./sec.; thus, related to 3 SM of visibility, you can see approximately 90 sec. ahead of your airplane.

            a)   This time decreases as your airspeed increases and/or visibility decreases.

7. **The applicant demonstrates the ability to identify, assess, and mitigate risks encompassing identification of weather conditions that may increase or reduce risk for the planned flight.**

    a.   Some situations that increase risk include unforecast en route weather conditions with heavy rain, turbulence, or conditions that do not allow for continued VFR flight; fuel capacity concerns due to higher than forecast headwinds; or deteriorating weather at your destination airport.

    b.   A close temperature-dew point spread indicates the probable formation of visible moisture in the form of dew, mist, fog, or clouds. The decrease in temperature (most frequently at night) can result in a close temperature-dew point spread and fast forming fog.

    c.   The destination airport reporting visibility below VFR minimums due to fog would increase risk for the planned flight.

        1)   Delaying departure would mitigate its risk.

    d.   If you plan a flight on a day with light rain forecast and the freezing level is at 1,000 ft., cancel the flight to eliminate risk.

    e.   A flight on a day forecast with light rain creates increased risk. You must evaluate if the ceiling is high enough to allow for adequate cloud clearance and if the visibility is above VFR minimums. Therefore, a light rain forecast would not automatically cause you to cancel the flight.

8. **The applicant demonstrates the ability to identify, assess, and mitigate risks encompassing establishing personal weather minimums based on the parameters of the flight (e.g., ceilings, visibility, crosswind component, etc.), and determining when existing and/or forecast weather conditions exceed these minimums.**

    a. Pilots should not be lulled into a false sense of security simply because they are in compliance with the regulations. Judgment and aeronautical decision-making serve as the bridge between regulatory compliance and safety. Deciding if or when to undertake any flight lies solely with the pilot in command (PIC). GA pilots should remember that FAA regulations designed to prevent accidents and incidents come out AFTER the accident or incident. One of the most important concepts that safe pilots understand is the difference between what is "legal" in terms of the regulations, and what is "smart" or "safe" in terms of pilot experience and proficiency. By establishing personal minimums, pilots can take a big step in managing risk.

        1) Step 1 – Review Weather Minimums

            a) Good VFR is ceilings greater than 3,000 ft. AGL and visibility greater than 5 mi.

            b) Marginal VFR is 1,000 to 3,000 ft. AGL and/or visibility 3 to 5 mi.

            c) IFR is less than 1,000 ft. AGL and/or visibility 1 mi. to less than 3 mi.

                i) A private pilot who is not instrument rated cannot fly under IFR.

        2) Step 2 – Assess Experience and Comfort Level

            a) Think about your flight training, certifications, and experience. Complete the FAA's Certification, Training, and Experience Summary chart.

Certification, Training, and Experience Summary

CERTIFICATION LEVEL
Certificate level (e.g., private, commercial, ATP)
Ratings (e.g., instrument, multiengine)
Endorsements (e.g., complex, high performance, high altitude)
TRAINING SUMMARY
Flight review (e.g., certificate, rating, Wings)
Instrument Proficiency Check
Time since checkout in airplane 1
Time since checkout in airplane 2
Time since checkout in airplane 3
Variation in equipment (e.g., GPS navigators, autopilot)
EXPERIENCE
Total flying time
Years of flying experience
RECENT EXPERIENCE (last 12 months)
Hours
Hours in this airplane (or identical model)
Landings
Night hours
Night landings
Hours flown in high density altitude
Hours flown in mountainous terrain
Crosswind landings
IFR hours
IMC hours (actual conditions)
Approaches (actual or simulated)

b) Think through your recent flying experience and make a note of the lowest weather conditions that you have comfortably experienced as a pilot in the last 6-12 months.

3) Step 3 – Consider Other Conditions

a) Include wind and turbulence as conditions needed to set personal minimums. Are there other conditions that you need to personally add to your personnel minimum checklist?

b) Moreover, you need to be honest with yourself when determining your comfort level. Some pilots do not like turbulence, for a variety of reasons, even though they may have the stick and rudder skills to endure more turbulence than they would mentally like to endure.

4) Step 4 – Assemble and Evaluate

a) After reviewing weather minimums, assessing experience and comfort level, and considering all conditions, assemble this information into a risk assessment matrix. Evaluate whether the combined effects of any conditions are below your personal minimums.

b) If an alternative course of action is possible, continue to make adjustments for the specific conditions.

5) Step 5 – Adjust for Specific Conditions

a) Any flight you have involves almost infinite combinations of pilot skill, experience, condition, and proficiency; aircraft equipment and performance; environmental conditions; and external influences. Both individually and in combination, these factors can compress the safety buffer provided by your baseline personal minimums. Consequently, you need a practical way to adjust your baseline personal minimums to accommodate specific conditions.

	If you are facing:		Adjust baseline personal minimums by:
Pilot	Illness, use of medication, stress, or fatigue; lack of currency (e.g., haven't flown for several weeks)	Add	*at least* 500 feet to ceiling
			at least ½ mile to visibility
Aircraft	An unfamiliar airplane or an aircraft with unfamiliar avionics or other equipment:		*at least* 500 ft to runway length
enVironment	Unfamiliar airports and airspace; different terrain or other unfamiliar characteristics	Subtract	*at least* 5 knots from winds
External Pressures	"Must meet" deadlines, pressures from passengers, etc.		

6) Step 6 – Stick to the Plan

a) Once you have personal minimums, you need to stick to them.

b) Having your personal minimums written makes it easier to explain to your passengers who may try to convince you to fly when it is unsafe to do so.

END OF RISK MANAGEMENT ELEMENT

12.3 SKILLS

A.   Task Objectives

1.   **The applicant demonstrates the ability to use available aviation weather resources to obtain an adequate weather briefing.**

 a.   Flight service stations (FSSs) are the primary source for obtaining preflight briefings and in-flight weather information.

  1)   Prior to your flight, and before you meet with your evaluator, you should call the nearest FSS for a complete briefing. The phone number is 1-800-WX-BRIEF.

  2)   Obtain the appropriate type of briefing for your departure flight time. It is recommended to obtain an abbreviated briefing prior to departure with the evaluator.

 b.   Many online resources are available for collecting weather information.

  1)   Some of these resources are approved sources for weather briefings.

  2)   If using online weather resources, be sure to review the issued and valid times on all products to ensure they are current.

 c.   Be able to explain to the evaluator how you obtained a weather briefing and how it is from approved sources.

  1)   For more information, see Subunit 12.1, item A.2.

2.   **The applicant demonstrates the ability to correlate weather information to determine alternate requirements.**

 a.   An alternate airport is required if your destination airport is not VFR or forecasted to not be VFR at the time of your arrival.

  1)   Consider alternate airports if your destination airport is expected to have marginal VFR.

 b.   If weather between departure airport and destination airport is marginal VFR or worse, determine alternate airport in case the weather prevents you from traversing it.

 c.   To have an airport as an alternate airport, current weather forecasts must indicate that, at your ETA at the alternate airport, the ceiling and visibility will be at or above basic VFR weather minimums.

3.   **The applicant demonstrates the ability to correlate available weather information to make a competent go/no-go or diversion decision.**

 a.   Every planned flight requires a go/no-go decision. To be able to make a decision based on weather conditions, you must first understand the overall weather situation and the dangers associated with the flight environment.

 b.   The best way to ensure a safe decision is made every time is to create personal minimums.

 c.   To use personal minimums as part of the weather-related decision-making process, compare the current and forecast weather to the personal minimums you have set.

  1)   If the weather is better than your minimums, you are a "go."
  2)   If the weather is below your minimums, you are a "no-go" for weather reasons.

 d.   Your evaluator will want to see how you make the go/no-go decision.

  1)   You may be given a specific scenario that will require you to make that decision.

  2)   Coming in to the practical test with a set of personal minimums will show the evaluator that you are prepared and safety conscious.

4. **The applicant demonstrates the ability to update/interpret weather in flight.**

    a. Weather briefing is an activity that begins prior to departure and continues until the flight is completed.

    b. With advanced avionics cockpit weather systems, safety can be increased by providing more information for you in an easier to interpret presentation.

        1) Tracking progress of significant weather encountered en route can be easily done with scroll and range control features that allow you to look ahead and check for weather condition along upcoming portions of the flight route.

        2) In addition, you can further investigate advisories received from HIWAS and other radio broadcasts. Another practical use of advanced cockpit weather systems is to check the METAR for a destination airport before flying in range of the airport's ATIS or AWOS/ASOS broadcast.

    c. Timely updating and correct interpretation of in-flight cockpit weather is essential for flight safety.

        1) Interpretation and confirmation of significant weather should be made by contacting FSS on 122.2 MHz.

    d. When you suspect that changing weather conditions have made continuation to the destination airport inadvisable, the radar and satellite features can be used to search for alternate airports.

    e. Keep in mind that FSSs offer many advantages over an advanced weather data system, so do not use advanced avionics weather data systems as a substitute for updated en route weather briefings from FSS.

        1) For example, when talking to an FSS weather briefer, it is possible to get a better overall picture of the weather system and pilot reports not yet entered into the system. The FSS briefer can also supply more Notice to Airmen (NOTAM) and other detailed information for your particular route of flight; without such briefing, the pilot might expend many precious moments searching for a critical bit of information, instead of managing the flight.

5. **The applicant demonstrates the ability to evaluate environmental conditions using valid and reliable information sources to be able to make a competent go/no-go or diversion decision.**

    a. Competent go/no-go decisions are made by the correct interpretation of the most up-to-date weather data from reliable weather sources.

    b. A good weather briefing begins with developing a total awareness of the overall big picture before obtaining a detailed or standard briefing.

    c. Many pilots start by monitoring weather patterns through commercial television, such as The Weather Channel, several days before the flight.

    d. The day or evening before the flight, pilots may wish to obtain an outlook briefing from FSS or electronically from a Direct User Access Terminal System (DUATS). You may choose to download weather and forecast charts from the Internet.

        1) Use official weather sources such as: www.duats.com or www.1800wxbrief.com

    e. When using DUATS or any other weather Internet sources, contact FSS to clarify any information you do not fully understand.

    f. As close to departure time as possible, call FSS or log on to DUATS for a standard briefing.

    g. When using weather products on the Internet or via other sources, first make sure that the menu of products is suitable for aviation use and the products are current.

h. If you obtain a standard briefing several hours before the flight or when the weather is questionable, it is a good practice to call an FSS for an abbreviated briefing just before takeoff.

i. If you are already in flight and need to obtain a standard briefing or update a previous briefing in flight, contact FSS on 122.2 MHz. Advise the specialist of the type of briefing you require (standard, abbreviated, etc.) and provide appropriate background information. The specialist will then provide information as specified in the type of briefing you request. PIREPs are a valuable source of in-flight weather information to help provide you with real-time weather information from other pilots.

j. Advanced avionics cockpit weather systems are designed to enhance safety–not to extend the limits of flight operations. The pilot must be able to evaluate weather conditions from the data presented during the all of the details of a displays, especially refresh rates and delays from data acquisition to presentation, to make en route weather decisions.

k. HIWAS, SIGMETs, and Center Weather Advisories (CWAs) combined with automated cockpit weather can help you make in-flight diversion decisions.

l. Destination/terminal area arrival weather can be obtained via radio and/or datalink from FSS, UNICOM, ATIS, AWOS/ASOS, and terminal area datalink and can be used to help make diversion decisions in a timely manner.

m. On-board data is never an adequate substitute for a timely and thorough en route weather briefing from an FSS and can aid you in seeing the "big picture" of where VFR conditions exits to maintain awareness of potential landing sites in the event that a diversion is necessary.

n. With the availability of weather information in the cockpit, a common pitfall is that the pilot can be tempted to skip the preflight weather briefing. Do not use advanced avionics weather data systems as a substitute for a pre-flight weather briefing. Always contact FSS at 1-800-WX-BRIEF for a standard weather brief before departure to aid in your go/no-go decision.

o. A common pitfall is if, while flying en route, the pilot does not clarify hazardous or adverse conditions from FSS and uses weather information that is not as current as that provided from FSS in weather decision making.

6. **The applicant demonstrates the ability to, given a scenario based on real-time weather, where it would be appropriate, divert.**

a. Using your best judgment based on the knowledge and risks discussed previously, answer the evaluator's weather scenario.

7. **The applicant demonstrates the ability to use cockpit displays of digital weather and aeronautical information, as applicable.**

a. Demonstrate how to use the cockpit displays of weather and aeronautical information inside your aircraft. This may include your hand-held devices.

END OF SKILLS ELEMENT

STUDY UNIT THIRTEEN
CROSS-COUNTRY FLIGHT PLANNING

Task	Task D. Cross-Country Flight Planning
References	14 CFR part 91; FAA-H-8083-2, FAA-H-8083-25; Navigation Charts; Chart Supplements U.S.; AIM; NOTAMs
Objective	To determine that the applicant exhibits satisfactory knowledge, risk management, and skills associated with cross-country flights and VFR flight planning.
Knowledge	The applicant demonstrates understanding of:
PA.I.D.K1	1. Route planning, including consideration of special use airspace.
PA.I.D.K2	2. Applying universal coordinated time (UTC) to flight planning.
PA.I.D.K3	3. Converting and calculating time relative to time zones and estimated time of arrival.
PA.I.D.K4	4. Calculating time, climb and descent rates, course, distance, heading, true airspeed and ground speed.
PA.I.D.K5	5. Fuel planning.
PA.I.D.K6	6. Altitude selection accounting for terrain and obstacles, glide distance of the aircraft, VFR cruising altitude, and the effect of wind.
PA.I.D.K7	7. Conditions conducive to icing.
PA.I.D.K8	8. Symbology found on VFR charts including airspace, obstructions and terrain features.
PA.I.D.K9	9. Elements of a VFR flight plan.
PA.I.D.K10	10. Procedures for activating and closing a VFR flight plan in controlled and non-controlled airspace.
PA.I.D.K11	11. Seasonal weather phenomena.
Risk Management	The applicant demonstrates the ability to identify, assess and mitigate risks, encompassing:
PA.I.D.R1	1. The pilot.
PA.I.D.R2	2. The aircraft.
PA.I.D.R3	3. The environment.
PA.I.D.R4	4. External pressures.
PA.I.D.R5	5. Lack of appropriate training when flight is planned in an area different from the pilot's local area, such as in mountains, congested airspace, or location with different weather and topography.
PA.I.D.R6	6. The tendency to complete the flight in spite of adverse change in conditions.
PA.I.D.R7	7. Failure to select the appropriate VFR altitude for the direction of flight.
PA.I.D.R8	8. Limitations of ATC services.
PA.I.D.R9	9. Improper fuel planning.
PA.I.D.R10	10. A route overflying significant environmental influences, such as mountains or large bodies of water.
PA.I.D.R11	11. Flight in areas unsuitable for landing or below personal minimums.
PA.I.D.R12	12. Seasonal weather patterns.
Skills	The applicant demonstrates the ability to:
PA.I.D.S1	1. Prepare, present and explain a cross-country flight plan assigned by the evaluator including a risk analysis based on real-time weather.
PA.I.D.S2	2. Transfer knowledge used for one region to another region (given local climate, terrain, etc.).
PA.I.D.S3	3. Update fuel planning/manage fuel.
PA.I.D.S4	4. Select appropriate routes, altitudes, and checkpoints.
PA.I.D.S5	5. Recalculate fuel reserves based on a scenario provided by the evaluator.
PA.I.D.S6	6. Create a navigation log and simulate filing a VFR flight plan.
PA.I.D.S7	7. Interpret departure, en route, arrival route with reference to appropriate and current charts.
PA.I.D.S8	8. Explain or demonstrate diversion to alternate.
PA.I.D.S9	9. Apply pertinent information from Chart Supplements U.S.; NOTAMs relative to airport, runway and taxiway closures; and other flight publications.
PA.I.D.S10	10. On the day of the practical test, the final flight plan shall be to the first fuel stop, based on the maximum allowable passengers, baggage, and/or cargo loads using real-time weather and appropriate and current aeronautical charts.
PA.I.D.S11	11. Properly identify airspace, obstructions, and terrain features.
PA.I.D.S12	12. Select appropriate navigation system/facilities and communication frequencies.

A.   General Information

1.   The objective of this task is for you to demonstrate your knowledge, risk management, and skills related to cross-country flights and VFR flight planning.

2.   See the Gleim *Pilot Handbook* for the following:

a.   Study Unit 9, "Navigation: Charts, Publications, Flight Computers," for a discussion of interpreting sectional charts, using flight publications, and using a manual flight computer

b.   Study Unit 11, "Cross-Country Flight Planning," for steps to perform in planning a cross-country flight and examples of a standard navigation log, an abbreviated navigation log, and an FAA flight plan form

3.   Some of the content of Subunits 13.1 and 13.2 is abbreviated based on the assumption that you have thoroughly read and understood pages 91-94 and the additional common task topics found in Part II. The task objectives and specific references are provided here for your convenience.

13.1 KNOWLEDGE

A.   Task Objectives

1.   **The applicant demonstrates understanding of route planning, including consideration of special use airspace.**

a.   Plot a course for your intended route of flight using a current sectional chart.

1)   Draw a course line from your departure airport to your destination on your sectional chart.

a)   Make sure the line is dark enough to read easily, but light enough not to obscure any chart information.

b)   If a fuel stop is required, show that airport as an intermediate stop or as the first leg of your flight.

2)   Once you have your course line(s) drawn, survey where your flight will be taking you.

a)   Look for available alternate airports en route.

b)   Look at the type of terrain, e.g., mountains, swamps, large bodies of water, that would have an impact if an off-airport landing became necessary.

c)   Mentally prepare for any type of emergency situation and the action to be taken during your flight.

d)   Be sure that your flight will not take you into restricted or prohibited airspace.

b.   You should be able to identify airspace, obstructions, and terrain features on your sectional chart.

1)   The topographical information featured on sectional charts consists of elevation levels and a great number of checkpoints.

a)   Checkpoints include populated places (i.e., cities, towns) drainage patterns (i.e., lakes, rivers), roads, railroads, and other distinctive landmarks.

2)   The aeronautical information on sectional charts includes visual and radio aids to navigation, airports, controlled airspace, special use airspace, obstructions, and related data.

c.   Within each quadrangle bounded by lines of longitude and latitude on the sectional chart are large, bold numbers that represent the maximum elevation figure (MEF).

1)   The MEF shown is given in thousands and hundreds of feet MSL.

a)   EXAMPLE: **1^9** means 1,900 ft. MSL.

2) The MEF is based on information available concerning the highest known feature in each quadrangle, including terrain and obstructions (trees, towers, antennas, etc.).

3) Because the sectional chart is published once every 6 months, you must also check the Aeronautical Chart Bulletin in the Chart Supplement for major changes to the sectional chart (e.g., new obstructions).

d. For information on special use airspace (SUA), see Knowledge item A.4.a. in Study Unit 14, Subunit 1.

2. **The applicant demonstrates understanding of applying universal coordinated time (UTC) to flight planning.**

a. Aviation uses an international standard time with a 24-hour clock system, called Universal Coordinated Time (UTC), to establish a common time.

1) The term "Zulu" (Z) may be used to denote UTC. This used to be referred to as Greenwich Mean Time (GMT).

b. The FAA uses UTC or Zulu time for all operations. Use the time conversion table below to find UTC. For daylight time, subtract 1 hour.

1) When converting from UTC or Zulu time to local time, subtract the hours.

Time Zone	UTC
Eastern Standard Time	+5 hr.
Central Standard Time	+6 hr.
Mountain Standard Time	+7 hr.
Pacific Standard Time	+8 hr.
Alaska Standard Time	+9 hr.
Hawaii Standard Time	+10 hr.

c. Convert your departure, checkpoint, and arrival times from local time to UTC.

3. **The applicant demonstrates understanding of converting and calculating time relative to time zones and estimated time of arrival.**

a. Be able to convert the times on a cross-country flight.

b. EXAMPLE: If you are departing Albuquerque, NM (Mountain Time) at 9 a.m. local time in June and arriving 5 hr. later in Phoenix, AZ, you need to understand both UTC and daylight savings time.

1) ANSWER: You are planning to depart Albuquerque at 15:00 UTC (0900 + 7 hr. − 1 hr.). Your arrival in Phoenix would be at 20:00 UTC, which is 13:00 (20:00 − 7) local time.

a) Arizona does not recognize daylight savings time.

4. **The applicant demonstrates understanding of calculating time, climb and descent rates, course, distance, heading, true airspeed, and ground speed.**

a. Use your flight computer to determine time, climb and descent rates, course, distance, heading, TAS, and ground speed.

b. Refer to the Gleim *Pilot Handbook*, Study Unit 9, Subunits 9-25, to review the Gleim flight computer and how to use it for your calculations.

5. **The applicant demonstrates understanding of fuel planning.**

a. Use your flight computer to determine the amount of fuel needed for your cross-country flight.

b. Remember, you must land with a reserve of 30 min. of fuel. You might need to plan to land to refuel before you reach your intended destination.

c. The Gleim *Pilot Handbook*, Study Unit 9, Subunit 13, explains how to calculate fuel using the Gleim flight computer.

6. **The applicant demonstrates understanding of altitude selection to account for terrain and obstacles, glide distance of aircraft, VFR cruising altitude, and the effect of wind.**

   a. By using what you learned in item A.1., you can determine proper altitude selection.

      1) Apply the hemispheric rule to altitude selection.

         a) Magnetic course 360° - 179°, use an odd thousand plus 500' altitude.
         b) Magnetic course 180° - 359°, use an even thousand plus 500' altitude.

   b. Your selection of the most favorable altitude is based on a number of factors, including

      1) Winds aloft
      2) Basic VFR weather minimums
      3) Obstacle and/or terrain clearance
      4) Reception of radio navigation aids to be used, if applicable
      5) VFR cruising altitudes, if applicable
      6) Airplane performance
      7) Special use airspace

7. **The applicant demonstrates understanding of conditions conducive to icing.**

   a. Review the freeze levels along your intended flight.

   b. Ensure there are no SIGMETs or PIREPs that suggest there is icing along your flight route.

   c. The Gleim *Aviation Weather and Weather Services*, Study Unit 33, "Forecast Icing Potential (FIP)," has more information.

8. **The applicant demonstrates understanding of symbology found on VFR charts, including airspace, obstructions, and terrain features.**

   a. For information on symbology found on VFR charts, including airspace, obstructions, and terrain features, see Section I Introduction, Knowledge, item B., beginning on page 93.

9. **The applicant demonstrates understanding of the elements of a VFR flight plan.**

   NOTE: Currently, pilots file flight plans in the U.S. under either a domestic or ICAO format. The FAA is proposing to implement flight plan filing for civil aircraft exclusively under the format used by the International Civil Aviation Organization (ICAO). This section includes information for both domestic and ICAO formats.

							Form Approved: OMB No. 2120-0034
U.S. DEPARTMENT OF TRANSPORTATION FEDERAL AVIATION ADMINISTRATION **FLIGHT PLAN**	(FAA USE ONLY)		☐ PILOT BRIEFING ☐ STOPOVER	☐ VNR		TIME STARTED	SPECIALIST INITIALS

1. TYPE	2. AIRCRAFT IDENTIFICATION	3. AIRCRAFT TYPE/ SPECIAL EQUIPMENT	4. TRUE AIRSPEED	5. DEPARTURE POINT	6. DEPARTURE TIME		7. CRUISING ALTITUDE
VFR IFR DVFR			KTS		PROPOSED (Z)	ACTUAL (Z)	

8. ROUTE OF FLIGHT

9. DESTINATION (Name of airport and city)	10. EST. TIME ENROUTE		11. REMARKS
	HOURS	MINUTES	

12. FUEL ON BOARD		13. ALTERNATE AIRPORT(S)	14. PILOT'S NAME, ADDRESS & TELEPHONE NUMBER & AIRCRAFT HOME BASE	15. NUMBER ABOARD
HOURS	MINUTES		17. DESTINATION CONTACT/TELEPHONE (OPTIONAL)	

16. COLOR OF AIRCRAFT	CIVIL AIRCRAFT PILOTS. FAR Part 91 requires you file an IFR flight plan to operate under instrument flight rules in controlled airspace. Failure to file could result in a civil penalty not to exceed $1,000 for each violation (Section 901 of the Federal Aviation Act of 1958, as amended). Filing of a VFR flight plan is recommended as a good operating practice. See also Part 99 for requirements concerning DVFR flight plans.

FAA Form 7233-1 (8-82)   CLOSE VFR FLIGHT PLAN WITH _____ FSS ON ARRIVAL

a.   A domestic flight plan requires the following 17 points of information:

   1)   Type -- VFR, IFR, DVFR

      a)   DVFR refers to defense VFR flights. They are VFR flights into air defense identification zones that require a VFR flight plan to be filed.

   2)   Airplane identification

   3)   Airplane type/special equipment

      a)   The following table contains the special equipment suffixes and their meanings:

/X	--	No transponder
/T	--	Transponder with no altitude-encoding capability
/U	--	Transponder with altitude-encoding capability
/D	--	DME, but no transponder
/B	--	DME and transponder, but no altitude-encoding capability
/A	--	DME and transponder with altitude-encoding capability
/I	--	RNAV and transponder with altitude-encoding capability
/C	--	RNAV and transponder, but no altitude-encoding capability
/W	--	RNAV, but no transponder
/G	--	GPS equipped with oceanic, en route, terminal, and GPS approach capability

   4)   True airspeed (kt.)

   5)   Departure point

   6)   Departure time in Universal Coordinated Time (UTC)

      a)   You supply the proposed departure time, and the FSS will fill in the actual departure time when you activate the flight plan after takeoff.

   7)   Cruising altitude

   8)   Route of flight

   9)   Destination airport identifier or airport name (name of airport and city if needed for clarity)

   10) Estimated time en route (hours and minutes)

   11) Remarks

   12) Fuel on board (total amount expressed in hours and minutes)

   13) Alternate airport(s) (NOTE: This is not required for a VFR flight plan.)

   14) Pilot's name, address, and telephone number, and airplane home base

   15) Number of people aboard

   16) Color of aircraft

   17) Destination contact/telephone (NOTE: This is optional, not required.)

Form Approved OMB No. 2120-0026
09/30/2006

U S Department of Transportation
Federal Aviation Administration

International Flight Plan

PRIORITY   ADDRESSEE(S)

<=FF

                                                                    <=

FILING TIME   ORIGINATOR

                                            <=

SPECIFIC IDENTIFICATION OF ADDRESSEE(S) AND / OR ORIGINATOR

3 MESSAGE TYPE   7 AIRCRAFT IDENTIFICATION   8 FLIGHT RULES   TYPE OF FLIGHT

<=(FPL   —   —   — **<=**

9 NUMBER   TYPE OF AIRCRAFT   WAKE TURBULENCE CAT.   10 EQUIPMENT

                                                    /   — / **<=**

13 DEPARTURE AERODROME   TIME

        —   **<=**

15 CRUISING SPEED   LEVEL   ROUTE

                                                                    <=

TOTAL EET

16 DESTINATION AERODROME   HR   MIN   ALTN AERODROME   2ND ALTN AERODROME

                                                                    <=

18 OTHER INFORMATION

—   **<=**

SUPPLEMENTARY INFORMATION (NOT TO BE TRANSMITTED IN FPL MESSAGES)

19   ENDURANCE   EMERGENCY RADIO
        HR   MIN   PERSONS ON BOARD   UHF   VHF   ELBA

—E/   **P/**   **R/**

        SURVIVAL EQUIPMENT   JACKETS
        POLAR DESERT MARITIME JUNGLE   LIGHT FLUORES UHF   VHF

                /

        DINGHIES
        NUMBER CAPACITY COVER   COLOR

D/   **<=**

AIRCRAFT COLOR AND MARKINGS

A/

N/   REMARKS   **<=**

C/   PILOT-IN-COMMAND   **)<=**

        FILED BY   ACCEPTED BY   ADDITIONAL INFORMATION

FAA Form 7233-4 (7-93)

b.   ICAO Flight Plan

1)   Flight plans contain specific information relating to the proposed flight of an aircraft, and controllers use them to provide air traffic services. The use of one format will simplify the process and align U.S. flight plans with ICAO standards.

2)   Switching from the domestic flight plan format to the ICAO format is relatively simple and aided by the fact that most of the fields in the domestic form are found in the international form.

3) While some wording is slightly different, pilots experienced with filing domestic plans will see close similarities with most of the international fields, allowing them to file ICAO plans with ease. The table below illustrates the similarity between domestic and ICAO fields.

Domestic Fields	ICAO Field Equivalents
Aircraft Identification	Aircraft Identification
Type (of Flight)	Flight Rules
Aircraft Type	Type of Aircraft
Special Equipment*	Equipment (COM/NAV)*
Departure Point	Departure Aerodrome**
Departure Time	Time
True Airspeed	Cruising Speed
Cruising Altitude	Level
Route of Flight	Route**
Destination	Destination Aerodrome**
Est Time Enroute	Total EET
Remarks	Other Information/Remarks
Fuel on Board	Endurance
Number Aboard	Persons on Board
Color of Aircraft	Aircraft Color and Markings
Pilot's Name & Other Information	Pilot in Command

*This field is optional
**ICAO IFR Flight Plans require 4 character location identifiers

4) For additional guidance, refer to the *Aeronautical Information Manual (AIM)* paragraph 5-1-9.

10. **The applicant demonstrates understanding of the procedures for activating and closing a VFR flight plan in controlled and non-controlled airspace.**

   a. Flight plans can be filed in the air by radio, but it is best to file a flight plan either in person at the FSS or by phone prior to departing.

      1) After takeoff, contact the FSS by radio on the appropriate frequency and report your takeoff time so your flight plan can be activated, or opened.

   b. When a VFR flight plan is filed, it will be held by the FSS until 1 hr. after the proposed departure time and then canceled unless

      1) The actual departure time is received (i.e., you notify FSS).

      2) A revised proposed departure time is received.

      3) At the time of filing, the FSS is informed that the proposed departure time will be met, but the actual time cannot be given because of inadequate communication.

         a) This procedure must be initiated by the pilot.

   c. Flight plans can be canceled in the air by radio by contacting FSS.

11. **The applicant demonstrates understanding of seasonal weather phenomena.**

   a. For information on seasonal weather phenomena, see Study Unit 9, Subunit 6, beginning on page 86.

END OF KNOWLEDGE ELEMENT

13.2 RISK MANAGEMENT

A.   Task Objectives

1.   **The applicant demonstrates the ability to identify, assess, and mitigate risks encompassing the pilot.**

   a.   For information on pilot risks, see Study Unit 5, Subunit 2, beginning on page 41.

2.   **The applicant demonstrates the ability to identify, assess, and mitigate risks encompassing the aircraft.**

   a.   For information on aircraft risks, see Study Unit 5, Subunit 2, beginning on page 41.

3.   **The applicant demonstrates the ability to identify, assess, and mitigate risks encompassing the environment.**

   a.   For information on environmental risks, see Study Unit 5, Subunit 2, beginning on page 41.

4.   **The applicant demonstrates the ability to identify, assess, and mitigate risks encompassing external pressures.**

   a.   For information on external pressures, see Study Unit 5, Subunit 2, beginning on page 41.

5.   **The applicant demonstrates the ability to identify, assess, and mitigate risks encompassing a lack of appropriate training when the flight is planned in an area different from the pilot's local area, such as in mountains, congested airspace, or a location with different weather and topography.**

   a.   If you are traveling to or through an area of the country that has environments you are not accustomed to,

   1)   You may need to do more research than normal or even take an online course.
   2)   Consider taking along a more experienced pilot or, at least, a pilot who can handle the radio and alleviate your workload and stress level.

6.   **The applicant demonstrates the ability to identify, assess, and mitigate risks encompassing the tendency to complete the flight in spite of an adverse change in conditions.**

   a.   Operational pitfalls are traps that pilots fall into, avoidance of which is actually simple in nature. A pilot should always have an alternate or plan B for where to land in case of an emergency on every flight. Make considerations for the unexpected.

   b.   Pilots have a tendency to fall victim to personal and external pressures.

   1)   Pilots must be flexible and, when confronted with unplanned or spontaneous situations, determine safe alternative courses of action.
   2)   "Get-there-itis" is a hazardous attitude where personal or external pressure clouds the vision and impairs judgment by causing a fixation on the original goal or destination combined with a total disregard for alternative courses of action.
   3)   According to the National Transportation Safety Board (NTSB), pilots on flights of more than 300 NM are 4.7 times more likely to be involved in an accident than pilots on flights 50 NM or less.
   4)   On long trips, you will most likely encounter different types of weather conditions.

   a)   Weather is the largest single cause of aviation fatalities. Most of these accidents occur to general aviation (GA) operators, usually one who is flying a light single- or twin-engine aircraft and encounters instrument meteorological conditions (IMC) while operating under VFR.
   b)   Over half the pilots involved in weather accidents did not receive an official weather briefing. Once the flight is under way, the number of pilots who receive a weather update from FSS is dismal.

5) Do not scud run or fly into IMC (unless you are cleared on an IFR flight plan).

    a) Scud running, or continued VFR flight into IFR conditions, pushes the pilot and aircraft capabilities to the limit when the pilot tries to make visual contact with the terrain. This is one of the most dangerous things a pilot can do and illustrates how poor aeronautical decision making links directly to a human factor that leads to an accident.

    b) Continuing VFR into IMC often leads to spatial disorientation or collision with ground/obstacles. It is even more dangerous when the pilot is not instrument rated or current.

7. **The applicant demonstrates the ability to identify, assess, and mitigate risks encompassing failure to select the appropriate VFR altitude for the direction of flight.**

    a. Failure to follow the hemispheric rule could put you on a collision course with other aircraft.

8. **The applicant demonstrates the ability to identify, assess, and mitigate risks encompassing limitations of ATC services.**

    a. ATC service is available in controlled airspace: Class A, Class B, Class C, Class D, and Class E.

    b. A controller's primary function is to provide safe separation between aircraft. Any additional service, such as weather avoidance assistance, can only be provided on a workload permitting basis.

       1) The separation workload is generally greater than normal when weather disrupts the usual flow of traffic. ATC radar limitations and frequency congestion may also be a factor in limiting the controller's capability to provide additional service.

    c. To the extent possible, controllers will issue pertinent weather information to assist pilots in avoiding such areas when requested.

       1) Pilots should respond to a weather advisory by either acknowledging the advisory or requesting an alternative course of action as follows:

          a) Request to deviate off course by stating the number of miles and the direction of the requested deviation.

          b) Request a new route to avoid the affected area.

          c) Request a change of altitude.

          d) Request radar vectors around the affected areas.

    d. Limitations and understanding what type of weather advisories controllers can provide.

       1) Controllers can select the level of weather to be displayed. Weather displays of higher levels of intensity make it difficult for controllers to see aircraft data blocks, so pilots should not expect ATC to keep weather displayed continuously.

       2) There are three kinds of radar systems ATC employs, which can provide some information to pilots concerning weather.

          a) The newest technology allows controller to describe precipitation as light, moderate, heavy (or extreme). However, due to the delay of radar, this can be up to 6 min. old.

          b) An older radar technology only allows controllers to describe precipitation as "moderate" and "heavy to extreme."

          c) Some ATC facilities cannot see intensity and controllers will describe precipitation as "intensity unknown."

       3) Radar cannot detect turbulence.

9. **The applicant demonstrates the ability to identify, assess, and mitigate risks encompassing improper fuel planning.**

    a. There are many aspects of a flight that pilots cannot predict, such as ATC providing vectors for traffic separation or deviations to remain in VFR.

    b. Thus, pilots should not strive to budget a 30-min. reserve. Instead, carry enough fuel as is reasonably practical to provide an additional margin of safety.

10. **The applicant demonstrates the ability to identify, assess, and mitigate risks encompassing a route overflying significant environmental influences, such as mountains or large bodies of water.**

    a. Routes over mountains and waterways require pilots to consider emergency equipment unique to these environments.

        1) Mountainous terrain typically has cold weather, so you should carry survival blankets, flashlights, food, water, and flares to help rescuers locate you.

            a) Mountainous terrain also has fewer places to make an off-airport landing in case of an emergency.

        2) When flying over water, life vests for every passenger are absolutely necessary.

            a) Also consider a raft with cover to help limit sun exposure during the day.

        3) Consider carrying a portable ELT that would send out a signal to help rescuers locate you and any passengers in the water.

    b. Look at the type of terrain and obstructions, e.g., mountains, swamps, large bodies of water, that could be a factor if an off-airport landing became necessary.

        1) Look for available alternate airports en route.

        2) Mentally prepare for any type of emergency situation and the action to be taken during your flight.

    c. By knowing the highest terrain and obstructions, you will know the minimum safe altitude to meet the requirements of 14 CFR 91.119.

    d. After looking at all of these aspects, you may choose an alternate route that offers fewer hazards and more safety options than your initial choice.

11. **The applicant demonstrates the ability to identify, assess, and mitigate risks encompassing flight in areas unsuitable for landing or below personal minimums.**

    a. If your chosen flight path covers areas where you cannot land, consider alternative flight paths.

        1) What happens if you or your passengers get sick? How would you land?

    b. Always have a plan on how to land safely in the event of an emergency.

12. **The applicant demonstrates the ability to identify, assess, and mitigate risks encompassing seasonal weather patterns.**

    a. Seasonal weather that pilots are not accustomed to traversing can be very dangerous. You should recognize and avoid weather for which you are not trained or experienced.

    b. For more information on seasonal weather phenomena, see Study Unit 9, Subunit 6, beginning on page 86.

END OF RISK MANAGEMENT ELEMENT

13.3 SKILLS

A. Task Objectives

1. **The applicant demonstrates the ability to prepare, present, and explain a cross-country flight plan assigned by the evaluator, including a risk analysis based on real-time weather.**

    a. Before meeting with your evaluator, you should complete your flight planning for your cross-country flight using the current weather.

        1) This assumes that you have asked for, and your evaluator has given you, a cross-country flight to plan before your practical test.

    b. Be able to provide and explain your flight plan to your evaluator.

2. **The applicant demonstrates the ability to transfer knowledge used for one region to another region (given local climate, terrain, etc.).**

    a. Identify terrain types that your flight path will take you.

        1) Mitigate any risks by explaining to your evaluator what steps you will take or how you will adjust your flight path as to not encounter this type of terrain.

    b. Identify seasonal weather or climate conditions that impact your planned flight.

        1) Mitigate any risks by explaining to your evaluator what steps you will take or how you will adjust your flight path to avoid this type of terrain.

3. **The applicant demonstrates the ability to update fuel planning/manage fuel.**

    a. Use your flight computer to calculate the necessary fuel and/or fuel stops to complete your cross-country flight.

4. **The applicant demonstrates the ability to select appropriate routes, altitudes, and checkpoints.**

    a. Select easily identifiable en route checkpoints.

        1) There is no set rule for selecting a landmark as a checkpoint. Every locality has its own peculiarities. The general rule to follow is never to place complete reliance on any single landmark.

            a) Use a combination of two or more, if available.

        2) Select prominent landmarks as checkpoints.

    b. Select the most favorable altitudes, considering weather conditions and equipment capabilities.

        1) Use your flight computer to determine headings, flight time, and fuel requirements.

    c. Select appropriate navigation systems/facilities and communication frequencies.

        1) From studying your course on your sectional chart, you can determine which navigation systems/facilities (e.g., VOR or GPS) you may use for navigation.

        2) You should use the Chart Supplement to determine the appropriate communication frequencies (e.g., ground, tower, radar facilities, etc.).

5. **The applicant demonstrates the ability to recalculate fuel reserves based on a scenario provided by the evaluator.**

    a. Recalculate fuel necessary and the amount of fuel reserves using your flight computer.

6. **The applicant demonstrates the ability to create a navigation log and simulate filing a VFR flight plan.**

    a. Always use a navigation log to assist you in planning and conducting a cross-country flight.

   b.   The final step in your cross-country flight planning is preparing to complete and file a VFR flight plan.

      1)   VFR flight plans are not mandatory, but they are highly recommended as a safety precaution. In the event you do not reach your destination as planned, the FAA will institute a search for you. This process begins 30 min. after you were scheduled to reach your destination.

      2)   This element requires that you simulate filing a VFR flight plan. Complete a VFR flight plan form and explain to your evaluator how you would file the flight plan.

7.   **The applicant demonstrates the ability to interpret departure, en route, and arrival route with reference to appropriate and current charts.**

   a.   Your sectional or approach chart may provide guidance on how ATC prefers you arrive or depart an airspace.

   b.   The Chart Supplement is a civil flight information publication published and distributed every 8 weeks by the FAA. It is a directory of all airports, seaplane bases, and heliports open to the public; communications data; navigational facilities; and certain special notices and procedures.

      1)   Use of the Chart Supplement is a vital part of your cross-country flight planning.

      2)   The Chart Supplement may also provide guidance on how to depart or arrive at certain airports.

8.   **The applicant demonstrates the ability to explain or demonstrate diversion to alternate.**

   a.   Given a scenario, be able to describe how you would divert to an alternate airport.

      1)   You may also demonstrate a diversion in-flight.

      2)   The evaluator may combine this diversion with an in-flight emergency, so be prepared and try to be cognizant of possible alternate airports and their communication frequencies.

9.   **The applicant demonstrates the ability to apply pertinent information from Chart Supplements U.S.; NOTAMs relative to airport, runway, and taxiway closures; and other flight publications.**

   a.   Conduct thorough flight planning and be aware of all NOTAMs. Make sure you write down all NOTAMs provided by your weather briefer.

10. **The applicant demonstrates the ability to, on the day of the practical test, prepare a final flight plan to the first fuel stop, based on the maximum allowable passengers, baggage, and/or cargo loads using real-time weather and appropriate and current aeronautical charts.**

   a.   Using your POH/AFM, have a weight and balance completed displaying the maximum number of passengers with maximum baggage.

      1)   The intent is for you to demonstrate your understanding of how many passengers you can take on a trip with the greatest number of bags.

11. **The applicant demonstrates the ability to properly identify airspace, obstructions, and terrain features.**

   a.   Use your knowledge of chart data and refer to the legends to identify features requested by the evaluator.

12. **The applicant demonstrates the ability to select appropriate navigation system/ facilities and communication frequencies.**

   a.   From studying your course on your sectional chart, you can determine which navigation systems/facilities (e.g., VOR, GPS) you may use for navigation.

   b.   You should use the Chart Supplement to determine the appropriate communication frequencies (e.g., ground, tower, radar facilities, etc.).

END OF SKILLS ELEMENT

STUDY UNIT FOURTEEN
NATIONAL AIRSPACE SYSTEM

Task	Task E. National Airspace System
References	14 CFR parts 71, 91, 93; FAA-H-8083-2; Navigation Charts; AIM
Objective	To determine that the applicant exhibits satisfactory knowledge, risk management, and skills associated with the National Airspace System operating under VFR as a private pilot.
Knowledge	The applicant demonstrates understanding of:
PA.I.E.K1	1. Types of airspace/airspace classes and basic VFR weather minimums.
PA.I.E.K2	2. Charting symbology.
PA.I.E.K3	3. Operating rules, pilot certification, and airplane equipment requirements for flying in different classes of airspace.
PA.I.E.K4	4. Special use, special flight rules areas, and other airspace areas.
PA.I.E.K5	5. Temporary flight restrictions.
PA.I.E.K6	6. Aircraft speed limitations in various classes of airspace.
Risk Management	The applicant demonstrates the ability to identify, assess and mitigate risks, encompassing:
PA.I.E.R1	1. Various classes of airspace.
PA.I.E.R2	2. Maintaining VFR at night.
PA.I.E.R3	3. Special use airspace.
PA.I.E.R4	4. Compliance with or avoidance of specific en route airspace.
Skills	The applicant demonstrates the ability to:
PA.I.E.S1	1. Determine the requirements for basic VFR weather minimums and flying in particular classes of airspace.
PA.I.E.S2	2. Determine the requirements for flying in special use airspace (SUA), and special flight rule areas (SFRA).
PA.I.E.S3	3 Properly identify airspace and operate accordingly with regards to communication and equipment requirements.
PA.I.E.S4	4. Accounts for SUA, SFRA, and temporary flight rules (TFR).

A. General Information

    1. The objective of this task is for you to demonstrate your knowledge, risk management, and skills related to the National Airspace System operating under VFR as a private pilot.

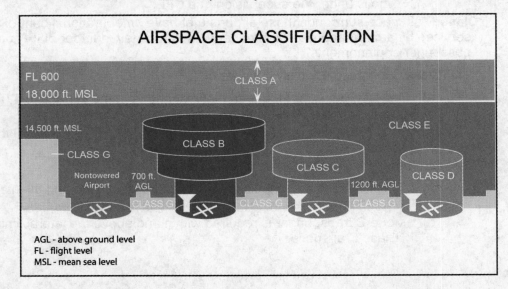

14.1 KNOWLEDGE

A.   Task Objectives

1.   **The applicant demonstrates understanding of types of airspace/airspace classes and basic VFR weather minimums.**

a.   For information on types of airspace/airspace classes and basic VFR weather minimums, see Section I Introduction, Knowledge, item A., beginning on page 92.

2.   **The applicant demonstrates understanding of charting symbology.**

a.   For information on charting symbology, see Section I Introduction, Knowledge, item B., beginning on page 93.

3.   **The applicant demonstrates understanding of operating rules, pilot certification, and airplane equipment requirements for flying in different classes of airspace.**

a.   **Class A** airspace is generally the airspace from 18,000 ft. MSL up to and including flight level (FL) 600, including the airspace overlying the waters within 12 NM of the coast of the 48 contiguous states and Alaska.

1)   Operating rules and pilot/equipment requirements

a)   An IFR clearance to enter and operate within Class A airspace is mandatory. Thus, you must be instrument-rated to act as PIC of an airplane in Class A airspace.

b)   Two-way radio communication, appropriate navigational capability, and a Mode C transponder are required.

b.   **Class B** airspace is generally the airspace from the surface to 10,000 ft. MSL surrounding the nation's busiest airports in terms of IFR operations or passenger enplanements (e.g., Atlanta, Chicago).

1)   The configuration of each Class B airspace area is individually tailored and consists of a surface area and two or more layers.

2)   Operating rules and pilot/equipment requirements for VFR operations

a)   An ATC clearance is required prior to operating within Class B airspace.

b)   Two-way radio communication capability is required.

c)   Mode C transponder is required within and above the lateral limits of Class B airspace and within 30 NM of the primary airport regardless of altitude.

d)   The PIC must be at least a private pilot, or a student or recreational pilot who is under the supervision of a CFI.

c.   **Class C** airspace surrounds those airports that have an operational control tower, are serviced by a radar approach control, and have a certain number of IFR operations or passenger enplanements.

1)   Class C airspace normally consists of

a)   A 5-NM radius surface area that extends from the surface to 4,000 ft. above the airport elevation

b)   A 10-NM radius shelf area that extends from 1,200 ft. to 4,000 ft. above the airport elevation

2)   Operating rules and equipment requirements

a)   Two-way radio communications must be established and maintained with ATC before entering and while operating in Class C airspace.

b)   Mode C transponder is required within and above the lateral limits of Class C airspace.

d. **Class D** airspace surrounds those airports that have both an operating control tower and weather services available, and are not associated with Class B or C airspace.

   1) Class D airspace normally extends from the surface up to and including 2,500 ft. AGL.

   2) Operating rules and pilot/equipment requirements

      a) Two-way communications must be established and maintained with ATC prior to entering and while operating in Class D airspace.

      b) No specific pilot certification is required.

e. **Class E** airspace is any controlled airspace that is not Class A, B, C, or D airspace.

   1) Except for 18,000 ft. MSL (the floor of Class A airspace), Class E airspace has no defined vertical limit, but rather it extends upward from either the surface or a designated altitude to the overlying or adjacent controlled airspace.

   2) There are no specific pilot certification or equipment requirements to operate under VFR in Class E airspace.

f. **Class G** airspace is that airspace that has not been designated as Class A, Class B, Class C, Class D, or Class E airspace (i.e., it is uncontrolled airspace).

   1) No specific pilot certification or airplane equipment is required to operate under VFR in Class G airspace.

NOTE: While generally there is no equipment required to operate VFR in Class E or Class G airspace, there are some airports located within the surface area of an airport with an operational control tower. In these circumstances, you must establish and maintain two-way radio communication with the control tower if you plan to operate to, from, or through an area within 4 NM from the airport, from the surface up to and including 2,500 ft. AGL.

4. **The applicant demonstrates understanding of special use, special flight rules areas, and other airspace areas.**

   a. **Special Use Airspace (SUA)**

      1) There are six types of SUA in the U.S. National Airspace System. You should be familiar with the types of SUA and any operation rules that apply (e.g., entry, transit, etc.).

      2) **Prohibited areas** -- airspace within which flight is prohibited. Such areas are established for security or other reasons of national welfare.

         a) Prohibited areas protect government interests as well as ecologically sensitive areas.

         b) Prohibited areas are often surrounded by large temporary flight restrictions (TFRs) when certain situations exist.

            i) Because prohibited areas protect areas the President often visits, pilots must be aware that large TFRs will be implemented around those areas when the President is present.

         c) Prohibited areas have varied ceilings but all begin at the surface. Depending on the area protected, prohibited area ceilings range from 1,000 feet MSL to 18,000 feet MSL.

         d) Notices of new, uncharted prohibited areas are disseminated via the NOTAM system.

      3) **Restricted areas** -- airspace within which flight, while not wholly prohibited, is subject to restrictions. Restricted areas denote the existence of unusual, often invisible hazards to aircraft such as artillery firing, aerial gunnery, or guided missiles.

         a) The size and shape of restricted airspace areas vary based on the operation areas they restrict.

    b)   Restricted areas are often placed next to, or stacked on top of, each other.

        i)   The altitudes of restricted areas vary based on the operations conducted within them.

    c)   If a restricted area is active, a pilot must receive prior permission of the controlling agency before attempting to fly through it.

        i)   Times and altitudes of operation as well as the name of the controlling agency can be found on the sectional aeronautical chart.

4)   **Warning areas** -- airspace of defined dimensions, extending from 3 NM outward from the coast of the U.S., which contains activity that may be hazardous to nonparticipating aircraft. The purpose of a warning area is to warn nonparticipating pilots of the potential danger (such as the hazards in restricted areas).

    a)   A warning area may be located over domestic or international waters or both.

    b)   Warning areas should be thought of exactly as restricted areas are.

        i)   Because they are outside the 3-NM airspace boundary of U.S. airspace, they cannot be regulated as restricted areas are.

    c)   Times and altitudes of operation can be found on the sectional aeronautical chart.

5)   **Military operations areas (MOAs)** -- airspace established to separate certain military training activities from IFR traffic.

    a)   Pilots operating under VFR should exercise extreme caution while flying within an MOA when military activity is being conducted.

        i)   Before beginning a flight that crosses an MOA, contact any FSS within 100 NM of the area to obtain accurate real-time information concerning the MOA hours of operation.

        ii)   Prior to entering an active MOA, contact the controlling agency for traffic advisories.

    b)   MOAs are often placed next to or stacked on top of each other.

        i)   The altitudes of MOAs vary based on the operations conducted within them.

        ii)   Times and altitudes of operation as well as the name of the controlling agency can be found on the sectional aeronautical chart.

    c)   MOAs are often found in conjunction with restricted areas.

        i)   Pay careful attention to such airspace when planning crossing flights to ensure you do not violate active restricted airspace.

6)   **Alert areas** -- areas depicted on aeronautical charts to inform nonparticipating pilots of areas that may contain a high volume of pilot training or an unusual type of aerial activity.

    a)   All activity within an alert area is conducted in accordance with Federal Aviation Regulations.

        i)   There is no specific controlling agency for an alert area nor is crossing clearance required/given.

    b)   Pilots of participating aircraft as well as pilots transiting the area are equally responsible for collision avoidance.

7) **Controlled firing areas** -- areas containing activities that, if not conducted in a controlled environment, could be hazardous to nonparticipating aircraft.

    a) The activities are suspended immediately when spotter aircraft, radar, or ground lookout positions indicate an aircraft might be approaching the area.

    b) These areas are not depicted on charts because the pilot is not required to take action.

b. **Special Flight Rules Areas (SFRAs)**

1) When necessary for safety or security, SFRAs will be established by the FAA to modify the rules for operating within a given airspace area.

    a) These are not actually a type of airspace, but merely modifications to existing airspace.

    b) Communication requirements, transponder usage, routing, speed limitations, and other like factors are all subject to change when special flight rules are in effect.

2) SFRAs are designated on sectional and terminal area charts using a blue line with blue shaded boxes on the inside, or protected side, of the area.

    a) A box can be found near the area identifying it as a SFRA.

    b) A regulatory reference will be provided as well to allow pilots to learn more about the rules in effect.

3) EXAMPLES:

    a) Grand Canyon National Park

        i) Due to the high number of aircraft operating near the Grand Canyon, special flight rules were enacted to prevent near misses and midair collisions.

        ii) 14 CFR Part 93, Subpart U, defines the boundaries and operating requirements within the Grand Canyon National Park Special Flight Rules Area.

            • The rule establishes minimum altitudes, explains the pilot authorization process, and identifies flight-free zones where all operations are prohibited.

    b) Los Angeles International Airport

        i) The Class B airspace around the LAX airport handles a very high volume of arriving and departing air traffic as well as flight instruction activities.

            • To accommodate simplicity in VFR operations, a special flight rules area was created to modify the communication requirements and entry/exit procedures of Class B airspace.

        ii) Operations within this area are governed by 14 CFR Part 93, Subpart G.

            • The regulation defines the affected area and provides conditions for operations within it.

c)   Washington, D.C.

i)   The airspace around the U.S. capital has changed many times since the events of September 11, 2001. In the interests of national security, a special flight rules area was established to permanently modify a specific area within the Tri-Area Class B airspace surrounding Washington, D.C.

- Formerly an ADIZ area, the SFRA imposes many of the old ADIZ entry, operation, and exit requirements, such as flight plan filing, discrete transponder codes, and pre-takeoff clearance at affected airports.

ii)   The D.C. SFRA is centered on the Reagan National VOR/DME station.

- The outer ring has a radius of 30 miles and is active 24 hr. a day from the surface to 18,000 ft. MSL.
- The inner ring is a flight restricted zone (FRZ) that can only be entered by pilots individually screened and approved by the Transportation Security Administration (TSA).

iii) Subpart V of 14 CFR Part 93 defines the boundaries and operating requirements within the Washington, D.C., Special Flight Rules Area.

d)   Other SFRAs exist as well. The previous examples were used only for illustrative purposes to show the wide range of causes for implementation of a special flight rules area.

4)   Before operating in a SFRA, you should become familiar with the regulations associated with it.

a)   Failure to comply with special flight rules can result in injury and destruction of property.

b)   Punitive, civil, and criminal charges may be brought against offending pilots, depending on the severity and intent of the infraction.

c.   **Other Airspace Areas**

1)   **Airport advisory areas** encompass the areas within 10 SM of airports that have no operating control towers but where FSSs are located. At such locations, the FSS provides advisory service to arriving and departing aircraft. Participation in the Local Airport Advisory (LAA) program is recommended but not required.

2)   **Military training routes (MTRs)** are developed for use by the military for the purpose of conducting low-altitude (below 10,000 ft. MSL), high-speed training (more than 250 kt.).

3)   **National security areas (NSAs)** -- airspace of defined vertical and lateral dimensions established at locations where there is a requirement for increased security and safety of ground facilities. Pilots are requested to voluntarily avoid flying through the depicted NSA.

a)   A NOTAM will be issued to prohibit flight in NSAs when it is necessary to provide a greater level of security and safety.

4)   Flight limitations in the proximity of space flight operations (14 CFR 91.143) are designated in a NOTAM.

5)   Tabulations of parachute jump areas in the U.S. are contained in the Chart Supplement.

6) **VFR flyway** is a general flight path not defined as a specific course but used by pilots planning flights into, out of, through, or near complex terminal airspace to avoid Class B airspace.

   a) VFR flyways are depicted on the reverse side of some of the VFR terminal area charts.

   b) An ATC clearance is not required to fly these routes since they are not in Class B airspace.

7) **VFR corridor** is airspace through Class B airspace, with defined vertical and lateral boundaries, in which aircraft may operate without an ATC clearance or communication with ATC. A VFR corridor is, in effect, a hole through the Class B airspace.

8) **Class B airspace VFR transition route** is a specific flight course depicted on a VFR terminal area chart for transiting a specific Class B airspace.

   a) These routes include specific ATC-assigned altitudes, and you must obtain an ATC clearance prior to entering the Class B airspace.

   b) On initial contact, you should inform ATC of your position, altitude, route name desired, and direction of flight.

      i) After a clearance is received, you must fly the route as depicted, and most importantly, follow ATC instructions.

9) **Terminal area VFR route** is a specific flight course for optional use by pilots to avoid Class B, Class C, and Class D airspace areas while operating in complex terminal airspace (e.g., Los Angeles).

   a) An ATC clearance is not required to fly these routes.

10) **Terminal radar service areas (TRSAs)** are not controlled airspace from a regulatory standpoint (i.e., they do not fit into any of the airspace classes) because TRSAs were never subject to the rulemaking process.

    a) Thus, TRSAs are not contained in 14 CFR Part 71 nor are there any TRSA operating rules in 14 CFR Part 91.

    b) TRSAs are areas where participating pilots can receive additional radar services, known as TRSA Service.

    c) The primary airport(s) within the TRSA are in Class D airspace.

       i) The remaining portion of the TRSA normally overlies Class E airspace beginning at 700 or 1,200 ft. AGL.

    d) Pilots operating under VFR are encouraged to participate in the TRSA service. However, participation is voluntary.

    e) TRSAs are depicted on sectional charts with a solid black line and with altitudes for each segment expressed in hundreds of feet MSL.

       i) The Class D portion is depicted with a blue segmented line.

5. **The applicant demonstrates understanding of temporary flight restrictions.**

   a. Temporary flight restrictions (TFRs) (14 CFR 91.137) contain airspace where the flight of aircraft is prohibited without advanced permission and/or an FAA waiver.

      1) This restriction exists because the area inside the TFR is often of key importance to national security or national welfare.

      2) TFRs may also be put into effect in the vicinity of any incident or event that, by its nature, may generate such a high degree of public interest that hazardous congestion of air traffic is likely.

    b.   TFRs are very different from other forms of airspace because they are often created, canceled, moved, and/or changed.

        1)   The temporary nature of TFRs can make keeping track of their locations and durations challenging.

        2)   TFRs protect government interests as well as the general public.

        3)   TFRs often surround other forms of airspace when extra security is necessary.

            a)   Because TFRs protect the President, pilots must be aware that large TFRs will be implemented around any area where the President is present.

    c.   A Notice to Airmen (NOTAM) implementing temporary flight restrictions will contain a description of the area in which the restrictions apply.

        1)   The size and shape of TFRs vary based on the areas they protect.

            a)   Most TFRs are in the shape of a circle and are designed to protect the center of that circle.

            b)   TFRs always have defined vertical and lateral boundaries as indicated in the NOTAMs.

6.   **The applicant demonstrates understanding of aircraft speed limitations in various classes of airspace.**

    a.   You may not operate an airplane at an indicated airspeed greater than 250 kt. if you are under 10,000 ft. MSL or operating within Class B airspace.

    b.   You may not operate an aircraft at or below 2,500 ft. above the surface within 4 NM of the primary airport of Class C or Class D airspace at an indicated airspeed of more than 200 kt.

    c.   You may not operate under Class B airspace or in a VFR corridor through such a Class B airspace area at an indicated airspeed greater than 200 kt.

    d.   If your minimum safe speed in your airplane is faster than the speed normally allowed, you may operate at that minimum safe speed.

END OF KNOWLEDGE ELEMENT

14.2 RISK MANAGEMENT

A.   Task Objectives

1.   **The applicant demonstrates the ability to identify, assess, and mitigate risks encompassing various classes of airspace.**

   a.   Airspace considerations are always important.

   1)   Check the airspace and any temporary flight restrictions (TFRs) along the route of flight.

   2)   Do not violate protected airspace.

   3)   If the weather deteriorates, will airspace restrictions allow you to maneuver around the weather?

2.   **The applicant demonstrates the ability to identify, assess, and mitigate risks encompassing maintaining VFR at night.**

   a.   Flying over airspace at night requires special considerations.

   1)   Will the flight conditions allow a safe emergency landing at night?

   2)   Can I circumnavigate clouds without violating airspace?

   3)   Can I maintain proper separation of terrain, obstacles, and VFR at night cloud clearance minimums?

3.   **The applicant demonstrates the ability to identify, assess, and mitigate risks encompassing special use airspace.**

   a.   Always ensure the special use airspace is "cold" if you plan to traverse this airspace.

   1)   Your safety and well-being could be in jeopardy.

   b.   If you're flying over special use airspace, remember to think of how you would perform an emergency landing.

   1)   Is there live fire happening below you?

4.   **The applicant demonstrates the ability to identify, assess, and mitigate risks encompassing compliance with or avoidance of specific en route airspace.**

   a.   Ensure you are aware of airways and VFR corridors.

   1)   If you are maneuvering and not using these airways, stay clear of them in order to avoid a higher risk of midair collisions.

   b.   There are certain areas areas not depicted as any particular special use airspace or other airspace type that should be avoided.

   1)   Wildlife refuges. Do not loiter around wildlife sanctuaries and avoid flight within 2,000' ft. AGL.

2)   Some areas should be avoided for reasons of national security. These may be associated with or near a restricted area, but not always.

    a)   The example below shows how such areas are depicted on a sectional chart.

    b)   Power plants should also be avoided.

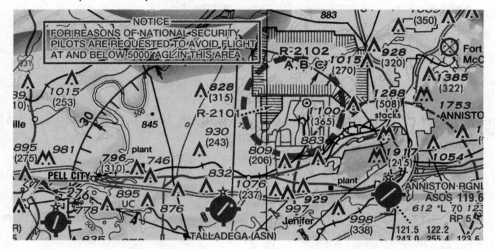

3)   Special military activity areas may be depicted with gray hashed lines. These areas may surround a military training route.

    a)   These areas may include unmanned aircraft, or other unusual activity.

    b)   The example below shows the depiction of these areas. The floor and ceiling in hundreds of feet are charted with an associated note to contact local flight service for activity status.

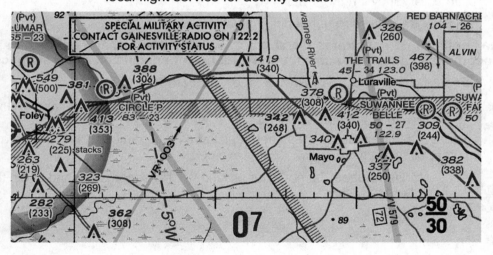

END OF RISK MANAGEMENT ELEMENT

14.3 SKILLS

A.   Task Objectives

1.   **The applicant demonstrates the ability to determine the requirements for basic VFR weather minimums and flying in particular classes of airspace.**

   a.   Based upon the scenario provided, use your knowledge to determine the requirements for basic VFR weather minimums and flying in particular classes of airspace.

2.   **The applicant demonstrates the ability to determine the requirements for flying in special use airspace (SUA) and special flight rule areas (SFRA).**

   a.   Based upon the scenario provided, use your knowledge to determine the requirements for flying in SUA and SFRAs.

3.   **The applicant demonstrates the ability to properly identify airspace and operate accordingly with regards to communication and equipment requirements.**

   a.   Use your knowledge to properly identify airspace and operate accordingly with regards to communication and equipment requirements.

4.   **The applicant demonstrates the ability to account for SUA, SFRAs, and temporary flight rules (TFRs).**

   a.   Use your knowledge to apply pertinent operations and requirements to account for SUA, SFRAs, and TFRs.

   b.   Explain to your evaluator how you determine these airspace areas and how you would remain clear of them or obtain permission to enter.

END OF SKILLS ELEMENT

STUDY UNIT FIFTEEN
PERFORMANCE AND LIMITATIONS

Task	Task F. Performance and Limitations
References	FAA-H-8083-1, FAA-H-8083-2, FAA-H-8083-3, FAA-H-8083-25; POH/AFM
Objective	To determine that the applicant exhibits satisfactory knowledge, risk management, and skills associated with operating an aircraft safely within the parameters of its performance capabilities and limitations.
Knowledge	The applicant demonstrates understanding of:
PA.I.F.K1	1. Elements related to performance and limitations (e.g., takeoff and landing, crosswind, tailwind and headwind, density altitude, glide performance, weight and balance, climb, cruise, descent, powerplant considerations) by explaining the use of charts, tables, and data to determine performance.
PA.I.F.K2	2. Factors affecting performance to include atmospheric conditions, pilot technique, aircraft condition, and airport environment.
PA.I.F.K3	3. The effects of loading on performance.
PA.I.F.K4	4. The effects of exceeding weight and balance limits.
PA.I.F.K5	5. The effects of weight and balance changes over the course of the flight.
PA.I.F.K6	6. Aerodynamics.
Risk Management	The applicant demonstrates the ability to identify, assess and mitigate risks, encompassing:
PA.I.F.R1	1. Performance charts.
PA.I.F.R2	2. Limitations.
PA.I.F.R3	3. Variations in flight performance resulting from weight and balance changes during flight.
PA.I.F.R4	4. Published aircraft performance data as it relates to expected performance.
Skills	The applicant demonstrates the ability to:
PA.I.F.S1	1. Compute weight and balance for a given scenario, which includes practical techniques to resolve out-of-limit calculations and determine if the weight and balance will remain within limits during all phases of flight.
PA.I.F.S2	2. Use aircraft manufacturer's approved performance charts, tables, and data.
PA.I.F.S3	3. Evaluate takeoff and landing performance based on the values calculated.
PA.I.F.S4	4. Evaluate environmental conditions.

A.   General Information

1.   The objective of this task is for you to demonstrate your knowledge, risk management, and skills related to operating an aircraft safely within the parameters of its performance capabilities and limitations.

2.   This task is make- and model-specific and applies to the airplane used on your practical test. This task covers Sections 2, 5, and 6 of your POH/AFM.

a.   Section 2: Limitations
b.   Section 5: Performance
c.   Section 6: Weight and Balance/Equipment List

3.   See Study Unit 5, "Airplane Performance and Weight and Balance," in *Pilot Handbook* for discussions on airplane performance and weight and balance.

15.1 KNOWLEDGE

A. Task Objectives

1. **The applicant demonstrates understanding of elements related to performance and limitations (e.g., takeoff and landing, crosswind, tailwind and headwind, density altitude, glide performance, weight and balance, climb, cruise, descent, powerplant considerations) by explaining the use of charts, tables, and data to determine performance.**

    a. Airplane performance can be defined as the ability to operate or function, i.e., the ability of an airplane to accomplish certain things that make it useful for certain purposes.

        1) The various items of airplane performance result from the combination of airplane and powerplant characteristics.

            a) The aerodynamic characteristics and weight of the airplane generally define the power and thrust requirements at various conditions of flight.

            b) Powerplant characteristics generally define the power and thrust available at various conditions of flight.

            c) The matching of these characteristics is done by the manufacturer.

    b. Operating limitations are found in Section 2, Limitations, of your airplane's POH/AFM. These limits establish the boundaries (i.e., flight envelope) in which your airplane must be operated.

        1) You should be able to explain the adverse effects of exceeding your airplane's limitations. These may include

            a) Attempting a takeoff or landing without a long enough runway

            b) Not having enough fuel to make your airport of intended landing, while cruising at a high power setting

            c) Exceeding your airplane's structural or aerodynamic limits by being over gross weight and/or outside center of gravity limits

    c. Performance charts, tables, and/or data are found in Section 5, Performance, of your airplane's POH/AFM.

        1) You must be able to explain the use of each chart, table, and/or data in your POH/AFM.

    d. You should be able to explain the operations and limitations of each system on your aircraft, including recognizing and managing abnormal conditions and system malfunctions.

        1) Operation of systems is discussed in more detail in Study Unit 16.

        2) Your aircraft's systems are found in Section 7, Systems Descriptions, of your airplane's POH/AFM.

        3) Systems emergencies specific to your aircraft are discussed in Section 3, Emergency Procedures, of your airplane's POH/AFM.

2. **The applicant demonstrates understanding of factors affecting performance to include atmospheric conditions, pilot technique, aircraft condition, and airport environment.**

   a. The characteristics of the atmosphere have a major effect on airplane performance. Atmospheric pressure and temperature are the two dominant factors that influence the density of the air.

      1) For information on the characteristics of atmospheric conditions that affect performance, see Study Unit 9, Subunit 1, beginning on page 77.

      2) **Effect of Air Density on Lift and Drag**

         a) Lift and drag vary directly with the density of the air.

            i) As air density increases, lift and drag increase.
            ii) As air density decreases, lift and drag decrease.

         b) Air density is affected by pressure, temperature, and humidity.

            i) At an altitude of 18,000 ft., the density of the air is one-half the density at sea level (given standard conditions). If an airplane is to maintain the same lift at high altitudes, the amount of air flowing over the wing must be the same as at lower altitudes. Thus, the speed of the air over the wings (airspeed) must be increased at high altitudes.

               • This is why an airplane requires a longer takeoff distance to become airborne at higher altitudes than with similar conditions at lower altitudes.

            ii) Because air expands when heated, warm air is less dense than cool air.

               • When other conditions remain the same, an airplane will require a longer takeoff run on a hot day than on a cool day.

            iii) Because water vapor weighs less than an equal amount of dry air, moist air (high relative humidity) is less dense than dry air (low relative humidity).

               • Therefore, when other conditions remain the same, the airplane will require a longer takeoff run on a humid day than on a dry day.

               • The condition is compounded on a hot, humid day because the expanded air can hold much more water vapor than on a cool day. The more moisture in the air, the less dense the air.

         c) Less dense air also causes other performance losses besides the loss of lift. Engine horsepower and propeller efficiency decrease because fewer air molecules are available for combustion, resulting in a loss of power, and because propeller blades (which are airfoils) are less effective when air is less dense.

            i) Since the propeller is not pulling with the same force and efficiency as when the air is dense, it takes longer to obtain the necessary forward speed to produce the lift required for takeoff.

               • Thus, the airplane requires a longer takeoff run.
               • The rate of climb will also be lower for the same reasons.

         d) From the above discussion, it is obvious that a pilot should beware of high, hot, and humid conditions, i.e., operations at airports at high altitudes, hot temperatures, and high moisture content (high relative humidity).

b. Pilot technique, aircraft condition, and the airport environment are also important factors to consider when calculating performance.

1) Information the manufacturer provides on performance charts has been gathered from test flights conducted in a new aircraft, under normal operating conditions while using average piloting skills, and with the aircraft and engine in good working order.

   a) It is important to remember that the data from the charts will not be accurate if the aircraft is not in good working order or when operating under adverse conditions. Be conservative and compensate for the performance numbers if the aircraft is not in good working order.

      i) Each aircraft performs differently, and, therefore, has different performance numbers. Compute the performance of the aircraft prior to every flight, as every flight is different.

   b) In addition, consider the necessity to compensate for the performance numbers if your piloting skills are below average.

2) Every chart is based on certain conditions and contains notes on how to adapt the information for flight conditions. It is important to compensate for actual conditions not addressed in the chart.

   a) Some of the airport environment conditions the manufacturer often addresses are

      i) High elevation
      ii) Wind
      iii) Operation from a dry grass runway
      iv) Paved, level, dry runway

3. **The applicant demonstrates understanding of the effects of loading on performance.**

a. The aircraft's weight and how that weight is positioned or loaded is important information for a pilot to evaluate.

b. Aircraft are certificated for weight and balance in part for the effects of the weight on airplane characteristics.

1) Takeoff/climb and landing performance of an aircraft are determined on the basis of its maximum allowable takeoff and landing weights.

2) A heavier gross weight results in a longer takeoff run, shallower climb, faster touchdown speed, and longer landing roll.

c. Even if an aircraft is loaded well within the maximum weight limitations, it is imperative that weight distribution be within the limits of CG location. An aircraft loaded to the rear limit of its permissible CG range handles differently in turns and stall maneuvers, and has different landing characteristics than when it is loaded near the forward limit. Within the allowable CG range you can expect the following differences:

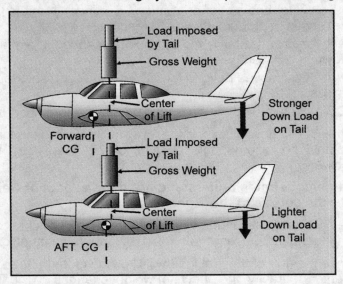

1) With a forward CG, a greater downward force on the tail is required to maintain level cruising flight.

a) "Nose-up" trim is required in most aircraft to maintain level cruise flight.

b) The total lift required from the wing is increased.

c) Thus, the wing flies at a higher angle of attack, which results in more drag and a higher indicated stall speed.

2) With an aft CG, less downward force on the tail is required and "nose-down" trim will be used, resulting in less lift required by the wing.

a) Thus, the wing flies at a lower angle of attack with less drag, allowing for a higher cruise speed.

4. **The applicant demonstrates understanding of the effects of exceeding weight and balance limits.**

a. Exceeding weight limits can be detrimental to ground and flight operations.

1) Even a minor overload can make it impossible to clear an obstacle that normally would not be a problem during takeoff under more favorable conditions.

2) Overloading has an adverse effect on all climb and cruise performance, which leads to overheating during climbs, added wear on engine parts, increased fuel consumption, slower cruise speeds, and reduced range.

3) Structural damage of or complete failure of the aircraft structure may occur

a) More often, overloading affects structural components progressively and is hard to detect during a preflight.

b) Cumulative stress and damage may eventually result in structural failure later during completely normal operations.

c) Accelerated metal fatigue failures often occur.

4) Seats, baggage compartments, and cabin floors are designed for a certain load or concentration of load and no more.

5) Overloading affects stability and controllability.

   a) The stability of many aircraft is completely unsatisfactory if the gross weight is exceeded and the CG within limits

b. In general, an airplane becomes less stable and controllable as the CG moves aft.

   1) The elevator has a shorter arm (i.e., distance) from the CG and requires greater deflection to produce the same result.

   2) Recovery from a stall is more difficult because the airplane's tendency to pitch down is reduced.

   3) If the CG is moved beyond the aft limit, stall and spin recovery may become impossible.

c. As the CG moves forward, the airplane becomes more nose-heavy.

   1) If the CG is moved beyond the forward limit, the elevator may no longer be able to hold the nose up, particularly at low airspeeds, e.g., takeoff, landing, and power-off glides.

5. **The applicant demonstrates understanding of the effects of weight and balance changes over the course of the flight.**

a. Over the course of a flight, the weight of the aircraft will change due to factors primarily including fuel burn. On larger aircraft, passengers might also move about the cabin.

   1) Since the arm of the fuel load will likely be different than the calculated aircraft center of gravity, the effects of weight changes during flight will also affect the balance of your aircraft.

   2) For each flight, your weight and balance should be calculated based on the load at takeoff, and also for landing at a different weight.

      a) If the loaded center of gravity is within limits for takeoff, but not for landing, you will need to determine the best method to place occupants or baggage to keep the aircraft within limits during the entire flight.

      b) You may need to carry ballast in a baggage area to help balance the aircraft.

b. Use caution when ensuring cargo is securely attached in the baggage area. Turbulence can cause baggage or cargo to shift which could adversely affect aircraft loading.

   1) This can cause the center of gravity to move outside of acceptable limits, which could cause loss of control or other unfavorable handling characteristics.

c. See *Pilot Handbook*, Study Unit 5, "Airplane Performance and Weight and Balance," for discussions on airplane performance and weight and balance.

6. **The applicant demonstrates understanding of aerodynamics.**

a. See *Pilot Handbook*, Study Unit 1, "Airplanes and Aerodynamics," for a discussion of aerodynamics.

END OF KNOWLEDGE ELEMENT

15.2 RISK MANAGEMENT

A.   Task Objectives

1.   **The applicant demonstrates the ability to identify, assess, and mitigate risks encompassing performance charts.**

a.   Consult the "Performance" section of your POH/AFM before takeoff, specifically taking into account the existing temperature, barometric pressure, field length, wind, type of runway surface, and airplane operating condition and weight.

1)   Since the performance charts assume average pilot technique, consider your personal proficiency.

2)   Recognize that, in some situations, you should decide NOT to attempt to take off because the margin of safety is too small. You may have to

a)   Remove fuel, people, or baggage;
b)   Wait for different wind and/or temperature conditions;
c)   Retain a more experienced pilot to make the flight; or
d)   Have the airplane moved to a safer takeoff location.

2.   **The applicant demonstrates the ability to identify, assess, and mitigate risks encompassing limitations.**

a.   As the PIC, you must know and understand your aircraft's performance limits. Specifically, you must know whether, under a given set of atmospheric conditions, your aircraft is capable of clearing terrain and obstacles near the airport on departure or during a go-around.

b.   This task item directly relates to the PAVE checklist as part of risk management, specifically the "A" element related to the aircraft.

1)   **P**ilot – Do you have the skill and confidence to operate safely in the environment you face?

2)   **A**ircraft – Is your aircraft capable (considering performance limits and cockpit instrumentation) of operating safely in the environment you face?

3)   en**V**ironment – Considering weather, terrain, and any other environmental factors, can you operate safely?

4)   **E**xternal pressures – Are there pressures acting on you affecting your decision to continue or terminate the flight?

3.   **The applicant demonstrates the ability to identify, assess, and mitigate risks encompassing variations in flight performance resulting from weight and balance changes during flight.**

a.   See Subunit 15.1, items A.3.-5., for a detailed discussion of this task item.

4.   **The applicant demonstrates the ability to identify, assess, and mitigate risks encompassing published aircraft performance data as it relates to expected performance.**

a.   Before takeoff, determine the aircraft performance for each phase of flight.

b.   During your flight, monitor your engine and systems to be sure everything is operating and performing as expected.

1)   Adjust your navigation logs as needed to account for variations from expected performance.

2)   Cross check your instruments and systems and refer to the POH/AFM to determine if actual aircraft performance is an indication of a system not functioning properly. If a system is determined to be operating improperly, you should land as soon as practical to have the problem examined.

END OF RISK MANAGEMENT ELEMENT

15.3 SKILLS

A.   Task Objectives

   1.   **The applicant demonstrates the ability to compute weight and balance for a given scenario, which includes practical techniques to resolve out-of-limits calculations and determine if the weight and balance will remain within limits during all phases of flight.**

   a.   You will need to use Section 6, Weight and Balance, in your airplane's POH/AFM to accomplish this element. You should calculate the weight and balance for takeoff, cruise, and landing.

   1)   The subject of weight and balance is concerned with not only the weight of the airplane but also the location of its center of gravity (CG). You should not attempt a flight until you are satisfied with the weight and balance condition.

   2.   **The applicant demonstrates the ability to use aircraft manufacturer's approved performance charts, tables, and data.**

   a.   Your evaluator will expect you to know how to work through every performance chart and table in the performance section of your POH/AFM.

   3.   **The applicant demonstrates the ability to evaluate takeoff and landing performance based on the values calculated.**

   a.   The minimum takeoff distance is of primary interest in the operation of any airplane because it defines the runway requirements.

   1)   The minimum takeoff distance is determined by using the minimum safe speed that allows for a sufficient safety margin above stall speed, provides satisfactory control, and an initial rate of climb.

   b.   The minimum landing distance is obtained by landing at the minimum safe speed that allows sufficient margin above the stall speed and provides satisfactory control and capability for a go-around.

   1)   Generally, the landing speed is some fixed percentage of the stall speed or minimum control speed for the airplane in the landing configuration. This airspeed is found in the airplane's POH/AFM.

   c.   Use your aircraft's POH/AFM to determine the takeoff and landing performance given the current environmental conditions.

   4.   **The applicant demonstrates the ability to evaluate environmental conditions.**

   a.   Air density is perhaps the single most important factor affecting airplane performance. The general rule is that as air density decreases, so does airplane performance.

   1)   Temperature, altitude, barometric pressure, and humidity all affect air density. The density of the air DECREASES

   a)   As air temperature INCREASES
   b)   As altitude INCREASES
   c)   As barometric pressure DECREASES
   d)   As humidity INCREASES

   2)   The engine produces power in proportion to the weight or density of the air.

   a)   As air density decreases, the power output of the engine decreases.

   i)   This is true of all engines not equipped with a supercharger or turbocharger.

3) The propeller produces thrust in proportion to the mass of air being accelerated through the rotating blades.

    a) As air density decreases, propeller efficiency decreases.

4) The wings produce lift as a result of the air passing over and under them.

    a) As air density decreases, the lift efficiency of the wing decreases.

b. At power settings of less than 75%, or at density altitudes above 5,000 ft., it is essential that normally aspirated engines be leaned for maximum power on takeoff, unless equipped with an automatic altitude mixture control.

1) The excessively rich mixture adds another detriment to overall performance.

2) Turbocharged engines need not be leaned for takeoff in high density altitude conditions because they are capable of producing manifold pressure equal to or higher than sea-level pressure.

3) At airports of higher elevations, such as those in the western U.S., high temperatures sometimes have such an effect on density altitude that safe operations may be impossible.

    a) Even at lower elevations with excessively high temperature or humidity, airplane performance can become marginal, and it may be necessary to reduce the airplane's weight for safe operations.

END OF SKILLS ELEMENT

STUDY UNIT SIXTEEN
OPERATION OF SYSTEMS

Task	Task G. Operation of Systems
References	FAA-H-8083-2, FAA-H-8083-3, FAA-H-8083-25; POH/AFM
Objective	To determine that the applicant exhibits satisfactory knowledge, risk management, and skills associated with the safe operation of systems on the airplane provided for the flight test.
Knowledge	The applicant demonstrates understanding of:
PA.I.G.K1	1. Major components of the systems:
PA.I.G.K1a	a. Primary flight controls and trim
PA.I.G.K1b	b. Flaps, leading edge devices, and spoilers as appropriate
PA.I.G.K1c	c. Powerplant and propeller (basic engine knowledge)
PA.I.G.K1d	d. Landing gear
PA.I.G.K1e	e. Fuel, oil, and hydraulic
PA.I.G.K1f	f. Electrical
PA.I.G.K1g	g. Avionics
PA.I.G.K1h	h. Pitot-static, vacuum/pressure and associated flight instruments
PA.I.G.K1i	i. Environmental
PA.I.G.K1j	j. Deicing and anti-icing
PA.I.G.K2	2. Normal operation of systems.
PA.I.G.K3	3. Common errors made by pilots.
PA.I.G.K4	4. Abnormal operation of systems (recognition of system failures/malfunctions).
PA.I.G.K5	5. Systems interaction and pilot monitoring of automated systems.
Risk Management	The applicant demonstrates the ability to identify, assess and mitigate risks, encompassing:
PA.I.G.R1	1. Mishandling a system failure.
PA.I.G.R2	2. Troubleshooting system failures/malfunctions.
PA.I.G.R3	3. Mismanagement of airplane systems, which can cause a problem or system failure.
PA.I.G.R4	4. Determining and/or declaring an emergency.
PA.I.G.R5	5. Failure to identify system malfunctions or failures.
PA.I.G.R6	6. Outside/environmental factors affecting the systems, including improper fueling, carburetor ice, extremely cold temperatures, and vapor lock.
PA.I.G.R7	7. Detection and management of threats and errors.
PA.I.G.R8	8. Ineffective monitoring of automation.
Skills	The applicant demonstrates the ability to:
PA.I.G.S1	1. Explain and operate the airplane's systems.
PA.I.G.S2	2. Use checklist procedures.
PA.I.G.S3	3. Use immediate action items during emergency operations, as applicable.

A. General Information

1. The objective of this task is for you to demonstrate satisfactory knowledge, risk management, and skills related to the safe operation of systems on the airplane provided for the flight test.

  a. This task is make- and model-specific, and applies to the airplane used on your practical test.

2.   See *Pilot Handbook* for the following:

   a.   Study Unit 1, "Airplanes and Aerodynamics," Subunit 5, "Flight Controls and Control Surfaces," for a discussion on the primary flight controls, trim devices, flaps, leading edge devices, and spoilers

   b.   Study Unit 2, "Airplane Instruments, Engines, and Systems," for a discussion of the operation of the various airplane instruments, engines, and systems

3.   To prepare for this task, systematically study, not just read, the following sections of your POH/AFM:

   a.   Section 1: General Information.
   b.   Section 7: Airplane and Systems Descriptions.
   c.   Section 8: Handling, Service, and Maintenance.
   d.   Section 9: Supplements (Optional Systems Description and Operating Procedures).

4.   Finally, make a list of the make and model of all avionics equipment in your training airplane. Make yourself conversant with the purpose, operation, and capability of each unit. You should be constantly discussing your airplane's systems with your CFI.

16.1 KNOWLEDGE

A.   Task Objectives

   1.   **The applicant demonstrates understanding of the major components of the following systems:**

      a.   **Primary flight controls and trim**

         1)   The airplane's attitude is controlled by the deflection of the primary flight controls.

            a)   The primary flight controls are the rudder, elevator (or stabilator on some airplanes), and ailerons.

         2)   Trim devices are commonly used to relieve you of the need of maintaining continuous pressure on the primary flight controls.

            a)   The most common trim devices used on trainer-type airplanes are trim tabs and anti-servo tabs located on the trailing edge of the primary flight control surfaces.

            b)   A manual trim control wheel or electric trim switch are used to operate trim systems.

      b.   **Flaps, leading edge devices, and spoilers as appropriate**

         1)   Wing flaps are used on most airplanes.

            a)   Flaps systems can be operated either electrically or manually.

               i)   Electrically operated systems include a flap switch and indicator, electric motor and associated circuit breaker, and cable/pulley system connected to the flap.

               ii)   Manually operated systems usually include a hand lever to extend/retract the flap via the cable/pulley system.

     b)   Flaps increase both lift and drag and have three important functions:

            i)   First, they permit a slower landing speed, which decreases the required landing distance.

           ii)   Second, they permit a comparatively steep angle of descent without an increase in speed. This makes it possible to clear obstacles safely when making a landing approach to a short runway.

           iii)   Third, they may also be used to shorten the takeoff distance and provide a steeper climb path.

  2)   Leading edge devices, like slats or slots, accelerate air over the wing, increasing lift. Some aircraft have full-span leading-edge slats. Others have slots that affect airflow over the ailerons. Most general aviation aircraft do not use slats or slots. However, these may be found on some short takeoff and landing (STOL) planes.

  3)   Spoilers are devices that can be deployed to spoil lift. They are used in some high-performance airplanes to allow them to descend while maintaining a relatively high speed. Gliders also make use of spoilers.

c.   **Powerplant and propeller (basic engine knowledge)**

  1)   An airplane's engine and propeller are commonly referred to as the powerplant. Not only does the engine provide power to propel the airplane, but it powers the units that operate a majority of the airplane's systems.

  2)   You should be able to explain your airplane's powerplant, including

     a)   The operation of the engine (including gearing, if applicable)
     b)   Engine type and horsepower
     c)   Ignition system
     d)   Induction system
     e)   Cooling system

  3)   The airplane propeller consists of two or more blades and a central hub to which the blades are attached. Each blade of an airplane propeller is essentially a rotating wing which produces forces that create the thrust to pull, or push, the airplane through the air.

     a)   Most light, trainer-type airplanes have a **fixed-pitch propeller**; i.e., the pitch of the propeller blades is fixed by the manufacturer and cannot be changed.

     b)   Some airplanes may feature a **ground-adjustable propeller** where blade pitch can be adjusted on the ground.

  4)   The power needed to rotate the propeller blades is furnished by the engine. The engine rotates the airfoils of the blades through the air at high speeds, and the propeller transforms the rotary power of the engine into forward thrust.

d.   **Landing gear**

  1)   The landing gear system supports the airplane during the takeoff run, landing, and taxiing, and when parked. The landing gear must be capable of steering, braking, and absorbing shock to the airframe.

     a)   Most light trainer-type airplanes are equipped with fixed landing gear.
     b)   Major components of a fixed landing gear system include

            i)   Steerable nosewheel
           ii)   Two main wheels and wheel fairings
           iii)   Shock absorbing landing gear struts and air/oil nose gear shock strut
           iv)   Hydraulically actuated single-disk brake on each inboard side of each wheel

e. **Fuel, oil, and hydraulic**

1) The fuel system stores fuel and transfers it to the airplane engine.

   a) Major components of a standard fuel system include

      i)   Two vented fuel tanks (one in each wing)
      ii)   Selector valve
      iii) Fuel strainer
      iv)   Manual primer
      v)   Carburetor

2) The oil system provides a means of storing and circulating oil throughout the internal components of a reciprocating engine.

   a) Each engine is equipped with an oil pressure gauge and an oil temperature gauge to be monitored to determine that the oil system is functioning properly.

3) Many small airplanes have an independent hydraulic brake system powered by master cylinders in each main landing gear wheel, similar to those in your car.

   a) An airplane with retractable landing gear normally uses hydraulic fluid in the operation of the landing gear.

4) You should be able to explain the fuel, oil, and hydraulic systems for your airplane, including

   a) Approved fuel grade(s) and quantity (usable and nonusable)
   b) Oil grade and quantity (minimum and maximum operating levels)
   c) Hydraulic systems (i.e., brakes, landing gear, etc.)

f. **Electrical**

1) Electrical energy is required to operate the starter, navigation and communication radios, lights, and other airplane equipment.

2) You should be able to explain the electrical system for your airplane, including

   a) Battery location, voltage, and capacity (i.e., amperage)
   b) Electrical system and alternator (or generator) voltage and capacity

      i) Advantages and disadvantages of an alternator/generator system

   c) Circuit breakers and fuses -- location and purpose
   d) Ammeter indications

g. **Avionics**

1) The avionics system is all of your airplane's aviation electronic equipment.

   a) Be able to explain how all of your communication and navigation systems operate.

   b) Make a list of the make, model, type of radio, and related equipment in your airplane. As appropriate, consult and study their instruction manuals.

h. **Pitot-static system, the vacuum/pressure system, and associated flight instruments**

1) The pitot-static system provides the source for the operation of the

   a) Altimeter
   b) Vertical speed indicator
   c) Airspeed indicator

2) The vacuum/pressure system is engine-driven and the major components include a vacuum pump, relief valve, and system air filter. Typically, the system provides the source for the operation of the following gyroscopic flight instruments:

   a) Heading indicator
   b) Attitude indicator

3) While not normally part of the vacuum/pressure system, the turn coordinator is a gyroscopic flight instrument but is normally powered by the electrical system.

i. **Environmental**

1) Heating in most training airplanes is accomplished by an air intake in the nose of the airplane.

    a) The air is directed into a shroud, where the air is heated by the engine.

    b) The heated air is then delivered through vents into the cabin or used for the defroster.

2) Cooling and ventilation are controlled by outlets.

    a) Some airplanes are equipped with an air conditioner for cooling.

    b) Outside air used for cooling and ventilation is normally supplied through air inlets that are located in the wings or elsewhere on the airplane.

    c) Learn how your airplane's system works by reading your POH/AFM.

3) Heat and defrost controls are located on the instrument panel, or within easy reach.

    a) Most airplanes are equipped with outlets that can be controlled by each occupant of the airplane.

    b) Your POH/AFM will explain the operation of the controls.

j. **Deicing and anti-icing**

1) Induction system (carburetor) ice-protection system is the basic, and probably the only, ice-protection system in your airplane.

    a) Carburetor heat warms the air before it enters the carburetor.

        i) It is used to remove and/or prevent ice formation.

        ii) Carburetor ice can occur at temperatures much warmer than freezing due to fuel vaporization and a drop in pressure through the carburetor venturi.

2) Fuel system icing results from the presence of water in the fuel system. This may cause freezing of screen, strainers, and filters. When fuel enters the carburetor, the additional cooling may freeze the water.

    a) Normally, proper use of carburetor heat can warm the air sufficiently in the carburetor to prevent ice formation.

    b) Some airplanes are approved to use anti-icing fuel additives.

        i) Remember that an anti-icing additive is not a substitute for carburetor heat.

3) Pitot heat is an electrically-powered system and may put a severe drain on the electrical system on some airplanes.

    a) Pitot heat is used to prevent ice from blocking the ram air hole of the pitot tube.

        i) Pitot heat should be used prior to encountering visible moisture.

    b) Monitor your ammeter for the effect pitot heat has on your airplane's electrical system.

4) Be emphatic with your evaluator that icing conditions are to be avoided both in flight planning and in the air!

    a) Most training airplanes have placards that prohibit flight into known icing conditions.

5) Check your POH/AFM for the appropriate system, if any, in your airplane.

2. **The applicant demonstrates understanding of normal operation of systems.**

   a. The normal operations of systems is detailed in the POH/AFM for your aircraft. Refer to the General Information section at the beginning of this study unit for additional study resources.

3. **The applicant demonstrates understanding of common errors made by pilots.**

   a. Failure to understand the systems and equipment in your airplane.

      1) You must know how the various systems and equipment operate in your airplane.

         a) Then, you will be able to analyze the malfunction correctly and take the appropriate steps to correct the situation.

         b) You will also understand the effect(s) it will have on the operation of your airplane.

         c) You will be able to avoid common errors made by pilots.

4. **The applicant demonstrates understanding of abnormal operation of systems (recognition of system failures/malfunctions).**

   a. The abnormal operation of systems is detailed in the POH/AFM for your aircraft. In addition to the resources listed in the General Information section at the beginning of this study unit, you should study your POH/AFM Section 3: Emergency Procedures.

   b. Refer to Study Unit 51, "Systems and Equipment Malfunctions," for a detailed discussion.

5. **The applicant demonstrates understanding of systems interaction and pilot monitoring of automated systems.**

   a. This task element requires that you apply aeronautical decision-making and judgment skills to the operation of systems.

   b. The evaluator will evaluate your ability to explain how aircraft systems interact and how the operation of a system may affect the operations of other system.

      1) EXAMPLE: Explain how the use of flaps requires a corresponding trim adjustment.

   c. In some situations, using automation to assist you can actually get you behind the airplane and cause you to miss important transmissions or course changes. You must use automation effectively or choose not to use it in some situations.

   d. See Study Unit 6, Subunit 3, for more information on automation management.

END OF KNOWLEDGE ELEMENT

16.2 RISK MANAGEMENT

A.   Task Objectives

1.   **The applicant demonstrates the ability to identify, assess, and mitigate risks encompassing mishandling a system failure.**

a.   The evaluator wants to see you make competent, confident decisions using a logical decision-making process when handling a system failure.

b.   Your analysis of why you determined to act in a certain way is a critical step in both the decision-making process and your ability to display satisfactory competence in this task.

c.   The evaluator will be testing your adaptability to unforeseen circumstances. (S)he will want to see that you can safely and effectively alter your plans when the situation demands it.

2.   **The applicant demonstrates the ability to identify, assess, and mitigate risks encompassing troubleshooting system failures/malfunctions.**

a.   If you suspect a system failure or malfunction, you can perform basic troubleshooting tasks to determine which system has failed, confirm whether it is a partial failure or a complete failure, and make a determination on how that failure might affect your flight.

b.   Always use the appropriate checklist in your POH/AFM to ensure you are applying the appropriate troubleshooting steps.

3.   **The applicant demonstrates the ability to identify, assess, and mitigate risks encompassing mismanagement of airplane systems, which can cause a problem or system failure.**

a.   Follow the approved normal operations procedures or abnormal operations procedures for an aircraft system failure/malfunction so as not to create a problem (or additional problem or system failure).

b.   If a system fails in flight and you have taken the appropriate steps to remedy the situation but the system still does not operate correctly, do not continue operating the system.

1)   EXAMPLE: A radio failure may be the result of a popped circuit breaker. If you reset the circuit breaker, and it pops again, do not attempt to reset it another time.

2)   Manage the failure by operating redundant systems or by taking alternative means of action.

c.   Do not allow system malfunctions to distract you from your responsibility to to fly the plane. Many accidents could have been avoided if this common sense principle were applied.

4.   **The applicant demonstrates the ability to identify, assess, and mitigate risks encompassing determining and/or declaring an emergency.**

a.   An emergency can be either a distress or urgency condition as defined in the Pilot/Controller Glossary.

1)   Distress is defined as a condition of being threatened by serious and/or imminent danger and requiring immediate assistance.

2)   Urgency is defined as a condition of being concerned about safety and requiring timely but not immediate assistance; a potential distress condition.

b.   Pilots do not hesitate to declare an emergency when faced with distress conditions, such as fire, mechanical failure, or structural damage. However, some are reluctant to report an urgency condition when encountering situations that may not be immediately perilous but are potentially catastrophic.

1)   An aircraft is in an urgent condition the moment that the pilot becomes doubtful about position, fuel endurance, weather, or any other condition that could adversely affect flight safety.

2)   The time for a pilot to request assistance is when an urgent situation may, or has just occurred, not after it has developed into a distress situation.

c.   The pilot in command (PIC) is responsible for crew, passengers, and operation of the aircraft at all times.

1)   14 CFR 91.3 allows deviations from regulations during emergencies so that the PIC can make the best decision to ensure safety of all personnel during these contingencies.

2)   By declaring an emergency during flight, that aircraft becomes a priority to land safely.

5.   **The applicant demonstrates the ability to identify, assess, and mitigate risks encompassing failure to identify system malfunctions or failures.**

a.   Failure to identify system failures and recognize problems as they develop may unnecessarily lead to a situation more hazardous than if detected while in development.

b.   Understanding your aircraft's systems and developing good habits to cross-check systems will enable you to identify system failures and recognize problems as they develop.

6.   **The applicant demonstrates the ability to identify, assess, and mitigate risks encompassing outside/environmental factors affecting the systems, including improper fueling, carburetor ice, extremely cold temperatures, and vapor lock.**

a.   The enVironment element of PAVE encourages us to consider all aspects of the environment that your aircraft will be operating in.

1)   Improper fueling: During the preflight procedures, you should ensure the aircraft is properly fueled. Verify the correct fuel quantity and grade of fuel, and check for contaminants.

2)   Carburetor ice: There is a high potential for carburetor ice when the ambient temperature is between 20° and 70° Fahrenheit with high humidity. Carburetor ice is possible in humid conditions when temperatures are as high as 100°.

3)   Extremely cold temperatures: Extremely cold environments may require modified systems operating procedures. Examples include modified starting procedures, use of a different grade of oil, engine preheat, and limitations on power settings at cold temperatures to avoid damaging the engine during start and warm up.

4)   Vapor lock: Operations during hot days may result in vapor lock. If the liquid fuel turns to gas while in the fuel delivery system, this can disrupt the operation of the fuel pump, causing loss of feed pressure to the carburetor or fuel injection system, resulting in transient loss of power or complete stalling. Restarting the engine from this state may be difficult.

7. **The applicant demonstrates the ability to identify, assess, and mitigate risks encompassing detection and management of threats and errors.**

    a. The evaluator wants to see you make competent, confident decisions using a logical decision-making process.

        1) The DECIDE and 3P models are covered in Study Unit 5, Subunit 1,.

    b. Your analysis of why you determined to act in a certain way is a critical step in both the decision-making process and your ability to display satisfactory competence in this task.

    c. See Study Unit 17, Subunit 2, item A.7., for a discussion of threats and errors.

8. **The applicant demonstrates the ability to identify, assess, and mitigate risks, encompassing ineffective monitoring of automation.**

    a. In some situations, using automation to assist you can actually get you behind the airplane and cause you to miss important transmissions or course changes. You must use automation effectively or choose not to use it in some situations.

    b. See Study Unit 6, Subunit 3, for more information on automation management.

END OF RISK MANAGEMENT ELEMENT

16.3 SKILLS

A.   Task Objectives

1.   **The applicant demonstrates the ability to explain and operate the airplane's systems.**

   a.   See Subunit 16.1, items 1.-2., for a detailed discussion on operating systems.

   b.   Understand that variances exist between different models and may also exist between similar variations of the same aircraft make and model. You should operate your aircraft systems in accordance with the POH/AFM for your specific aircraft.

2.   **The applicant demonstrates the ability to use checklist procedures.**

   a.   For information on using checklists, see Study Unit 6, Subunit 4, beginning on page 54.

3.   **The applicant demonstrates the ability to use immediate action items during emergency operations, as applicable.**

   a.   Use the appropriate checklist for system and equipment malfunctions, which are in Section 3, Emergency Procedures, of your POH/AFM.

   b.   Memorize the immediate action items and, after completion, refer to the appropriate checklist.

   c.   Your emergency checklists must be readily available to you while you are in your airplane.

END OF SKILLS ELEMENT

STUDY UNIT SEVENTEEN
HUMAN FACTORS

Task	Task H. Human Factors
References	FAA-H-8083-2, FAA-H-8083-25; AIM
Objective	To determine that the applicant exhibits satisfactory knowledge, risk management, and skills associated with personal health, flight physiology, aeromedical and human factors, as it relates to safety of flight.
Knowledge	The applicant demonstrates understanding of:
PA.I.H.K1	1. The symptoms, recognition, causes, effects, and corrective actions associated with aeromedical and physiological issues including:
PA.I.H.K1a	a. Hypoxia
PA.I.H.K1b	b. Hyperventilation
PA.I.H.K1c	c. Middle ear and sinus problems
PA.I.H.K1d	d. Spatial disorientation
PA.I.H.K1e	e. Motion sickness
PA.I.H.K1f	f. Carbon monoxide poisoning
PA.I.H.K1g	g. Stress and fatigue
PA.I.H.K1h	h. Dehydration and nutrition
PA.I.H.K1i	i. Hypothermia
PA.I.H.K1j	j. Optical illusions
PA.I.H.K2	2. The effects of alcohol, drugs, and over-the-counter medications, and associated regulations.
PA.I.H.K3	3. The effects of dissolved nitrogen in the bloodstream of a pilot or passenger in flight following scuba diving.
PA.I.H.K4	4. The effects of hazardous attitudes on aeronautical decision-making.
PA.I.H.K5	5. Collision avoidance, scanning, obstacle and wire strike avoidance.
PA.I.H.K6	6. The pilot/airplane interface to include: pilot monitoring duties and the interaction with charts and avionics equipment.
Risk Management	The applicant demonstrates the ability to identify, assess and mitigate risks, encompassing:
PA.I.H.R1	1. The impact of environmental factors on medication's physiological effects.
PA.I.H.R2	2. Personal risk factors and the conflict between being goal oriented and adhering to personal limitations.
PA.I.H.R3	3. Optical illusions.
PA.I.H.R4	4. The circumstances of the flight (day/night, hot/cold) that affect the pilot's physiology.
PA.I.H.R5	5. Continued VFR flight into Instrument Meteorological Conditions (IMC).
PA.I.H.R6	6. Hazardous attitudes.
PA.I.H.R7	7. Failure to detect and manage threats and errors associated with human factors.
PA.I.H.R8	8. Ineffective monitoring of automation.
PA.I.H.R9	9. Distractions.
Skills	The applicant demonstrates the ability to:
PA.I.H.S1	1. Perform a self assessment including whether the pilot is fit for flight.
PA.I.H.S2	2. Show sound decision-making and judgment (based on reality of circumstances).
PA.I.H.S3	3. Demonstrate automation management and effective monitoring of automated systems.
PA.I.H.S4	4. Establish personal limitations.

A.   General Information

   1.   The objective of this task is for you to demonstrate your knowledge, risk management, and skills related to personal health, flight physiology, and aeromedical and human factors, as they relate to safety of flight.

17.1   KNOWLEDGE

A.   Task Objectives

1.   **The applicant demonstrates understanding of the symptoms, recognition, causes, effects, and corrective actions associated with aeromedical and physiological issues including:**

a.   **Hypoxia** is a state of oxygen deficiency in the body sufficient to impair functions of the brain and other organs. Prolonged hypoxia may result in unconsciousness.

1)   Significant effects of altitude hypoxia usually do not occur in the normal, healthy pilot below 12,000 ft. MSL.

a)   A deterioration in night vision occurs as low as 5,000 ft. MSL.

2)   From 12,000 to 15,000 ft. MSL (without supplemental oxygen), judgment, memory, alertness, coordination, and ability to make calculations are impaired. Headache, drowsiness, dizziness, and either a sense of well-being (euphoria) or belligerence occur.

3)   At altitudes above 15,000 ft. MSL, the periphery of the visual field turns gray. Only central vision remains (tunnel vision). A blue color (cyanosis) develops in the fingernails and lips.

4)   Corrective action if hypoxia is suspected or recognized includes

a)   Use of supplemental oxygen
b)   An emergency descent to a lower altitude

5)   Recovery from hypoxia is almost immediate. The person suffering from hypoxia will regain his or her faculties very quickly after sufficient oxygen is available.

b.   **Hyperventilation** is an abnormal increase in the volume of air breathed in and out of the lungs, resulting in insufficient carbon dioxide in the blood. Hyperventilation can occur subconsciously when you encounter a stressful situation in flight.

1)   This abnormal breathing flushes from your lungs and blood much of the carbon dioxide your system needs to maintain the proper degree of blood acidity.

a)   The resulting chemical imbalance in the body produces dizziness, rapid heart rate, tingling of the fingers and toes, hot and cold sensations, drowsiness, nausea, suffocation, and ultimately unconsciousness. Often you may react to these symptoms with even greater hyperventilation.

2)   It is important to realize that early symptoms of hyperventilation and hypoxia are similar. Also, hyperventilation and hypoxia can occur at the same time.

3)   The symptoms of hyperventilation subside within a few minutes after the rate and depth of breathing are consciously brought back under control.

a)   This can be hastened by controlled breathing in and out of a paper bag held over the nose and mouth. Also, talking, singing, or counting aloud often helps.

c.   **Middle ear and sinus problems**

1)   As the cabin pressure decreases during ascent, the expanding air in the middle ear pushes the Eustachian tube open and escapes down it to the nasal passages, thus equalizing ear pressure with the cabin pressure.

a)   Either an upper respiratory infection (e.g., a cold or sore throat) or nasal allergies can produce enough congestion around the Eustachian tube to make equalization difficult if not impossible.

b) The difference in pressure between the middle ear and the airplane's cabin can build to a level that will hold the Eustachian tube closed. This problem, commonly referred to as "ear block," produces severe ear pain and loss of hearing that can last from several hours to several days.

    i) Rupture of the ear drum can occur in flight or after landing.
    ii) Fluid can accumulate in the middle ear and become infected.

c) During descent, the pilot must periodically reopen the Eustachian tube to equalize pressure.

    i) This can be accomplished by swallowing, yawning, tensing muscles in the throat, or if these do not work, by the combination of closing the mouth, pinching the nose closed, and swallowing slowly.

    ii) If these actions fail to equalize the pressure, a Valsava maneuver should be performed, which entails closing the mouth, pinching the nostrils closed, and blowing air through the nose. This forces air up the Eustachian tube and into the middle ear.

2) During ascent and descent, air pressure in the sinuses equalizes with aircraft cabin pressure through small openings that connect the sinuses to the nasal passages.

a) Either an upper respiratory infection (e.g., a cold or sinusitis) or nasal allergies can produce enough congestion around one or more of these small openings to slow equalization.

b) As the difference in pressure between the sinus and the cabin mounts, the opening may become plugged, resulting in "sinus block." A sinus block, experienced most frequently during descent, can occur in the frontal sinuses, located above each eyebrow, or in the maxillary sinuses, located in each upper cheek.

    i) It usually produces excruciating pain over the sinus area.
    ii) A maxillary sinus block can also make the upper teeth ache.
    iii) Bloody mucus may discharge from the nasal passages.

c) If a sinus block or an ear block does not clear shortly after landing, a physician should be consulted.

3) Middle ear and sinus problems are prevented by not flying with an upper respiratory infection or nasal allergic condition.

a) Adequate protection is not provided by decongestant spray or drops to reduce congestion around the Eustachian tubes or the sinus openings.

b) Oral decongestants have side effects that can significantly impair pilot performance.

d. **Spatial disorientation** is a state of temporary spatial confusion resulting from misleading information sent to the brain by various sensory organs. If you lose outside visual references and become disoriented, you are experiencing spatial disorientation. To a pilot, this means simply the inability to tell "which way is up," which is why spatial disorientation can be a dangerous condition.

1) Sight, the semicircular canals of the inner ear, and pressure-sensitive nerve endings (located mainly in your muscles and tendons) are used to maintain spatial orientation.

a) During periods of limited visibility, such as at night, in clouds or in dust, conflicting information among these senses makes you susceptible to spatial disorientation.

      2) Your brain relies primarily on sight when there is conflicting information.

         a) When outside references are limited due to limited visibility and/or darkness, the brain will rely on other input for orientation information.

      3) Spatial disorientation can be corrected by relying on and believing your airplane's instruments or by focusing on reliable, fixed points on the ground.

e. **Motion sickness,** or air sickness, is caused by continued stimulation of the tiny portion of the inner ear that controls your sense of balance.

      1) Motion sickness symptoms are progressive.

         a) First, the desire for food is lost.
         b) Then, saliva collects in the mouth and you begin to perspire freely.
         c) Eventually, you become nauseated and disoriented.
         d) The head aches and there may be a tendency to vomit.

      2) If suffering from airsickness, you should

         a) Open the air vents.
         b) Loosen clothing.
         c) Use supplemental oxygen, if available.
         d) Keep the eyes on a point outside the airplane.
         e) Avoid unnecessary head movements.
         f) Cancel the flight and land as soon as possible.

      3) Although motion sickness is uncommon among experienced pilots, it does occur occasionally.

         a) Most importantly, it jeopardizes your flying efficiency, particularly in turbulent weather.

         b) Student pilots are frequently surprised by an uneasiness usually described as motion sickness.

            i) This sickness probably results from combining anxiety, unfamiliarity, and the vibration or shaking received from the airplane. These sensations are usually overcome with experience.

         c) Pilots who are susceptible to airsickness should NOT take the preventive drugs which are available over the counter or by prescription.

            i) Research has shown that most motion sickness drugs cause a temporary deterioration of navigational skills or ability to perform other tasks demanding keen judgment.

f. **Carbon monoxide** is a colorless, odorless, and tasteless gas contained in exhaust fumes and tobacco smoke.

      1) When inhaled even in minute quantities over a period of time, it can significantly reduce the ability of the blood to carry oxygen.

         a) Consequently, the effects of hypoxia occur.

      2) Most heaters in light aircraft work by air flowing over the exhaust manifold.

         a) Using these heaters when exhaust fumes are escaping through manifold cracks and seals is responsible every year for both nonfatal and fatal aircraft accidents from carbon monoxide poisoning.

         b) If you detect the odor of exhaust or experience symptoms of headache, drowsiness, or dizziness while using the heater, you should suspect carbon monoxide poisoning and immediately shut off the heater and open the air vents.

            i) Loss of consciousness and death are very real possibilities if the exposure to carbon monoxide continues.

            ii) If symptoms are severe or continue after landing, medical treatment should be sought.

g.   **Stress and fatigue**

   1)   Stress from the pressures of everyday living can impair pilot performance, often in very subtle ways.

   a)   Difficulties can occupy thought processes so as to decrease alertness.

   b)   Distraction can interfere with judgment so that unwarranted risks are taken.

   c)   When you are under more stress than usual, you should consider delaying flight until your difficulties have been resolved.

   d)   Stress is an inevitable and necessary part of life that encourages motivation and heightens a pilot's response to meet any challenge.

   e)   Additionally, stress effects are cumulative, eventually adding up to an intolerable burden unless coped with adequately.

   2)   Stress is a term used to describe the body's nonspecific response to demands placed on it, whether pleasant or unpleasant, by physical, physiological, or psychological factors known as stressors.

   a)   Physical stressors include conditions associated with the environment, such as temperature and humidity extremes, noise, vibration, and lack of oxygen.

   b)   Physiological stressors include fatigue, lack of physical fitness, sleep loss, missed meals (leading to low blood sugar levels), and illness.

   c)   Psychological stressors are related to social or emotional factors, such as a death in the family, the birth of a baby, a divorce, etc.

   i)   Also, they may be related to mental workload, such as analyzing a problem, navigating an aircraft, or making decisions.

   3)   Individuals who are overstressed (not coping adequately) often show symptoms in three ways: emotional, physical, and behavioral.

   4)   Cockpit stress management techniques include

   a)   Avoid situations that distract you from flying the aircraft.

   b)   Reduce your workload to reduce stress levels. A manageable workload will create a proper environment in which to make good decisions.

   c)   If an emergency does occur, be calm. Think for a moment, weigh the alternatives, and then act.

   d)   Maintain proficiency in your aircraft; proficiency builds confidence. Familiarize yourself thoroughly with your aircraft, its systems, and emergency procedures.

   e)   Know and respect your own personal limits.

   f)   Do not let little mistakes bother you until they build into a big issue. Wait until after you land; then "debrief" and analyze past actions.

   g)   If flying is adding to your stress, either stop flying or seek professional help to manage your stress within acceptable limits.

   5)   Fatigue can be treacherous because it may not be apparent to you until serious errors are made.

   a)   It is best described as either acute (short-term) or chronic (long-term).

   6)   Acute fatigue is the everyday tiredness felt after long periods of physical or mental strain.

   a)   Consequently, coordination and alertness can be reduced.

   b)   Acute fatigue is prevented by adequate rest and sleep, as well as regular exercise and proper nutrition.

7)   Chronic fatigue occurs when there is not enough time for full recovery between episodes of acute fatigue.

    a)   Performance continues to fall off, and judgment becomes impaired.

    b)   Recovery from chronic fatigue requires a prolonged period of rest.

8)   Stress and fatigue can be a deadly combination.

h.   **Dehydration and nutrition**

1)   Dehydration is the lack of adequate body fluids for the body to carry on normal functions at an optimal level.

    a)   Dehydration occurs by either inadequate intake of fluids or loss of fluids through perspiration, vomiting, diarrhea, excessive urination, or illness.

        i)   Vomiting, diarrhea, and excessive urination are separate health problems that usually preclude piloting activities.

        ii)   As the atmosphere becomes thinner, it contains less moisture and more body fluids are lost.

        iii)   Fluid loss can occur in any environment. Causes include hot cockpits and flight lines, high humidity, diuretic drinks (i.e., coffee, tea, soda), as well as improper attire.

    b)   Losses of only a few percent of body fluids can adversely affect both mental and physical processes.

    c)   Dehydration acts as a stressor and can degrade your decision-making ability.

    d)   Common signs and symptoms of dehydration include headache, fatigue, cramps, sleepiness, dizziness, and with severe dehydration, lethargy, and coma.

    e)   On all extended flights, carry water or other suitable liquids to consume as appropriate.

2)   Nutrition

    a)   Proper nutrition is important for everyone, but even more so for pilots who add the physical and mental demands of flying to their daily lives.

        i)   While simply eating the correct food is vital to health and wellbeing, it is also important to eat on a regular schedule and to eat proper portions based on the time of day.

    b)   Besides the benefits of safety in the cockpit, eating right poses general health benefits, such as blood pressure and cholesterol stabilization, heart disease prevention, weight management, and diabetes prevention or control, among other benefits.

        i)   All of these benefits also keep you in compliance with and eligible for medical certification.

    c)   Eating regularly and correctly will provide you with mental and physical support in the cockpit.

i.   **Hypothermia** occurs when your body is unable to maintain its normal temperature. An internal temperature of 96°F or lower signals hypothermia.

1)   Some signs that a person is experiencing hypothermia include

    a)   Extreme shivering

    b)   Stiffness of the arms or legs

    c)   Confusion or sleepiness

    d)   Slow, slurred speech

    e)   Poor control over body movements

2)   A pilot or passenger does not have to experience extreme cold to succumb to hypothermia. A drafty cockpit, and especially an open-cockpit aircraft, can cause a poorly prepared pilot or passenger to experience hypothermia in temperatures that might seem moderate when standing on the ground with no wind.

3)   Hypothermia can be prevented by dressing appropriately. Pilots and passengers should be aware that the temperature at altitude is usually lower than the temperature on the ground, and the wind blowing through the cockpit will cause more difficulty in maintaining a normal body temperature.

j.   **Optical illusions**

1)   **Spatial disorientation and illusions.** The most hazardous illusions are those that lead to spatial disorientation.

a)   Vestibular (inner ear) related illusions: Under normal flight conditions, when there is a visual reference to the horizon and ground, the sensory system in the inner ear helps to identify the pitch, roll, and yaw movements of the aircraft. When visual contact with the horizon is lost, the vestibular system becomes unreliable.

b)   Visual illusions are especially hazardous because pilots rely on their eyes for correct information. Two illusions that lead to spatial disorientation that are concerned only with the visual system are:

i)   False horizon
ii)   Autokinesis

c)   Remedy for spatial disorientation:

i)   Prevention is usually the best course of action.
ii)   Avoid flight in reduced visibility or at night when the horizon is not visible.
iii) Training and awareness.
iv)   Learning to rely totally on flight instruments.

d)   For a detailed discussion of spatial disorientation and illusions, refer to *Pilot Handbook*, Study Unit 6, Subunits 9-10.

2)   **Optical Illusions and Landing Errors**

a)   Various terrain features and atmospheric conditions can create optical illusions primarily associated with landing.

b)   Because pilots must transition from reliance on instruments to visual cues outside the flight deck for landing, it is imperative they be aware of the potential problems associated with these illusions and take appropriate corrective action.

c)   The major illusions leading to landing errors include

i)   Runway width illusion
ii)   Runway and terrain slopes illusion
iii) Featureless terrain illusion
iv)   Water refraction
v)   Haze and fog
vi)   Ground lighting illusions

d)   Landing illusions particular to night flight. Anticipate and be aware of the various illusions that can lead to landing errors. Some of them include

i)   Featureless terrain at night
ii)   Elements that cause any type of visual obscuration (fog, haze, rain, and a dark runway environment), can cause a low approach

        iii)   Regularly spaced lights along a road can be mistaken for a runway

        iv)   Bright runway or approach lighting systems can create the illusion that the airplane is closer to the runway

   e)   To prevent these illusions and their potentially hazardous consequences during landing, pilots can

        i)   Anticipate the possibility of visual illusions during approaches to unfamiliar airports, particularly at night or in adverse weather conditions

        ii)   Consult airport diagrams and the Chart Supplement for runway slope, terrain, and lighting information

        iii)   Frequently reference the altimeter during approaches during day and night.

        iv)   Conduct an aerial visual inspection of unfamiliar airports before landing

        v)   Use the VASI or PAPI, or electronic glide slope when when available

        vi)   Recognize that an emergency or other activity can be a distraction from usual procedures

        vii)   Maintain optimum proficiency in landing procedures

   f)   For a detailed discussion of optical illusions while landing, refer to *Pilot Handbook*, Study Unit 6, Subunit 10.

2.   **The applicant demonstrates understanding of the effects of alcohol, drugs, and over-the-counter medications and associated regulations.**

   a.   There is only one safe rule to follow with respect to combining flying and drinking -- **DON'T**.

      1)   As little as 1 oz. of liquor, 1 bottle of beer, or 4 oz. of wine can impair flying skills.

        a)   Even after your body has completely destroyed a moderate amount of alcohol, you can still be impaired for many hours by hangover.

        b)   Alcohol also renders you much more susceptible to disorientation and hypoxia.

      2)   The 14 CFRs prohibit pilots from performing cockpit duties within 8 hr. after drinking any alcoholic beverage or while under the influence of alcohol.

        a)   An excellent rule is to allow at least 12 to 24 hr. "from bottle to throttle," depending on how much you drank.

   b.   Pilot performance can be seriously impaired by prescription drugs and over-the-counter (OTC) medications.

      1)   Many medications have primary or side effects that may impair judgment, memory, alertness, coordination, vision, and the ability to make calculations.

      2)   Any medication that depresses the nervous system (i.e., sedative, tranquilizer, antihistamine) can make you more susceptible to hypoxia.

      3)   The safest rule is not to fly while taking any medication, unless approved by the FAA.

      4)   In Study Unit 6, "Aeromedical Factors and Aeronautical Decision Making (ADM)," of *Pilot Handbook*, see page 328 for a table listing the most commonly experienced side effects and interactions of OTC medications.

   c.   For summaries of 14 CFRs related to alcohol and drugs (Secs. 61.15, 61.19, 91.17, and 91.19), see *Pilot Handbook*, Study Unit 4, Subunits 6 and 8.

3.   **The applicant demonstrates understanding of the effects of dissolved nitrogen in the bloodstream of a pilot or passenger in flight following scuba diving.**

   a.   If you or one of your passengers intends to fly after scuba diving, you should allow the body sufficient time to rid itself of excess nitrogen absorbed during diving.

      1)   If this is not done, decompression sickness due to evolved gas (i.e., the nitrogen changes from a liquid to a gas and forms bubbles in the bloodstream) can occur at low altitudes and create a serious in-flight emergency.

   b.   The recommended waiting time before flight to altitudes of up to 8,000 ft. is at least 12 hr. after a dive that has not required controlled ascent (nondecompression diving).

      1)   You should allow at least 24 hr. after diving that has required controlled ascent (decompression diving).

      2)   The waiting time before flight to flight altitudes above 8,000 ft. should be at least 24 hr. after any scuba diving.

   c.   The recommended altitudes are actual flight altitudes above mean sea level (MSL), not pressurized cabin altitudes. These recommendations take into consideration the risk of decompression of aircraft during flight.

4.   **The applicant demonstrates understanding of the effects of hazardous attitudes on aeronautical decision making.**

   a.   Being fit to fly depends on more than just a pilot's physical condition and recent experience. For example, attitude will affect the quality of decisions. Attitude is a motivational predisposition to respond to people, situations, or events in a given manner.

   b.   Five hazardous attitudes have been identified that can cloud pilot judgment and decision making.

      1)   Antiauthority (Don't tell me!)
      2)   Impulsivity (Do something quickly!)
      3)   Invulnerability (It won't happen to me.)
      4)   Macho (I can do it.)
      5)   Resignation (What's the use?)

   c.   For information on the effects of these hazardous attitudes on aeronautical decision making, see Study Unit 5, Subunit 3, beginning on page 46.

   d.   For additional information on the effects of hazardous attitudes on aeronautical decision making, see *Pilot Handbook*, Study Unit 6.

5.   **The applicant demonstrates understanding of collision avoidance, scanning, and obstacle and wire strike avoidance.**

   a.   For information on collision avoidance and scanning, see Study Unit 7, Subunit 4, beginning on page 66.

   b.   For information on wire strike avoidance, see Study Unit 7, Subunit 6, beginning on page 68.

6. **The applicant demonstrates understanding of the pilot/airplane interface, including pilot monitoring duties and the interaction with charts and avionics equipment.**

    a. Pilot Monitoring Duties

        1) It is important for pilots to continually monitor their flight instruments and gauges in order to assess the aircraft's attitude, systems, and performance.

        2) When using automated systems in aircraft, pilots need to be especially vigilant to not become complacent.

    b. Pilot Interaction with Navigation and Performance

        1) It is important for pilots to be proficient in the use of both manual and automated navigation and performance charts.

        2) Multi-function displays (MFDs) are capable of displaying moving maps that mirror sectional charts. These detailed displays are so descriptive that many pilots fall into the trap of relying solely on the moving maps for navigation.

        3) Paper charts should be folded to the route, neatly organized, and easily accessible in the cockpit.

    c. Pilot Interaction with Avionics Equipment

        1) Pilots need to be mindful of the benefits and limitations of advanced avionics on board their aircraft.

            a) The availability of global positioning systems (GPS) and moving map systems, coupled with traffic and near real-time weather information in the flight deck, may lead pilots to believe they are protected from the dangers inherent to operating in marginal weather conditions.

            b) Although advanced flight deck technologies may mitigate certain risks, it is by no means a substitute for sound ADM.

        2) If a pilot is unfamiliar with any aircraft systems, this will add to the workload and may contribute to a loss of situational awareness.

        3) It is important to remember that electronic flight displays do not replace basic flight knowledge and skills. They are tools for improving flight safety. Risk increases when the pilot believes the equipment will compensate for lack of skill and knowledge.

END OF KNOWLEDGE ELEMENT

17.2 RISK MANAGEMENT

A.   Task Objectives

1.   **The applicant demonstrates the ability to identify, assess, and mitigate risks encompassing the impact of environmental factors on medication's physiological effects.**

   a.   Medications can reduce the oxygen-carrying capacity of the blood to the degree that the amount of oxygen provided to body tissues will already be equivalent to the oxygen provided to the tissues when exposed to cabin pressure altitudes of several thousand feet.

   b.   Low doses of certain drugs can, through their depressant action, render the brain much more susceptible to hypoxia.

   c.   Extreme heat and cold increase the body's demand for oxygen, and hence its susceptibility to hypoxia compounding the physiological effects of medication at altitude.

   d.   As with all drugs, side effects may vary with the individual and with changes in altitude and other flight conditions.

   e.   The safest rule is not to fly while taking medication, unless approved by the FAA.

2.   **The applicant demonstrates the ability to identify, assess, and mitigate risks encompassing personal risk factors and the conflict between being goal oriented and adhering to personal limitations.**

   a.   Decisions should be made in the context of why the flight is being made, how critical it is to maintain the schedule, and whether or not the trip is worth the risks.

   b.   Use a personal checklist, such as the I'M SAFE checklist, to determine personal risks. For more information, see Study Unit 5, Subunit 2, item D., beginning on page 41.

   c.   Pilots, particularly those with considerable experience, as a rule always try to complete a flight as planned, please passengers, meet schedules, and generally demonstrate that they have the "right stuff."

      1)   The basic drive to demonstrate the "right stuff" can have an adverse effect on safety and can impose an unrealistic assessment of piloting skills under stressful conditions.

      2)   These tendencies ultimately may lead to practices that are dangerous and often illegal and may lead to a mishap.

   d.   Get-there-itis. This tendency, common among pilots, clouds the vision and impairs judgment by causing a fixation on the original goal or destination, combined with a total disregard for any alternative course of action.

   e.   Most pilots are goal oriented and when asked to accept a flight, they have a tendency to deny personal limitations while adding weight to issues not germane to the mission.

   f.   Pilots often discount the fatigue factor because they are goal oriented and tend to deny personal limitations when asked to accept a flight.

   g.   To effectively manage risk and not create hazards, pilots must conduct an effective evaluation of their personal limitations for each flight.

3.   **The applicant demonstrates the ability to identify, assess, and mitigate risks encompassing optical illusions.**

   a.   The pilot should take care to limit the effects of optical illusions.

   b.   Awareness of the potential for optical illusions is necessary to limit the effects of optical illusions.

c. Consider the following in order to help prevent and prepare for optical illusions:

1) Make sure you are fit to fly (healthy, rested, and not under the effects of medication).

2) Avoid flight in reduced visibility or at night when the horizon is not visible.

3) Consult airport diagrams and the Chart Supplement for runway slope, terrain, and lighting information.

4) Be proficient and comfortable flying solely by reference to instruments.

5) Familiarize yourself with the local terrain.

6) Anticipate and be aware of the various illusions that can lead to landing errors.

7) Anticipate the possibility of visual illusions during approaches to unfamiliar airports, particularly at night or in adverse weather conditions.

8) During approach to landing, frequently reference the altimeter during day and night conditions.

9) Use approach lighting like VASI and PAPI when available.

10) Maintain optimum proficiency in landing procedures.

11) Use the visual descent point (VDP) found on many nonprecision instrument approach procedure charts.

d. Sloping cloud formations, an obscured horizon, a dark scene spread with ground lights and stars, and certain geometric patterns of ground light can create illusions of not being aligned correctly with the actual horizon.

1) Various surface features and atmospheric conditions encountered in landing can create illusions of being on the wrong approach path.

2) Landing errors due to these illusions can be prevented by anticipating them during approaches, inspecting unfamiliar airports before landing, using electronic glideslope or VASI systems when available, and maintaining proficiency in landing procedures.

e. The pilot must monitor the flight instruments onboard the aircraft in order to compensate for, and limit the effects of, optical illusions.

4. **The applicant demonstrates the ability to identify, assess, and mitigate risks encompassing the circumstances of the flight (day/night, hot/cold) that affect the pilot's physiology.**

a. The circumstances, or environment of the flight, and how it can affect the pilot's physiology should be considered.

b. Utilize the 5P process (see Study Unit 5, Subunit 2, item G.) to help you recognize the physiological situation before takeoff, during flight, and at the end of the flight.

1) Once risks are identified, the pilot is better equipped to make alternate plans that lessen the effects of these factors and provide a safer solution.

c. Consider some of the following factors that may affect the pilot's physiology:

1) Airport – Mitigate risk by careful study of charts and the Chart Supplement during your preflight preparation.

2) Weather – Fly within your personal limitations for weather.

3) Day vs. night flight – The eyes are the first part of the body to suffer from low oxygen at altitude because the capillaries are very small and have a limited capacity to carry oxygen.

4) Physical stressors – Be aware of conditions associated with the environment, such as temperature and humidity extremes, noise, vibration, and lack of oxygen that can create physical demands on the body.

      5)   Turbulent weather and/or the new sensations of flight – This situation can cause motion sickness in the inexperienced pilot.

      6)   Altitude – It can contribute to hypoxia.

         a)   Be aware that the effects of hypoxia can occur at even lower altitudes given one or more of the following factors:

            i)   Carbon monoxide inhaled in smoking or from exhaust fumes

            ii)   Small amounts of alcohol and low doses of certain drugs (e.g., antihistamines, tranquilizers, sedatives, and analgesics)

            iii)   Extreme heat or cold, fever, and/or anxiety

5.   **The applicant demonstrates the ability to identify, assess, and mitigate risks encompassing continuing VFR flight into Instrument Meteorological Conditions (IMC).**

    a.   For more information on continuing VFR flight into IMC, see Study Unit 5, Subunit 4, beginning on page 47.

6.   **The applicant demonstrates the ability to identify, assess, and mitigate risks, encompassing hazardous attitudes.**

    a.   For information on the effects of hazardous attitudes, see Study Unit 5, Subunit 3, beginning on page 46.

7.   **The applicant demonstrates the ability to identify, assess, and mitigate risks encompassing failure to detect and manage threats and errors associated with human factors.**

    a.   The FAA calls this threat and error management.

    b.   A threat is any condition that increases the complexity of the operation.

      1)   Threats, if not managed properly, can decrease safety margins and can lead to errors.

      2)   There are two types of threats:

         a)   External threats – Those outside of your control (e.g., weather, lack of equipment, hard to understand documentation, system errors, inadequate lighting)

         b)   Internal (human) threats – Those within our control (e.g., fatigue, loss of situation awareness, stress, disregard for following procedures)

    c.   An error is a mistake that is made when threats are mismanaged.

      1)   There are five types of errors:

         a)   Intentional non-compliance errors
         b)   Procedural errors
         c)   Communication errors
         d)   Proficiency errors
         e)   Operational decision errors

    d.   There are two aspects to threat management:

      1)   Recognizing that a threat exists.

      2)   Coming up with a strategy to deal with the threat, so that it does not reduce safety margins or contribute to an error.

e.   Error management is the mitigation or reduction in seriousness of the outcome.

    1)   The resist and resolve filters or defense mechanisms may be applied to an existing error before it becomes consequential to safety.

    2)   By applying the resist and resolve filters in the analysis of an error, you may improve strategies or counter-measures to identify and manage both internal and external threats, such as fatigue, condition of ground equipment, etc.

f.   There are three types of error outcomes:

    1)   Inconsequential – The error has no immediate effect on safety.

    2)   Undesired state – Risk or unsafe operational conditions are increased.

    3)   Additional error – The error causes another error(s).

8.   **The applicant demonstrates the ability to identify, assess, and mitigate risks encompassing ineffective monitoring of automation.**

a.   For information on the monitoring of automation, see Study Unit 6, Subunit 3, beginning on page 51.

9.   **The applicant demonstrates the ability to identify, assess, and mitigate risks encompassing distractions.**

a.   Distractions inside and outside the aircraft can come in many different forms.

b.   Distractions are obstacles to maintaining situational awareness.

c.   Avoid programming cockpit automation or completing checklists while the aircraft is moving on the ground.

    1)   Ideally, all programming and all checklist items that can be completed prior to taxi should be accomplished prior to leaving the ramp area.

    2)   Head-down time during taxi operations is a very serious distraction that can result in missing a routing assignment, bumping into an airplane, or just getting behind and forgetting something important prior to takeoff/shutdown.

d.   Avoid distractions during taxi. Control or eliminate distractions by doing the following:

    1)   Politely ask passengers to wait for a better time to converse.

    2)   Ask ATC to standby or ask for taxi instructions to an airport holding area where you could stop the airplane and complete the necessary conversation with ATC.

    3)   Write down ATC taxi instructions and make use of airport diagrams to ensure you are following the correct taxi route.

    4)   Use proper scanning techniques and minimize head-down time while taxiing.

    5)   Complete after-landing procedures only after you have cleared the runway and have the opportunity to stop and perform tasks in an orderly fashion without distractions.

e.   Maintain a sterile cockpit free of distractions throughout the entire course of your flight.

f.   Distractions interrupting a visual inspection could lead to missing items on the checklist or not recognizing a discrepancy.

    1)   You must keep your thoughts on the preflight inspection.

    2)   If you are distracted, either start at the beginning of the preflight inspection or repeat the preceding two or three items.

g.   In order to avoid potentially dangerous distractions when flying with advanced avionics, the pilot must know how to manage the course deviation indicator (CDI), navigation source, autopilot, and any version of FMS installed in the airplane.

h.   Improper automation use can result in distractions and/or loss of situational awareness.

   1)   You must program automation at times when workload allows.

      a)   Trying to set up the autopilot while maintaining the final approach course is inappropriate and unsafe.

      b)   Trying to program the flight plan into a flight management system (FMS) during climbout shows poor task management and automation management.

   2)   Overloading yourself puts you in danger of exceeding your capabilities and losing situational awareness.

i.   There is an attitude among many pilots that they are required to demonstrate their single-handed control of the airplane without using cockpit resources. This is absolutely false.

   1)   If your airplane is equipped with an autopilot, not only should you use it to reduce your workload, but also the evaluator will expect and in some cases require you to use the autopilot during the practical test.

   2)   There is no need to fumble around with a sectional chart in the cockpit when you have a current terrain database capable of providing you with terrain and obstacle references based on your current position and flight path.

   3)   Such resources reduce distractions and allow you to maintain positive control of the airplane, especially in emergency situations where terrain avoidance becomes critical to the safety of the flight.

j.   Many flight deck distractions begin as a minor problem, such as a gauge that is not reading correctly, but result in accidents as the pilot diverts attention to the perceived problem and neglects to properly control the aircraft.

k.   Just like instrument fixation during instrument flight can lead to disorientation, situational fixation can lead to missed cues of hazards in flight that could impact safety.

END OF RISK MANAGEMENT ELEMENT

17.3 SKILLS

A.   Task Objectives

    1.   **The applicant demonstrates the ability to perform a self-assessment including whether the pilot is fit for flight.**

        a.   Use a personal checklist, such as the I'M SAFE checklist, to determine if you are fit for flight (see Study Unit 5, Subunit 2, item D., beginning on page 41).

        b.   Aircraft accident statistics show that pilots should conduct preflight checklists on themselves as well as their aircraft. Pilot impairment contributes to many more accidents than do failures of aircraft systems.

        c.   Use a risk assessment matrix, such as the one on page 37 in Study Unit 5, Subunit 1.

    2.   **The applicant demonstrates the ability to show sound decision-making and judgment (based on reality of circumstances).**

        a.   The DECIDE model is a good tool to use to help remember the elements of the decision-making process.

            1)   **D** etect. The decision maker detects the fact that change has occurred.

            2)   **E** stimate. The decision maker estimates the need to counter or react to the change.

            3)   **C** hoose. The decision maker chooses a desirable outcome (in terms of success) for the flight.

            4)   **I** dentify. The decision maker identifies actions that could successfully control the change.

            5)   **D** o. The decision maker takes the necessary action.

            6)   **E** valuate. The decision maker evaluates the effect(s) of his or her action countering the change.

        b.   The six elements of the DECIDE model should be treated as a continuous loop. If a pilot practices the DECIDE model in all decision making, its use can become very natural and result in better decisions being made under all types of situations.

        c.   For more information on sound decision making and judgment, see Study Unit 5, Subunits 1 and 2, beginning on page 35.

    3.   **The applicant demonstrates the ability to demonstrate automation management and effective monitoring of automated systems.**

        a.   You should be able to explain and demonstrate how altitude changes are made with your autopilot.

            1)   You will likely have to select a vertical speed or airspeed setting for the autopilot to climb to the armed altitude.

            2)   The autopilot should automatically capture the armed altitude and switch to altitude hold mode.

            3)   If for any reason something unexpected happens, you should demonstrate adequate systems knowledge by getting the autopilot into the desired flight condition or taking manual control of the airplane, if necessary.

        b.   The evaluator may ask you during any phase of flight to report on the current mode or status of cockpit automation as well as to explain what the next mode or status will be.

        c.   You should demonstrate adequate system knowledge by being able to answer without becoming distracted from your other tasks.

            1)   If the evaluator asks you to report on the automation status during a particularly demanding phase of flight, you should politely ask the evaluator to stand by until you have accomplished all necessary tasks.

    d. The evaluator will be monitoring your performance to see how you utilize the available automation resources to manage your workload during all phases of flight, including emergencies.

    e. If any abnormal mode changes should occur or anticipated mode change not occur, you should recognize it quickly, report it to the evaluator, and resolve the situation.

    f. If you are unable to effectively correct the error without undue distraction, you must revert to manual flight control and reinstate automation when your workload allows.

    g. For more information on automation management and the effective monitoring of automation, see Study Unit 6, Subunit 3, beginning on page 51.

    h. Be prepared to operate using alternative means of navigation.

        1) The evaluator may simulate equipment failures, such as an inoperative GPS.

            a) Demonstrate how to verify if the GPS is receiving a reliable signal.

4. **The applicant demonstrates the ability to establish personal limitations.**

    a. Personal limitations can be limitations with

        1) Your own body

            a) To make effective decisions regarding the outcome of a flight, a pilot should be aware of personal limitations, such as health, recency of experience, skill level, and attitude. A personal checklist can help determine if a pilot is prepared for a particular flight.

            b) Prior to flight, pilot fitness should be assessed the same way in which the airplane's airworthiness is evaluated.

            c) For more information, see Study Unit 5, Subunit 2, beginning on page 41.

        2) Your knowledge of the aircraft

        3) Experience/flight time

        4) Experience with the information and avionics of the aircraft

        5) Weather/personal minimums

            a) An example of a personal weather minimums checklist is available in Study Unit 5, Subunit 2.

END OF SKILLS ELEMENT

PART III
SECTION II:
PREFLIGHT PROCEDURES

Study Units 18 through 22 of Section II explain the five FAA ACS tasks (A-D, F) of Preflight Procedures. These tasks include knowledge, risk management, and skill. Your evaluator is required to test you on all five of these tasks.

STUDY UNIT EIGHTEEN
PREFLIGHT ASSESSMENT

Task	Task A. Preflight Assessment
References	FAA-H-8083-2, FAA-H-8083-3; POH/AFM; AC 00-6
Objective	To determine that the applicant exhibits satisfactory knowledge, risk management, and skills associated with preparing for safe flight accounting for pilot, aircraft, environment, and external factors.
Knowledge	The applicant demonstrates understanding of:
PA.II.A.K1	1. Pilot self assessment.
PA.II.A.K2	2. The process to determine if the aircraft is appropriate for the mission by considering load, range, equipment and aircraft capability.
PA.II.A.K3	3. Aircraft preflight inspection including:
PA.II.A.K3a	a. Which items must be inspected
PA.II.A.K3b	b. The reasons for checking each item
PA.II.A.K3c	c. How to detect possible defects
PA.II.A.K3d	d. The associated regulations
PA.II.A.K4	4. Environmental factors that could affect the flight plan:
PA.II.A.K4a	a. Terrain
PA.II.A.K4b	b. Route selection
PA.II.A.K4c	c. Obstruction
PA.II.A.K4d	d. Weather
PA.II.A.K5	5. External pressures.
PA.II.A.K6	6. Seasonal weather phenomena.
Risk Management	The applicant demonstrates the ability to identify, assess and mitigate risks, encompassing:
PA.II.A.R1	1. Environmental factors.
PA.II.A.R2	2. External pressures.
PA.II.A.R3	3. Pilot-related factors.
PA.II.A.R4	4. Aircraft-related factors.
PA.II.A.R5	5. Aviation security concerns.
PA.II.A.R6	6. Seasonal weather patterns.
Skills	The applicant demonstrates the ability to:
PA.II.A.S1	1. Make proper use of the checklists, and systematically identify and manage pilot-related risks and personal minimums associated with the flight.
PA.II.A.S2	2. Inspect the airplane with reference to an appropriate checklist, explaining which items must be inspected, the reasons for checking each item, and how to detect possible defects.
PA.II.A.S3	3. Verify the airplane is airworthy and in condition for safe flight.
PA.II.A.S4	4. Assess the factors related to the environment (e.g., terrain, route selection, obstruction, weather).
PA.II.A.S5	5. Given the requirements of the flight the applicant uses the appropriate charts, tables, and graphs to determine performance.
PA.II.A.S6	6. Identify seasonal weather phenomena.

A.   General Information

1.   The preflight assessment concerns all elements contributing to the ability to conduct a flight safely. These areas include the pilot, aircraft, environment, and external factors.

2.   The pilot in command (PIC) is responsible for determining whether the airplane is airworthy and safe to fly. 14 CFR 91.7 states, "The pilot in command is responsible for determining whether that aircraft is in condition for safe flight."

3.   The PIC also must satisfactorily demonstrate the ability to evaluate himself or herself and environmental conditions, and to identify and manage hazardous external pressures.

18.1 KNOWLEDGE

A.   Task Objectives

   1.   **The applicant demonstrates understanding of pilot self assessment.**

      a.   Pilot personal minimums should be based on a clear assessment of pilot certification, experience, proficiency, and currency.

         1)   Each pilot should establish personal weather minimums, which may be (and often are) above FAA legal minimums.

      b.   When a pilot obtains a new rating or upgrades a certificate, or when current experience level changes, self-assessment factors should be reviewed (at least annually).

      c.   A detailed discussion of the processes used for pilot self assessment is available in Study Unit 5, Subunit 2, beginning on page 41.

   2.   **The applicant demonstrates understanding of the process to determine if the aircraft is appropriate for the mission by considering load, range, equipment, and aircraft capability.**

      a.   The aircraft preflight process begins well before you arrive at the airport to inspect the aircraft.

         1)   You should use all available information concerning your flight to determine if the aircraft is capable of satisfying the mission. Knowing where and when you are flying, the number of passengers, and the amount of cargo is necessary to calculate performance.

         2)   Operating limitations are found in Section 2, Limitations, of your airplane's POH/AFM. These limits establish the boundaries (i.e., flight envelope) in which your airplane must be operated.

         3)   Performance charts, tables, and/or data are found in Section 5, Performance, of your airplane's POH/AFM.

         4)   Use Section 6, Weight and Balance/Equipment List, in your airplane's POH/AFM to calculate the weight and balance. You should calculate the weight and balance for all phases of flight, including takeoff, cruise, and landing.

         5)   Ensure your aircraft is properly equipped to utilize the appropriate navigation facilities along your intended route.

      b.   For more information, see Study Unit 15, "Performance and Limitations."

   3.   **The applicant demonstrates understanding of aircraft preflight inspection, including (a) which items must be inspected, (b) the reasons for checking each item, (c) how to detect possible defects, and (d) the associated regulations.**

      a.   According to 14 CFR 91.7, no person may operate a civil aircraft unless it is in an airworthy condition. As the PIC, you are responsible for determining that the aircraft is in a condition for safe flight.

      b.   Additionally, according to 14 CFR 91.407, following maintenance, the operator must ensure the aircraft is approved for return to service. Ensure the proper endorsements are recorded in the aircraft logbooks.

      c.   The objective of the preflight inspection is to ensure that your airplane has no obvious problems prior to taking off. The preflight is carried out in a systematic walk around the airplane, beginning in the cockpit and using the appropriate checklist.

         1)   Make sure all necessary documents, maps, safety equipment, etc., are aboard.

         2)   Check to ensure all inspections are current (e.g., 100-hr., annual, transponder).

         3)   Make sure your airplane has the required equipment for your flight, e.g., Mode C transponder for an operation in Class B or Class C airspace.

d.   Next, inspect items outside of the airplane to determine that the airplane is in condition for safe flight.

1)   Fuel Quantity and Grade

a)   You should check the level of fuel in the tanks to visually verify the approximate fuel gauge indications.

b)   Every aircraft engine has been designed to use a specific grade of aviation fuel for satisfactory performance. Refer to your POH/AFM for the manufacturer's recommendation regarding the minimum grade. Dyes are added by the refinery to help you identify the various grades of aviation fuel.

i)   Fuel grade 100LL is blue.
ii)   Jet fuel is clear.

c)   DO NOT USE AUTOMOTIVE FUEL unless an FAA supplemental type certificate (STC) has been obtained for your airplane that approves auto gas use.

2)   Fuel Contamination Safeguards

a)   Always assume that the fuel in your airplane may be contaminated. A transparent container should be used to collect a generous fuel sample from each sump drainage valve at the lowest point of each tank and from other parts of the fuel system.

b)   Water, the most common fuel contaminant, is usually caused by condensation inside the tank.

i)   Since water is heavier than the fuel, it will be located at the lowest levels in the fuel system.

ii)   If water is found in the first sample, drain further samples until no water appears.

iii)   Do not hold your fuel sample cup up to the sky to check for water contamination. If the sample is 100% water (no fuel at all), it may appear to be 100% fuel when seen against the blue sky.

c)   Also check for other contaminants, e.g., dirt, sand, rust.

i)   Keep draining until no trace of the contaminant appears.

ii)   A preventive measure is to avoid refueling from cans and drums, which may introduce fuel contaminants such as dirt or other impurities.

d)   Wait at least 15 min. after your airplane has been refueled before you take a fuel sample.

i)   This will allow time for any contaminants to settle to the bottom of the tank.

3)   Fuel Venting

a)   Fuel tank vents allow air to replace the fuel consumed during flight, so the air pressure inside the tank remains the same as outside the tank. It is very important that you visually inspect these vents to ensure that they are not blocked.

i)   Any degree of blockage (partial or complete) can cause a vacuum to form in the fuel tank and prevent the flow of fuel to the engine.

b) Rather than a vent tube, some systems have a small vent hole in the fuel cap.

    i) Some of these vents face forward on the fuel cap, and, if replaced backwards with the tube facing rearward, fuel-flow difficulty or in-flight siphoning may occur.

c) Fuel tanks also have an overflow vent that prevents the rupture of the tank due to fuel expansion, especially on hot days.

    i) This vent may be combined with the fuel tank vent or separate from it.

d) Study your POH/AFM to learn the system on your airplane.

4) Oil Quantity, Grade, and Type

a) Usually the oil is stored in a sump at the bottom of the engine crankcase. An opening to the oil sump is provided through which oil can be added, and a dipstick is provided to measure the oil level.

    i) Your POH/AFM will specify the quantity of oil needed for safe operation.

    ii) Always make certain that the oil filler cap and the oil dipstick are secure after adding oil and/or checking the oil level. If these are not properly secured, oil loss may occur.

b) Use only the type and grade of oil recommended by the engine manufacturer, or its equivalent. Never use any oil additive that has not been recommended by the engine manufacturer or authorized by the FAA.

    i) The type and grade of oil to use can be found in your POH/AFM or on placards on or near the oil filler cap.

c) The wrong type of oil or an insufficient oil supply may interfere with any or all of the basic oil functions and can cause serious engine damage and/or an engine failure during flight.

5) Fuel, Oil, and Hydraulic Leaks

a) Check to see that there are no oil puddles or other leakages under your airplane, inside the engine cowling, or on the wheel struts.

b) Ask someone more experienced and/or knowledgeable to look at any leakage. Know the cause and make the necessary repairs before flying.

6) Flight Controls

a) Visually inspect the flight control surfaces (ailerons, elevator, rudder) to ensure that they move smoothly and freely for their entire movement span.

    i) They also must be securely attached with no missing, loose, or broken nuts, bolts, or rivets.

b) Inspect any mass balance weights on control surfaces (designed to keep the control surface's center of gravity forward of the hinge so as to preclude possible flutter).

c) Check to see that the control yoke moves in the proper direction as the control surfaces move.

d) Place the flaps in the down position to examine the attaching bolts, control rods, and the entire flap surface.

    i) Ensure that the flaps operate correctly with the flap control and that they lock into position.

7) Structural Damage

    a) Check for dents, cracks, tears (cloth cover), or bubbles (composite structures) on all surfaces of the airplane. These can disrupt the smooth airflow and change your airplane's performance.

        i) Surface deformities can lead to, or may be caused from, structural weakness and/or failures due to the stress that is put on the airplane during flight.

            • These deformities result from bent or broken underlying structure.

        ii) One method of checking the wings on a cloth-covered airplane is to grasp the wing spars at the wing tip and gently push down and pull up.

            • Any damage may be evident by sound and/or wrinkling of the skin.

    b) Inspect the propeller for nicks and/or cracks. A small nick that is not properly repaired can become a stress point where a crack could develop and cause the blade to break.

    c) If you have any doubts, get assistance from a qualified mechanic.

8) Exhaust System

    a) Check the exhaust system for visible damage and/or holes, which could lead to carbon monoxide poisoning.

9) Tiedown, Control Lock, and Wheel Chock Removal

10) Ice and Frost Removal

    a) Frost, ice, frozen rain, or snow may accumulate on parked airplanes. All of these must be removed before takeoff.

        i) Ice is removed by parking the airplane in a hangar or spraying deicing compounds on the airplane.

        ii) Frost must be removed from all airfoils before flight. Even small amounts can disrupt airflow, increase stall speed, and reduce lift.

11) Security of Baggage, Cargo, and Equipment

    a) Secure all baggage, cargo, and equipment during the preflight inspection. Make sure everything is in its place and secure.

        i) You do not want items flying around the cockpit if you encounter turbulence.

        ii) Cargo and baggage should be secured to prevent movement that could damage the airplane and/or cause a shift in the airplane's center of gravity.

        iii) An item of cargo is not more secure because it is heavy; it is more dangerous because it moves with greater force.

4. **The applicant demonstrates understanding of environmental factors that could affect the flight plan: (a) terrain, (b) route selection, (c) obstructions, and (d) weather.**

   a. Properly identify airspace, obstructions, and terrain features.

      1) You should be able to identify airspace, obstructions, and terrain features on your sectional chart and determine safe altitudes in advance.

      2) Within each quadrangle bounded by lines of longitude and latitude on the sectional chart are large, bold numbers that represent the maximum elevation figure (MEF).

      3) Your selected route should ensure that you are able to maintain the minimum safe altitudes for your flight set forth by 14 CFR 91.119.

      4) For information on identifying airspace, obstructions, and terrain features on charts, see Section I Introduction, Knowledge, item B., beginning on page 93.

   b. Make a competent "go/no-go" decision based on available weather information.

      1) You should know how to obtain and interpret a preflight weather briefing.

      2) The best way to ensure a safe decision is made every time is to have personal minimums and not exceed them.

      3) To use personal minimums as part of the weather-related decision-making process, compare the current and forecast weather to the personal minimums you have set.

      4) Your evaluator will want to see how you make the go/no-go decision.

         a) You may be given a specific scenario that will require you to make that decision.

         b) Coming in to the practical test with a set of personal minimums will show the evaluator that you are prepared and safety conscious.

   c. Refer to Study Unit 12, "Weather Information," and Study Unit 13, "Cross-Country Flight Planning," for in-depth discussions of these items.

5. **The applicant demonstrates understanding of external pressures.**

   a. For information on external pressures, see Study Unit 5, Subunit 2, beginning on page 41.

6. **The applicant demonstrates understanding of seasonal weather phenomena.**

   a. For information on seasonal weather phenomena, see Study Unit 9, Subunit 6, beginning on page 86.

END OF KNOWLEDGE ELEMENT

18.2 RISK MANAGEMENT

A. Task Objectives

1. **The applicant demonstrates the ability to identify, assess, and mitigate risks encompassing (a) environmental factors, (b) external pressures, (c) pilot-related factors, and (d) aircraft-related factors.**

    a. For information on these items, see Study Unit 5, Subunits 1-2, beginning on page 35.

2. **The applicant demonstrates the ability to identify, assess, and mitigate risks encompassing aviation security concerns.**

    a. In the wake of the attacks of September 11, 2001, general aviation (GA) and GA airports have come under great scrutiny relating to their security.

        1) Therefore, increased vigilance on the part of all pilots is essential to maintain a safe and secure GA environment.

    b. GA should be and is part of the Homeland Security solution and not the problem.

        1) As a whole, general aviation is a safe and secure environment. GA airports are, in themselves, small communities that present the kind of security features that a "neighborhood watch" would, wherein the local residents maintain a watchful vigil over all activities.

        2) The Transportation Security Administration (TSA) has implemented a toll-free hotline that anyone can use to report out-of-the-ordinary or suspicious activity at GA airports. The hotline number is

        (866) GA-SECURE
        (866) 427-3287

        3) Other ways of increasing the security of GA airports include getting to know your airport community, introducing yourself to strangers as well as your fellow pilots, and keeping an active flow of communication within your airport community. Remember, crimes occur due to an opportunity. Do your part to limit the opportunities criminals have available to them.

            a) Measures such as locking aircraft doors and installing prop/throttle locks can go a long way toward helping us all.

3. **The applicant demonstrates the ability to identify, assess, and mitigate risks encompassing seasonal weather patterns.**

    a. For information on seasonal weather patterns, see Study Unit 9, Subunit 6, beginning on page 86.

END OF RISK MANAGEMENT ELEMENT

18.3 SKILLS

A.   Task Objectives

1.   **The applicant demonstrates the ability to make proper use of the checklists and systematically identify and manage pilot-related risks and personal minimums associated with the flight.**

a.   Systematically identify and manage pilot-related risks and personal minimums.

1)   Use the I'M SAFE checklist to evaluate your fitness for flight.

a)   See Study Unit 5, Subunit 2, for a discussion on the I'M SAFE checklist.

2)   Use the PAVE checklist to help you examine areas of potential hazard and risk.

a)   See Study Unit 5, Subunit 2, for a discussion on the PAVE checklist.

3)   The best way to ensure a safe decision is made every time is to create personal minimums.

a)   See Study Unit 5, Subunit 2, for a discussion of creating personal minimums.

2.   **The applicant demonstrates the ability to inspect the airplane with reference to an appropriate checklist, explaining which items must be inspected, the reasons for checking each item, and how to detect possible defects.**

a.   Inspect your airplane with reference to your checklist.

1)   Each airplane has a specific list of preflight procedures recommended by the airplane manufacturer, which is found in the "Normal Procedures" section of your POH/AFM.

a)   The written checklist is a systematic set of procedures.
b)   Always have your checklist in hand and follow it item by item.

b.   Your CFI will instruct you in a systematic method of performing a preflight inspection. This inspection will most likely be more detailed than the checklist in your POH/AFM.

1)   Always have your checklist in hand to be used as a reference to ensure that all items have been checked. If you become distracted during the preflight inspection, you should use the checklist to determine the last item to be checked.

3.   **The applicant demonstrates the ability to verify the airplane is airworthy and in condition for safe flight.**

a.   Verify that your airplane is in condition for safe flight.

1)   During your preflight inspection of your airplane, you must note any discrepancies and make sound judgments on the airworthiness of your airplane.

a)   As pilot in command, you are responsible for determining that the airplane is airworthy.

b)   If you have any doubt, you should ask someone with more experience and/ or knowledge.

c)   Do not attempt a flight unless you are completely satisfied that the airplane is safe and airworthy.

2)   After you have completed the preflight inspection, take a step back and look at your entire airplane.

a)   During your inspection, you were looking at individual items for airworthiness. Now you should look at the airplane as a whole and ask, "Is this airplane safe to fly?"

4. **The applicant demonstrates the ability to assess the factors related to the environment (e.g., terrain, route selection, obstruction, weather).**

   a. Weather is a major environmental consideration. Set your personal minimums and thoroughly evaluate the weather to determine if the flight is a "go or no-go."

      1) EXAMPLE: Consider a scenario where the aircraft has been tied down on the ramp overnight. It rained until past midnight, the temperature has dropped throughout the night, and it is currently 28°F. Light freezing rain has begun to fall. The aircraft has no deice or anti-ice capabilities.

         a) With no means of deicing wings or propellers, and freezing rain falling, the flight would violate regulations that prohibit flight into known icing by aircraft that are unequipped to deal with those conditions.

         b) The safety of this flight would be compromised. The flight should be postponed until more reasonable weather conditions exist.

   b. Continue to analyze and assess the flight environment with the evaluation of terrain, route selection, and obstructions.

   c. The term environment is all encompassing. Additional factors to evaluate include air traffic control (ATC), navigational aids (NAVAIDs), and takeoff and landing areas.

5. **The applicant demonstrates the ability to, given the requirements of the flight, use the appropriate charts, tables, and graphs to determine performance.**

   a. Be familiar with all of the performance data contained in your POH/AFM.

      1) Section 5, Performance, of your POH/AFM contains charts, tables, and/or graphs for you to use to determine airplane performance (e.g., takeoff/landing distance, climb, cruise, etc.).

      2) Additionally, Section 4, Normal Procedures, of your POH/AFM contains takeoff, climb, cruise, and landing power settings and airspeeds.

   b. For more information on using performance data for your airplane, see Study Unit 3, Subunit 6.

6. **The applicant demonstrates the ability to identify seasonal weather phenomena.**

   a. Review the possible weather possibilities expected for the season and conduct your preflight weather brief alert for these items.

      1) During your weather briefing from FSS, ask and/or confirm weather that appears to be seasonal in nature

         a) Ask the FSS briefer about which product or chart (s)he is using to help you better examine the particular weather phenomena for that season (e.g., Lifted K Index during the summertime months to determine stability of the atmosphere and, thus, thunderstorm possibility).

      2) Talk with fellow pilots, family, and friends about the current weather to help you analyze and identify seasonal weather phenomena.

   b. For information on seasonal weather patterns, see Study Unit 9, Subunit 6, beginning on page 86.

END OF SKILLS ELEMENT

18.4 COMMON ERRORS

A.   Common Errors during the Preflight Assessment

1.   **Failure to use, or the improper use of, the checklist**

a.   Checklists are guides for use in ensuring that all necessary items are checked in a logical sequence.

b.   You must not get the idea that the list is merely a crutch for poor memory.

2.   **Hazards that may result from allowing distractions to interrupt a preflight inspection**

a.   Distractions could lead to missing items on the checklist or not recognizing a discrepancy.

1)   You must keep your thoughts on the preflight inspection.

b.   If you are distracted, either start at the beginning of the preflight inspection or repeat the preceding two or three items.

3.   **Inability to recognize discrepancies**

a.   You must understand what you are looking at during the preflight inspection.

b.   Look for smaller items such as missing screws, drips of oil, etc.

4.   **Failure to assure servicing with the proper fuel and oil**

a.   It is easy to determine whether the correct grade of fuel has been used. Even if you are present during fueling, you should be in the habit of draining a sample of fuel from the airplane to check for the proper grade and for any contamination.

b.   Oil is not color-coded for identification. You will need to check the proper grade before you or any line personnel add oil to the airplane.

END OF COMMON ERRORS

STUDY UNIT NINETEEN
COCKPIT MANAGEMENT

Task	**Task B. Cockpit Management**
References	FAA-H-8083-2, FAA-H-8083-3; POH/AFM
Objective	To determine that the applicant exhibits satisfactory knowledge, risk management, and skills associated with safe cockpit management practices.
Knowledge	The applicant demonstrates understanding of:
PA.II.B.K1	1. Pilot and passenger safety restraint systems, requirements, and operational considerations.
PA.II.B.K2	2. Oxygen use regulations, system operational guidelines, and system checks, if applicable.
PA.II.B.K3	3. Safety system rules and operational considerations.
PA.II.B.K4	4. Passenger briefing requirements and appropriate information.
PA.II.B.K5	5. PIC responsibility to have available material for the flight as planned.
PA.II.B.K6	6. The purpose of a checklist.
Risk Management	The applicant demonstrates the ability to identify, assess and mitigate risks, encompassing:
PA.II.B.R1	1. Failure to positively exchange the flight controls.
PA.II.B.R2	2. Use of portable electronic devices.
PA.II.B.R3	3. Use of automation.
PA.II.B.R4	4. Inappropriate use of technology.
PA.II.B.R5	5. The impact of reported discrepancies.
PA.II.B.R6	6. Passenger behavior that could negatively affect safety.
Skills	The applicant demonstrates the ability to:
PA.II.B.S1	1. Ensure all loose items in the cockpit and cabin are secured.
PA.II.B.S2	2. Organize, access, and determine suitability of material, equipment, and technology in an efficient manner.
PA.II.B.S3	3. Brief occupants on the use of safety belts, shoulder harnesses, doors, sterile cockpit, and flight control freedom of movement, and emergency procedures.
PA.II.B.S4	4. Properly program the navigational equipment available to the pilot on that particular aircraft.
PA.II.B.S5	5. Brief and execute positive exchange of flight controls and PIC responsibility to include identification of the PIC.
PA.II.B.S6	6. Conduct an appropriate pre take off briefing.

A. General Information

1. The objective of this task is for you to demonstrate your knowledge, risk management, and skills related to safe cockpit management practices.

a. This includes both maintaining an organized cockpit and understanding the aeronautical decision-making process.

2. In Study Unit 6, "Aeromedical Factors and Aeronautical Decision Making (ADM)," of *Pilot Handbook*, see Subunits 12 through 17 for a discussion of the aeronautical decision-making process and related topics.

19.1 KNOWLEDGE

A.   Task Objectives

1.   **The applicant demonstrates understanding of pilot and passenger safety restraint systems, requirements, and operational considerations.**

   a.   You should be familiar with the requirements of 14 CFR 91.107, Use of Safety Belts, Shoulder Harnesses, and Child Restraint Systems.

      1)   Each person must occupy an approved seat or berth with a safety belt and, if installed, shoulder harness, properly secured about him or her during movement on the surface, takeoff, and landing.

         a)   A child who has not reached his or her second birthday may be held by an adult who is occupying an approved seat or berth.

         b)   14 CFR 91.107 also describes the types of child restraint systems that are acceptable.

2.   **The applicant demonstrates understanding of oxygen use regulations, system operational guidelines, and system checks, if applicable.**

   a.   Supplemental oxygen requirements for flight crew and passengers when operating non-pressurized airplanes:

      1)   You may not operate a civil U.S.-registered airplane

         a)   At cabin pressure altitudes above 12,500 ft. MSL, up to and including 14,000 ft. MSL, unless the required minimum flight crew uses supplemental oxygen for that part of the flight at those altitudes that is longer than 30 min.

         b)   At cabin pressure altitudes above 14,000 ft. MSL unless the required minimum flight crew uses supplemental oxygen during the entire time at those altitudes

         c)   At cabin pressure altitudes above 15,000 ft. MSL unless each occupant is provided with supplemental oxygen

      2)   Supplemental oxygen use is more stringent under 14 CFR Parts 121 and 135.

   b.   The identification and differences between "aviators' breathing oxygen" and other types of oxygen:

      1)   Aviators' breathing oxygen is specified at 99.5% pure oxygen and not more than .005 mg of water per liter.

         a)   Oxygen bottles containing aviators' breathing oxygen should be clearly labeled.

      2)   Medical oxygen contains too much water, which can collect in various parts of the supplemental oxygen system and freeze.

         a)   Freezing may reduce, or stop, the flow of oxygen.

      3)   Industrial oxygen is not intended for breathing.

c. The operational characteristics of continuous flow, demand, and pressure-demand oxygen systems:

1) The continuous flow oxygen system is the most common system found in general aviation airplanes. There are currently two types.

a) The mask system is designed so the oxygen can be diluted with ambient air by allowing the user to exhale around the face piece, and it comes with a rebreather bag that allows the individual to reuse part of the exhaled oxygen.

i) Although certificated up to 41,000 ft., careful attention to system capabilities is required when using this type of system above 25,000 ft.

b) A cannula has hollow flexible tubes positioned just under the user's nose. The tube has oxygen outlets under the nose and provides a very comfortable oxygen delivery method that does not interfere with headsets, microphones, drinking, or eating. It is certified for use up to 18,000 ft.

d. Prior to every flight, you should perform the "PRICE" check on your oxygen system.

1) **P**ressure - ensure that there is enough oxygen pressure and quantity to complete the flight.

2) **R**egulator - inspect the oxygen regulator for proper function. If you are using a continuous-flow system, make sure the outlet assembly and plug-in coupling are compatible.

3) **I**ndicator - most oxygen delivery systems indicate oxygen flow by use of flow indicators. Flow indicators may be located on the regulator or within the oxygen delivery tube. Don the mask and check the flow indicator to assure a steady flow of oxygen.

4) **C**onnections - ensure that all connections are secured. This includes oxygen lines, plug-in coupling, and the mask.

5) **E**mergency - have oxygen equipment in the aircraft ready to use for those emergencies that call for oxygen (hypoxia, decompression sickness, smoke and fumes, and rapid decompressions). This step should include briefing passengers on the location of oxygen and its proper use.

e. General operational guidelines include

1) Keep equipment clean.
2) Protect oxygen masks from direct sunlight and dust, and store properly.
3) No smoking! Oxygen is highly flammable! Ensure that the aircraft is properly grounded.
4) Mix and match system components with caution – ensure compatibility.

3. **The applicant demonstrates understanding of safety system rules and operational considerations.**

a. Know the operating requirements, limitations, and procedures for each safety system installed in your aircraft.

1) Beyond seat belts, this could include SRS (supplemental restraint system/airbags), supplemental oxygen, and ballistic recovery systems (whole aircraft parachutes).

a) Some systems may be limited in duration for use, attitude, or speed restrictions.

4. **The applicant demonstrates understanding of passenger briefing requirements and appropriate information.**

    a. Brief your passengers on the use of safety belts, shoulder harnesses, doors, and emergency procedures.

        1) As PIC, you must ensure that before takeoff each person is briefed on how to fasten and unfasten that person's safety belt and, if installed, shoulder harness (14 CFR 91.107).

        2) In addition, before moving the aircraft on the surface, takeoff, or landing, you must ensure that each person has been notified to fasten his or her safety belt and, if installed, shoulder harness (14 CFR 91.107).

    b. Brief passengers using the SAFETY list:

S: Seat belts fastened for taxi, takeoff, landing Shoulder harness fastened for takeoff, landing Seat position adjusted and locked in place. **A:** Air vents (location and operation) All environmental controls (discussed) Action in case of any passenger discomfort **F:** Fire extinguisher (location and operation) **E:** Exit doors (how to secure; how to open) Emergency evacuation plan Emergency/survival kit (location and contents) **T:** Traffic (scanning, spotting, notifying pilot) Talking ("sterile flight deck" expectations) **Y:** Your questions? (Speak up!)

        1) In addition, discuss the use of portable electronic devices and the details of the flight (time enroute, weather, etc.)

5. **The applicant demonstrates understanding of PIC responsibility to have available material for the flight as planned.**

    a. As pilot in command, you are directly responsible for, and the final authority as to, the operation of the aircraft. This includes having the necessary materials and equipment to conduct the flight safely (i.e., charts, publications, flashlights, batteries, pencil, and paper) available for the planned flight.

6. **The applicant demonstrates understanding of the purpose of a checklist.**

    a. For information on checklists, see Study Unit 6, Subunit 4, beginning on page 54.

END OF KNOWLEDGE ELEMENT

19.2 RISK MANAGEMENT

A.   Task Objectives

1.   **The applicant demonstrates the ability to identify, assess, and mitigate risks encompassing failure to positively exchange the flight controls.**

   a.   Before starting the aircraft, be sure to state that you will be using the positive exchange of flight controls procedures.

      1)   This procedure is designed to ensure that all parties know who will be actively controlling the airplane at any given point in time.

      2)   This positive exchange ensures that someone is always controlling the airplane and that only one person at a time will be making control inputs unless otherwise required.

   b.   There are three verbal steps in exchanging the flight controls. Consider an example in which you pass the flight controls to your instructor.

      1)   You state, "You have the flight controls."
      2)   The instructor responds, "I have the flight controls."
      3)   You reaffirm, "You have the flight controls."

         a)   Visually check to ensure the other person actually has the flight controls.

2.   **The applicant demonstrates the ability to identify, assess, and mitigate risks encompassing use of portable electronic devices.**

   a.   Consider 14 CFR 91.21 for the implications of portable electronic devices.

      1)   Portable electronic devices other than portable voice recorders, hearing aids, pacemakers, electric shavers, etc., may not be operated on aircraft operated IFR or aircraft operated by holders of an air carrier operating certificate or an operating certificate.

      2)   The pilot in command or operator of the aircraft can make certain exceptions to this rule so long as the electronic devices will not interfere with the communication or navigation systems of the aircraft.

   b.   Make sure you brief your passengers on what items are acceptable and the appropriate times for use.

3.   **The applicant demonstrates the ability to identify, assess, and mitigate risks encompassing use of automation.**

   a.   You must program automation at times when workload allows.

      1)   Trying to set up the autopilot while maintaining the final approach course is inappropriate and unsafe.

      2)   Likewise, trying to program the flight plan into a flight management system (FMS) during climbout shows poor task management and automation management.

      3)   Plan in advance when and where programming should (and should not) occur.

         a)   Your familiarity with the equipment, the route, the local ATC environment, and personal expectations with the automation should drive when, where, and how the automation is programmed and used.

   b.   Overloading yourself puts you in danger of exceeding your capabilities and losing situational awareness.

   c.   Consider programming portable electronic flight bags before entering your cockpit.

      1)   The cockpit is not the place to learn how to use your portable electronics.

      2)   Minimize the amount of head-down time you spend operating portable equipment. It should not become a distraction to your duties as PIC (i.e., interfering with collision avoidance procedures).

4. **The applicant demonstrates the ability to identify, assess, and mitigate risks encompassing inappropriate use of technology.**

   a. Advanced avionics offer multiple levels of automation from strictly manual flight to highly automated flight.

      1) No one level of automation is appropriate for all flight situations, but in order to avoid potentially dangerous distractions when flying with advanced avionics, the pilot must know how to manage the course deviation indicator (CDI), navigation source, autopilot, and any version of FMS installed in the airplane.

      2) It is important for a pilot to know the peculiarities of the particular automated system being used. This ensures that the pilot knows what to expect, how to monitor for proper operation, and how to promptly take appropriate action if the system does not perform as expected.

   b. Do not passively monitor automated systems.

      1) Be aware that when passively monitoring an automated system for faults, abnormalities, or other infrequent events, humans perform poorly.

      2) The more reliable the system is, the worse the human performance becomes.

         a) For example, the pilot monitors only a backup alert system, rather than the situation that the alert system is designed to safeguard.

         b) It is a paradox of automation that technically advanced avionics can both increase and decrease pilot awareness.

   c. Do not replace basic flight knowledge and skills with the reliance on automation. Be proficient in basic flight knowledge and flight skills. Automation is a tool for improving flight safety not a replacement for knowledge and skill.

      1) Risk increases when the pilot believes the gadgets compensate for lack of skill and knowledge.

      2) It is especially important to recognize there are limits to what the electronic systems in any light GA aircraft can do.

      3) Being PIC requires sound ADM, which sometimes means saying "no" to a flight.

   d. Get properly trained on the automation you will be using.

      1) The automated cockpit offers many new capabilities and simplifies the basic flying tasks, but only if the pilot is properly trained and all the equipment is working properly.

5. **The applicant demonstrates the ability to identify, assess, and mitigate risks encompassing the impact of reported discrepancies.**

   a. During your preflight inspection of your airplane, you must note any discrepancies and make sound judgments on the airworthiness of your airplane.

      1) As pilot in command, you are responsible for determining that the airplane is airworthy.

      2) If you have any doubt, you should ask someone with more experience and/or knowledge.

      3) Do not attempt a flight unless you are completely satisfied that the airplane is safe and airworthy.

6. **The applicant demonstrates the ability to identify, assess, and mitigate risks encompassing passenger behavior that could negatively affect safety.**

    a. Hazards may result from allowing distractions to interrupt a visual inspection.

        1) This could lead to missing items on the checklist or not recognizing a discrepancy.

            a) You must keep your thoughts on the preflight inspection.

        2) If you are distracted, either start at the beginning of the preflight inspection or repeat the preceding two or three items.

    b. Recognize when pressures from passenger demands may have a negative impact on judgment and flight safety.

        1) No one ever intends to have an accident and many accidents result from poor judgment.

        2) Since passengers are often at arm's length in the cockpit, they can easily create distractions.

            a) During your passenger preflight brief, explain the "sterile cockpit" procedures for times of high workload.

            b) If passengers are capable, you can redirect their attention by asking them to help scan for other traffic.

            c) Ask your passengers to hold their questions and conversation with you for a later time.

            d) Use the pilot or pilot/crew isolate function on your intercom (if equipped) to turn off passenger noise from your headset.

    c. Passenger curiosity or the unfamiliarity of flying in an airplane could lead passengers to touch switches/knobs, adjust his or her seat at an inappropriate time (during climbout), or grab the yoke when adjusting his or her seat.

        1) Brief passengers to not touch knobs/switches and to consult you when they have a need.

END OF RISK MANAGEMENT ELEMENT

19.3 SKILLS

A.   Task Objectives

1.   **The applicant demonstrates the ability to ensure all loose items in the cockpit and cabin are secured.**

a.   The cockpit and/or cabin should be checked for loose articles or cargo that may be tossed about if turbulence is encountered and must be secured.

2.   **The applicant demonstrates the ability to organize, access, and determine suitability of material, equipment, and technology in an efficient manner.**

a.   On every flight, you should be in the habit of organizing and neatly arranging your materials and equipment in an efficient manner that makes them readily available.

b.   Be in the habit of "good housekeeping."

1)   A disorganized cockpit will complicate even the simplest of flights.

c.   Organization will contribute to safe and efficient flying.

3.   **The applicant demonstrates the ability to brief occupants on the use of safety belts, shoulder harnesses, and doors; sterile cockpit; flight control freedom of movement; and emergency procedures.**

a.   You are required to brief each passenger on how to fasten and unfasten the safety belt and, if installed, the shoulder harness (14 CFR 91.107).

b.   You cannot taxi, take off, or land before notifying each passenger to fasten his or her safety belt and, if installed, shoulder harness and ensuring that (s)he has done so (14 CFR 91.107).

c.   At this time, you need to brief the occupants on the airplane's emergency procedures that are relevant to them.

d.   Remember, you must brief your evaluator on these items as you would any passenger.

4.   **The applicant demonstrates the ability to properly program the navigational equipment available to the pilot on that particular aircraft.**

a.   You must be familiar with and be able to program all navigational equipment available on your airplane.

b.   For a detailed discussion of programming the navigational equipment, see Study Unit 36, "Navigation Systems and Radar Services."

5.   **The applicant demonstrates the ability to brief and execute positive exchange of flight controls and PIC responsibility to include identification of the PIC.**

a.   Make sure there is always a clear understanding of who has control of the aircraft, whether it is in a flight with your instructor, with your FAA evaluator, or another pilot. Prior to the flight, the pilots involved should conduct a briefing that includes reviewing the procedures for exchanging flight controls. The FAA recommends a positive three-step process for exchanging flight controls between pilots:

1)   When one pilot seeks to have the other pilot take control of the aircraft, he or she will say, "You have the flight controls."

2)   The second pilot acknowledges immediately by saying, "I have the flight controls."

3)   The first pilot again says, "You have the flight controls."

6. **The applicant demonstrates the ability to conduct an appropriate pre-takeoff briefing.**

    a.   In addition to briefing your passengers, take the time to brief your takeoff and departure plan.

    b.   Include the departure heading, climb attitudes, distance, and time to the first checkpoint.

    c.   Include a discussion of emergency procedures should the engine fail at different phases of the takeoff and departure.

        1)   For more information on emergency procedures, see Study Unit 8, Subunit 2.

END OF SKILLS ELEMENT

19.4 COMMON ERRORS

A.   Common Errors in Cockpit Management

1.   **Failure to place and secure essential materials and equipment for easy access during flight**

   a.   Do not use the top of the instrument panel as a storage area.
   b.   Maintain an organized cockpit and stress the safety factors of being organized.

2.   **Failure to brief passengers**

   a.   Always brief your passengers on the use of their safety belts and shoulder harnesses.
   b.   Also brief your passengers on emergency procedures.
   c.   For the practical test, the evaluator is a passenger. You must perform a standard passenger briefing before leaving the ramp area.

      1)   Practice giving your instructor a passenger briefing to get used to this action before test day.

END OF COMMON ERRORS

STUDY UNIT TWENTY
ENGINE STARTING

Task	Task C. Engine Starting
References	FAA-H-8083-2, FAA-H-8083-3, FAA-H-8083-25; POH/AFM
Objective	To determine that the applicant exhibits satisfactory knowledge, risk management, and skills associated with recommended engine starting procedures including proper airplane positioning.
Knowledge	The applicant demonstrates understanding of:
PA.II.C.K1	1. Starting under various atmospheric conditions, using external power and hand propping safety.
PA.II.C.K2	2. Starting procedures for carbureted, fuel injected, diesel, Full Authority Digital Engine Control (FADEC), or turbine engines, as applicable.
PA.II.C.K3	3. Equipment limitations (such as starter cycles).
PA.II.C.K4	4. Proper positioning of the airplane.
Risk Management	The applicant demonstrates the ability to identify, assess and mitigate risks, encompassing:
PA.II.C.R1	1. Propeller safety and awareness to include passenger briefing and dangers associated with hand propping.
PA.II.C.R2	2. Implications of engine(s) starting with a weak or depleted battery, including considerations for use of external power.
PA.II.C.R3	3. Abnormal start.
PA.II.C.R4	4. Hot and cold weather operation.
PA.II.C.R5	5. Electrical system failure following aircraft engine starts.
PA.II.C.R6	6. Engine fires related to over priming/cold weather starting.
Skills	The applicant demonstrates the ability to:
PA.II.C.S1	1. Position the airplane properly considering structures, other aircraft, and the safety of nearby persons and property.
PA.II.C.S2	2. Utilize the checklist as appropriate during engine start.
PA.II.C.S3	3. Start the engine under various atmospheric conditions.

A. General Information

1. The objective of this task is for you to demonstrate your knowledge, risk management, and skills related to recommended engine starting procedures including proper airplane positioning.

2. In Study Unit 2, "Airplane Instruments, Engines, and Systems," of *Pilot Handbook*, see Subunit 15, "Ignition System," for a discussion on hand-propping procedures.

20.1 KNOWLEDGE

A.   Task Objectives

   1.   **The applicant demonstrates understanding of starting under various atmospheric conditions, using external power and hand propping safety.**

      a.   Refer to item A.3. in Subunit 20.3 for information on engine starting under various atmospheric conditions.

      b.   Some airplanes are equipped with an external power receptacle.

         1)   This allows you to connect an external power (battery) to your airplane's electrical system without accessing the battery in the airplane.

         2)   You can also use an external battery and connect it to the airplane's battery to provide power to the starter.

         3)   Read your POH/AFM for the correct procedures.

      c.   Even though most airplanes are equipped with an electric starter, some can also be started by hand propping. Before you attempt to hand prop an airplane, you should be instructed on the procedures and safety precautions.

         1)   The airplane should be tied down and/or chocked while a qualified pilot is seated at the controls with the brakes on. The person turning the propeller should have experience doing this procedure.

   2.   **The applicant demonstrates understanding of starting procedures for carbureted, fuel injected, diesel, Full Authority Digital Engine Control (FADEC), or turbine engines, as applicable.**

      a.   The correct engine starting procedure for your airplane is explained in your POH/AFM.

   3.   **The applicant demonstrates understanding of equipment limitations (such as starter cycles).**

      a.   Know the limitations, if any, that are applicable to the starting system on your airplane.

         1)   Some starting systems are limited to the amount of time they can be on before a mandatory cool down period.

            a)   For example, this may allow 30 sec. of cranking, followed by 30 sec. of rest, followed by another 30 sec. of cranking, followed by 2 min. of rest.

         2)   Another limitation may include a life-limited starter. This may require inspections or maintenance after a prescribed number of starter cycles.

         3)   Read your POH/AFM to determine the limitations for your aircraft.

   4.   **The applicant demonstrates understanding of proper positioning of the airplane.**

      a.   For information on proper position of the airplane, see item A.1. in Subunit 20.3.

END OF KNOWLEDGE ELEMENT

20.2 RISK MANAGEMENT

A.   Task Objectives

1.   **The applicant demonstrates the ability to identify, assess, and mitigate risks encompassing propeller safety and awareness to include passenger briefing and dangers associated with hand propping.**

   a.   When starting an engine, the rules of safely and courtesy should be strictly observed.

      1)   One of the most important considerations is to make sure there is no one near the propeller during engine start.

         a)   The pilot should look in all directions to be sure that nothing is or will be in the vicinity of the propeller. This includes nearby persons and aircraft that could be struck by the propeller blast or the debris it might pick up from the ground.

         b)   The pilot should always call "CLEAR" out of the side window and wait for a response from persons who may be nearby before activating the starter.

      2)   Do not allow passengers to load or disembark while the engine is running.

      3)   Never walk in front of an operating propeller on an airplane or behind the operating tail rotor of a helicopter.

      4)   Explain to your passengers that when an aircraft beacon is on, its engine is running and the propeller is turning or the engine is about to be started.

      5)   Passengers should be briefed on the "clear prop" call-out by pilots so that they are aware that an engine may be starting in their vicinity.

   b.   Due to the hazards associated with hand propping, this method should be used only when absolutely necessary and the proper precautions have been taken.

      1)   Always use procedures in accordance with the manufacturer's recommendations and checklists.

      2)   Only two people, both familiar with the airplane and hand propping techniques, should attempt the procedure; never attempt this procedure alone.

         a)   Mitigate risks of miscommunication and avoid confusion during noisy or windy conditions by confirming procedures and commands to be used.

         b)   Decide who is in charge. The person pulling the propeller faces the greatest risks and should direct all activity.

         c)   Never allow a person unfamiliar with the controls to occupy the pilot's seat.

      3)   The person doing the hand propping should make sure (s)he is not too far away from the blade, because it would cause the need to lean forward in an unbalanced manner, which could cause the person to fall forward into the rotating blades when the engine starts.

         a)   To prevent the possibility of being pulled into the propeller when it momentarily rotates in the opposite direction during a misfire, you should always push downward with the palms of both hands and not grip the propeller with your fingers.

         b)   Always step backward, away from the prop as it is pushed down.

      4)   If the engine doesn't start, do not reposition the blade for another attempt unless the ignition/magneto switch is turned OFF.

      5)   Consider what the aircraft will do once it starts. Are the brakes set and wheels chocked?

      6)   After starting, when removing the chocks, remember that the prop is essentially invisible.

         a)   Make sure the throttle is at idle.
         b)   Approach the chocks from the rear of the propeller.
         c)   Never approach from the front or the side.

2.   **The applicant demonstrates the ability to identify, assess, and mitigate risks encompassing implications of engine(s) starting with a weak or depleted battery, including considerations for use of external power.**

a.   When the battery is weak, starting may not be possible, or may not be permitted by the aircraft manufacturer.

1)   If the battery is depleted or below a minimum threshold for starting, it should be serviced prior to attempting an engine start.

2)   If the battery is weak, and external power is available, it should be used in accordance with the aircraft manufacturer's recommendations.

a)   Read the POH/AFM for the correct operating procedures.

b)   The power source must be of the correct grounding type and voltage or your airplane.

c)   When using external power, ensure only trained personal are assisting to connect and disconnect the external power source.

d)   Line service personal should be briefed regarding propeller safety and hand signals used when starting with external power.

3.   **The applicant demonstrates the ability to identify, assess, and mitigate risks encompassing abnormal start.**

a.   Be able to recognize and discuss abnormal starting situations.

1)   Consider how to determine the indications of an abnormal starting condition.

a)   A starter that will not engage may make a whining sound without actually turning the propeller.

b)   Be alert to the possibility of an engine fire, especially if the engine backfires during starting.

2)   If the engine doesn't start while handpropping, do not reposition the blade for another attempt unless the ignition/magneto switch is turned OFF.

4.   **The applicant demonstrates the ability to identify, assess, and mitigate risks encompassing hot and cold weather operation.**

a.   Your airplane may have different procedures for starting when the ambient temperature is hot or cold.

1)   During hot weather, or when the engine is already hot, follow the procedures listed in your airplane's POH/AFM for hot starts.

a)   A common issue when conducting a hot start is too much fuel.
b)   Use caution not to over prime or flood the engine, which could cause an engine fire.

b.   During cold weather, the oil in your airplane's engine becomes very thick. There are several methods to assist in starting a cold engine. Check your POH/AFM for the recommended procedure.

1)   One method is that the propeller should be pulled through (turned) several times to draw oil through the system.

a)   This saves battery energy, which is already low due to the cold temperature.

b)   When performing this procedure, a loose or broken groundwire on either magneto could cause the engine to fire or backfire.

i)   Ensure that the ignition/magneto switch is off, throttle is closed, mixture is in lean/idle cut-off position, nobody is standing in or near the propeller arc, the parking brake is on, and the airplane is chocked and/or tied down.

5. **The applicant demonstrates the ability to identify, assess, and mitigate risks encompassing electrical system failure following aircraft engine starts.**

   a. Operating your starter motor for long periods of time may cause it to overheat and/or completely drain your battery.

      1) Follow the recommendations and procedures that are in your POH/AFM.

   b. Pilots should be aware of the possibility of total electrical system failure after aircraft engine start due to the starter relay (solenoid) failed mechanically in the "on" position.

      1) This condition causes the starter to run, and if allowed to continue, can result in electrical system overload, overheating of components, and in some cases complete failure of the assembly. Destruction of the starter drive shaft and gear assemble may also damage the aircraft engine.

      2) To aid in the prevention of accidents or incidents due to this issue, some safety suggestions include

         a) During maintenance activities, inspect the starter motor, electrical cables, and starter relay areas for evidence of over-heating and damage.

         b) Pilots should be completely familiar with instrument readings, cockpit sounds, and other indicators following normal engine starting periods.

         c) Indications that problems are developing in the starter system may include

            i) Low voltage
            ii) High ammeter or loadmeter readings
            iii) Dimming of lights
            iv) Excessive noise in radio receivers

         d) A noted change in such known normal conditions could indicate prolonged starter motor running and the engine should be shut down. Do not attempt further flight operations until the cause is determined and repaired.

6. **The applicant demonstrates the ability to identify, assess, and mitigate risks encompassing engine fires related to over-priming/cold weather starting.**

   a. Using incorrect starting procedures could be very hazardous. It could also lead to over priming or priming your engine when it is not necessary.

      1) Over priming can lead to an excess of fuel, especially in a carburetor intake. If the engine backfires, a fire could occur.

   b. Should a fire occur during starting, you should continue cranking the engine.

      1) This should suck the flames into the induction system and extinguish the blaze.

      2) If the engine starts, allow it to run for about a minute before shutting down and having the aircraft inspected for damage.

      3) If the engine does not start, shut down the electrical system and evacuate the aircraft. Use a fire extinguisher to put out the fire if it is still burning.

END OF RISK MANAGEMENT ELEMENT

20.3 SKILLS

A.   Task Objectives

1.   **The applicant demonstrates the ability to position the airplane properly considering structures, other aircraft, and the safety of nearby persons and property.**

a.   Always start the engine with enough room in front of the airplane so you can turn off the engine if the brakes fail.

b.   Do not start the engine with the tail of the airplane pointed toward an open hangar door, parked cars, or a group of bystanders (i.e., think about direction of prop blast).

1)   It is a violation of 14 CFR 91.13 to operate your airplane on any part of the surface of an airport in a careless or reckless manner that endangers the life or property of another.

c.   Be cautious of loose debris, e.g., rocks or dirt, that can become projectiles when you start the engine.

d.   To avoid damage to the propeller and property, the aircraft should be in an area where the propeller will not stir up gravel or dust.

2.   **The applicant demonstrates the ability to utilize the checklist as appropriate during engine start.**

a.   You should use the appropriate checklist, provided in your POH/AFM, for engine starting (e.g., normal start, cold weather start, hot start, flooded engine start, etc.).

b.   For more information on the the use of checklists, see Study Unit 6, Subunit 4, beginning on page 54.

3.   **The applicant demonstrates the ability to start the engine under various atmospheric conditions.**

a.   You must be able to explain engine starting procedures under various atmospheric conditions (i.e., cold or hot weather).

1)   Cold weather starting can be made easier by preheating the engine.

a)   Many FBOs in cold weather locations offer this service.

b)   Small, portable heaters are available to blow hot air into the engine to warm it.

c)   This is generally required when outside air temperatures are below 0°F and is recommended by most engine manufacturers when the temperature is below 20°F.

2)   To start a cold engine, prime it with fuel first.

a)   In carburetor engines, the primer is a small manual or electric pump that draws fuel from the tanks and vaporizes it directly into one or two of the cylinders through small fuel lines.

i)   Continuous priming may be required to keep the engine running until sufficient engine heat is generated to vaporize the fuel.

b)   After a cold engine has been started, it should be idled at low RPM for 2 to 5 min. and the oil temperature indication should be in the "green" to allow the oil to warm and begin circulating throughout the system.

3) During hot weather and/or with a hot engine, the cylinders tend to become overloaded with fuel. This could lead to a flooded engine situation.

   a) Follow the appropriate checklist for either a HOT or FLOODED engine in your POH/AFM.

      i) A flooded engine normally requires you to have the mixture in the lean position and the throttle full open.

         • This helps clear the cylinders of the excess fuel and allows the engine to start.

      ii) As the engine starts, ensure that you close the throttle and move the mixture to rich.

END OF SKILLS ELEMENT

20.4 COMMON ERRORS

A.   Common Errors during Engine Starting

   1.   **Failure to use, or the improper use of, the checklist**

      a.   You must be in the habit of properly using the correct checklist for engine starting.

      b.   This ensures that every item is completed and checked in a logical order.

   2.   **Excessively high RPM after starting**

      a.   You should constantly monitor the engine instruments while the engine is operating.

   3.   **Improper preheat of the engine during severe cold weather conditions**

      a.   Severe cold weather will cause a change in the viscosity of engine oils, batteries may lose a high percentage of their effectiveness, and instruments may stick.

      b.   During preheat operations, do not leave the airplane unattended, and keep a fire extinguisher nearby.

      c.   There is a tendency to over prime, which washes down cylinder walls, and scoring of the walls may result.

      d.   Icing on the spark plug electrodes can short them out. The only remedy is heat.

   4.   **Failure to ensure proper clearance of the propeller**

      a.   During the visual inspection, the propeller path should be checked for debris or obstructions, especially on the ground.

      b.   Before starting, ensure that no person or object will be struck by the propeller.

END OF COMMON ERRORS

STUDY UNIT TWENTY-ONE
TAXIING

Task	Task D. Taxiing
References	FAA-H-8083-2, FAA-H-8083-3, FAA-H-8083-25; POH/AFM; AC 91-73; Chart Supplements U.S.; AIM
Objective	To determine that the applicant exhibits satisfactory knowledge, risk management, and skills associated with safe taxi operations, including runway incursion avoidance.
Knowledge	The applicant demonstrates understanding of:
PA.II.D.K1	1. Positioning aircraft controls for wind.
PA.II.D.K2	2. Airport markings, signs, and lights.
PA.II.D.K3	3. Aircraft lighting.
PA.II.D.K4	4. Safe taxi procedures at towered and non-towered airports:
PA.II.D.K4a	a. Maneuvering
PA.II.D.K4b	b. Maintain taxiway/runway alignment
PA.II.D.K4c	c. Situational awareness to avoid runway incursions
PA.II.D.K4d	d. Taxiing to avoid other aircraft/vehicles and hazards
PA.II.D.K5	5. Visual indicators for wind.
PA.II.D.K6	6. Airport information resources including Chart Supplements U.S., airport diagrams, and appropriate publications.
PA.II.D.K7	7. Good cockpit discipline during taxi, including maintaining a sterile cockpit, proper speed, separation between other aircraft and vehicles, and communication procedures.
PA.II.D.K8	8. Procedures for appropriate cockpit activities while taxiing including taxi route planning, briefing the location of Hot Spots, communicating and coordinating with ATC.
PA.II.D.K9	9. Rules for entering or crossing runways.
PA.II.D.K10	10. Procedures unique to night operations.
PA.II.D.K11	11. Hazards of low visibility operations.
PA.II.D.K12	12. Proper engine management including leaning, per manufacturer's recommendations.
Risk Management	The applicant demonstrates the ability to identify, assess and mitigate risks, encompassing:
PA.II.D.R1	1. Distractions during aircraft taxi.
PA.II.D.R2	2. Improper task management during taxi.
PA.II.D.R3	3. Confirmation or expectation bias as related to taxi instructions.
PA.II.D.R4	4. Taxi instructions/clearances.
PA.II.D.R5	5. Improper resource management.
Skills	The applicant demonstrates the ability to:
PA.II.D.S1	1. Perform a brake check immediately after the airplane begins moving.
PA.II.D.S2	2. Position the flight controls properly for the existing wind conditions.
PA.II.D.S3	3. Control direction and speed without excessive use of brakes.
PA.II.D.S4	4. Control the airplane during ground operations.
PA.II.D.S4a	a. Maneuvering
PA.II.D.S4b	b. Maintaining taxiway/runway alignment
PA.II.D.S4c	c. Maintaining situational awareness to avoid runway incursions
PA.II.D.S4d	d. Taxiing to avoid other aircraft/vehicles and hazards
PA.II.D.S5	5. Exhibit proper positioning of the aircraft relative to hold lines.
PA.II.D.S6	6. Exhibit procedures to ensure clearances/instructions are received, recorded, and read back correctly.
PA.II.D.S7	7. Exhibit situational awareness and taxi procedures in the event the aircraft is on a taxiway that is between parallel runways.
PA.II.D.S8	8. Use an airport diagram or taxi chart during taxi.
PA.II.D.S9	9. Comply with airport/taxiway markings, signals, ATC clearances and instructions.
PA.II.D.S10	10. Use procedures to minimize pilot workload during taxi operations.
PA.II.D.S11	11. Demonstrate briefing procedures to avoid runway incursions.

A.   General Information

    1.   The objective of this task is for you to demonstrate your knowledge, risk management, and skills related to safe taxi operations, including runway incursion avoidance.

21.1 KNOWLEDGE

A.   Task Objectives

    1.   **The applicant demonstrates understanding of positioning aircraft controls for wind.**

       a.   When taxiing in windy conditions, you must position the control surfaces as shown in the diagram below.

          1)   When the wind is from any forward direction, the control yoke should be turned or pushed fully toward the wind.

             a)   The aileron on the side from which the wind is coming will be up, and the wind flowing over the wing will hold the wing down (rather than lifting the wing, which would permit the wind to get under the wing and possibly blow the airplane over on its back).

             b)   The elevators should be in a neutral position, i.e., the control yoke held neither forward nor back, to permit the nosewheel to carry its normal weight and be used for directional control.

                i)   On tailwheel airplanes, the elevators should be up, i.e., control yoke or stick pulled back, to keep the tail firmly down so the tailwheel can provide directional control.

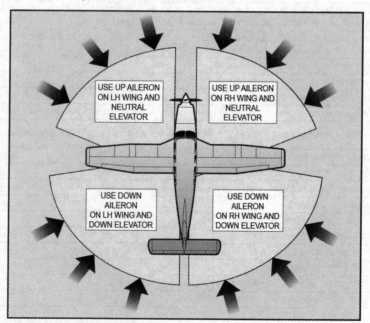

          2)   When the wind is from any rearwind direction, the control yoke should be turned or pushed fully away from the wind.

             a)   The aileron on the side from which the wind is coming will be down, which will help keep the wind from getting under the wing and lifting it.

             b)   The elevator should be down, i.e., the control yoke pushed full forward, to deter the wind from getting under the tail, raising the tail, and possibly blowing the airplane over (tail over front).

                i)   On tailwheel airplanes, the control yoke or stick is also held full forward to keep the tailwheel firmly on the ground for directional control.

    3) Your heading indicator provides a helpful reference for positioning the flight controls during taxi.

        a) Make note of the reported wind direction's location on the face of your heading indicator.

            i) Be sure that your heading indicator has been set to match your compass.

            ii) Verify the reported wind direction with a wind sock or other wind direction indicator.

        b) As your airplane changes direction during taxi turns, the relative position of the wind (i.e., headwind or tailwind, left or right) is shown on the heading indicator.

        c) Simply position your airplane's flight controls using the memory aid, "make a level turn into a quartering headwind and dive away from a quartering tailwind."

2. **The applicant demonstrates understanding of airport markings, signs, and lights.**

    a. You need to be able to identify and interpret the various runway and taxiway markings and airport lighting since you may be flying in and out of various airports.

    b. The ultimate purpose of your understanding of these visual aids is to promote positive situational awareness, which will help you avoid runway incursions.

    c. The following are illustrated/explained in Study Unit 3, "Airports, Air Traffic Control, and Airspace," in *Pilot Handbook*:

        1) Runway markings include

            a) Runway designation marking
            b) Runway centerline marking
            c) Runway aiming point marker
            d) Runway touchdown zone marker
            e) Runway side stripe marking
            f) Runway shoulder markings
            g) Runway threshold markings
            h) Runway threshold bar
            i) Demarcation bar
            j) Chevrons

        2) Taxiway markings include

            a) Taxiway centerline
            b) Taxiway edge markings
            c) Taxiway shoulder markings
            d) Surface painted taxiway direction signs
            e) Surface painted location signs
            f) Geographic position markings

        3) Holding position markings include

            a) Runway holding position markings
            b) Holding position markings for instrument landing system
            c) Holding position markings for taxiway/taxiway intersections
            d) Surface painted holding position signs

        4) Other airport markings include

            a) Vehicle roadway markings
            b) VOR receiver checkpoint markings
            c) Non-movement area boundary markings
            d) Marking and lighting of permanently closed runways and taxiways
            e) Temporarily closed runway and taxiway markings
            f) Helicopter landing area markings

5) There are six types of airport signs:

    a) Mandatory instruction signs
    b) Location signs
    c) Direction signs
    d) Destination signs
    e) Information signs
    f) Runway distance remaining signs

6) Airport lighting includes

    a) Approach light system
    b) Runway lights/runway edge lights
    c) Touchdown zone lighting
    d) Runway centerline lighting
    e) Threshold lights
    f) Runway end identifier lights
    g) Various types of visual approach slope indicator lights
    h) Airport rotating beacon

Airport Signs and Markings Quick Reference Guide

EXAMPLE	TYPE OF SIGN	PURPOSE	LOCATION/CONVENTION
4 - 22	Mandatory: Hold position for taxiway/ runway intersection.	Denotes entrance to runway from a taxiway.	Located L side of taxiway within 10 feet of hold position markings.
22 - 4	Mandatory: Holding position for runway/runway intersection.	Denotes intersecting runway.	Located L side of rwy prior to intersection, & R side if rwy more than 150' wide, used as taxiway, or has "land & hold short" ops.
4 - APCH	Mandatory: Holding position for runway approach area.	Denotes area to be protected for aircraft approaching or departing a runway.	Located on taxiways crossing thru runway approach areas where an aircraft would enter an RSA or apch/ departure airspace.
ILS	Mandatory: Holding position for ILS critical area/precision obstacle free zone.	Denotes entrance to area to be protected for an ILS signal or approach airspace.	Located on twys where the twys enter the NAVAID critical area or where aircraft on taxiway would violate ILS apch airspace (including POFZ).
⊖	Mandatory: No entry.	Denotes aircraft entry is prohibited.	Located on paved areas that aircraft should not enter.
B	Taxiway Location.	Identifies taxiway on which the aircraft is located.	Located along taxiway by itself, as part of an array of taxiway direction signs, or combined with a runway/ taxiway hold sign.
22	Runway Location.	Identifies the runway on which the aircraft is located.	Normally located where the proximity of two rwys to one another could cause confusion.
(hatched marking)	Runway Safety Area / OFZ and Runway Approach Area Boundary.	Identifies exit boundary for an RSA / OFZ or rwy approach.	Located on taxiways on back side of certain runway/ taxiway holding position signs or runway approach area signs.
(striped marking)	ILS Critical Area/POFZ Boundary.	Identifies ILS critical area exit boundary.	Located on taxiways on back side of ILS critical area signs.
J →	Direction: Taxiway.	Defines designation/direction of intersecting taxiway(s).	Located on L side, prior to intersection, with an array L to R in clockwise manner.
↖ L	Runway Exit.	Defines designation/direction of exit taxiways from the rwy.	Located on same side of runway as exit, prior to exit.
22 ↑	Outbound Destination.	Defines directions to take-off runway(s).	Located on taxi routes to runway(s). Never collocated or combined with other signs.
FBO ↘	Inbound Destination.	Defines directions to airport destinations for arriving aircraft.	Located on taxi routes to airport destinations. Never collocated or combined with other types of signs.
NOISE ABATEMENT PROCEDURES IN EFFECT 2300 - 0500	Information.	Provides procedural or other specialized information.	Located along taxi routes or aircraft parking/staging areas. May not be lighted.
(hatched marker)	Taxiway Ending Marker.	Indicates taxiway does not continue beyond intersection.	Installed at taxiway end or far side of intersection, if visual cues are inadequate.
7	Distance Remaining.	Distance remaining info for take-off/landing.	Located along the sides of runways at 1000' increments.

EXAMPLE	TYPE OF MARKING	PURPOSE	LOCATION/CONVENTION
	Holding Position.	Denotes entrance to runway from a taxiway.	Located across centerline within 10 feet of hold sign on taxiways and on certain runways.
	ILS Critical Area/POFZ Boundary.	Denotes entrance to area to be protected for an ILS signal or approach airspace.	Located on twys where the twys enter the NAVAID critical area or where aircraft on taxiway would violate ILS apch airspace (including POFZ).
	Taxiway/Taxiway Holding Position.	Denotes location on taxiway or apron where aircraft hold short of another taxiway.	Used at ATCT airports where needed to hold traffic at a twy/twy intersection. Installed provides wing clearance.
	Non-Movement Area Boundary.	Delineates movement area under control of ATCT, from non-movement area.	Located on boundary between movement and non-movement area. Located to ensure wing clearance for taxiing aircraft.
Taxiway Edge.		Defines edge of usable, full strength taxiway.	Located along twy edge where contiguous shoulder or other paved surface NOT intended for use by aircraft.
Dashed Taxiway Edge.		Defines taxiway edge where adjoining pavement is usable.	Located along twy edge where contiguous paved surface or apron is intended for use by aircraft.
	Surface Painted Holding Position.	Denotes entrance to runway from a taxiway.	Supplements elevated holding position signs. Required where hold line exceeds 200'. Also useful at complex intersections.
	Enhanced Taxiway Centerline.	Provides visual cue to help identify location of hold position.	Taxiway centerlines are enhanced 150' prior to a runway holding position marking.
	Surface Painted Taxiway Direction.	Defines designation/direction of intersecting taxiway(s).	Located L side for turns to left. R side for turns to right. Installed prior to intersection.
	Surface Painted Taxiway Location.	Identifies taxiway on which the aircraft is located.	Located R side. Can be installed on L side if combined with surface painted hold sign.

3. **The applicant demonstrates understanding of aircraft lighting.**

   a. Cockpit panel lighting can include electronically lit display units, individual instrument post lighting, and/or overhead flood light type panel lighting.

      1) Cockpit lighting should be adjusted to a minimum brightness that will allow the pilot to read the instruments and switches and yet not hinder the pilot's outside vision.

         a) This will also eliminate light reflections on the windshield and windows.

   b. For information on aircraft lighting outside the cockpit, see Study Unit 53, Subunit 1, item A.4, beginning on page 671.

4. **The applicant demonstrates understanding of safe taxi procedures at towered and non-towered airports, including (a) maneuvering, (b) maintaining taxiway/runway alignment, (c) situational awareness to avoid runway incursions, and (d) taxiing to avoid other aircraft/vehicles and hazards.**

   a. Taxiing is the controlled movement of the airplane under its own power while on the ground.

      1) Taxiway centerline and edge markings are yellow.

         a) When yellow taxiing centerline stripes are provided, they should be observed unless necessary to clear obstructions or airplanes.

      2) Markings for runways are white.

         a) Maintain runway alignment by following the white runway centerline markings.

   b. Usually when operating on a soft or muddy field, you must maintain the taxi speed or power slightly above that required under normal field operations; otherwise, the airplane may come to a stop.

    c.   Special Considerations for Tower-Controlled Airports

        1)   Acknowledge and read back all ATC instructions/clearances.

        2)   Write down ATC taxi instructions and make use of airport diagrams to visualize your taxi route, especially at complex and/or busy airports.

        3)   Hold short of all runways unless explicitly cleared by ATC to cross them.

        4)   Always stop and query ATC if you have questions or doubts regarding your clearance.

        5)   Request progressive taxi instructions from ATC when unsure of the taxi route.

    d.   Special Considerations for Non-Towered Airports

        1)   Visually confirm the area around the aircraft is clear before moving.

        2)   Pay attention to local radio transmissions while taxiing to determine what other aircraft are operating in the area.

        3)   Transmit your intentions to let others know of your movement on the ground.

        4)   Do not develop the mentality that taxiing at a non-towered airport requires less mental focus than when operating at a tower-controlled airport.

    e.   Use a standard clearing procedure before initiating movement on the surface.

        1)   Look to your left, scan the area for other traffic, and announce "clear left" if it is in fact clear.

        2)   Repeat this same procedure for both the front and right of the aircraft.

        3)   Check for traffic before crossing any runway hold line and before entering a taxi.

    f.   Make use of airport diagrams for unfamiliar airports.

        1)   Know your intended taxi route, but also be aware of other ramp areas, common entry/exit points from ground vehicles, and points where you can safely stop the aircraft so as not to convenience other traffic.

    g.   Review NOTAM for information on runway/taxiway closures and construction areas.

    h.   Turn on aircraft lights and the rotating beacon or strobe lights while taxing.

    i.   Review charted Hot Spots before you begin taxiing.

    j.   For information on avoiding runway incursions, see Study Unit 7, Subunit 2, beginning on page 61.

5.   **The applicant demonstrates understanding of visual indicators for wind.**

    a.   For information on visual indicators for wind, see Study Unit 9, Subunit 2, beginning on page 78.

6.   **The applicant demonstrates understanding of airport information resources including Chart Supplements U.S., airport diagrams, and appropriate publications.**

    a.   It is important to review the current data for the airports at which you will be operating. Three common sources of information include

        1)   Aeronautical Charts
        2)   Chart Supplements
        3)   Notices to Airmen (NOTAMs)

    b.   The Chart Supplement is a civil flight information publication published every 56 days designed to be used in conjunction with charts.

        1)   It is a directory of all airports, seaplane bases, and heliports open to the public; communications data; navigational facilities; and certain special notices and procedures.

        2)   A digital Chart Supplement can be accessed on the FAA website at www.faa.gov/air_traffic/flight_info/aeronav/digital_products.

7. **The applicant demonstrates understanding of good cockpit discipline during taxi, including maintaining a sterile cockpit, proper speed, separation between other aircraft and vehicles, and communication procedures.**

    a.   Taxiing is a unique airplane operation in that, unlike when you are in the air, you are basically confined to a particular path to get from point A to point B.

        1)   While there may be multiple taxiways between the ramp and the runway, you will either taxi in the most efficient manner possible or under the guidance of ATC.

        2)   Because taxiways are essentially one lane roads, you must be sure your taxi route is clear all the way to your destination.

        3)   Two airplanes that find themselves head-to-head on a taxiway may have little to no room to maneuver.

    b.   Unlike when you are in the air, you know that you will have other aircraft operating in close proximity to you when you are taxiing.

        1)   Collision avoidance procedures, even if you are under the direction of air traffic control, should still be used during taxi operations.

            a)   During taxi, the pilot's eyes should be looking outside the airplane, to the sides, as well as the front.

            b)   Be aware of the entire area around the airplane to ensure that the airplane will clear all obstacles and other aircraft.

        2)   The expectation of other aircraft and vehicles operating around you gives good cause for increased awareness and vigilance when operating on the ground.

    c.   ATC taxi instructions are generally given all at once, identifying your entire route of taxi from the ramp to the runway (or vice versa), rather than in single instructions, such as "turn to a heading of 320 degrees."

        1)   Due to the complexity of some taxi instructions, it is always a good idea to write the instructions down for future reference.

    d.   Good cockpit discipline includes the use of proper communications phraseology and procedures, including the proper voice cadence.

        1)   Monitor ATC clearances/instructions issued to other aircraft.

        2)   Listen carefully to avoid taking a clearance/instruction intended for someone else.

        3)   Look for light gun signals from the tower if you suspect radio problems or experience radio failure.

    e.   Taxi operations require constant vigilance and continual awareness of the movement and location of other aircraft and vehicles on the airport movement area.

        1)   Focus attention and have your "head up and eyes out" of the cockpit when taxiing.

    f.   Minimize discussions, questions, and conversations during taxi (maintain a "sterile cockpit"). See Study Unit 6, Subunit 2, for more information on sterile cockpit.

    g.   Good cockpit discipline includes taxiing at a safe speed.

8. **The applicant demonstrates understanding of procedures for appropriate cockpit activities while taxiing, including taxi route planning, briefing the location of Hot Spots, and communicating and coordinating with ATC.**

    a.   First, be sure that the activities you are conducting during taxi operations are essential and do not cause any undue distraction for you as the pilot in command.

    b.   Your taxi route, including where to hold short, should be determined and firmly established in your mind before you leave the ramp.

        1)   Review the appropriate airport diagrams and Hot Spots and have the diagram out and available for immediate reference during taxi.

        2)   Review current ATIS for any taxiway closures, runway closures, construction activity, or other airfield specific risks.

3) Copy the taxi clearance and use the airport diagram to review the taxi route to the assigned runway prior to releasing brakes and beginning taxi; clarify any instructions you are unsure of.

4) STOP aircraft on the taxiway and request ATC clarification if there is confusion regarding aircraft position or ATC taxi clearance.

5) Request a progressive taxi if necessary.

9. **The applicant demonstrates understanding of rules for entering or crossing runways.**

   a. At a non-towered field, prior to entering or crossing runway, announce your intentions and look both ways for traffic.

   b. At a towered field, read back all runway crossing and/or holding instructions.

      1) Do not solely rely on the tower to keep you clear of other traffic. Continue to be vigilant while checking for traffic.

   c. Turn on additional aircraft lights, i.e., strobe lights, navigation light, or landing light when entering or crossing runways.

10. **The applicant demonstrates understanding of procedures unique to night operations.**

   a. Without the aid of the sun in helping you identify aircraft, you must know how to spot and track other aircraft at night.

      1) As with nighttime flight operations, the aircraft position lights will help you determine how the aircraft is oriented and what direction the aircraft is moving in.

      2) Aircraft landing/taxi lights are also very good indicators of the direction the aircraft is moving in.

   b. Be courteous to other pilots at night and turn off landing/taxi lights as well as strobe lights when they will cause a distraction or prevent the other pilot from seeing where (s)he is going.

      1) Ensure your position lights and anticollision lights remain on.

   c. Due to the importance of aircraft lights when operating at night, be sure to properly preflight the aircraft and ensure your lights are operating properly prior to conducting night operations.

   d. If taxi lines are painted on the ramp or taxiway, these lines should be followed to ensure a proper path along the route.

11. **The applicant demonstrates understanding of hazards of low visibility operations.**

   a. Like driving a car in low visibility conditions, taxi operations can be problematic as it is harder to see airport signs and markings, obstructions, and other aircraft.

   b. Ultimately, a non-instrument rated pilot should not be operating in poor visibility conditions.

   c. If you should you find yourself taxiing in conditions that limit your visibility, be sure that you accurately communicate your position and intentions and make smart use of aircraft exterior lights.

   d. Be extra careful at night or during low visibility conditions. Focus on safe operation of the aircraft as it is moving. Running checklists and nonessential communication should be deferred until aircraft is stopped and brakes are set.

12. **The applicant demonstrates understanding of proper engine management, including leaning, per manufacturer's recommendations.**

   a. Since the process of adjusting the mixture can vary from one aircraft to another, you should refer to the POH/AFM to determine the specific procedures for a given aircraft.

END OF KNOWLEDGE ELEMENT

21.2 RISK MANAGEMENT

A.   Task Objectives

1.   **The applicant demonstrates the ability to identify, assess, and mitigate risks encompassing distractions during aircraft taxi.**

   a.   You must be vigilant during taxi operations due to reasons that have already been identified and discussed.

      1)   Head-down time during taxi operations is a very serious distraction that can result in missing a routing assignment, bumping into an airplane, or just getting behind and forgetting something important prior to takeoff/shutdown.

   b.   The evaluator will expect to see that you can accomplish all required tasks while filtering out nonessential tasks, such as unnecessary conversation or cell phone use.

   c.   Focus on the task at hand and do not allow yourself to be distracted.

      1)   Be aware that the evaluator may try to distract you with questions during taxi. Politely ask the evaluator to standby while you accomplish safe taxi procedures.

2.   **The applicant demonstrates the ability to identify, assess, and mitigate risks encompassing improper task management during taxi.**

   a.   Improper task management can create unnecessary hazards and greatly affect the safety of taxi operations. Good cockpit habits in planning, prioritizing, and sequencing of tasks must be formed early in training to prevent runway incursions and the possibility of a ground collision.

   b.   For more information on task management, see Study Unit 6, Subunit 1.

3.   **The applicant demonstrates the ability to identify, assess, and mitigate risks encompassing confirmation or expectation bias as related to taxi instructions.**

   a.   For information on expectation bias, see Study Unit 7, Subunit 5.

4.   **The applicant demonstrates the ability to identify, assess, and mitigate risks encompassing taxi instructions/clearances.**

   a.   Write down all instructions and clearances from ATC to ensure you get the correct message. Doing so will also help to read back instructions or a clearance to ATC.

      1)   Whenever in doubt, ask for clarification.
      2)   Avoid a collision course by always reading back clearances.

   b.   Do not become distracted by the taxi chart. Reference it appropriately, but do not allow yourself to focus exclusively on the chart to the detriment of safe taxi operations.

5.   **The applicant demonstrates the ability to identify, assess, and mitigate risks encompassing improper resource management.**

   a.   The evaluator will assess your ability throughout the practical test to use good ADM procedures in order to evaluate risks. The evaluator will accomplish this requirement by developing a scenario that incorporates as many ACS tasks as possible.

      1)   Useful tools and sources of information may not always be readily apparent. Pilots must learn to identify and develop the skills to evaluate whether it is time to use a particular resource and the impact its use has on safety.

      2)   Modern cockpit environments have many resources available; however, you must use these resources wisely.

         a)   Avoid distractions by not having unnecessary conversations.
         b)   Maintain situational awareness by keeping your head up.
         c)   Avoid programming avionics while taxiing.

   b.   For more information on resource management, see Study Unit 6.

END OF RISK MANAGEMENT ELEMENT

21.3 SKILLS

A. Task Objectives

1. **The applicant demonstrates the ability to perform a brake check immediately after the airplane begins moving.**

    a. To perform a brake check on your airplane, you need to begin moving your airplane forward by gradually adding power (moving the throttle forward slowly) to increase the engine RPM.

        1) Reduce the power to idle as soon as your airplane begins rolling, and gently apply the brakes to stop the forward motion of your airplane.

    b. If there is any question about the operation of the brakes, shut down the engine immediately and have them checked.

2. **The applicant demonstrates the ability to position the flight controls properly for the existing wind conditions.**

    a. The wind is a very important consideration when operating your airplane on the ground. The objective is to keep your airplane firmly on the ground, i.e., not to let the wind blow the airplane around and/or weathervane, and to have better controllability and steerability.

        1) If a wind from the side gets under the wing, it can lift the wing up and even blow the airplane over sideways. A wind from the rear can get under the tail of the airplane and blow the airplane over to the front.

        2) Caution is recommended. Avoid sudden bursts of power and sudden braking.

3. **The applicant demonstrates the ability to control direction and speed without excessive use of brakes.**

    a. Your taxi speed should be approximately as fast as a brisk walk.

        1) The primary requirement is safe, positive control -- the ability to stop or turn where and when desired.

        2) Normally, the speed should be at a rate at which movement of the airplane is dependent on the throttle, that is, slow enough so that when the throttle is closed, the airplane can be stopped promptly.

    b. Very sharp turns or attempting to turn at too great a speed must be avoided as both tend to exert excessive pressure on the landing gear, and such turns are difficult to control once started.

4. **The applicant demonstrates the ability to control the airplane during ground operations, including maneuvering, maintaining taxiway/runway alignment, maintaining situational awareness to avoid runway incursions, and taxiing to avoid other aircraft/vehicles and hazards.**

    a. The evaluator wants to see that you have thought ahead and know how you will accomplish your ground operations at the airport.

        1) You should expect scenario-based questioning on busy airport operations whether or not you are operating out of a complex airport.

    b. Maneuver the aircraft either from the ramp to the runway or from the runway to the ramp while simultaneously ensuring that you comply with ATC requirements and taxi in a manner that promotes ground safety (e.g., considering crosswinds, other aircraft or vehicles, and appropriate speeds) and eliminates the risk of a runway incursion.

    c. Consider highlighting your route on an airport diagram printout so you can visually comprehend your taxi route, thus encouraging positive situational awareness.

    d. Taxi so as to avoid other aircraft and hazards.

        1) Maintaining awareness of the location and movement of all other aircraft and vehicles along the taxi path and in the traffic pattern is essential to safety.

2) Visually scan the area around you and constantly look for other traffic and/or obstructions. At this time, you should be looking outside your airplane while spending a minimum amount of time looking in the cockpit to check your engine and flight instruments.

   a) Indicate your awareness of traffic and/or obstructions by pointing them out to your evaluator.

e. Be sure that your airplane's wings will clear all other airplanes or obstructions.

   1) If in doubt, stop.

f. Avoid prop washing people, aircraft, or vehicles while taxiing.

   1) 14 CFR 91.13 prohibits you from operating your airplane in a careless or reckless manner that endangers the life or property of another.

   2) Be polite when operating around people and/or property.

g. Monitor the appropriate radio frequency for traffic and possible conflicts.

5. **The applicant demonstrates the ability to exhibit proper positioning of the aircraft relative to hold lines.**

a. Recall that hold short markings (Detail 1 in the image below) represent an invisible plane that no part of your aircraft may cross without an ATC clearance (at tower-controlled airports) or visual verification that the runway environment is clear (at non-towered airports).

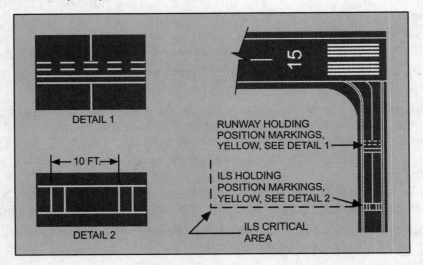

b. Hold short markings have two sets of dotted lines and two sets of solid lines.

   1) When you are approaching from the dotted side, that means you are exiting a runway.

   2) When you are approaching from the solid side, that means you are entering the runway.

   3) Do not cross the double solid lines without an explicit ATC clearance (at tower-controlled airports) or visual verification that the runway environment is clear (at non-towered airports).

c. ILS critical area boundary markings (Detail 2 in the figure above) denote where you should stop if an ILS approach is in use.

   1) At a tower-controlled airport, ATC will advise if you should stop at ILS critical area markings.

   2) At a non-towered airport, you should hold at the ILS critical area markings if you have heard another aircraft transmitting its intentions to shoot the ILS instrument approach to that runway.

6. **The applicant demonstrates the ability to exhibit procedures to ensure clearances/instructions are received, recorded, and read back correctly.**

   a.   Whether you are operating at a tower-controlled airport or not, make it a habit early in your training to write down your taxi route to your intended takeoff runway or to the ramp after landing.

      1)   Consider drawing your taxi route on an airport diagram to aid your situational awareness during your taxi.

      2)   Make note of ATC taxi instructions, especially when they involve multiple turns, so that you do not get lost, take a wrong turn, and/or cause a ground traffic incident.

   b.   Whenever you are assigned taxi instructions by ATC, read back the instructions in a clear tone of voice so the controller is sure you know what is expected of you.

      1)   Avoid rushing through your radio transmissions. The controller is much more interested in the fact that you understood and acknowledge the correct taxi route than in your speed of delivery.

      2)   Be sure to clearly announce your acknowledgment of holding instructions in a timely manner.

7. **The applicant demonstrates the ability to exhibit situational awareness and taxi procedures in the event the aircraft is on a taxiway that is between parallel runways.**

   a.   When taxiing between parallel runways, be aware that landing traffic can come from either direction onto the taxiway.

   b.   Listen closely for ATC instructions/advisories and be sure that you visually clear intersections before crossing runways or other taxiways at non-towered airports.

8. **The applicant demonstrates the ability to use an airport diagram or taxi chart during taxi.**

   a.   Always make use of airport diagrams for unfamiliar airports, especially large, complex ones, so that you are well aware of your position on the airport and the location of your destination when operating on the ground.

   b.   Mark ATC taxi instructions on the diagram and use it to ensure you are following those instructions.

   c.   Do not become distracted by the chart. Reference it appropriately, but do not allow yourself to focus exclusively on the chart to the detriment of safe taxi operations.

9. **The applicant demonstrates the ability to comply with airport/taxiway markings, signals, ATC clearances, and instructions.**

   a.   You must comply with airport markings and signals.

   b.   If you are operating at a tower-controlled airport, you must comply with ATC clearances.

10. **The applicant demonstrates the ability to use procedures to minimize pilot workload during taxi operations.**

   a.   Avoid programming cockpit automation or completing checklists while the aircraft is moving on the ground.

      1)   Ideally, all programming and all checklist items that can be completed prior to taxi should be accomplished prior to leaving the ramp area.

      2)   Head-down time during taxi operations is a very serious distraction that can result in missing a routing assignment, bumping into an airplane, or getting behind and forgetting something important prior to takeoff/shutdown.

   b.   Repeat all ATC instructions and ask clarification for any instructions that you do not understand.

    c.   Focus on the task at hand and do not allow yourself to be distracted.

        1)   Be aware that the evaluator may try to distract you with questions during taxi. Politely ask the evaluator to standby while you accomplish safe taxi procedures.

11. **The applicant demonstrates the ability to demonstrate briefing procedures to avoid runway incursions.**

    a.   First, be sure that the activities you are conducting during taxi operations are essential and do not cause any undue distraction for you as the pilot in command.

    b.   Your taxi route, including where to hold short, should be determined and firmly established in your mind before you leave the ramp.

        1)   Make use of airport diagrams to review runway incursion hot spots (if any).

        2)   If you are operating at a non-towered airport, be sure that you fit into the flow of ground traffic and choose the most appropriate taxi route to and from the active runway.

END OF SKILLS ELEMENT

21.4 COMMON ERRORS

A.   Common Errors during Taxiing

    1.   **Improper use of brakes**

        a.   The most common error is the tendency to ride the brakes while taxiing.

           1)   Correct this by using the throttle to slow the airplane down, and use the brakes to stop the airplane completely.

           2)   Obviously, more braking will be necessary in castoring nosewheel and tailwheel airplanes.

    2.   **Improper positioning of flight controls for various wind conditions**

        a.   Always know the direction of the wind in relation to the airplane. Use all available means to determine direction, such as wind sock and/or ground control.

        b.   Picture the wind relative to your airplane at any given time by means of the heading indicator.

           1)   EXAMPLE: If the airplane is heading 090° and the wind is from 240°, you can use the heading indicator to determine that the wind is a right-quartering tailwind.

    3.   **Hazards of taxiing too fast**

        a.   This occurs from the improper use of the throttle and sometimes by feeling rushed to get to the run-up area.

        b.   Taxi slowly in the ramp area and at a speed at which you can stop or turn where and when you desire.

           1)   Normally it should be at such a speed that, when the throttle is closed, the airplane can be stopped promptly.

4.   **Failure to comply with markings, signals, or clearances**

    a.   Before starting to taxi at a controlled airport, ask yourself if the taxi instructions make sense and that you understand the clearance.

        1)   Contact ground control for clarification.

    b.   While taxiing, identify markings and signals to your evaluator. Explain what you are doing as you do it so the evaluator is confident you are in control.

5.   **Failure to maintain situational awareness throughout the taxi**

    a.   Accomplish all checklist items from the ramp area or at appropriate times when the aircraft is in a designated area for stopping on the airport, such as a run-up area.

    b.   Program and set all cockpit avionics and instruments before leaving the ramp area to avoid distractions while taxiing and delays when waiting for takeoff.

    c.   Write down ATC taxi instructions and make use of airport diagrams to ensure you are following the correct taxi route.

6.   **Failure to maintain situational awareness throughout ground operations**

    a.   Accomplish all checklist items from the ramp area or at appropriate times when the aircraft is in a designated area for stopping on the airport, such as a run-up area.

    b.   Program and set all cockpit avionics and instruments before leaving the ramp area to avoid distractions while taxiing and delays when waiting for takeoff.

    c.   Write down ATC taxi instructions and make use of airport diagrams to ensure you are following the correct taxi route.

7.   **Failure to follow standard runway incursion avoidance procedures**

    a.   Always acknowledge and read back ATC instructions promptly.

        1)   You do not have to flatly accept all ATC clearances, but you do need to respond quickly to either accept the clearance or request a different clearance.

    b.   Write down all ATC instructions so you can refer to them later if needed.

    c.   Use an airport diagram to ensure you are taxiing along the prescribed taxi route.

    d.   Use aircraft lights appropriately when operating at night.

    e.   Visually confirm that the runway and its approach path are clear before taxiing onto it to cross it or to take off.

END OF COMMON ERRORS

STUDY UNIT TWENTY-TWO
BEFORE TAKEOFF CHECK

Task	Task F. Before Takeoff Check
References	FAA-H-8083-2, FAA-H-8083-3; POH/AFM
Objective	To determine that the applicant exhibits satisfactory knowledge, risk management, and skills associated with the before takeoff check, including the reasons for checking each item, detecting malfunctions, and ensuring the airplane is in safe operating condition as recommended by the manufacturer.
Knowledge	The applicant demonstrates understanding of:
PA.II.F.K1	1. Purpose of the run up.
PA.II.F.K2	2. Aircraft performance given expected conditions.
PA.II.F.K3	3. The purpose of a checklist, to include the reasons for checking each item and how to detect malfunctions.
PA.II.F.K4	4. Wake turbulence avoidance.
PA.II.F.K5	5. An emergency locator transmitter (ELT).
Risk Management	The applicant demonstrates the ability to identify, assess and mitigate risks, encompassing:
PA.II.F.R1	1. Division of attention and scanning.
PA.II.F.R2	2. Different than expected runway.
PA.II.F.R3	3. Failure to properly exchange the flight controls.
PA.II.F.R4	4. Wake turbulence.
PA.II.F.R5	5. Improper automation management.
Skills	The applicant demonstrates the ability to:
PA.II.F.S1	1. Position the airplane properly considering other aircraft, vessels, and wind.
PA.II.F.S2	2. Divide attention between inside and outside the cockpit.
PA.II.F.S3	3. Ensure that powerplant and instrumentation are suitable for run up and takeoff, including temperature(s) and pressure(s).
PA.II.F.S4	4. Accomplish the before takeoff checklist, ensure the airplane is in safe operating condition as recommended by the manufacturer, and provide the departure briefing.
PA.II.F.S5	5. Review takeoff performance, such as airspeeds, takeoff distance, departure, and emergency procedures.
PA.II.F.S6	6. Avoid runway incursions and ensure no conflict with traffic prior to taxiing into takeoff position.

A. General Information

1. The objective of this task is for you to demonstrate your knowledge, risk management, and skills related to the before takeoff check, including the reasons for checking each item, detecting malfunctions, and ensuring the airplane is in safe operating condition as recommended by the manufacturer.

22.1 KNOWLEDGE

A.   Task Objectives

   1.   **The applicant demonstrates understanding of the purpose of the run up.**

   a.   The before takeoff check is the systematic procedure for making a last-minute check of the engine, controls, systems, instruments, and radio prior to flight.

      1)   Normally, it is performed after taxiing to a position near the takeoff end of the runway.

      2)   Taxiing to that position usually allows sufficient time for the engine to warm up to at least minimum operating temperatures and ensures adequate lubrication of the internal moving parts of the engine before operating the engine at high power settings.

   2.   **The applicant demonstrates understanding of aircraft performance given expected conditions.**

   a.   Your POH/AFM will explain the proper operating limitations while you are performing your before takeoff check.

      1)   Any deviation from these normal operating limits means that there is a possible malfunction, and you should return to the ramp to determine the cause.

   3.   **The applicant demonstrates understanding of the purpose of a checklist, including the reasons for checking each item and how to detect malfunctions.**

   a.   For information on using checklists, see Study Unit 6, Subunit 4, beginning on page 54.

   4.   **The applicant demonstrates understanding of wake turbulence avoidance.**

   a.   For information on wake turbulence avoidance, see Study Unit 7, Subunit 7, beginning on page 69.

   5.   **The applicant demonstrates understanding of an emergency locator transmitter (ELT).**

   a.   For information on ELTs, see Section IX Introduction, Knowledge, item D., beginning on page 624.

END OF KNOWLEDGE ELEMENT

22.2 RISK MANAGEMENT

A. Task Objectives

1. **The applicant demonstrates the ability to identify, assess, and mitigate risks encompassing division of attention and scanning.**

    a. Be sure that the activities you are conducting during taxi operations are essential and do not cause any undue distraction for you as the pilot in command.

        1) Head-down time during taxi operations is a very serious distraction that can result in missing a routing assignment, bumping into an airplane, or just getting behind and forgetting something important prior to takeoff/shutdown.

    b. The evaluator will expect to see that you can accomplish all required tasks while filtering out the non-essential tasks, such as unnecessary conversation or cell phone use.

    c. Focus on the task at hand and do not allow yourself to be distracted.

        1) Be aware that the evaluator may try to distract you with questions during taxi. Politely ask the evaluator to standby while you accomplish safe taxi procedures.

    d. Divide your attention inside and outside of the cockpit, especially during the engine run up.

        1) If the parking brake slips, or if the application of the toe brakes is inadequate for the amount of power applied, the airplane could move forward unnoticed if your attention is fixed inside the airplane.

    e. For information on scanning, see Study Unit 7, Subunit 4, item G., on page 67.

2. **The applicant demonstrates the ability to identify, assess, and mitigate risks encompassing use of a different than expected runway.**

    a. If you operate out of one airport regularly, you may become overly pre-programmed to certain departure and arrival procedures.

        1) Be sure that you always listen critically for weather information and ATC instructions. Do not assume anything.

    b. When you operate into unfamiliar airports, be ready for your plan to change, either due to ATC instructions or other aircraft in the area.

3. **The applicant demonstrates the ability to identify, assess, and mitigate risks encompassing failure to properly exchange the flight controls.**

    a. For information on proper exchange of the flight controls, see Study Unit 19, Subunit 2.

4. **The applicant demonstrates the ability to identify, assess, and mitigate risks encompassing wake turbulence.**

    a. For information on wake turbulence, see Study Unit 7, Subunit 7, beginning on page 69.

5. **The applicant demonstrates the ability to identify, assess, and mitigate risks encompassing improper automation management.**

    a. For information on automation management, see Study Unit 6, Subunit 3, beginning on page 51.

END OF RISK MANAGEMENT ELEMENT

22.3 SKILLS

A. Task Objectives

1. **The applicant demonstrates the ability to position the airplane properly considering other aircraft, vessels, and wind.**

    a. As you taxi to the active runway, turn your airplane somewhat diagonal to the runway so you will not prop blast any aircraft behind you.

    b. The FAA recommends that you position your airplane into the wind, as nearly as possible, to obtain more accurate operating indications and to minimize engine overheating when the engine is run up.

    c. You should position your airplane on a firm surface (smooth turf or paved surface) that is free of debris.

        1) Otherwise, the propeller will pick up pebbles, dirt, mud, sand, or other loose particles and hurl them backward, not only damaging the tail of the airplane, but often inflicting damage to the propeller itself.

    d. Straighten your nosewheel before stopping, as your ignition check requires an engine run-up that puts considerable stress on your nosewheel (which is better absorbed with the nosewheel straight).

2. **The applicant demonstrates the ability to divide attention between inside and outside the cockpit.**

    a. Divide your attention inside and outside of the cockpit, especially during engine run up.

        1) If the parking brake slips, or if your application of brake pressure is inadequate for the amount of power applied, the airplane could move forward unnoticed if your attention is fixed inside the airplane.

3. **The applicant demonstrates the ability to ensure that powerplant and instrumentation are suitable for run up and takeoff, including temperature(s) and pressure(s).**

    a. Most of the engine warm-up will have been conducted during taxi.

    b. Any additional warm-up should be restricted to the before takeoff check.

        1) The takeoff can be made when the throttle can be advanced to full power without the engine faltering.

    c. Powerplant and instrumentation temperatures and pressures should be checked to be certain they are within suitable parameters for takeoff by following the appropriate before takeoff checklist and ensuring indications are within the proper limitations.

4. **The applicant demonstrates the ability to accomplish the before takeoff checklist, ensure the airplane is in safe operating condition as recommended by the manufacturer, and provide the departure briefing.**

    a. You, as the pilot in command, are responsible for determining whether your airplane is in condition for safe flight (14 CFR 91.7). Remember that everything on your checklist is very important to ensure that your airplane is safe for flight.

    b. Use the approved checklist from the POH/AFM to perform the before takeoff checks.

    c. Exercise sound judgment in determining that your airplane is safe for flight.

        1) If you have any doubts, explain them to your evaluator and return to the ramp for further investigation.

    d. Perform a departure briefing that is specific for that flight and avoid following a checklist to become routine and create complacency. Make sure you include a plan of action for a powerplant failure during takeoff or initial climb.

        1) Consider the following to include in your takeoff briefing:

            a) Airport info: runway conditions, traffic activities, and airspace complexities.

            b) Identify V speeds: V_Y, V_X, V_R, and best glide should be considered for current conditions prior to takeoff.

      c) Terrain/obstructions: Mountains, powerlines, trees, or towers may become obstructions during emergencies; identify them prior to takeoff.

      d) Abort point: Establish an abort point prior to takeoff. Abort if you haven't achieved 70% takeoff speed by the runway midpoint.

      e) After liftoff: Once the information above is determined, brief your plan for an engine failure during and after takeoff.

5. **The applicant demonstrates the ability to review takeoff performance, such as airspeeds, takeoff distance, departure, and emergency procedures.**

    a. Review the V_R, V_X, V_Y, and other takeoff performance airspeeds for your airplane.

      1) As you reach these airspeeds, plan to call them out loud.

    b. From your preflight planning, you have already determined the expected takeoff distance for the conditions. Review this performance data.

    c. Takeoff emergency procedures are set forth in Section 3, Emergency Procedures, of your POH/AFM. Prepare ahead for all contingencies. Be prepared at all times to execute an emergency landing if you lose an engine. Remember, **maintain airspeed** so you control your situation rather than enter a stall/spin.

      1) The most common emergency on takeoff is the loss of engine power during the takeoff roll or during the takeoff climb.

         a) If engine power is lost during the takeoff roll, pull the throttle to idle, apply the brakes, and slow the airplane to a stop.

         b) If you are just lifting off the runway and you lose your engine power, try to land the airplane on the remaining runway. Leave it in the flare attitude that it is already in. It will settle back down to the ground; i.e., land it like a normal landing.

           i) It is very important not to lower the nose because you do not want to land on the nosewheel.

         c) If engine power is lost any time during the climbout, a general rule is that, if the airplane is above 500 to 1,000 ft. AGL, you may or may not have enough altitude to turn back and land on the runway from which you have just taken off. This decision must be based on distance from airport, wind condition, obstacles, etc.

           i) Many airplanes will lose over 1,000 ft. of altitude during a power-off 180° turn.

           ii) Watch your airspeed! Avoiding a stall is the most important consideration. Remember that the control yoke should be forward (nose down) for more airspeed.

         d) If the airplane is below 500 ft. AGL, do not try to turn back. If do, you will probably either stall or hit the ground before you get back to the runway.

           i) The best thing to do is to land the airplane straight ahead. Land in a clear area, if possible.

           ii) If you have no option but to go into trees, slow the airplane to just above the stall speed (as close to the treetops as possible) to strike the trees with the slowest forward speed possible.

    d. You should review your departure procedure before you depart the run-up area.

      1) Know your initial direction of flight after takeoff.

      2) At a controlled airport, ATC will issue you a clearance on how to depart the traffic pattern.

      3) At an uncontrolled airport, you should depart the traffic pattern by continuing straight out or exiting with a 45° left turn (right turn if the runway has a right-hand traffic pattern) beyond the departure end of the runway, after reaching traffic pattern altitude.

6. **The applicant demonstrates the ability to avoid runway incursions and ensure no conflict with traffic prior to taxiing into takeoff position.**

    a. Prior to taxiing onto the runway, you must make certain that the takeoff area and path are clear of other aircraft, vehicles, persons, livestock, wildlife (including birds), etc.
    b. At controlled airports, this is a function of ATC, but you must also check for conflicts with other aircraft or other hazards.
    c. At uncontrolled airports, you should announce your intentions on the appropriate CTAF, and clear the area by looking in every direction of the runway traffic pattern for other aircraft.

END OF SKILLS ELEMENT

22.4 COMMON ERRORS

A. Common Errors during the Before Takeoff Check

1. **Failure to use, or the improper use of, the checklist**

    a. You must be in the habit of properly using the appropriate checklist.
    b. This ensures that every item is completed and checked in a logical order.

2. **Improper positioning of the airplane**

    a. Position your airplane so you will not prop blast any aircraft behind you.
    b. The FAA recommends that the airplane be positioned into the wind as nearly as possible.
    c. The airplane should be on a surface that is firm and free of debris.

3. **Acceptance of marginal engine performance**

    a. You may feel that you have to complete this flight at this time and thus accept marginal engine performance.

        1) Marginal engine performance is not acceptable and may lead to a hazardous condition.

4. **Improper check of flight controls**

    a. The flight controls should be visually checked for proper positioning and movement.
    b. The control yoke should move freely in the full range of positions.
    c. Call aloud the proper position and visually check it.

5. **Hazards of failure to review takeoff and emergency procedures**

    a. Before taxiing onto the runway, review the critical airspeeds used for takeoff, the takeoff distance required, and takeoff emergency procedures.
    b. You will then be thinking about this review during the takeoff roll. It helps prepare you for any type of emergency that may occur.

6. **Failure to check for hazards and other traffic**

    a. You, the pilot in command, are responsible for collision avoidance.

        1) ATC is not responsible for collision avoidance but works with pilots to maintain separation.
    b. Other airplanes are not the only hazards you must look for. Vehicles, persons, and livestock could be in a hazardous position during the takeoff.

END OF COMMON ERRORS

PART III
SECTION III:
AIRPORT OPERATIONS

Study Units 23 and 24 of Section III explain the two FAA ACS tasks (A-B) of Airport Operations. These tasks include knowledge, risk management, and skill. Your evaluator is required to test you on both tasks.

FAA terminology and conventional aviation terminology are often different. While we do not recommend any use of slang, there are some common terms that may be used interchangeably. Preferences vary among evaluators, so you should rely on your instructor for specific guidance applicable to your local area. In this text, the terms "controlled airport" and "tower-controlled airport" refer to an airport with an operating control tower. "Uncontrolled airport" and "non-towered airport" refer to an airport without an operating control tower.

STUDY UNIT TWENTY-THREE
COMMUNICATIONS AND LIGHT GUN SIGNALS

Task	Task A. Communications and Light Gun Signals
References	14 CFR part 91; FAA-H-8083-2, FAA-H-8083-25; AIM
Objective	To determine that the applicant exhibits satisfactory knowledge, risk management, and skills associated with normal and emergency radio communications and ATC light gun signals to conduct radio communications safely while operating the aircraft.
Knowledge	The applicant demonstrates understanding of:
PA.III.A.K1	1. How to obtain proper radio frequencies.
PA.III.A.K2	2. Communication procedures and ATC phraseology.
PA.III.A.K3	3. ATC light signal recognition.
PA.III.A.K4	4. Transponders.
PA.III.A.K5	5. Radar assistance.
PA.III.A.K6	6. Lost communication procedures.
PA.III.A.K7	7. Use of automated weather and airport information.
Risk Management	The applicant demonstrates the ability to identify, assess and mitigate risks, encompassing:
PA.III.A.R1	1. Human factors associated with communication.
PA.III.A.R2	2. Human factors associated with declaring an emergency.
PA.III.A.R3	3. Equipment issues that could cause loss of communication.
PA.III.A.R4	4. Improper automation management.
PA.III.A.R5	5. Single-pilot resource management (SRM) and/or crew resource management (CRM).
Skills	The applicant demonstrates the ability to:
PA.III.A.S1	1. Select appropriate frequencies.
PA.III.A.S2	2. Transmit using phraseology and procedures as specified in the AIM.
PA.III.A.S3	3. Acknowledge radio communications and comply with instructions.

A.   General Information

1.   The objective of this task is for you to demonstrate your knowledge, risk management, and skills related to normal and emergency radio communications and ATC light signals to conduct radio communications safely while operating the aircraft.

23.1 KNOWLEDGE

A.   Task Objectives

1.   **The applicant demonstrates understanding of how to obtain proper radio frequencies.**

a.   Your preflight planning should include looking up the frequencies of all facilities that you might use and/or need during your flight.

1)   This information can be obtained from a current Chart Supplement, sectional charts, etc.

2)   Write this information on your navigation log, or organize it so you can locate it.

2.   **The applicant demonstrates understanding of communications procedures and ATC phraseology.**

a.   Radio communications are a critical link in the ATC system. The link can be a strong bond between you and the controller, or it can be broken with surprising speed and disastrous results.

1)   The single most important factor in pilot-controller communications is understanding.

a)   Good phraseology enhances safety and is a mark of a professional pilot.

b)   Jargon, chatter, and "CB" slang have no place in ATC communications.

b.   Pilot/Controller Glossary

1)   Using proper radio phraseology and procedures contribute to a pilot's ability to operate safely and efficiently in the airspace system.

2)   A review of the Pilot/Controller Glossary contained in the *Aeronautical Information Manual (AIM)* assists a pilot in the use and understanding of standard terminology.

3)   The *AIM* also contains many examples of radio communications.

c.   **Phonetic Alphabet**

1)   You should use the phonetic alphabet when identifying your airplane during initial contact with air traffic control facilities.

A	.-	Alpha	(AL-FAH)		T	-	Tango	(TANG-GO)
B	-...	Bravo	(BRAH-VOH)		U	..-	Uniform	(YOU-NEE-FORM)
C	-.-.	Charlie	(CHAR-LEE) or (SHAR-LEE)		V	...-	Victor	(VIK-TAH)
D	-..	Delta	(DELL-TAH)		W	.--	Whiskey	(WISS-KEY)
E	.	Echo	(ECK-OH)		X	-..-	Xray	(ECKS-RAY)
F	..-.	Foxtrot	(FOKS-TROT)		Y	-.--	Yankee	(YANG-KEY)
G	--.	Golf	(GOLF)		Z	--..	Zulu	(ZOO-LOO)
H	....	Hotel	(HOH-TEL)					
I	..	India	(IN-DEE-AH)					
J	.---	Juliett	(JEW-LEE-ETT)		1	.----	One	(WUN)
K	-.-	Kilo	(KEY-LOH)		2	..---	Two	(TOO)
L	.-..	Lima	(LEE-MAH)		3	...--	Three	(TREE)
M	--	Mike	(MIKE)		4	....-	Four	(FOW-ER)
N	-.	November	(NO-VEM-BER)		5	.....	Five	(FIFE)
O	---	Oscar	(OSS-CAH)		6	-....	Six	(SIX)
P	.--.	Papa	(PAH-PAH)		7	--...	Seven	(SEV-EN)
Q	--.-	Quebec	(KEH-BECK)		8	---..	Eight	(AIT)
R	.-.	Romeo	(ROW-ME-OH)		9	----.	Nine	(NIN-ER)
S	...	Sierra	(SEE-AIR-RAH)		0	-----	Zero	(ZEE-RO)

2)   Additionally, use the phonetic equivalents for single letters and for spelling out groups of letters or difficult words during adverse communication conditions.

d. **Figures**

1) Figures indicating hundreds and thousands in round numbers up to 9,900, such as for ceiling heights and upper wind levels, are spoken in accordance with the following:

     a) EXAMPLES: 500 is "FIVE HUNDRED"
               4,500 is "FOUR THOUSAND FIVE HUNDRED"

2) Numbers above 9,900 are spoken by separating the digits preceding the word "thousand."

     a) EXAMPLES: 10,000 is "ONE ZERO THOUSAND"
               13,500 is "ONE THREE THOUSAND FIVE HUNDRED"

3) When a radio frequency contains a decimal point, the decimal point is spoken as "POINT."

     a) EXAMPLE: 122.1 is "ONE TWO TWO POINT ONE"

e. **Altitudes and Flight Levels**

1) Up to but not including 18,000 ft. MSL, state the separate digits of the thousands, plus the hundreds, if appropriate.

     a) EXAMPLES: 12,000 is "ONE TWO THOUSAND"
               12,500 is "ONE TWO THOUSAND FIVE HUNDRED"

f. **Directions.** The three digits of bearing, course, heading, and wind direction should always be magnetic. The word "TRUE" must be added when it applies.

1) EXAMPLES:

     a) (Magnetic course) 005 is "ZERO ZERO FIVE"
     b) (True course) 050 is "ZERO FIVE ZERO TRUE"
     c) (Magnetic bearing) 360 is "THREE SIX ZERO"
     d) (Magnetic heading) 100 is "ONE ZERO ZERO"
     e) (Wind direction) 220 is "TWO TWO ZERO"

g. In virtually all situations, your radio broadcasts can be thought of as

1) To whom you are talking
2) Who you are
3) Where you are
4) What you want to do
5) To whom you are talking (when making common traffic advisories in uncontrolled airport areas)

3. **The applicant demonstrates understanding of ATC light signal recognition.**

   a. ATC light signals are used to communicate with aircraft that have no radios or have experienced radio communication equipment failure at an airport with an operating control tower.

   1) ATC light signals have the meaning shown in the following table:

LIGHT GUN SIGNALS			
COLOR AND TYPE OF SIGNAL	**MOVEMENT OF VEHICLES, EQUIPMENT, AND PERSONNEL**	**AIRCRAFT ON THE GROUND**	**AIRCRAFT IN FLIGHT**
STEADY GREEN	Cleared to cross, proceed, or go	Cleared for takeoff	Cleared to land
FLASHING GREEN	Not applicable	Cleared for taxi	Return for landing (to be followed by steady green at the proper time)
STEADY RED	STOP	STOP	Give way to other aircraft and continue circling
FLASHING RED	Clear the taxiway/runway	Taxi clear of the runway in use	Airport unsafe, do not land
FLASHING WHITE	Return to starting point on airport	Return to starting point on airport	Not applicable
ALTERNATING RED AND GREEN	Exercise Extreme Caution!!!!	Exercise Extreme Caution!!!!	Exercise Extreme Caution!!!!

4. **The applicant demonstrates understanding of transponders.**

   a. The transponder is an airborne radar beacon transmitter receiver. It automatically receives signals from ground radar stations and replies with your airplane's altitude and the transponder code. This helps ATC understand the airplane's position and altitude.

   b. Since most airplanes you will fly will be equipped with a transponder, you should understand the proper operating procedures.

   1) Transponders have five operating modes.

      a) OFF -- turns the transponder off.

      b) STY or SBY (standby) -- turns the transponder on for equipment warm-up. The transponder does not reply to interrogations in this position.

      c) ON -- turns the transponder on and allows the transponder to reply to Mode A (no altitude reporting) interrogations.

      d) ALT -- turns the transponder on and allows the transponder to transmit either Mode A or Mode C (altitude reporting) replies as requested by the interrogating signal.

      e) TEST -- checks operation of the transponder.

   2) The reply/monitor light flashes to indicate when the transponder is replying to interrogations.

   3) The IDENT (ID) switch, when depressed, sends a signal that allows the controller to confirm an aircraft identity or to identify an aircraft.

      a) The IDENT signal should be used only at the request of a controller.

   4) Code selector knobs (four) allow you to set the proper four-digit transponder code.

c.   **Mode C (Automatic Altitude Reporting)**

1)   This system converts your airplane's altitude to coded digital information, which is transmitted to the radar facility.

2)   If your airplane is Mode C-equipped, you must set your transponder to reply Mode C (i.e., set function switch to ALT) unless ATC requests otherwise.

a)   If ATC requests that you "STOP ALTITUDE SQUAWK," you should set the function switch from ALT to ON.

d.   You can learn more about transponders in *Pilot Handbook*, Study Unit 3, Subunit 22.

5.   **The applicant demonstrates understanding of radar assistance.**

a.   ATC radar facilities provide a variety of services to participating VFR aircraft on a workload-permitting basis.

1)   To participate, you must be able to communicate with ATC, be within radar coverage, and be radar identified by the controller.

2)   Among the services provided are

a)   VFR radar traffic advisory service (commonly known as flight following)
b)   Terminal radar programs
c)   Radar assistance to lost aircraft

b.   **VFR Flight Following**

1)   To obtain flight following, you should contact ATC on the appropriate frequency after leaving the traffic area of your departure airport.

a)   Use the departure frequency listed for the airport in the Chart Supplement.

b)   Inform ATC that you are requesting VFR flight following, and announce your departure point and destination.

c)   The controller will assign you a transponder code and ask your aircraft type and cruising altitude.

2)   When you are using flight following, ATC will advise you of any traffic that may be in a position to warrant your attention.

c.   **Terminal Radar Programs**

1)   Terminal radar programs for VFR aircraft are classified as basic, TRSA, Class C, and Class B service.

a)   Basic radar service provides safety alerts, traffic advisories, and limiting vectoring on a workload-permitting basis.

b)   TRSA service provides sequencing and separation for all participating VFR aircraft operating within a Terminal Radar Service Area (TRSA).

2)   When arriving, you should contact approach control on the published frequency and state your position, altitude, and destination, and indicate that you have received the ATIS (if available).

a)   The proper frequency may be found on the sectional chart or in the Chart Supplement.

b)   Approach control will specify when to contact the tower.

3)   When departing, you should inform ground control or clearance delivery of your destination and/or route of flight and proposed cruising altitude.

a)   ATC will normally advise participating VFR aircraft when leaving the geographical limits of the controller's radar. Radar service is not terminated unless specifically stated by the controller.

    d.   If you are unable to establish communications with an ATC facility, you may need to utilize the emergency frequency 121.5 MHz before the situation worsens. This frequency is monitored by all ATC facilities.

    e.   You must clearly understand that these programs in no way relieve you of your primary responsibility of flying the airplane legally and safely.

        1)   It is still your task to

            a)   See and avoid other traffic

            b)   Adjust your operations and flight path as necessary to avoid wake turbulence

            c)   Maintain appropriate terrain and obstruction clearance

            d)   Maintain basic VFR visibility and distance from clouds

        2)   If ATC assigns a route, heading, and/or altitude that will make you compromise your responsibilities in the above areas, you must contact the controller to advise him or her and obtain a revised clearance or instructions.

    f.   For information on radar assistance available to lost aircraft, see Study Unit 38, Subunit 1, item A.2.

    g.   You can learn more about radar services to VFR aircraft in *Pilot Handbook*, Study Unit 3, Subunit 23.

6.   The applicant demonstrates understanding of lost communication procedures.

    a.   Lost Communication Procedures at Tower Controlled Airports

        1)   Arriving Aircraft

            a)   If you receive no response to your transmission inbound, you may have radio failure.

            b)   If you are receiving tower transmissions but none are directed toward you, you should suspect a transmitter failure.

                i)   Determine the direction and flow of traffic, enter the traffic pattern, and look for light signals. Change your transponder code to 7600.

                ii)   During daylight, acknowledge tower transmissions or light signals by rocking your wings. At night, acknowledge by blinking the landing or navigation lights.

                iii)   After landing, telephone the tower to advise them of the situation.

            c)   If you are receiving no transmissions on tower or ATIS frequency, suspect a receiver failure.

                i)   Transmit to the tower in the blind your position, situation, and intention to land.

                ii)   Determine the flow of traffic, enter the pattern, and wait for light signals.

                iii)   Acknowledge signals as described above and by transmitting in the blind.

                iv)   After landing, telephone the tower to advise them of the situation.

2) Departing Aircraft

    a) If you experience radio failure prior to leaving the parking area, make every effort to have the equipment repaired.

    b) If you are unable to have the malfunction repaired, call the tower by telephone and request authorization to depart without two-way radio communications.

        i) If tower authorization is granted, you will be given departure information and requested to monitor the tower frequency or watch for light signals, as appropriate.

        ii) During daylight, acknowledge tower transmissions or light signals by promptly executing action authorized by light signals.

            • When in the air, rock your wings.

        iii) At night, acknowledge by blinking the landing or navigation lights.

    c) If your radio malfunctions after departing the parking area (ramp), watch the tower for light signals or monitor the appropriate (ground or tower) frequency. However, you should return to the ramp.

b. At a non-towered airport, use extra caution since you may not be able to self-announce your position.

    1) Maintain additional vigilance in and approaching the traffic pattern.

    2) Continue to announce your position since your transmitter may still be operational.

        a) Use the phrase "In the blind" with your transmissions to advise others that your receiver may be inoperative.

7. **The applicant demonstrates understanding of the use of automated weather and airport information.**

a. **Automated weather reporting systems** are increasingly being installed at airports. These systems consist of various sensors, a processor, a computer-generated voice subsystem, and a transmitter to broadcast local, minute-by-minute weather data directly to the pilot.

    1) Automated surface observation systems can provide pilots with weather information over discrete VHF frequencies or over the voice portion of a local NAVAID.

    2) These systems provide information that can be used by flight crews to make approach decisions, and by the National Weather Service to generate aviation routine weather reports (METARs).

b. Two common types of automated systems are used throughout the country:

    1) **Automated Weather Observing System (AWOS)**

        a) Transmits on a discrete VHF radio frequency.

        b) Transmits a 20 to 30 second weather message updated each minute.

            i) Pilots monitor the designated frequency for the automated weather broadcast.

            ii) There is no two-way communication capability.

      2) **Automated Surface Observing System (ASOS)/Automated Weather Sensor System (AWSS)**

         a) Primary surface weather observing system of the U.S.

           i) AWSS is a follow-on program that provides identical data as ASOS.

           ii) ASOS/AWSS is more sensitive and provides more information than AWOS.

         b) Designed to support aviation operations and weather forecast activities.

           i) ASOS/AWSS will provide continuous minute-by-minute observations and perform the basic observing functions necessary to generate a METAR and other aviation weather information.

         c) Transmitted and received by the pilot in exactly the same way as AWOS.

8. **Automatic Terminal Information Service (ATIS)**

    a. If available, the ATIS frequency is listed on the sectional chart just under the tower control frequency for the airport, e.g., ATIS 125.05. ATIS provides a continuous transmission that provides information for arriving and departing aircraft, including

      1) Time of the latest weather report
      2) Sky conditions, visibility, and obstructions to visibility
      3) Temperature and dewpoint (degrees Celsius)
      4) Wind direction (magnetic) and velocity
      5) Altimeter
      6) Other pertinent remarks, instrument approach, and runway in use

    b. The purpose of ATIS is to relieve the ground controllers' and approach controllers' workload. They need not repeat the same information.

    c. The ATIS broadcast is updated whenever any official weather is received, regardless of content or changes, or when a change is made in other pertinent data, such as a runway change. Each new broadcast is labeled with a letter of the alphabet at the beginning of the broadcast; e.g., "This is information alpha" or "information bravo."

    a. Every aircraft arriving at or departing from an airport with ATIS should monitor ATIS to receive that airport's weather information before contacting approach, tower, clearance delivery, or ground control.

END OF KNOWLEDGE ELEMENT

23.2 RISK MANAGEMENT

A.   Task Objectives

1.   **The applicant demonstrates the ability to identify, assess, and mitigate risks encompassing human factors associated with communication.**

   a.   For information on human factors associated with communication and expectation bias, see Study Unit 7, Subunit 5, on page 68.

2.   **The applicant demonstrates the ability to identify, assess, and mitigate risks encompassing human factors associated with declaring an emergency.**

   a.   The pilot in command (PIC) is responsible for crew, passengers, and operation of the aircraft at all times. 14 CFR 91.3 allows deviations from regulations during emergencies, which allows the PIC to make the best decision to ensure safety of all personnel during these contingencies.

   b.   An emergency can be either a distress or urgency condition as defined in the the FAA's Pilot/Controller Glossary. Pilots should not hesitate to declare an emergency when faced with distress conditions, such as fire, mechanical failure, or structural damage.

      1)   Based on post-incident interviews with pilots, there is hesitation from some pilots to declare an emergency with ATC when needed. Pilots fear facing the FAA and having to account for the actions that led to the emergency situation. There may also be a general fear of the paperwork required after declaring an emergency.

      2)   Some pilots may be reluctant to report an urgency condition when encountering situations that may not be immediately perilous but are potentially catastrophic.

   c.   Pilots who become apprehensive for their safety for any reason should request assistance immediately. Air traffic controllers and FSS are the best external resources during flight. Assistance is available in the form of radio, radar, direction finding (DF) stations, and other aircraft.

      1)   The services provided by ATC cannot only decrease pilot workload, but also help pilots make informed inflight decisions.

   d.   If your airplane is experiencing an emergency such as loss of power, if you become doubtful about any condition that could adversely affect flight safety, or if you become apprehensive about your safety for any reason, use the emergency frequency, which is 121.5 MHz.

   e.   If an emergency does occur, be calm. Think for a moment, weigh the alternatives, and then act.

3.   **The applicant demonstrates the ability to identify, assess, and mitigate risks encompassing equipment issues that could cause loss of communication.**

   a.   Preventing aircraft system malfunctions that might lead to an in-flight emergency begins with a thorough preflight inspection.

   b.   The loss of electrical power can deprive the pilot of numerous critical systems, including radios and other communication devices.

      1)   If a generator failure is detected, the pilot must reduce electrical load on the battery and land as soon as practical.

      2)   The pilot can attempt to troubleshoot generator failure by following established procedures published in the appropriate POH/AFM.

c.   Incorrect operation of the avionics and audio panel can also lead to loss of communication. For example,

1)   Setting the incorrect ATC frequency
2)   Not turning the volume up to a sufficient level
3)   Incorrect radio selection on the audio panel
4)   Headset jacks not completely plugged in
5)   Faulty push to talk switch

4.   **The applicant demonstrates the ability to identify, assess, and mitigate risks encompassing improper automation management.**

a.   For information on automation management, see Study Unit 6, Subunit 3, beginning on page 51.

5.   **The applicant demonstrates the ability to identify, assess, and mitigate risks encompassing single pilot resource management (SRM) and/or crew resource management (CRM).**

a.   **SRM** is defined as the art of managing all the resources (both onboard the aircraft and from outside sources) available to a single pilot prior to and during flight to ensure a successful flight.

1)   The following six items are areas of SRM:

a)   Aeronautical decision making (ADM)
b)   Risk management
c)   Task management
d)   Situational awareness
e)   Controlled flight into terrain (CFIT) awareness
f)   Automation management

b.   A single pilot does not have the advantages of the oversight of a crew. Therefore, a single pilot must be more alert to cancel out any personal bias or skewed judgment during preflight planning and the discussion of weather parameters. If the single pilot does not comprehend or perceive the risk, (s)he will make no attempt to mitigate it.

c.   To make informed decisions during flight operations, a pilot must also become aware of the resources found inside and outside the flight deck.

1)   One of the most underutilized resources may be the person in the right seat, even if the passenger has no flying experience. Passengers can assist by

a)   Watching for traffic or reading checklist items.
b)   Providing information in an irregular situation, especially if familiar with flying. A strange smell or sound may alert passengers to a potential problem.
c)   Confirming after the pilot that the landing gear is down.
d)   Learning to look at the altimeter for a given altitude in a descent.
e)   Listening to logic or lack of logic.

2)   ATC and FSSs are the best external resources during flight.

a)   The assistance of ATC may be very useful if a pilot becomes lost, but in an emergency situation, there may be no time to contact ATC.

3)   An internal resource is verbal communication. It has been established that verbal communication reinforces an activity; touching an object further enhances the probability an activity has been accomplished.

4)   Checklists are essential flight deck internal resources.

5)   The ability to manage workload is the most valuable resource a pilot has.

d. SRM sounds good on paper, but it requires a way for pilots to understand and use it in their daily flights. One practical application is the 5P model, which looks at five key elements in the SRM process: Plan, Plane, Pilot, Passengers, and Programming.

    1) Each of these areas consists of a set of challenges and opportunities that face a single pilot.

    2) For detailed information on the 5P model, see Study Unit 5, Subunit 2.

e. SRM is a set of skill competencies that must be evident in all tasks in the ACS, as applied to single-pilot operations.

f. **CRM** refers to making use of all available resources to safely conduct a flight.

    1) Anyone you can communicate with is a potential resource, including passengers, ATC, and Flight Service Stations.

    2) Non-human resources include any sources of information to aid in situational awareness and monitoring environmental conditions.

        a) Examples include displays, charts, checklists, POH/AFM, weather datalink, radar, and ADS-B In.

END OF RISK MANAGEMENT ELEMENT

23.3 SKILLS

A. Task Objectives

1. **The applicant demonstrates the ability to select appropriate frequencies.**

    a. You should always continue to work to make your radio technique as professional as possible. Selecting the appropriate frequency is obviously essential.

    b. Your preflight planning should include looking up the frequencies of all facilities that you might use and/or need during your flight.

        1) This information can be obtained from a current Chart Supplement, sectional charts, etc.

        2) Write this information on your navigation log, or organize it so you can locate it easily in the cockpit.

    c. You may still have to look up frequencies while you are flying.

    d. Always plan ahead as to frequencies needed.

        1) Listen to hand-offs by your controller to airplanes ahead of you.
        2) Look up frequencies before you need them.

    e. Use the standby frequency window in your radio, if equipped, for selecting your next needed frequency.

2. **The applicant demonstrates the ability to transmit using phraseology and procedures as specified in the *AIM*.**

    a. Radio communications is a very important task of flying, especially when you are working with ATC. The single most important concept in radio communication is understanding.

        1) Using standard phraseology enhances safety and is a mark of professionalism in a pilot.

            a) Jargon, chatter, and "CB" slang has no place in aviation radio communications.

    b. In virtually all situations, radio broadcasts can be thought of as

        1) Whom you are calling
        2) Who you are
        3) Where you are
        4) What you want to do

    c. Refer to Study Unit 3, "Airports, Air Traffic Control, and Airspace," in *Pilot Handbook* for specific phraseology recommendations.

3. **The applicant demonstrates the ability to acknowledge radio communications and comply with instructions.**

    a. Make sure your radios, speakers, and/or headset are in good working order so you can plainly hear radio communications. Acknowledge all ATC clearances by repeating key points, e.g., "Taxi to (or across) Runway 10," "Line up and wait," "Clear for takeoff Runway 24," "Hold short," or "Left downwind 6," followed by your call sign.

        1) Always repeat altitudes and headings.

        2) Do not hesitate with "Say again" if your clearance was blocked or you did not hear or understand it.

        3) As appropriate, ask for amplification or clarification; e.g., ask for **progressives** if you need taxi instructions.

    b.   14 CFR 91.123 states that once you, as pilot in command, obtain a clearance from ATC, you may not deviate from that clearance except in an emergency.

           1)   You have the responsibility for the safe operation of your airplane.

           2)   If you cannot accept a clearance from ATC (e.g., flying into clouds), inform ATC using the proper phraseology, "UNABLE," and state the reason you cannot accept and obtain a new clearance.

    c.   14 CFR 91.3 states that you, the pilot in command, are directly responsible for, and the final authority as to, the operation of your airplane.

           1)   As a safe and competent pilot, you should obtain clarification on any clearance that you do not understand or that you feel would put you in a bad situation.

END OF SKILLS ELEMENT

23.4 COMMON ERRORS

A.   Common Errors with Communications and Light Gun Signals

1.   **Use of improper frequencies**

   a.   This is caused by inadequate planning, misreading the frequency on the chart or flight log, or mistuning the frequency on the radio.

   b.   Double-check and read aloud the frequency numbers that are to be set in the radio.

      1)   Monitor the frequency before transmitting. Often you can confirm the correct frequency by listening to other transmissions.

2.   **Improper procedure and phraseology when using radio voice communications**

   a.   Think about what you are going to say before you transmit.

   b.   Be sensitive to the controller's workload, and tailor your broadcasts to match. Often pilots are taught correct phraseology only and never taught how to abbreviate transmissions on busy ATC frequencies.

3.   **Failure to acknowledge or properly comply with ATC clearances and other instructions**

   a.   This normally occurs because you did not hear or understand the message.

   b.   Developing your ability to divide your attention properly will help you not to miss ATC messages.

   c.   Ask ATC to repeat its message or ask for clarification. Do not assume what ATC meant or instructed.

4.   **Failure to understand or comply properly with ATC light signals**

   a.   Periodically review the different light gun signals and their meanings.

   b.   If you operate where you can ask ground control to direct some practice light signals toward you, this will help you learn them.

   c.   Reviewing and practicing (if possible) will help you understand and comply with ATC light signals.

END OF COMMON ERRORS

STUDY UNIT TWENTY-FOUR
TRAFFIC PATTERNS

Task	Task B. Traffic Patterns
References	14 CFR part 91; FAA-H-8083-2, FAA-H-8083-25; AIM
Objective	To determine that the applicant exhibits satisfactory knowledge, risk management, and skills associated with traffic patterns.
Knowledge	The applicant demonstrates understanding of:
PA.III.B.K1	1. Towered and non-towered airport operations and runway selection.
PA.III.B.K2	2. Airport signs and markings, lighting, and wind indicators.
PA.III.B.K3	3. Collision avoidance, scanning, obstacle and wire strike avoidance.
PA.III.B.K4	4. Right-of-way rules.
PA.III.B.K5	5. Wake turbulence recognition and resolution.
PA.III.B.K6	6. Wind shear avoidance.
PA.III.B.K7	7. Runway incursion avoidance.
PA.III.B.K8	8. Use of automated weather and airport information.
PA.III.B.K9	9. Use of radio for proper communications.
PA.III.B.K10	10. Parachuting operations.
PA.III.B.K11	11. Approach and landing considerations for different types of aircraft.
Risk Management	The applicant demonstrates the ability to identify, assess and mitigate risks, encompassing:
PA.III.B.R1	1. Collision avoidance, scanning, obstacle and wire strike avoidance.
PA.III.B.R2	2. Wake turbulence.
PA.III.B.R3	3. Failure to maintain situational awareness.
PA.III.B.R4	4. Failure to maintain separation from other aircraft.
PA.III.B.R5	5. Operating considerations of various aircraft types.
PA.III.B.R6	6. Go-around or rejected takeoff, if appropriate.
Skills	The applicant demonstrates the ability to:
PA.III.B.S1	1. Properly identify and interpret airport runways, taxiways, markings, and lighting.
PA.III.B.S2	2. Comply with proper traffic pattern procedures.
PA.III.B.S3	3. Maintain proper spacing from other aircraft.
PA.III.B.S4	4. Correct for wind drift to maintain the proper ground track.
PA.III.B.S5	5. Maintain orientation with the runway/landing area in use.
PA.III.B.S6	6. Maintain traffic pattern altitude, ±100 feet, and the appropriate airspeed, ±10 knots.
PA.III.B.S7	7. Maintain an awareness of the position of other aircraft in the pattern.

A. General Information

1. The objective of this task is for you to demonstrate your knowledge, skills, and risk management related to traffic patterns.

2. See Study Unit 3, "Airports, Air Traffic Control, and Airspace," in *Pilot Handbook* for a discussion of airport traffic patterns, wake turbulence, and collision avoidance.

3. Safety first! Commit to it and practice it. Always look for traffic and talk about it (even when you are solo). Ask your evaluator to watch for traffic.

4. Some of the content of Subunits 24.1 and 24.2 is abbreviated based on the assumption that you will thoroughly read and understand pages 287 through 304 and the additional common task topics found in Part II. The task objectives and specific references are provided here for your convenience.

24.1 KNOWLEDGE

A. Task Objectives

1. **The applicant demonstrates understanding of towered and non-towered airport operations and runway selection.**

    a. Established airport traffic patterns assure that air traffic flows into and out of an airport in an orderly manner. Airport traffic patterns establish

    1) The direction and placement of the pattern

        a) At airports without an operating control tower, left traffic is required unless otherwise indicated by the traffic pattern indicators in the segmented circle.

            i)   The Chart Supplement will indicate right traffic when applicable.

        b) At airports with an operating control tower, the direction of the traffic pattern will be specified by ATC.

    2) The altitude at which the pattern is to be flown

        a) The normal traffic pattern altitude for small airplanes is 1,000 ft. AGL unless otherwise specified in the Chart Supplement.

    3) The procedures for entering and departing the pattern

        a) At airports without an operating control tower, the FAA recommends entering the pattern at a 45° angle abeam the midpoint of the runway on the downwind leg.

            i)   When departing the traffic pattern, continue straight out or exit with a 45° left turn (right turn for right traffic pattern) beyond the departure end of the runway after reaching pattern altitude.

        b) At airports with an operating control tower, ATC will specify pattern entry and departure procedures.

    b. Pilots should consult the Chart Supplement and NOTAMs for runway closures, preferred runways, and noise abatement procedures.

    c. Because all landings and takeoffs should be performed into the wind, the pilot should first determine wind direction.

    1) For information on wind direction indicators, see Study Unit 9, Subunit 2, beginning on page 78.

    d. Some airports have a landing direction indicator (tetrahedron or landing tee) that is manually set by the airport operator to show the direction of landings and takeoffs.

    e. The segmented circle system, if installed, provides traffic pattern information at airports without operating control towers. It consists of the following:

    1) The **segmented circle** is located in a position affording maximum visibility to pilots in the air and on the ground. A wind and/or landing direction indicator is usually in the center.

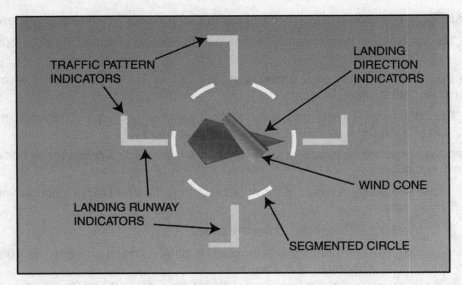

2) **Landing runway (strip) indicators** are installed in pairs as shown in the segmented circle above and are used to show the alignment of runways.

3) **Traffic pattern indicators** are arranged in pairs with the landing runway indicators and are used to indicate the direction of turns when there is a variation from the normal left traffic pattern.

   a) If the airport has no segmented circle, traffic pattern indicators may be installed on or near the runway ends.

4) EXAMPLE: In the figure above, the wind is blowing from the bottom right of the box, and the airport operator has adjusted the tetrahedron to show the horizontal runway to be in use, with landings and departures to the right of the box.

   a) The traffic pattern indicators show the left traffic pattern is to be used on this runway.

2. **The applicant demonstrates understanding of airport signs and markings, lighting, and wind indicators.**

   a. See Study Unit 3, "Airports, Air Traffic Control, and Airspace," in *Pilot Handbook* for a discussion on airport signs, markings, and lighting.

   b. For information on wind indicators, see Study Unit 9, Subunit 2, beginning on page 78.

3. **The applicant demonstrates understanding of collision avoidance, scanning, and obstacle and wire strike avoidance.**

   a. For information on collision avoidance, scanning, and obstacle avoidance, see Study Unit 7, Subunit 4, beginning on page 66.

   b. For information on wire strikes, see Study Unit 7, Subunit 6, beginning on page 68.

4. **The applicant demonstrates understanding of right-of-way rules.**

   a. For information on right-of-way rules, see Section IV Introduction, Risk Management, item F., beginning on page 300.

5. **The applicant demonstrates understanding of wake turbulence.**

   a. For information on wake turbulence, see Study Unit 7, Subunit 7, beginning on page 69.

6. **The applicant demonstrates understanding of wind shear avoidance.**

   a. For information on wind shear avoidance, see Study Unit 9, Subunit 4, beginning on page 81.

7. **The applicant demonstrates understanding of runway incursion avoidance.**

    a. For information on runway incursion avoidance, see Study Unit 7, Subunit 2, beginning on page 61.

8. **The applicant demonstrates understanding of the use of automated weather and airport information.**

    a. For information on the use of automated weather and airport information, see Study Unit 23, Subunit 1, item A.7., beginning on page 271.

9. **The applicant demonstrates understanding of the use of radio for proper communications.**

    a. Some key points to remember about use of radio and proper communications in the traffic pattern are

        1) Airports with operating control tower

            a) Repeat back the "numbers" in all ATC transmissions, i.e. runways, headings, and altitudes.

            b) Understand and use proper phraseology. For example, know the difference between "Roger" and "Wilco."

        2) Airports without operating control tower

            a) Listening is more important than talking. Take time to listen for traffic calls before broadcasting. You can learn a lot about the traffic, winds, etc., by listening first.

            b) When the pattern is busy with aircraft, do not clutter the frequency with unnecessary calls.

        3) See Study Unit 3, "Airports, Air Traffic Control, and Airspace" in *Pilot Handbook* for a detailed discussion on radio phraseology and communications at airports with and without an operating control tower.

10. **The applicant demonstrates understanding of parachuting operations.**

    a. Pilots can learn about parachuting activity by checking NOTAMs, Chart Supplements, and sectional charts.

    b. Maintain a listening watch CTAF/UNICOM.

    c. It is the responsibility of everyone to watch for and avoid each other.

        1) Because skydivers free fall at a speed of 120 mph or more, they are extremely difficult to spot from other aircraft.

    d. Unless you are flying into, or out of, an airport where skydiving is taking place, it is best to avoid overflying such an airport by at least 2 mi.

11. **The applicant demonstrates understanding of approach and landing considerations for different types of aircraft.**

    a. The normal traffic pattern for small aircraft is 1,000 ft. AGL.

    b. Faster and larger aircraft typically fly a wider and higher pattern than slower aircraft and in many cases will make a straight-in approach for landing.

    c. Faster and larger aircraft have longer landing distances, and aircraft arriving behind them should allow more time for them to exit the runway.

END OF KNOWLEDGE ELEMENT

24.2 RISK MANAGEMENT

A.   Task Objectives

1.   **The applicant demonstrates the ability to identify, assess, and mitigate risks encompassing collision avoidance, scanning, and obstacle and wire strike avoidance.**

   a.   For information on collision avoidance, scanning, and obstacle avoidance, see Study Unit 7, Subunit 4, beginning on page 66.

   b.   For information on wire strikes, see Study Unit 7, Subunit 6, beginning on page 68.

2.   **The applicant demonstrates the ability to identify, assess, and mitigate risks encompassing wake turbulence.**

   a.   For information on wake turbulence, see Study Unit 7, Subunit 7, beginning on page 69.

3.   **The applicant demonstrates the ability to identify, assess, and mitigate risks encompassing failure to maintain situational awareness.**

   a.   For information on situational awareness, see Study Unit 7.

4.   **The applicant demonstrates the ability to identify, assess, and mitigate risks encompassing failure to maintain separation from other aircraft.**

   a.   In Class B, C, and TRSA airspace, you must remain vigilante of other aircraft even when ATC is providing aircraft separation services.

   b.   Proper aircraft separation is critical in wake turbulence avoidance.

   c.   Runway incursions can also compromise aircraft separation.

   d.   Make sure to display the correct altimeter setting is set in the altimeter.

   e.   The "See and Avoid" concept should always be used.

5.   **The applicant demonstrates the ability to identify, assess, and mitigate risks encompassing operating considerations of various aircraft types.**

   a.   The normal traffic pattern for small aircraft is 1,000 ft. AGL.

   b.   Faster and larger aircraft typically fly a wider and higher pattern than slower aircraft and in many cases will make a straight in approach for landing.

   c.   Faster and larger aircraft have longer landing distances and aircraft arriving behind them should allow more time for them to exit the runway.

6.   **The applicant demonstrates the ability to identify, assess, and mitigate risks encompassing go-around or rejected takeoff, if appropriate.**

   a.   For information on go-around and rejected takeoff, see Section IV Introduction, Risk Management, items E. and G., beginning on page 300.

END OF RISK MANAGEMENT ELEMENT

24.3 SKILLS

A.   Task Objectives

1.   **The applicant demonstrates the ability to properly identify and interpret airport runways, taxiways, markings, and lighting.**

   a.   For more information on airport runways, taxiways, markings, and lighting, see Study Unit 3, "Airports, Air Traffic Control, and Airspace," in *Pilot Handbook*.

2.   **The applicant demonstrates the ability to comply with proper traffic pattern procedures.**

   a.   Skills learned in flying a rectangular course are used in flying a correct traffic pattern. Key points include

   1)   Entering the pattern

   a)   At airports without an operating control tower, the FAA recommends entering the pattern at a 45° angle abeam the midpoint of the runway on the downwind leg.

   2)   Exiting the pattern

   a)   Know your initial direction of flight after takeoff.

   b)   At a controlled airport, ATC will issue you a clearance on how to depart the traffic pattern.

   c)   At an uncontrolled airport, you should depart the traffic pattern by continuing straight out or exiting with a 45° left turn (right turn if the runway has a right-hand traffic pattern) beyond the departure end of the runway after reaching traffic pattern altitude.

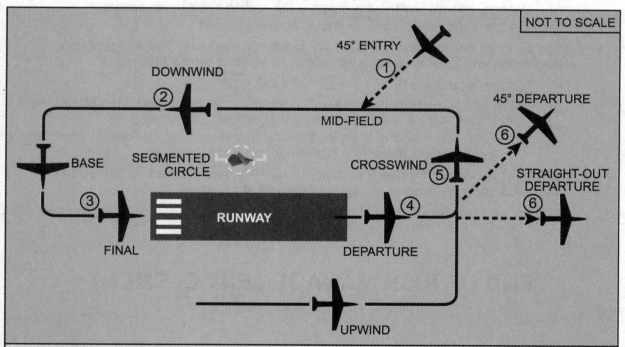

Key:
1. Enter pattern in level flight, abeam the midpoint of the runway, at pattern altitude.
2. Maintain pattern altitude until abeam approach end of the landing runway on the downwind leg.
3. Complete turn to final at least 1/4 mi. from the runway.
4. Continue straight ahead until beyond departure end of runway.
5. If remaining in the traffic pattern, commence turn to crosswind leg beyond the departure end of the runway, within 300 ft. of pattern altitude.
6. If departing the traffic pattern, continue straight out, or exit with a 45° left turn (right turn for right traffic pattern) beyond the departure end of the runway, after reaching pattern altitude.

    b.   At airports with operating control towers, ATC will specify pattern entry and departure procedures.

    c.   There is a basic rectangular airport traffic pattern that you should use unless modified by ATC or by approved visual markings at the airport. Thus, all you need to know is

        1)   The basic rectangular traffic pattern

        2)   Visual markings and typical ATC clearances that modify the basic rectangular pattern

        3)   Reasons for modifying the basic pattern

3.   **The applicant demonstrates the ability to maintain proper spacing from other aircraft.**

    a.   As you fly in the traffic pattern, you must observe other traffic and maintain separation, especially when smaller airplanes may have relatively slower approach speeds than your airplane.

        1)   Faster aircraft typically fly a wider pattern than slower aircraft.

    b.   At an airport with an operating control tower, the controller may instruct you to adjust your traffic pattern to provide separation.

    c.   Remember, whether you are at an airport with or without an operating control tower, you are responsible for seeing and avoiding other aircraft.

4.   **The applicant demonstrates the ability to correct for wind drift to maintain the proper ground track.**

    a.   For information on correcting for wind drift to maintain the proper ground track, see Study Unit 34, Subunit 1, item A.5., beginning on page 454.

5.   **The applicant demonstrates the ability to maintain orientation with the runway/landing area in use.**

    a.   While conducting airport traffic pattern operations, you must remain oriented with the runway in use.

    b.   Know which runway is in use, plan to enter properly, and remain in the correct traffic pattern.

    c.   When approaching an airport, visualize your position from the airport and the relative direction of the runway. Use the airplane's heading indicator to assist you.

6.   **The applicant demonstrates the ability to maintain traffic pattern altitude, ±100 feet, and the appropriate airspeed, ±10 knots.**

    a.   You must maintain the traffic pattern altitude until you are abeam the touchdown point on the downwind leg.

    b.   Maintain the proper airspeed for the portion of the traffic pattern prescribed in your POH/AFM.

        1)   If ATC requests that you maintain a specified airspeed, and you determine it is safe for your operation, then maintain that airspeed.

7.   **The applicant demonstrates the ability to maintain an awareness of the position of other aircraft in the pattern.**

    a.   Remember the "See and Avoid" concept.

        1)   Keep your head on a swivel.

        2)   Do not become fixated on something inside the airplane to the detriment of seeing aircraft outside the aircraft.

    b.   Monitor the tower frequency or CTAF and make a mental picture of where other aircraft are located based on their transmissions.

END OF SKILLS ELEMENT

24.4 COMMON ERRORS

A. Common Errors during Traffic Patterns

1. **Failure to comply with traffic pattern instructions, procedures, and rules**

   a. Your noncompliance with ATC instructions may be caused by not understanding or hearing radio communications.

      1) You must learn to divide your attention while in the traffic pattern among flying, collision avoidance, performing checklists, and radio communications.

2. **Improper correction for wind drift**

   a. Remember that a traffic pattern is no more than a rectangular course and should be performed in the same manner.

3. **Inadequate spacing from other traffic**

   a. This occurs when you turn onto a traffic pattern leg too soon or you are flying an airplane that is faster than the one you are following.

4. **Poor altitude or airspeed control**

   a. Know the airspeeds at various points in the traffic pattern.
   b. Check the flight and engine instruments.

END OF COMMON ERRORS

PART III
SECTION IV:
TAKEOFFS, LANDINGS, AND GO-AROUNDS

Study Units 25 through 32 of Section IV explain the eight FAA ACS tasks (A-F, M, and N) of Takeoffs, Landings, and Go-Arounds. These tasks include knowledge, risk management, and skill. Your evaluator is required to test you on all eight of these tasks.

This section explains and describes the factors involved and the technique required for safely taking your airplane off the ground and departing the takeoff area under normal conditions, as well as in various situations in which maximum performance of your airplane is essential. Although the takeoff and climb maneuver is one continuous process, it can be divided into three phases.

1.   The **takeoff roll** is that portion of the maneuver during which your airplane is accelerated to an airspeed that provides sufficient lift for it to become airborne.

2.   The **liftoff**, or rotation, is the act of becoming airborne as a result of the wings lifting the airplane off the ground or your rotating the nose up, increasing the angle of attack to start a climb.

3.   The **initial climb** begins when your airplane leaves the ground and a pitch attitude is established to climb away from the takeoff area. Normally, it is considered complete when your airplane has reached a safe maneuvering altitude or an en route climb has been established.

This section also discusses the factors that affect your airplane during the landing approach under normal and critical circumstances, and the technique for positively controlling these factors. The approach and landing can be divided into five phases.

1.   The **base leg** is that portion of the traffic pattern during which you must accurately judge the distance in which your airplane must descend to the landing point.

2.   The **final approach** is the last part of the traffic pattern during which your airplane is aligned with the landing runway and a straight-line descent is made to the point of touchdown. The descent rate (descent angle) is governed by your airplane's height and distance from the intended touchdown point and by the airplane's groundspeed.

3.   The **roundout**, or **flare**, is that part of the final approach during which your airplane makes a transition from the approach attitude to the touchdown or landing attitude.

4.   The **touchdown** is the actual contact or touching of the main wheels of your airplane on the landing surface, as the full weight of the airplane is being transferred from the wings to the wheels.

5.   The **after-landing roll**, or **rollout**, is the forward roll of your airplane on the landing surface after touchdown while the airplane's momentum decelerates to a normal taxi speed or a stop.

The tasks in this section have several common items, listed and explained here instead of repeated throughout the text.

KNOWLEDGE

A. **The applicant demonstrates understanding of takeoff distance.**

1. The minimum takeoff distance is of primary interest in the operation of any airplane because it defines the runway requirements.

    a. The minimum takeoff distance is determined by using the minimum safe speed that allows for a sufficient safety margin above stall speed, provides satisfactory control, and an initial rate of climb.

2. To obtain minimum takeoff distance, the forces that act on the airplane must provide the maximum acceleration during the takeoff roll. Any item that alters the takeoff speed or acceleration rate during the takeoff roll will affect the takeoff distance.

    a. The effect of gross weight on takeoff distance is significant, and proper consideration of this item must be made.

        1) Increased gross weight produces a threefold effect on takeoff performance.

            a) A higher takeoff speed is necessary to produce the greater lift required to get the airplane airborne.

            b) There is a greater mass to accelerate; thus, the rate of acceleration is reduced.

            c) Retarding force (drag and ground friction) is increased; thus, the takeoff distance is increased.

3. Takeoff distances in an airplane's POH/AFM are based on paved, dry, level runway conditions.

    a. A rough, dirt, or grass landing strip will retard acceleration and will considerably lengthen the takeoff distance.

    b. Standing water, snow, or slush on a paved runway or an uphill-sloping runway will also increase the takeoff distance.

4. The effect of proper takeoff speed is especially important when runway lengths and takeoff distances are critical.

    a. The takeoff speed specified in the airplane's POH/AFM is generally the minimum safe speed at which the airplane can become airborne.

    b. Attempting to take off below the recommended airspeed could mean that the airplane may stall, be difficult to control, or have a very low initial rate of climb.

        1) In some cases, an excessive angle of attack may not allow the airplane to climb out of ground effect.

    c. An excessive airspeed may improve the initial rate of climb and feel of the airplane, but it will produce an undesirable increase in takeoff distance.

B. **The applicant demonstrates understanding of available landing distance.**

1. You should always understand the available landing distance at your destination airport.

    a. Make sure you get information on runway lengths at airports of intended use, data on takeoff and landing distances, weather reports and forecasts, and fuel requirements; and

    b. Plan for alternatives if the planned flight cannot be completed or if you encounter delays.

2.   The runway condition and slope will also affect the landing distance.

   a.   A wet, icy, or snow-covered runway (concrete or grass) will not allow good braking and therefore will increase the landing distance.

      1)   All braking effectiveness may be lost if the airplane's tires are hydroplaning, which is caused by a thin layer of water that separates the tires from the runway.

         a)   Hydroplaning speed (in knots) is about nine times the square root of the tire pressure.

         b)   Typically, the nosewheel tire will continue to hydroplane after the main wheels have stopped, which leads to steering difficulties.

   b.   A downsloping runway will increase the landing distance because the touchdown may be a little farther down the runway and the braking is not as effective going downhill as on a level or upsloping runway.

3.   The most critical conditions of landing performance are the result of some combination of high gross weight, high density altitude, and unfavorable wind.

   a.   These conditions produce the greatest landing distance and provide critical levels of energy dissipation required of the brakes.

   b.   In all cases, it is necessary to make an accurate prediction of minimum landing distance to compare with the available runway.

4.   Landing distance graphs or tables are found in the airplane's POH/AFM. Most assume a dry, paved, level runway surface. If these surface conditions do not exist, some charts will have correction factors. For those that do not, note that the actual landing performance will not match the values listed in the performance chart.

   a.   The data on the chart is based on the listed associated conditions, i.e., power, flaps, gear, runway, weight, and approach speed.

   b.   You need to distinguish between distances for clearing a 50-ft. obstacle and distances for ground roll.

      1)   Ground roll is the distance from touchdown until the airplane comes to a stop by using the recommended braking technique.

   c.   Normal Landing Distances Chart

      1)   Headwind alternatives are 0, 15, and 30 kt. If the actual headwind is between these figures, you must interpolate.

      2)   The altitudes given are sea level, 2,000, 4,000, 6,000, and 8,000 ft. MSL. If your altitude is between these figures, you must interpolate.

      3)   For each headwind and altitude, five outside air temperatures are given. You must interpolate if the current temperature is between two of these figures.

4) Ground roll is approximately 45% of the total distance over a 50-ft. obstacle (see Note 1 on the Normal Landing Distances chart below).

NORMAL LANDING DISTANCES

ASSOCIATED CONDITIONS

POWER	OFF
FLAPS	35°
GEAR	DOWN
RUNWAY	PAVED, LEVEL, DRY SURFACE
WEIGHT	2750 POUNDS
APPROACH SPEED	85 MPH/74 KTS IAS

NOTES:

1. GROUND ROLL IS APPROXIMATELY 45% OF TOTAL DISTANCE OVER 50-FT. OBSTACLE
2. FOR EACH 100 LBS. BELOW 2750 LBS., REDUCE TABULATED DISTANCE BY 3% AND APPROACH SPEED BY 1 MPH.

WIND COMPONENT DOWN RUNWAY KNOTS	SEA LEVEL		2000 FT		4000 FT		6000 FT		8000 FT	
	OAT °F	TOTAL OVER 50-FT OBSTACLE FEET	OAT °F	TOTAL OVER 50-FT OBSTACLE FEET	OAT °F	TOTAL OVER 50-FT OBSTACLE FEET	OAT °F	TOTAL OVER 50-FT OBSTACLE FEET	OAT °F	TOTAL OVER 50-FT OBSTACLE FEET
0	23	1578	16	1651	9	1732	2	1820	6	1916
	41	1624	34	1701	27	1787	20	1880	13	1983
	59	1670	52	1752	45	1842	38	1942	31	2050
	77	1717	70	1804	63	1899	56	2004	49	2118
	95	1764	88	1856	81	1956	74	2066	66	2187
15	23	1329	16	1397	9	1472	2	1555	6	1644
	41	1372	34	1444	27	1524	20	1611	13	1707
	59	1414	52	1491	45	1575	38	1668	31	1770
	77	1458	70	1540	63	1626	56	1727	49	1833
	95	1502	88	1588	81	1682	74	1784	66	1898
30	23	1079	16	1142	9	1212	2	1289	6	1372
	41	1119	34	1186	27	1260	20	1341	13	1430
	59	1158	52	1230	45	1308	38	1395	31	1489
	77	1199	70	1275	63	1357	56	1449	49	1548
	95	1240	88	1320	81	1407	74	1502	66	1608

5) EXAMPLE: Given a weight of 2,750 lb., a 15-kt. headwind at 2,000 ft., and 52°F, the landing distance over a 50-ft. obstacle would be 1,491 ft. Ground roll would be 671 ft. (45% × 1,491 ft.).

C. **The applicant demonstrates understanding of takeoff power.**

1. Power should be added smoothly and continuously–without hesitation–to allow for a controllable transition to flying airspeed.

    a. The airplane should be allowed to roll with its full weight on the main wheels and accelerated to the lift-off speed.

    b. As the takeoff roll progresses, the airplane's pitch attitude and angle of attack should be adjusted to that which results in the minimum amount of drag and the quickest acceleration. In nosewheel-type airplanes, this involves little use of the elevator control because the airplane is already in a low drag attitude.

    c. Applying power too quickly can cause engine surging, backfiring, and a possible overboost situation (turbocharged engines). These conditions cause unnecessary engine wear as well as possible failure.

2. Engine instruments must be monitored during the entire maneuver.

    a. Listen for any indication of power loss or engine roughness.

    b. Monitoring enables you to notice immediately any malfunctions or indications of insufficient power or other potential problems. Do not commit liftoff unless all engine indications are normal.

    c. Never take off unless oil is in normal operating range because the oil may not be warm enough to circulate freely through the engine, causing damage or possible engine failure when increasing power for takeoff and climbout.

D. **The applicant demonstrates understanding of stabilized approach and interpretation and use of visual glide slope instruments.**

1. The term **stabilized approach** means that your airplane is in a position where minimum input of all controls will result in a safe landing.

    a. Excessive control input at any juncture could be an indication of improper planning.
    b. Remember, you must make simultaneous adjustments to both pitch and power.
    c. Large adjustments will result in over-controlling and chasing the glide slope.

2. A stabilized approach is one in which the pilot establishes and maintains a constant angle glidepath towards a predetermined point on the landing runway.

    a. It is based on the pilot's judgment of certain visual clues, and depends on the maintenance of a constant final descent airspeed and configuration.
    b. The objective of a stabilized approach is to select an appropriate touchdown point on the runway, and adjust the glidepath so that the true aiming point and the desired touchdown point basically coincide.
    c. To do this you must maintain your selected glide path and airspeed.

3. During a stabilized approach, the runway shape does not change.

    a. If the approach becomes shallower, however, the runway will appear to shorten and become wider. Conversely, if the approach is steepened, the runway will appear to become longer and narrower.

4. Lock in your airspeed and glide path as soon as possible.

    a. Never let your airspeed go below your approach speed.
    b. Never let your airplane sink below your selected glide path or the glide path of a visual approach slope indicator (i.e., VASI or PAPI).

5. Immediately after rolling out on the final approach, the pilot should adjust the pitch attitude and power so that the airplane is descending directly toward the aiming point at the appropriate airspeed.

    a. The airplane should be in the landing configuration, and trimmed for "hands off" flight.
    b. The pilot will be free to devote full attention toward outside references.

        1) The pilot should not stare at any one place, but rather scan from one point to another, such as from the aiming point to the horizon, to the trees and bushes along the runway, to an area well short of the runway, and back to the aiming point.

    c. It is essential that deviations from the desired glidepath be detected early, so that only slight and infrequent adjustments to glidepath are required.

        1) The closer the airplane gets to the runway, the larger (and possibly more frequent) the required corrections become, resulting in an **unstabilized approach**.

    d. Because you will not have the option of adding power, it becomes paramount that you maintain a stabilized approach.
    e. Consider keeping a higher than normal approach, which you can bleed off later, or an aim point farther down the runway.

6. Airspeed control is the most important factor in achieving landing precision. A well-executed landing begins in the traffic pattern with the proper setup and a stabilized approach.

    a. An excessive amount of airspeed may result in touchdown too far from the runway threshold or an after-landing roll that exceeds the available landing area.
    b. Once on final approach, slight adjustments in pitch and power may be necessary to maintain the descent attitude and the desired airspeed.

    c.   On final approach, you should use the airspeed in your POH/AFM. In the absence of the manufacturer's recommended airspeed, a speed equal to 1.3 V_{s0} should be used.

        1)   EXAMPLE: If V_{s0} in your airplane is 40 kt. (45 mph), multiply that by 1.3 to determine that the airspeed on final approach should be 52 kt. (60 mph).

In your airplane, final approach speed (POH/AFM) _____, or 1.3 V_{s0} _____.

        2)   Make necessary adjustments to that speed if you are in turbulent air or strong, gusty winds.

        3)   Inform your evaluator of your final approach airspeed.

7.   Most of the visual glideslope indicators use a system of lights positioned normally on the left side of the runway near the designated touchdown point.

    a.   Once you understand the principles and color code of the lighting system, you simply note the colors and adjust your airplane's glide path (i.e., rate of descent) to remain on the visual glideslope.

    b.   Visual glideslope indicators are very effective during either daytime or nighttime, especially during approaches over water or featureless terrain where sources of visual references are lacking or misleading.

        1)   Visual glideslope indicators provide optimal descent guidance during the approach and minimize the possibility of undershooting or overshooting the designated touchdown area.

    c.   When using a visual glideslope indicator, you should not begin your descent until you are aligned with the runway.

        1)   Lateral guidance is provided by the runway or runway edge lights.

    d.   When you make an approach to land on a runway at a controlled airport that has an operating visual slope indicator, you are required to remain at or above the glideslope until it is necessary to descend for a safe landing.

        1)   This requirement does not prohibit you from making normal corrections above or below the glideslope for the purpose of remaining on the glideslope.

8.   The **visual approach slope indicator (VASI)** is a system of lights arranged to provide visual descent guidance during an approach.

    a.   The VASI system uses color differentiation between red and white.

        1)   Each light unit projects a beam of light having a white segment in the upper part of the beam and a red segment in the lower part of the beam.

        2)   The VASI lights are normally located on the left side of the runway.

    b.   Most VASI systems consist of two bars (near and far) that provide one visual glide path, which is normally set at 3°.

        1)   From a position below the glide path, you will see all the light bars as red. From above the glide path, all the light bars will appear white.

        2)   Passing through the glide path from a low position, you will see a transition in color from red to white. This transition will occur if you maintain or gain altitude.

        3)   Passing through the glide path from a high position, you will see a transition in color from white to red. This transition will occur if you begin above the VASI glide path and your rate of descent is too great (i.e., exceeds the VASI glide path).

BELOW GLIDE PATH   ON GLIDE PATH   ABOVE GLIDE PATH

2-BAR VASI

c.   Some VASI systems consist of three bars (near, middle, and far), which provide an additional glide path to accommodate high cockpit aircraft.

1)   The lower glide path is provided by the near and middle bars and is normally set at 3°, while the upper glide path, provided by the middle and far bars, is normally 1/4° higher.

a)   This higher glide path is intended for use only by high cockpit aircraft to provide a sufficient threshold crossing height.

2)   When using a three-bar VASI, it is not necessary to use all three bars. The near and middle bars constitute a two-bar VASI for using the lower glide path. Also, the middle and far bars constitute a two-bar VASI for using the upper glide path.

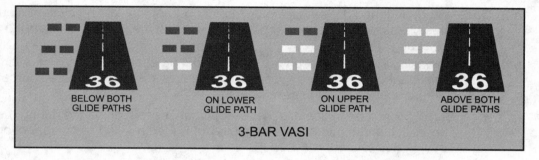

d.   The figure below illustrates some of the VASI variations you may encounter.

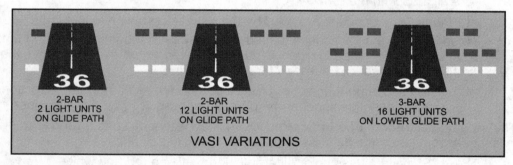

9.   The **precision approach path indicator (PAPI)** uses lights similar to the VASI but in a single row of either two or four lights.

a.   The row of light units is normally installed on the left side of the runway.
b.   The glide path indications are depicted below.

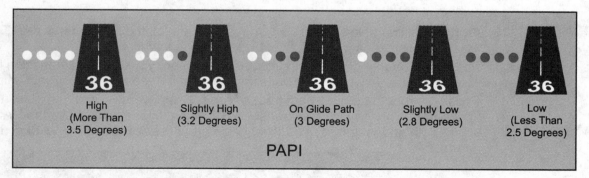

10. Additional, less common types of visual approach slope indicators include tri-color VASI, pulsating VASI, and alignment of elements system.

a.   If any of these systems are used in your area, refer to *Pilot Handbook*, Study Unit 3, for more details.

E. **The applicant demonstrates understanding of application of V$_X$ or V$_Y$ and variations with altitude.**

1. Two airspeeds important to climb performance are the best angle-of-climb speed (V$_X$) and the best rate-of-climb speed (V$_Y$).

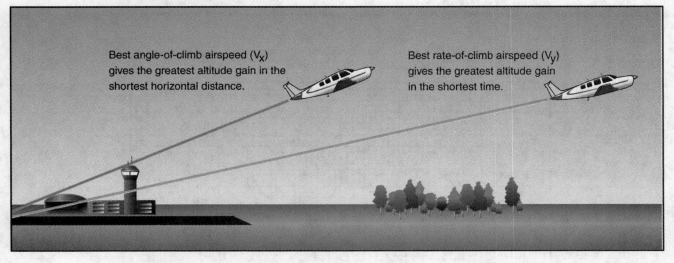

Best angle-of-climb airspeed (V$_x$) gives the greatest altitude gain in the shortest horizontal distance.

Best rate-of-climb airspeed (V$_y$) gives the greatest altitude gain in the shortest time.

a. V$_X$ provides the greatest gain in altitude for distance traveled over the ground and is used to clear obstacles immediately after takeoff on short-length runways.

b. V$_Y$ provides the greatest gain in altitude over a period of time and is used during a normal takeoff or after clearing all obstacles during departure when V$_X$ was used.

c. These airspeeds are found in the airplane's POH/AFM.

2. The climb performance of an airplane is affected by certain variables. Climb performance is most critical with high gross weight, at high altitude, in obstructed takeoff areas, or during malfunction of an engine in a multiengine airplane.

a. The conditions of the airplane's maximum climb angle or maximum climb rate occur at specific speeds, and variations in speed will produce variations in climb performance.

b. Weight has a very pronounced effect on airplane performance.

    1) If weight is added to the airplane, it must fly at a higher angle of attack to maintain a given altitude and speed.

        a) A higher angle of attack increases induced drag (due to the additional lift being produced) as well as parasite drag (due to the additional fuselage area exposed to the relative wind).

            i) Additional power is needed to overcome increased drag, which means that less reserve power is available for climbing.

    2) Generally, an increase in weight will reduce the maximum rate of climb achievable and require a higher climb speed.

c.   An increase in altitude will also increase the power required and decrease the power available. Thus, altitude greatly affects climb performance.

    1)   The speeds for maximum rate of climb and maximum angle of climb vary with altitude.

        a)   As altitude increases, V_X increases.

        b)   As altitude increases, V_Y decreases.

        c)   As altitude increases, these various speeds finally converge at the absolute ceiling of the airplane.

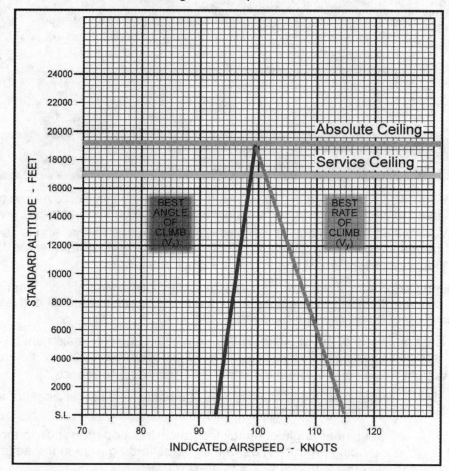

    2)   The **service ceiling** is the altitude at which the airplane is limited to a climb rate of 100 feet per minute (fpm).

    3)   At the **absolute ceiling**, there is no excess of power, and only one speed will allow steady level flight. Thus, the rate of climb is zero.

3. Climb performance charts are found in the airplane's POH/AFM.

   a. A climb performance chart provides information at various gross weights, altitudes, and temperatures. It states the indicated airspeed, the rate of climb (fpm), and gallons of fuel used.

   b. In the example chart below, the gross weights of 1,700, 2,000, and 2,300 lb. are given on the left. Interpolate as necessary.

   c. Altitudes of sea level, 5,000, 10,000, and 15,000 ft. are given. Interpolate as necessary.

   d. The notes give important information. In the example chart, Note 3 says to decrease rate of climb by 20 fpm for each 10°F above the standard temperatures.

   e. EXAMPLE: With a gross weight of 2,000 lb. and pressure altitude of 5,000 ft. with a temperature of 61°F, the rate of climb is 570 fpm. The 610-fpm rate of climb must be reduced by 40 fpm because the temperature of 61°F is 20°F above the standard temperature of 41°F.

MAXIMUM RATE-OF-CLIMB DATA

GROSS WEIGHT POUNDS	AT SEA LEVEL & 59°F			AT 5,000 FT. & 41°F			AT 10,000 FT. & 23°F			AT 15,000 FT. & 5°F		
	IAS MPH	RATE OF CLIMB FT/MIN	GAL. OF FUEL USED	IAS MPH	RATE OF CLIMB FT/MIN	FROM S.L. FUEL USED	IAS MPH	RATE OF CLIMB FT/MIN	FROM S.L. FUEL USED	IAS MPH	RATE OF CLIMB FT/MIN	FROM S.L. FUEL USED
2300	82	645	1.0	81	435	2.6	79	230	4.8	78	22	11.5
2000	79	840	1.0	79	610	2.2	76	380	3.6	75	155	6.3
1700	77	1085	1.0	76	825	1.9	73	570	2.9	72	315	4.4

NOTES: 1. Flaps up, full throttle, mixture leaned for smooth operation above 3,000 ft.
2. Fuel used includes warm up and takeoff allowance.
3. For hot weather, decrease rate of climb 20 ft./min. for each 10°F above standard day temperature for particular altitude.

F. **The applicant demonstrates understanding of land and hold short operations (LAHSO) or option to refuse LAHSO restriction.**

1. **Land and hold short operations (LAHSO)** take place at some airports with an operating control tower in order to increase airport capacity and improve the flow of traffic.

   a. LAHSO require that you land and hold short of an intersecting runway, an intersecting taxiway, or some other designated point on a runway.

   b. Before accepting a clearance to land and hold short, you must determine that you can safely land and stop within the available landing distance.

   c. Student pilots should not participate in the LAHSO program.

   d. The pilot in command has the final authority to accept or decline any LAHSO clearance.

      1) You are expected to decline a LAHSO clearance if you determine it will compromise safety.

   e. You should receive a LAHSO clearance only when there is a minimum ceiling of 1,000 ft. and visibility of 3 SM.

      1) The intent of having basic VFR weather conditions is to allow pilots to maintain visual contact with other aircraft and ground vehicle operations.

2. **Land and hold short lights** are used to indicate the hold short point on certain runways that are approved for LAHSO. Land and hold short lights consist of a row of pulsing white lights installed across the runway at the hold short point. Where installed, the lights are on anytime LAHSO is in effect and off when LAHSO is not in effect.

G. **The applicant demonstrates understanding of effects of runway surface.**

1.   Runway conditions affect takeoff and landing performance. Any surface that is not hard and smooth will increase the ground roll during takeoff. This is due to the inability of the tires to roll smoothly along the runway.

    a. Takeoff distances in an airplane's POH/AFM are based on paved, dry, level runway conditions.

        1) A rough, dirt, or grass landing strip will retard acceleration and will considerably lengthen the takeoff distance.

        2) Standing water, snow, or slush on a paved runway or an uphill-sloping runway will also increase the takeoff distance.

    b. Landing on fields that are rough or have soft surfaces (e.g., snow, mud, sand, or tall grass) requires special techniques.

        1) When landing on such surfaces, you must control your airplane in a manner such that the wings support the weight of the airplane as long as practicable.

            a) Supporting the airplane's weight with the wings minimizes drag and stress put on the landing gear from the rough or soft surfaces.

        2) If the need arises to make a soft-field departure, consult the recommendations provided by the manufacturer in your airplane's POH/AFM. It will most likely have recommendations for operation on different runway surfaces.

    c. Inspect your taxi route and your takeoff runway. Normally, you should walk the entire route carefully.

        1) Note wet or soft spots and mark them as necessary (use pieces of cloth or paper tied to objects, e.g., fence posts, or anchor them to the ground at the side of the runway with stakes, sticks, etc.).

        2) Determine and mark your takeoff abort point—exactly where you will cut power if not airborne.

            a) Seventy-five percent of V_R by the halfway point on the runway is a general rule.

    d. Potholes or other ruts in the pavement can be the cause of poor tire movement along the runway.

    e. Obstructions such as mud, snow, or standing water reduce the airplane's acceleration down the runway.

        1) Although muddy and wet surface conditions can reduce friction between the runway and the tires, they can also act as obstructions and reduce the landing distance.

    f. Braking effectiveness is another consideration when dealing with various runway types. The condition of the surface affects the braking ability of the aircraft.

RISK MANAGEMENT

A. **The applicant demonstrates the ability to identify, assess, and mitigate risks encompassing selection of runway based on wind, pilot capability, and aircraft limitations.**

1. Wind. Are there runways suitable for the wind direction?

    a. Ensure that you can get a reasonable headwind on landing and the crosswind is not perpendicular, or nearly, to the available runway.

2. Pilot capability. What are your personal minimums?

    a. Are the winds greater than your personal minimums?

    b. Are there any conditions outside of your personal minimums?

    c. The hazard is often not the challenges presented, but the pilot being overly confident and complacent as to his or her responsibilities.

    d. The first and key step in preparing for a new situation is to recognize that you may not have the required skill set–the step of recognizing personal limitations.

3. Aircraft limitations. What limitations will the aircraft impose upon the trip?

    a. Are the wind component, runway length, and runway conditions acceptable for this aircraft?

    b. Can this aircraft use the runways available for the trip with an adequate margin of safety under the conditions to be flown? For instance, consider a POH/AFM for an aircraft that indicates a maximum demonstrated crosswind component of 15 kt. What does this mean to a pilot? This is the maximum crosswind that the manufacturer's test pilot demonstrated in the aircraft's certification.

B. **The applicant demonstrates the ability to identify, assess, and mitigate risks encompassing go/no go decision making.**

1. Every planned flight requires a go/no-go decision. To be able to make a decision based on conditions, you must first understand the overall situation and the dangers associated with the flight environment.

2. The best way to ensure a safe decision is made every time is to create personal minimums.

    a. Personal minimums define your self-imposed limitations on a variety of flight factors, including weather.

    b. This includes your health, the level of physical and mental stress you are experiencing, your fatigue level, and even your emotional state. Each of these factors has to be considered when you make any go/no go decisions.

    c. EXAMPLE: You would make a go/no go decision based on the maximum crosswind component listed for your aircraft in the POH/AFM. If the crosswind were above that maximum crosswind component, you would not fly. If it were below the maximum crosswind component, you would base your decision on your level of experience, the terrain, and the existence of obstacles in the area that might cause a safety issue. If in doubt, you would not fly.

C. **The applicant demonstrates the ability to identify, assess, and mitigate risks encompassing low altitude maneuvering.**

1. A smart pilot is always prepared for an emergency and minimizes low altitude activity.

    a. A common phrase is "altitude is our friend." The higher you are, the more time you have to make decisions in an emergency.

2. Maintaining coordinated flight is especially critical during low altitude maneuvering. Uncoordinated turns during slow speed flight can result in an accelerated stall and subsequent spin, which may not be recoverable from a low altitude.

3. For information on controlled flight into terrain (CFIT), see Part II, Study Unit 7, Subunit 3.

D. **The applicant demonstrates the ability to identify, assess, and mitigate risks encompassing obstacles on departure and approach and landing paths.**

1. You must consider the performance capabilities of your airplane, and plan your departure and arrival procedures accordingly.

    a. Be aware of where obstacles are located near your departure and destination airports, and plan to use runways that provide maximum obstacle clearance.

    b. Be sure to consider atmospheric factors, such as high density altitude, when planning for obstacle clearance.

2. The practical test is like any other flight. Safety is your first priority. If there are obstacles on your route of flight, maintain V_X until you clear them, then transition to V_Y, to continue your climb.

3. You must use all available outside references, including looking behind, to maintain a track of the runway centerline extension.

    a. This will assist you in avoiding hazardous obstacles or preventing drifting into the path of another airplane, which may be taking off from a parallel runway.

    b. Cross-check with the airplane's heading indicator, using enough right rudder to maintain heading with the wings level.

E. **The applicant demonstrates the ability to identify, assess, and mitigate risks encompassing recognition of the need for rejected takeoff and identification of takeoff abort criteria.**

1. Always be prepared to abort the takeoff at any time.

    a. If you decide to abort the takeoff, commit to that decision.

2. Prior to takeoff, determine and mark your takeoff abort point -- exactly where you will cut power if not airborne.

    a. Seventy-five percent of V_R by the halfway point on the runway is a general rule.

3. Engine instruments must be monitored during the entire maneuver.

    a. Monitoring enables you to notice immediately any malfunctions or indication of insufficient power or other potential problems.

    b. Listen for any indication of power loss or engine roughness.

    c. Do not hesitate to abort the takeoff if all engine indications are not normal.

F. **The applicant demonstrates the ability to identify, assess, and mitigate risks encompassing right-of-way.**

1. You must apply right-of-way rules and maintain adequate spacing behind other aircraft.

    a. Generally, the right-of-way rules apply the same on the runway and in the air; i.e., approaching head-on, alter course to the right; yield to an airplane on the right.

        1) Ground control (at an airport with an operating control tower) may instruct one aircraft to stop or yield to another.

        2) If in doubt, always yield to other aircraft. Be safe.

    b. Avoid being too close to another airplane's prop or jet wash, which could cause you to lose control of your airplane. Maintain a safe separation.

2. Aircraft on final approach to land or while landing have the right-of-way over other aircraft in flight or on the ground.

    a. When two or more aircraft are approaching the airport for landing, the lower aircraft has the right-of-way.

        1) You may not take advantage of this rule to cut in front of another aircraft that is on final approach or to overtake that aircraft.

G. **The applicant demonstrates the ability to identify, assess, and mitigate risks encompassing recognition of the need for go-around/rejected landing.**

 1. Occasionally it will be advisable, for safety reasons, to discontinue your approach and make another approach under more favorable conditions. Unfavorable conditions may include

 a. Extremely low base-to-final turn

 b. Too high or too low final approach

 c. The unexpected appearance of hazards on the runway, e.g., another airplane failing to clear the runway on time

 d. Wake turbulence from a preceding aircraft

 e. Wind-shear encounter

 f. Overtaking another aircraft on final approach

 g. ATC instructions to "go around"

 2. The need to discontinue an approach and landing may arise at any point in the approach and landing process. A timely decision must be made.

 a. The earlier you recognize a dangerous situation, the sooner you can decide to reject the landing and start the go-around, the safer this maneuver will be.

 b. If you decide to go around, stick to your plan. Do not attempt a landing after an unsafe approach.

 c. Never wait until the last possible moment to make a decision.

 3. As soon as it becomes clear that a go-around may be advisable, it is reasonable to then announce that you are going around and begin the process. The lower you carry the approach, the less margin of safety is provided. It is better to decide to go around earlier than to wait until you are on short final, at low altitude, and/or potentially slower than you would like to be for initiating a climb to begin the go-around.

 4. You must touch down at or within 200 ft. beyond a specified point; not doing so would constitute a failure of the task.

 5. When takeoff power is applied in the go-around, you must cope with undesirable pitch and yaw.

 a. Since you have trimmed your airplane for the approach (i.e., nose-up trim), the nose may rise sharply and veer to the left.

 1) Proper elevator pressure must be applied to maintain a safe climbing pitch attitude.

 2) Right rudder pressure must be increased to counteract torque, or P-factor, and to keep the nose straight.

H. **The applicant demonstrates the ability to identify, assess, and mitigate risks encompassing low altitude stall/spin.**

 1. Pilots have inadvertently stalled during landing when performing the following:

 a. Attempting to "stretch" a glide in a power-off approach

 b. Improper airspeed control on final approach or in other segments of the traffic pattern

 c. Attempting to recover from a high sink rate on final approach by only increasing pitch attitude

 d. Crossed-control turns (aileron pressure in one direction, rudder pressure in the opposite direction) from base leg to final approach, which results in a skidding or slipping (uncoordinated) turn

2. Pilots must ensure their turns in the pattern are coordinated, especially the base-to-final turn. The hazard of stalling during uncoordinated flight is that you may enter a spin.

    a. Normally, it is recommended that the angle of bank not exceed a medium bank because the steeper the angle of bank, the higher the airspeed at which the airplane stalls.

    b. Often a wing will drop at the beginning of a stall, and the nose of your airplane will attempt to move (yaw) in the direction of the low wing.

        1) The correct amount of opposite rudder must be applied to keep the nose from yawing toward the low wing.

    c. If you maintain directional control (coordinated flight), the wing will not drop further before the stall is broken, thus preventing a spin.

3. The likelihood of stalling in uncoordinated flight is increased during such maneuvers as go-arounds and power-on stalls is due to the greater torque from high pitch attitude, high power setting, and low airspeed.

    a. Some maneuvers result in one wing dropping.
    b. Maintaining directional control with rudder is vital to avoiding a spin.
    c. Remember that, in order to spin, both of the airplane's wings must first be stalled; then one wing becomes less stalled than the other.

        1) The correct amount of opposite rudder must be applied to keep the nose from yawing toward the low wing.

    d. If you maintain directional control (coordinated flight), the wing will not drop further before the stall is broken, thus preventing a spin.

    e. It is essential to learn to apply immediate corrective action anytime it is apparent that the airplane is nearing stall/spin conditions.

    f. At times, recovery from a spin may not be possible due to the low altitude.

4. Be careful of cross-controlled stalls that can lead to inadvertent spins.

    a. This is a stall that is most apt to occur during a poorly planned and executed base-to-final approach turn, and often is the result of overshooting the centerline of the runway during that turn.

    b. At the relatively low altitude of a base-to-final approach turn, improperly trained pilots may be apprehensive of steepening the bank to increase the rate of turn, and rather than steepening the bank, they hold the bank constant and attempt to increase the rate of turn by adding more rudder pressure in an effort to align it with the runway.

5. **Stall/Spin Awareness**

    a. You should be aware and demonstrate your awareness of possible conditions that could lead to the aircraft stalling or spinning.

    b. You should emphasize those conditions in which pilots most often accidentally encounter stalls and/or spins, such as

        1) Just after takeoff (from steep climb angles)
        2) Base to final traffic pattern turn
        3) Just before touchdown (as in flat, slow approaches)
        4) While practicing stalls

I. **The applicant demonstrates the ability to identify, assess, and mitigate risks encompassing criticality of takeoff distance available.**

    1. The minimum takeoff distance is of primary interest in the operation of any aircraft because it defines the runway requirements. The minimum takeoff distance is obtained by taking off at some minimum safe speed that allows sufficient margin above stall and provides satisfactory control and initial rate of climb.

2. Takeoff distance should be calculated when considering the following factors:

    a. Aft/forward center of gravity

    b. Runway conditions (soft/normal)

    c. Wind

    d. Wake turbulence

    e. Length of runway

3. In all cases, the pilot must make an accurate prediction of takeoff distance from the performance data of the POH/AFM, regardless of the runway available, and strive for a polished, professional takeoff procedure.

J. **The applicant demonstrates the ability to identify, assess, and mitigate risks encompassing land and hold short operations.**

1. Always review the Chart Supplement for your destination airport so you are aware of potential LAHSO operations.

2. Before accepting a clearance to land and hold short, you must determine that you can safely land and stop within the available landing distance.

3. Student pilots should not participate in the LAHSO program.

4. You, as pilot in command, have the final authority to accept or decline any LAHSO clearance.

    a. You are expected to decline a LAHSO clearance if you determine it will compromise safety.

K. **The applicant demonstrates the ability to identify, assess, and mitigate risks encompassing operating from other than a hard surfaced runway.**

1. A runway that is not hard-surfaced can be considered a soft field. You must take in to account a hard-packed turf or a wet, high grass turf. Know the condition of the landing surface you will be operating into.

    a. If a surface is soft or wet, consider what effect that will have if you perform a crosswind landing, when one main wheel touches down before the other main wheel.

2. Proper planning will ensure knowledge of the landing surface condition, e.g., wet, dry, loose, hard packed.

    a. The landing surface will affect your airplane's braking/stopping distance.

    b. The soft or rough surface itself will normally provide sufficient friction to reduce your airplane's forward speed.

    c. Brakes may not be needed on a soft field and may need to be avoided.

    d. On a very soft surface, you may need to maintain higher power to avoid stopping and/or becoming bogged down on the landing surface.

3. You must maintain enough speed while taxiing to prevent becoming bogged down on the soft surface.

    a. You will often need to increase power after landing on a very soft surface to keep your airplane moving and prevent being stuck.

    b. Care must be taken not to taxi excessively fast because, if you taxi onto a very soft area, your airplane may bog down and bend the landing gear and/or nose over.

    c. Keep your airplane moving at all times until you are at the point where you will be parking your airplane.

4. Use your POH/AFM to determine the appropriate airspeeds and performance for a soft-field approach and landing.

5. The most common error, as well as the easiest to avoid, is to attempt a landing that is beyond the capabilities of your airplane and/or your flying skills. Be sure that the surface of the field you plan to use is suitable for landing.

6.   It may be necessary to plan the touchdown and rollout more carefully. The goal is to minimize the distance needed to taxi on the soft field to prevent unnecessary wear or damage to the aircraft.

7.   Before taking off at a soft (other than hard-surfaced) runway, determine your capability to take off in your airplane from that surface. Also, consider the possibility of damage and extra wear on your airplane. You may decide to wait until the takeoff surface conditions improve.

     a.   If the need arises to make a soft-field departure, consult the recommendations provided by the manufacturer in your airplane's POH/AFM.

          1)   Practice and perfect soft-field takeoffs.

8.   If your airplane is parked on a soft surface, other airplanes or the wind may have blown unwanted debris onto your airplane. Such materials, when trapped in the control surfaces, may jam the controls or limit their travel, which can cause disaster.

     a.   Soft fields are often remote fields. Birds and animals may seek refuge or build nests (even overnight) under the cowling, in landing gear wheel wells, and elsewhere.

     b.   Also, be cautious of possible vandalism of your airplane at remote airfields.

9.   Inspect your taxi route and your takeoff runway. Normally, you should walk the entire route carefully.

     a.   Note wet or soft spots and mark them as necessary (use pieces of cloth or paper tied to objects, e.g., fence posts, or anchor them to the ground at the side of the runway with stakes, sticks, etc.).

     b.   Determine and mark your takeoff abort point -- exactly where you will cut power if not airborne.

          1)   Seventy-five percent of V_R by the halfway point on the runway is a general rule.

10. If the airplane wheels have settled into the ground, move the airplane forward before getting into the cockpit.

     a.   Use leverage of the wing by holding the wingtip and rocking the wingtip back and forth.

     b.   Be careful not to stress the nose wheel with side loads (have someone lift the nose or push down on the tail).

     c.   Use help as available.

11. When taxiing to take off on a soft field, you do not want to come to a complete stop or let the power bleed off to the point that the aircraft bogs down in the soft ground. Therefore, keep the aircraft moving, but in a safe manner.

     a.   Always clear the area, but do so without stopping.

12. When taxiing on a soft field, it may take very near full power to get the aircraft to begin rolling. From that point, adjust the power as needed to keep the aircraft moving at a speed that is safe, but do not allow the aircraft's wheels to bog down in the soft ground.

13. In a tricycle-gear aircraft, as you advance the power to takeoff power,

     a.   Get the aircraft off the ground and into ground effect as soon as possible. Level off and allow the aircraft to accelerate to V_Y in ground effect, then pitch up to climb out normally.

     b.   During the takeoff roll, hold the yoke (stick) back to get the nosewheel off the ground as soon as possible. This reduces friction and drag caused by the wheel rolling along the ground, lowers the chances of damaging the nosewheel as the aircraft accelerates, and increases lift due to the higher angle of attack.

STUDY UNIT TWENTY-FIVE
NORMAL TAKEOFF AND CLIMB

Task	**Task A. Normal Takeoff and Climb**
References	FAA-H-8083-2, FAA-H-8083-3; POH/AFM
Objective	To determine that the applicant exhibits satisfactory knowledge, risk management, and skills associated with a normal takeoff, climb operations, and rejected takeoff procedures. *Note: If a crosswind condition does not exist, the applicant's knowledge of crosswind elements must be evaluated through oral testing.*
Knowledge	The applicant demonstrates understanding of:
PA.IV.A.K1	1. Takeoff distance.
PA.IV.A.K2	2. Takeoff power.
PA.IV.A.K3	3. Atmospheric conditions.
PA.IV.A.K4	4. Wind conditions and effects.
PA.IV.A.K5	5. The application of V_X or V_Y and variations with altitude.
PA.IV.A.K6	6. The manufacturer's recommended emergency procedures for relating to the takeoff sequence.
Risk Management	The applicant demonstrates the ability to identify, assess and mitigate risks, encompassing:
PA.IV.A.R1	1. Selection of runway based on wind, pilot capability, and aircraft limitations.
PA.IV.A.R2	2. The demonstrated crosswind component for the aircraft.
PA.IV.A.R3	3. Windshear.
PA.IV.A.R4	4. Tailwind.
PA.IV.A.R5	5. Wake turbulence.
PA.IV.A.R6	6. Go/no-go decision-making.
PA.IV.A.R7	7. Task management.
PA.IV.A.R8	8. Low altitude maneuvering.
PA.IV.A.R9	9. Wire strikes.
PA.IV.A.R10	10. Obstacles on the departure path.
PA.IV.A.R11	11. A rejected takeoff and predetermining takeoff abort criteria.
PA.IV.A.R12	12. Handling engine failure during takeoff and climb.
PA.IV.A.R13	13. Criticality of takeoff distance available.
PA.IV.A.R14	14. Plans for engine failure after takeoff.
PA.IV.A.R15	15. Sterile cockpit environment.
Skills	The applicant demonstrates the ability to:
PA.IV.A.S1	1. Verify ATC clearance and no aircraft is on final before crossing the hold line.
PA.IV.A.S2	2. Verify aircraft is on the assigned/correct runway.
PA.IV.A.S3	3. Ascertain wind direction with or without visible wind direction indicators.
PA.IV.A.S4	4. Determine if the crosswind component is beyond the pilot's ability or aircraft manufacturer maximum demonstrated value.
PA.IV.A.S5	5. Position the flight controls for the existing wind conditions.
PA.IV.A.S6	6. Clear the area; taxi into the takeoff position and align the airplane on the runway centerline/takeoff path.
PA.IV.A.S7	7. Confirm takeoff power; and proper engine and flight instrument indications prior to rotation.
PA.IV.A.S8	8. Rotate and lift-off at the recommended airspeed and accelerate to V_Y (or other speed as appropriate for aircraft).
PA.IV.A.S9	9. Establish a pitch attitude that will maintain V_Y +10/-5 knots (or other airspeed as appropriate for aircraft).
PA.IV.A.S10	10. Retract the landing gear and flaps in accordance with manufacturer's guidance.
PA.IV.A.S11	11. Maintain takeoff power and V_Y +10/-5 knots or to a safe maneuvering altitude.
PA.IV.A.S12	12. Maintain directional control and proper wind drift correction throughout the takeoff and climb.
PA.IV.A.S13	13. Comply with responsible environmental practices, including noise abatement and published departure procedures.
PA.IV.A.S14	14. Complete the appropriate checklist.
PA.IV.A.S15	15. Comply with manufacturer's recommended emergency procedures related to the takeoff sequence.

A.   General Information

  1.   The objective of this task is for you to demonstrate your knowledge, risk management, and skills related to a normal takeoff, climb operations, and rejected takeoff procedures.

      a.   NOTE: If a crosswind condition does not exist, your knowledge of crosswind procedures will be orally tested.

  2.   The content of Subunits 25.1 and 25.2 is abbreviated based on the assumption that you have thoroughly read and understood pages 287 through 304 and the additional common task topics found in Part II. The task objectives and specific references are provided here for your convenience.

25.1 KNOWLEDGE

A.   Task Objectives

  1.   **The applicant demonstrates understanding of takeoff distance.**

      a.   For information on takeoff distance, see Section IV Introduction, Knowledge, item A., beginning on page 289.

  2.   **The applicant demonstrates understanding of takeoff power.**

      a.   For information on takeoff power, see Section IV Introduction, Knowledge, item C., beginning on page 291.

  3.   **The applicant demonstrates understanding of atmospheric conditions.**

      a.   For information on atmospheric conditions, see Study Unit 9, Subunit 1, beginning on page 77.

  4.   **The applicant demonstrates understanding of wind conditions and effects.**

      a.   For information on wind conditions and effects, see Study Unit 9, Subunit 3, beginning on page 80.

  5.   **The applicant demonstrates understanding of the application of V_X or V_Y and variations with altitude.**

      a.   For information on the application of V_X or V_Y and variations with altitude, see Section IV Introduction, Knowledge, item E., beginning on page 295.

  6.   **The applicant demonstrates understanding of the manufacturer's recommended emergency procedures relating to the takeoff sequence.**

      a.   For information on the manufacturer's recommended emergency procedures relating to the takeoff sequence, see Study Unit 8, Subunit 2, item C., beginning on page 73.

END OF KNOWLEDGE ELEMENT

25.2 RISK MANAGEMENT

A. Task Objectives

1. **The applicant demonstrates the ability to identify, assess, and mitigate risks encompassing selection of runway based on wind, pilot capability, and aircraft limitations.**

   a. For information on selection of runway based on wind, pilot capability, and aircraft limitations, see Section IV Introduction, Risk Management, item A., beginning on page 299.

2. **The applicant demonstrates the ability to identify, assess, and mitigate risks encompassing the demonstrated crosswind component for the aircraft.**

   a. For information on crosswind component, see Study Unit 9, Subunit 3, item C., beginning on page 80.

3. **The applicant demonstrates the ability to identify, assess, and mitigate risks encompassing windshear.**

   a. For information on windshear, see Study Unit 9, Subunit 4, beginning on page 81.

4. **The applicant demonstrates the ability to identify, assess, and mitigate risks encompassing tailwind.**

   a. For information on tailwind, see Study Unit 9, Subunit 3, beginning on page 80.

5. **The applicant demonstrates the ability to identify, assess, and mitigate risks encompassing wake turbulence.**

   a. For information on wake turbulence, see Study Unit 7, Subunit 7, beginning on page 69.

6. **The applicant demonstrates the ability to identify, assess, and mitigate risks encompassing go/no-go decision making.**

   a. For information on go/no-go decision making, see Section IV Introduction, Risk Management, item B., beginning on page 299.

7. **The applicant demonstrates the ability to identify, assess, and mitigate risks encompassing task management.**

   a. For information on task management, see Study Unit 6, Subunit 1, beginning on page 49.

8. **The applicant demonstrates the ability to identify, assess, and mitigate risks encompassing low-altitude maneuvering.**

   a. For information on low-altitude maneuvering, see Section IV Introduction, Risk Management, item C., beginning on page 299.

9. **The applicant demonstrates the ability to identify, assess, and mitigate risks encompassing wire strikes.**

   a. For information on wire strikes, see Study Unit 7, Subunit 6, beginning on page 68.

10. **The applicant demonstrates the ability to identify, assess, and mitigate risks encompassing obstacles on the departure path.**

    a. For information on obstacles on the departure path, see Section IV Introduction, Risk Management, item D., beginning on page 300.

11. **The applicant demonstrates the ability to identify, assess, and mitigate risks encompassing a rejected takeoff and predetermining takeoff abort criteria.**

    a. For information on rejected takeoffs and predetermining takeoff abort criteria, see Section IV Introduction, Risk Management, item E., beginning on page 300.

12. **The applicant demonstrates the ability to identify, assess, and mitigate risks encompassing handling engine failure during takeoff and climb.**

   a.   For information on handling engine failure during takeoff and climb, see Study Unit 8, Subunit 2, beginning on page 73.

13. **The applicant demonstrates the ability to identify, assess, and mitigate risks encompassing criticality of takeoff distance available.**

   a.   For information on criticality of takeoff distance available, see Section IV Introduction, Risk Management, item I., beginning on page 302.

14. **The applicant demonstrates the ability to identify, assess, and mitigate risks encompassing plans for engine failure after takeoff.**

   a.   For information on plans for engine failure after takeoff, see Study Unit 8, Subunit 2, beginning on page 75.

15. **The applicant demonstrates the ability to identify, assess, and mitigate risks encompassing sterile cockpit environment.**

   a.   For information on sterile cockpit environment, see Study Unit 6, Subunit 2, beginning on page 51.

END OF RISK MANAGEMENT ELEMENT

25.3 SKILLS

A. Task Objectives

1. **The applicant demonstrates the ability to verify ATC clearance and that no aircraft is on final before crossing the hold line.**

   a. Use a standard clearing procedure before initiating movement on the surface.

      1) Look to your left, scan the area for other traffic, and announce "clear left" if it is in fact clear.
      2) Repeat this same procedure for both the front and right of the aircraft.
      3) Any time you stop moving, use this procedure (or one like it) before rolling again.

   b. Read back all ATC clearances. If any ATC takeoff instructions seem unclear or appear to conflict with other instructions that have been issued, stop and ask for clarification.

   c. At non-towered airports, visually check the runway and the approach path to ensure the area is clear before you taxi onto the runway for takeoff.

   d. Refer to the runway number and the magnetic heading of the aircraft as you taxi onto the runway and center the aircraft with the runway centerline to ensure you are using the correct/assigned runway.

2. **The applicant demonstrates the ability to verify the aircraft is on the assigned/correct runway.**

   a. Refer to the runway number and the magnetic heading of the aircraft as you taxi onto the runway and center the aircraft with the runway centerline to ensure you are using the correct/assigned runway.

   b. Runway safety is a significant challenge and a top priority for everyone in aviation. In the U.S., an average of three runway incursions occur daily.

   c. A runway incursion is any occurrence at an aerodrome involving the incorrect presence of an aircraft, vehicle, or person on the protected area of a surface designated for the landing and takeoff of aircraft.

   d. Never cross a hold line without explicit ATC instructions. Controllers are required to issue explicit instructions to cross or hold short of each runway, including inactive and closed runways that intersect a taxi route.

   e. As you line up on the runway, confirm your compass and heading indicator agree you are on the correct runway.

3. **The applicant demonstrates the ability to ascertain wind direction with or without visible wind direction indicators.**

   a. Make use of airport wind direction indicators if they are available and/or listen to automated weather broadcasts, where installed, to get timely wind information.

   b. If necessary, you can contact ATC for a wind check prior to takeoff at tower-controlled airports.

   c. If you have no ability to reference wind direction indicators, weather broadcasts, or ATC advisories, you can use various outside references, such as rising smoke, tree motion, or just the basic physical sensation of where the wind is blowing from.

   d. Always reverify wind direction as you taxi onto the runway by observing the windsock or other wind direction indicators, which may include grass or bushes.

4. **The applicant demonstrates the ability to determine if the crosswind component is beyond the pilot's ability or aircraft manufacturer's maximum demonstrated value.**

    a. The aircraft's demonstrated crosswind component can be determined from Section 4, Normal Procedures, and/or Section 5, Performance, in your POH/AFM via a textual description in Section 4 and/or a graph in Section 5.

        1) Bear in mind that a numerical value for the crosswind component of the aircraft is likely the maximum demonstrated crosswind component for a direct 90° crosswind.

        2) The chart presented in Section 5 of the POH/AFM is the best way to determine the actual crosswind component that will be affecting the aircraft during your takeoff.

    b. Beyond what the aircraft is capable of, you have to be aware of what your skill level will allow.

        1) You should establish and follow personal minimums that are based on your comfort levels when dealing with crosswinds.

        2) You should regularly re-evaluate your personal minimums and determine if they need to be updated.

        3) Show the evaluator you are aware of your personal abilities by explaining your personal minimums when it comes to crosswind components.

5. **The applicant demonstrates the ability to position the flight controls for the existing wind conditions.**

    a. Always reverify wind direction as you taxi onto the runway by observing the windsock or other wind direction indicator, which may include grass or bushes.

    b. For a crosswind takeoff, the ailerons should be FULLY deflected at the start of the takeoff roll.

        1) The aileron should be up on the upwind side of the airplane (i.e., the control yoke turned toward the wind).

        2) This will impose a downward force on the upwind wing to counteract the lifting force of the crosswind and prevent that wing from rising prematurely.

        3) Aileron deflection should be gradually reduced as you accelerate during the takeoff roll.

    c. Wing flaps may be in the retracted position or at some intermediate extension for normal and crosswind takeoffs and climbs.

        1) If flaps are used, they should be extended prior to your taxiing onto the active runway, and they should always be visually checked.

    d. Follow the procedures prescribed in your POH/AFM.

6. **The applicant demonstrates the ability to clear the area, taxi into the takeoff position, and align the airplane on the runway centerline/takeoff path.**

    a. Before taxiing onto the runway, make certain that you have sufficient time to execute the takeoff before any aircraft in the traffic pattern turns onto the final approach.

        1) Check that the runway is clear of other aircraft, vehicles, persons, or other hazards.

        2) This should be done at both airports with and without an operating control tower.

    b. Before beginning your takeoff roll, study the runway and related ground reference points, such as nearby buildings, trees, runway lights (at night), etc.

        1) This will give you a frame of reference for directional control during takeoff.
        2) You will feel more confident about having everything under control.

    c. After taxiing onto the runway, your airplane should be aligned with the runway centerline, and the nosewheel (or tailwheel) should be straight (or centered).

7. **The applicant demonstrates the ability to confirm takeoff power and proper engine and flight instrument indications prior to rotation.**

    a.   Recheck that the mixture is set in accordance with your POH/AFM.

    b.   Power should be added smoothly to allow for a controllable transition to flying airspeed.

        1)   Applying power too quickly can cause engine surging, backfiring, and a possible overboosting situation (turbocharged engines). These conditions cause unnecessary engine wear as well as possible failure.

        2)   Applying power too slowly wastes runway length.

    c.   Use the power setting that is recommended in your POH/AFM, usually full power with the throttle fully open.

    d.   Engine instruments must be monitored during the entire maneuver.

        1)   Listen for any indication of power loss or engine roughness.

        2)   Monitoring enables you to notice immediately any malfunctions or indication of insufficient power or other potential problems. Do not commit to liftoff unless all engine indications are normal.

8. **The applicant demonstrates the ability to rotate and lift off at the recommended airspeed and accelerate to V_Y (or other speed as appropriate for the aircraft).**

    a.   As your airplane accelerates, check your airspeed indicator to ensure that the needle is moving and operating properly.

        1)   Call out your airspeed as you accelerate to V_R, e.g., "40, 60, 80."

        2)   Do not focus all of your attention on your airspeed. Remember to look outside and ensure the airplane is tracking down the runway centerline.

    b.   The best takeoff attitude requires only minimal pitch adjustments just after liftoff to establish the best-rate-of-climb airspeed, V_Y. The airplane should be allowed to fly off the ground in its normal takeoff (i.e., best-rate-of-climb) attitude, if possible.

Your airplane's V_R _____.

    c.   If your POH/AFM does not recommend a V_R, use the following procedure from the FAA's *Airplane Flying Handbook* (FAA-H-8083-3).

        1)   When all the flight controls become effective during the takeoff roll in a nosewheel-type airplane, back elevator pressure should be gradually applied to raise the nosewheel slightly off the runway, thus establishing the liftoff attitude. This is referred to as rotating.

            a)   In tailwheel-type airplanes, the tail should first be allowed to rise off the ground slightly to permit the airplane to accelerate more rapidly.

        2)   At this point, the position of the nose in relation to the horizon should be noted; then elevator pressure should be applied as necessary to hold this attitude.

            a)   On both types of airplanes, the wings must be kept level by applying aileron pressure as necessary.

    d.   Forcing your airplane into the air by applying excessive back elevator pressure only results in an excessively high pitch attitude and may delay the takeoff.

        1)   Excessive and rapid changes in pitch attitude result in proportionate changes in the effects of torque, thus making the airplane more difficult to control.

        2)   If you force your airplane to leave the ground before adequate speed is attained, the wing's angle of attack may be excessive, causing the airplane to settle back onto the runway or to stall.

        3)   Also, jerking the airplane off the ground reduces passenger comfort.

e.   If insufficient back pressure is held to maintain the correct takeoff attitude or the nose is allowed to lower excessively, the airplane may settle back to the runway. This occurs because the angle of attack is decreased and lift is diminished to the point where it will not support the airplane.

f.   Some airplanes and many high-performance airplanes require conscious rearward elevator pressure at V_R to establish the liftoff.

1)   Without this conscious control pressure, the airplane may start to wheelbarrow (i.e., the main wheels break ground before the nose wheel).

2)   Note that, in general, high-performance airplanes have heavier control pressures and require more deliberate application of control movements.

g.   During takeoffs in a strong, gusty wind, increase V_R to provide an additional margin of safety in the event of sudden changes in wind direction immediately after liftoff.

9.   **The applicant demonstrates the ability to establish a pitch attitude that will maintain V_Y +10/-5 knots (or other airspeed as appropriate for the aircraft).**

a.   Apply the right amount of pressure to the yoke to maintain V_Y.

Your airplane's V_Y _____.

b.   By looking outside the airplane to keep the same view of the horizon, it will be easier to maintain V_Y than staring at the airspeed indicator.

10.   **The applicant demonstrates the ability to retract the landing gear and flaps in accordance with manufacturer's guidance.**

a.   Landing gear retraction is normally started when you can no longer land on the remaining runway and a positive rate of climb is established on the VSI.

b.   Before retracting the landing gear, apply the brakes momentarily to stop the rotation of the wheels to avoid excessive vibration on the gear mechanism.

1)   Centrifugal force caused by the rapidly rotating wheels expands the diameter of the tires, and if mud or other debris has accumulated in the wheel wells, the rotating wheels may rub as they enter.

c.   An airplane with retractable landing gear may have a V_Y for both gear up and gear down.

Your airplane's V_Y (gear down) _____.
V_Y (gear up)   _____.

d.   Make any necessary pitch adjustment to maintain the proper V_Y.

e.   Follow the gear retraction procedure in your POH/AFM.

1)   The landing gear is normally retracted before the flaps.

f.   The wing flaps are normally retracted after the surrounding terrain and obstacles have been cleared.

1)   Retract the flaps smoothly and make the needed pitch adjustments to maintain V_Y.

11.   **The applicant demonstrates the ability to maintain takeoff power and V_Y +10/-5 knots or to a safe maneuvering altitude.**

a.   After the recommended climbing airspeed (V_Y) has been well established and a safe maneuvering altitude has been reached (normally 500 to 1,000 ft. AGL), the power should be adjusted to the recommended climb setting and the pitch adjusted for cruise climb airspeed.

1)   Cruise climb offers the advantages of higher airspeed for increased engine cooling, higher groundspeed, better visibility ahead of the airplane, and greater passenger comfort.

b.   Most trainer-type airplane manufacturers recommend maintaining maximum power until reaching your selected cruising altitude.

c.   Follow the procedures in your POH/AFM.

12. **The applicant demonstrates the ability to maintain directional control and proper wind-drift correction throughout the takeoff and climb.**

    a. Maintain directional control on the runway centerline.

        1) Rudder pressure must be promptly and smoothly applied to counteract yawing forces (from wind and/or torque) so that your airplane will continue straight down the center of the runway.

        2) During a crosswind takeoff roll, you will normally apply downwind rudder pressure since, on the ground, your airplane (especially tailwheel-type) will tend to weathervane into the wind.

        3) When takeoff power is applied, torque, which yaws the airplane to the left, may be sufficient to counteract the weathervaning tendency caused by a right crosswind.

            a) On the other hand, it may also aggravate the tendency to swerve left with a left crosswind.

    b. Adjust aileron deflection during acceleration.

        1) During crosswind takeoffs, the aileron deflection into the wind should be decreased as appropriate airspeed increases.

            a) As the forward speed of your airplane increases and the crosswind becomes more of a relative headwind, holding of full aileron into the wind should be reduced.

        2) You will feel increasing pressure on the controls as the ailerons become more effective.

            a) Your objective is to release enough pressure to keep the wings level.

            b) The crosswind component does not completely vanish, so some aileron pressure will need to be maintained to prevent the upwind wing from rising.

                i) This will hold that wing down so that your airplane will, immediately after liftoff, be slipping into the wind enough to counteract drift.

    c. In a crosswind takeoff, as the nosewheel or tailwheel rises off the runway, holding the aileron control into the wind should result in the downwind wing rising and the downwind main wheel lifting off the runway first, with the remainder of the takeoff roll being made on the other main wheel (i.e., on the side from which the wind is coming).

        1) This is preferable to side skipping (which would occur if you did not turn the control yoke into the wind and use opposite rudder).

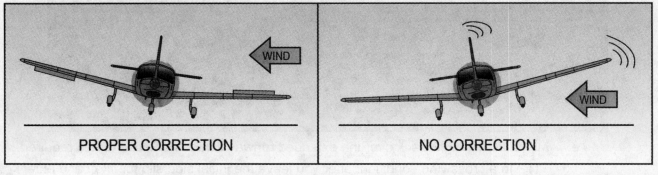

PROPER CORRECTION   NO CORRECTION

        2) If a significant crosswind exists, the main wheels should be held on the ground slightly longer than in a normal takeoff so that a smooth but very definite liftoff can be made.

            a) Accomplish this by applying slightly less back pressure on the control yoke as you near V_R.

      b)   This procedure will allow the airplane to leave the ground under more positive control so that it will definitely remain airborne while the proper amount of drift correction is established.

      c)   More importantly, it will avoid imposing excessive side loads on the landing gear and prevent possible damage that would result from the airplane settling back to the runway while drifting (due to the crosswind).

    3)   As both main wheels leave the runway and ground friction no longer resists drifting, the airplane will be slowly carried sideways with the wind unless you maintain adequate drift correction.

d.   In the initial crosswind climb, the airplane will be slipping (upwind wing down to prevent drift and opposite rudder to align your flight path with the runway) into the wind sufficiently to counteract the drifting effect of the wind and to increase stability during the transition to flight.

    1)   After your airplane is safely off the runway and a positive rate of climb is established, the airplane should be headed toward the wind to establish just enough crab to counteract the wind, and then the wings should be rolled level.

    2)   The climb while in this crab should be continued so as to follow a ground track aligned with the runway centerline.

    3)   Center the ball in the inclinometer with proper rudder pressure throughout the climb.

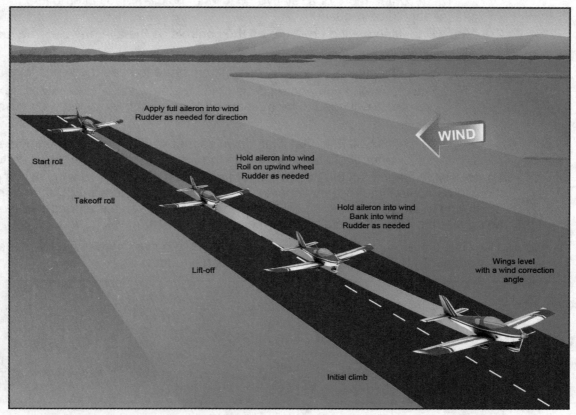

e.   Maintain a straight track over the extended runway centerline until a turn is required.

    1)   In a crosswind condition, after you leave the initial side slip for liftoff and enter the crab for climbout, the crab should be maintained as needed to continue along the extended runway centerline until a turn on course or the crosswind leg is initiated.

    2)   It is important to remain aligned with the runway to avoid the hazards of drifting into obstacles or the path of another aircraft that may be taking off from a parallel runway.

13. **The applicant demonstrates the ability to comply with responsible environmental practices, including noise abatement and published departure procedures.**

    a. When taking off and climbing, follow published departure procedures, including any established noise abatement procedures.

        1) You must comply with any established noise abatement procedures.

            a) A noise abatement policy is developed by the airport authority or city and is a local ordinance. Thus, you can be cited by the city for violation of the policy.

            b) Flying over towns and communities can create noise complaints.

            c) Many airports have been forced to provide noise mitigation to properties in their surrounding communities. These can be very expensive, resulting in higher fees for airports and aircraft operators.

            d) For example, the Hartsfield-Jackson Atlanta International Airport has provided sound insulation and/or relocated residents at a cost.

    b. The Chart Supplement will list that an airport has a noise abatement procedure in effect under "airport remarks."

        1) Other pilot guides may contain more detailed information on an airport's noise abatement procedures.

    c. A key to complying with noise abatement is to put as much distance as possible between you and the ground, as quickly as possible.

        1) Use the longest runway available.
        2) Rotate at V_R and climb out at V_X or V_Y, as recommended in your POH/AFM.
        3) Reduce power to climb power, and transition to a cruise climb as appropriate.

            a) The reduction to climb power will reduce the noise of your engine, and the transition to cruise climb airspeed will reduce the time you are over the noise monitors and noise sensitive areas.

    d. If you are flying from an unfamiliar airport that has a noise abatement policy, you should contact the airport's noise abatement office for details.

    e. You should conduct your operations responsibly with respect to the environment.

        1) For example, when taking fuel samples during preflight preparation, do not dump fuel on the ground. Consider reusing the fuel if it is clean, or dispose of it properly. Your local FBO or airport manager can advise about proper disposal methods.

14. **The applicant demonstrates the ability to complete the appropriate checklist.**

    a. Use and complete your takeoff and climb checklist from Section 4, Normal Procedures, of your POH/AFM.

15. **The applicant demonstrates the ability to comply with the manufacturer's recommended emergency procedures related to the takeoff sequence.**

    a. The key to successful management of an emergency situation and/or preventing a non-normal situation from progressing into a true emergency is a thorough familiarity with, and adherence to, the procedures developed by the airplane manufacturer and contained in the POH/AFM for the particular make and model airplane.

        1) For example, one particular procedure could entail engine failure on takeoff. Before a safe maneuvering altitude is attained, it is usually inadvisable to attempt to turn back to the field from where the takeoff was made. Instead, it is safer to immediately establish the proper glide attitude and select a field directly ahead or slightly to either side of the takeoff path.

END OF SKILLS ELEMENT

25.4 COMMON ERRORS

A.   Common Errors during a Normal Takeoff and Climb

1.   **Improper initial positioning of flight controls and wing flaps**

   a.   If a crosswind is present, FULL aileron should be held into the wind initially.

   b.   Flaps should be visually checked to ensure that they are in the proper position recommended by your POH/AFM.

   1)   If used, position the flaps prior to taxiing onto the active runway.

2.   **Improper power application**

   a.   Power should be applied smoothly.

   b.   Applying power too quickly can cause engine surging, backfiring, and a possible overboost situation (turbocharged engines).

   c.   Applying power too slowly wastes runway length.

3.   **Inappropriate removal of hand from throttle**

   a.   Throughout this maneuver, your hand should remain on the throttle.

   b.   Exceptions are raising the wing flaps and landing gear, and/or adjusting the trim during the climb. After completing these, your hand should return to the throttle.

4.   **Poor directional control**

   a.   Directional control is made with smooth, prompt, positive rudder corrections.

   1)   The effects of torque at the initial power application tend to pull the nose to the left.

   b.   The rudder will become more effective as airspeed increases.

   c.   A tendency to overcorrect will find you meandering back and forth across the centerline.

5.   **Improper use of ailerons**

   a.   As the forward speed of the airplane increases and the ailerons become more effective, the mechanical holding of full aileron should be reduced.

   b.   Some aileron pressure must be maintained to keep the upwind wing from rising.

   c.   If the upwind wing rises, a "skipping" action may develop.

   1)   This side skipping imposes severe side stresses on the landing gear and could result in structural failure.

6.   **Neglecting to monitor all engine and flight instruments**

   a.   Develop a quick scan of the engine gauges to detect any abnormality.

   1)   Perform the scan several times during your ground roll and then several times during climbout.

   a)   Engine temperatures: EGT, cylinder head, and oil
   b)   RPM and fuel pressure
   c)   Oil pressure

   2)   Call out full power when you attain it on the takeoff roll, e.g., "Max RPM."

   3)   In a glass cockpit airplane, watch for engine caution and warning annunciators, but do not rely on them completely. Maintain a vigilant scan as well.

   b.   Call out your airspeed as you accelerate.

7. **Improper pitch attitude during liftoff**

   a. Applying excessive back pressure will result only in an excessively high pitch attitude and delay the takeoff.

   b. If not enough elevator pressure is held to maintain the correct attitude, your airplane may settle back onto the runway, and this will delay the climb to a safe altitude.

   c. Improper trim setting will make it harder for you to maintain the proper takeoff attitude by causing an increase in control pressure that you must hold.

      1) In a tailwheel airplane with improper trim set, you may need to use forward elevator pressure to raise the tail and then lower the tail for takeoff attitude, thus leading to directional problems.

8. **Failure to establish and maintain proper climb configuration and airspeed**

   a. Use your POH/AFM checklists to determine the proper climb configuration and airspeed.

   b. Maintain airspeed by making small pitch changes using outside visual references; then cross-check with the airspeed indicator.

9. **Raising the landing gear before a positive rate of climb is established**

   a. Airplanes, especially in windy conditions, can become airborne in ground effect before sufficient airspeed is attained to sustain flight.

      1) If the landing gear is immediately raised on liftoff, the airplane may settle back down and strike the runway.

   b. Also, if an engine problem develops immediately after liftoff, the airplane should be landed immediately.

      1) If you have to wait for the landing gear to extend, there may be insufficient time and/or runway available.

10. **Drift during climb**

   a. You must use all available outside references, including looking behind, to maintain a track of the runway centerline extension.

   b. This will assist you in avoiding hazardous obstacles or preventing drifting into the path of another airplane that may be taking off from a parallel runway.

   c. Cross-check with the airplane's heading indicator, using enough right rudder to maintain heading with the wings level.

END OF COMMON ERRORS

STUDY UNIT TWENTY-SIX
NORMAL APPROACH AND LANDING

Task	Task B. Normal Approach and Landing
References	FAA-H-8083-2, FAA-H-8083-3; POH/AFM
Objective	To determine that the applicant exhibits satisfactory knowledge, risk management, and skills associated with a normal approach and landing with emphasis on proper use and coordination of flight controls. **Note:** If a crosswind condition does not exist, the applicant's knowledge of crosswind elements must be evaluated through oral testing.
Knowledge	The applicant demonstrates understanding of:
PA.IV.B.K1	1. Available landing distance.
PA.IV.B.K2	2. Stabilized approach and interpretation and use of visual glide scope indicators.
PA.IV.B.K3	3. Energy management.
PA.IV.B.K4	4. Atmospheric conditions.
PA.IV.B.K5	5. Wind conditions and effects.
PA.IV.B.K6	6. Emergency procedures during approach and landing.
PA.IV.B.K7	7. Land and hold short operations (LAHSO) or option to refuse LAHSO restriction.
Risk Management	The applicant demonstrates the ability to identify, assess and mitigate risks, encompassing:
PA.IV.B.R1	1. Failure to select the appropriate runway based on wind, pilot capability, and airplane limitations.
PA.IV.B.R2	2. Exceeding the manufacturer's maximum demonstrated crosswind component.
PA.IV.B.R3	3. Windshear.
PA.IV.B.R4	4. Tailwind.
PA.IV.B.R5	5. Wake turbulence.
PA.IV.B.R6	6. Task management.
PA.IV.B.R7	7. Low altitude maneuvering.
PA.IV.B.R8	8. Collision avoidance, scanning, obstacle and wire strike avoidance.
PA.IV.B.R9	9. Failure to follow the right-of-way rules.
PA.IV.B.R10	10. Obstacles on approach and landing paths.
PA.IV.B.R11	11. Failure to recognize the need to perform a go-round/rejected landing.
PA.IV.B.R12	12. Low altitude stall/spin.
PA.IV.B.R13	13. Land and hold short operations (LAHSO).
PA.IV.B.R14	14. Failure to adhere to sterile cockpit requirement.
Skills	The applicant demonstrates the ability to:
PA.IV.B.S1	1. Ensure the aircraft is on the correct/assigned runway.
PA.IV.B.S2	2. Scan the landing runway/areas and adjoining areas for possible obstructions for landing.
PA.IV.B.S3	3. Complete the appropriate checklist.
PA.IV.B.S4	4. Consider the wind conditions, landing surface, and obstructions to select a suitable touchdown point.
PA.IV.B.S5	5. Establish the recommended approach and landing configuration and airspeed, and adjust pitch attitude and power as required.
PA.IV.B.S6	6. Maintain a stabilized approach and recommended airspeed, or in its absence, not more than 1.3 V_{SO}, with wind gust factor applied +10/-5 knots, or as recommended by the aircraft manufacturer for the aircraft type and gust velocity.
PA.IV.B.S7	7. Make smooth, timely, and correct control applications:
PA.IV.B.S7a	a. During the round out and touchdown.
PA.IV.B.S8	8. Touch down smoothly at a speed that provides little or no aerodynamic lift.
PA.IV.B.S9	9. Touch down within the available runway area, within 400 feet beyond a specified point with no drift, and with the airplane's longitudinal axis aligned with and over the runway centerline.
PA.IV.B.S10	10. Maintain crosswind correction and directional control throughout the approach and landing sequence.
PA.IV.B.S11	11. Execute a timely go-around decision when the approach cannot be made within the tolerances specified above or for any other condition that may result in an unsafe approach or landing.
PA.IV.B.S12	12. Utilize after landing runway incursion avoidance procedures.

A. General Information

    1. The objective of this task is for you to demonstrate your knowledge, risk management, and skills related to a normal approach and landing with emphasis on proper use and coordination of flight controls.

        a. NOTE: If a crosswind condition does not exist, your knowledge of crosswind procedures will be orally tested.

    2. The content of Subunits 26.1 and 26.2 is abbreviated based on the assumption that you have thoroughly read and understood pages 287 through 304, and the additional common task topics found in Part II. The task objectives and specific references are provided here for your convenience.

26.1 KNOWLEDGE

A. Task Objectives

    1. **The applicant demonstrates understanding of available landing distance.**

        a. For information on available landing distance, see Section IV Introduction, Knowledge, item B., beginning on page 289.

    2. **The applicant demonstrates understanding of stabilized approach and interpretation and use of visual glide scope indicators.**

        a. For information on stabilized approach and interpretation and use of visual glide scope indicators, see Section IV Introduction, Knowledge, item D., beginning on page 292.

    3. **The applicant demonstrates understanding of energy management.**

        a. For information on energy management, see Study Unit 8, Subunit 1, beginning on page 71.

    4. **The applicant demonstrates understanding of atmospheric conditions.**

        a. For information on atmospheric conditions, see Study Unit 9, Subunit 1, beginning on page 77.

    5. **The applicant demonstrates understanding of wind conditions and effects.**

        a. For information on wind conditions and effects, see Study Unit 9, Subunit 3, beginning on page 80.

    6. **The applicant demonstrates understanding of emergency procedures during approach and landing.**

        a. For information on emergency procedures during approach and landing, see Study Unit 8, Subunit 2, item G., on page 76.

    7. **The applicant demonstrates understanding of land and hold short operations (LAHSO) or option to refuse LAHSO restriction.**

        a. For information on LAHSO or the option to refuse LAHSO restriction, see Section IV Introduction, Knowledge, item F., beginning on page 297.

END OF KNOWLEDGE ELEMENT

26.2 RISK MANAGEMENT

A.   Task Objectives

1.   **The applicant demonstrates the ability to identify, assess, and mitigate risks encompassing failure to select the appropriate runway based on wind, pilot capability, and airplane limitations.**

   a.   For information on selecting the appropriate runway based on wind, pilot capability, and airplane limitations, see Section IV Introduction, Risk Management, item A., beginning on page 299.

2.   **The applicant demonstrates the ability to identify, assess, and mitigate risks encompassing exceeding the manufacturer's maximum demonstrated crosswind component.**

   a.   For information on crosswind component, see Study Unit 9, Subunit 3, beginning on page 80.

3.   **The applicant demonstrates the ability to identify, assess, and mitigate risks encompassing windshear.**

   a.   For information on windshear, see Study Unit 9, Subunit 4, beginning on page 81.

4.   **The applicant demonstrates the ability to identify, assess, and mitigate risks encompassing tailwind.**

   a.   For information on tailwind, see Study Unit 9, Subunit 3, beginning on page 80.

5.   **The applicant demonstrates the ability to identify, assess, and mitigate risks encompassing wake turbulence.**

   a.   For information on wake turbulence, see Study Unit 7, Subunit 7, beginning on page 69.

6.   **The applicant demonstrates the ability to identify, assess, and mitigate risks encompassing task management.**

   a.   For information on task management, see Study Unit 6, Subunit 1, beginning on page 49.

7.   **The applicant demonstrates the ability to identify, assess, and mitigate risks encompassing low altitude maneuvering.**

   a.   For information on low altitude maneuvering, see Section IV Introduction, Risk Management, item C., beginning on page 299.

8.   **The applicant demonstrates the ability to identify, assess, and mitigate risks encompassing collision avoidance, scanning, and obstacle and wire strike avoidance.**

   a.   For information on collision avoidance, scanning, and obstacle avoidance, see Study Unit 7, Subunit 4, beginning on page 66.

   b.   For information on wire strikes, see Study Unit 7, Subunit 6, beginning on page 68.

9.   **The applicant demonstrates the ability to identify, assess, and mitigate risks encompassing failure to follow the right-of-way rules.**

   a.   For information on right-of-way rules, see Section IV Introduction, Risk Management, item F., beginning on page 300.

10.   **The applicant demonstrates the ability to identify, assess, and mitigate risks encompassing obstacles on approach and landing paths.**

   a.   For information on obstacles on approach and landing paths, see Section IV Introduction, Risk Management, item D., beginning on page 300.

11. **The applicant demonstrates the ability to identify, assess, and mitigate risks encompassing failure to recognize the need to perform a go-around/rejected landing.**

   a.   For information on failure to recognize the need to perform a go-around/rejected landing, see Section IV Introduction, Risk Management, item G., beginning on page 301.

12. **The applicant demonstrates the ability to identify, assess, and mitigate risks encompassing low altitude stall/spin.**

   a.   For information on low altitude stall/spin, see Section IV Introduction, Risk Management, item H., beginning on page 301.

13. **The applicant demonstrates the ability to identify, assess, and mitigate risks encompassing land and hold short operations (LAHSO).**

   a.   For information on LAHSO, see Section IV Introduction, Risk Management, item J., beginning on page 303.

14. **The applicant demonstrates the ability to identify, assess, and mitigate risks encompassing failure to adhere to sterile cockpit requirements.**

   a.   For information on sterile cockpit requirements, see Study Unit 6, Subunit 2, beginning on page 51.

END OF RISK MANAGEMENT ELEMENT

26.3 SKILLS

A. Task Objectives

1. **The applicant demonstrates the ability to ensure the aircraft is on the correct/ assigned runway.**

    a. The FAA has established standard airport and runway markings. Because most airports are marked in this manner, it is important for you to know and understand these markings.

        1) This same standardization is also found in airport lighting and other airport visual aids.

    b. The segmented circle system, if installed, provides traffic pattern information at airports without operating control towers. It consists of the following:

        1) The **segmented circle** is located in a position affording maximum visibility to pilots in the air and on the ground. A wind and/or landing direction indicator is usually in the center.

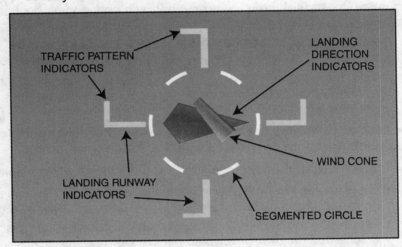

        2) **Landing runway (strip) indicators** are installed in pairs as shown in the segmented circle above and are used to show the alignment of runways.

    c. Maintain orientation with the runway in use.

        1) While conducting airport traffic pattern operations, you must remain oriented with the runway in use.

        2) Know which runway is in use, and plan to enter properly and remain in the correct traffic pattern.

        3) When approaching an airport, you should visualize your position from the airport and the relative direction of the runway. Use the airplane's heading indicator to assist you.

    d. Confirm runway number with heading indicator during all traffic pattern legs.

    e. At airports with operating control towers, pilots can ensure the aircraft is on the correct/ assigned runway by

        1) Understanding and following ATC instructions and clearances;

        2) Using an airport diagram;

        3) Knowing the meaning of the visual aids available at the airport, such as airfield markings, signs, and lighting; and

        4) If it doesn't look right, sound right, or feel right, it probably isn't right. STOP AND ASK!

    f. When on final, check your runway entrance against the primary signs and your expected route. Make one last instrument scan to ensure that the aircraft heading is aligned with the heading bug and/or runway heading.

2. **The applicant demonstrates the ability to scan the landing runway/areas and adjoining areas for possible obstructions for landing.**

    a.   During your approach, look for any hazards or obstructions and then evaluate how they may affect your approach and selection of a suitable touchdown point.

    b.   The pilot must avoid runway incursions and ensure that there is no conflict with other traffic prior to landing.

        1)   Prior to landing, scan to make certain that the landing area and path are clear of other aircraft, vehicles, persons, livestock, wildlife (including birds), etc.

        2)   At controlled airports, this is a function of ATC, but you must also check for conflicts with other aircraft or other hazards.

        3)   At uncontrolled airports, you should announce your intentions on the appropriate CTAF.

3. **The applicant demonstrates the ability to complete the appropriate checklist.**

    a.   Use the before-landing checklist in your POH/AFM to ensure that you follow the proper sequence in establishing the correct approach and landing configuration for your airplane.

    b.   You should initially start the checklist at midpoint on the downwind leg with the power reduction beginning once you are abeam your intended point of landing.

        1)   By the time you turn on final and align your airplane with the runway centerline, you should be in the final landing configuration. Confirm this by completing your checklist once again.

4. **The applicant demonstrates the ability to consider the wind conditions, landing surface, and obstructions to select a suitable touchdown point.**

    a.   You should consider the wind conditions and obstacles when planning your approach.

        1)   If there is going to be a strong headwind on final, you should position the base leg closer to the runway than you would if the wind were light.

        2)   Obstacles along the final approach path will cause you to plan to be at a higher altitude on final than you would if there were no obstacles.

    b.   After considering the conditions, you should select a touchdown point that is beyond the runway's landing threshold but well within the first one-third portion of the runway.

        1)   After you select your point, you should identify it to your evaluator.

    c.   Once you have selected your touchdown point, you need to select your aim point. The aim point will be the point at the end of your selected glide path, not your touchdown point. Thus, your aim point will be short of your touchdown point.

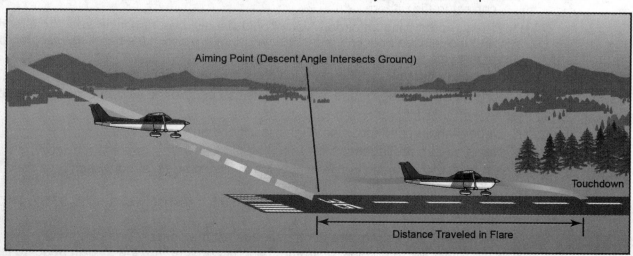

Aiming Point (Descent Angle Intersects Ground)

Touchdown

Distance Traveled in Flare

5. **The applicant demonstrates the ability to establish the recommended approach and landing configuration and airspeed, and adjust pitch attitude and power as required.**

    a. Properly configuring your airplane throughout the various approach segments will assist you in flying a stabilized approach.

        1) On the downwind leg, you should complete the before-landing checklist in your POH/AFM, which includes gear extension (if retractable).

            a) When abeam of your intended landing point, you should reduce the power and hold altitude constant. As the airspeed slows below the maximum flap extended speed (V_{FE}), you should partially lower the flaps and begin your descent.

In your airplane, V_{FE} ———.

        2) On the base leg, the flaps may be extended farther, but full flaps are not recommended at this point in the pattern due to increasing drag, decreasing speed, and the need to turn 90° onto the final approach course, which will reduce the vertical component of lift.

        3) Once aligned with the runway centerline on the final approach, you should make the final flap selection. This is normally full flaps.

            a) In turbulent air or strong gusty winds, you may elect not to use full flaps. This will allow you to maintain control more easily at a higher approach speed.

                i) With less than full flaps, your airplane will be in a higher nose-up attitude.

    b. The approach and landing configuration means that the gear is down (if retractable), wing flaps are extended, and you are maintaining a reduced power setting.

    c. The objective of a good final approach is to descend at an angle and airspeed that will permit your airplane to reach the desired touchdown point at an airspeed that will result in a minimum of floating just before touchdown.

        1) A fundamental key to flying a stabilized approach is the interrelationship of pitch and power.

            a) This interrelationship means that any changes to one element in the approach equation (e.g., airspeed, attitude) must be compensated for by adjustments in the other.

        2) Power should be adjusted as necessary to control the sink rate or to attain the desired altitudes along the approach path, and the pitch attitude should be adjusted SIMULTANEOUSLY to control the airspeed

            a) By lowering the nose of your airplane and reducing power to keep your approach airspeed constant, you can descend at a higher rate to correct for being too high in the approach.

        3) The important point is never to let your airspeed drop below the proper approach speed and never to let your airplane sink below the selected glide path.

d.   When you are established on final, you should use pitch to fly your airplane to the aim point.

1)   If the aim point has no apparent movement in your windshield, then you are on a constant glide path to the aim point. No pitch correction is needed.

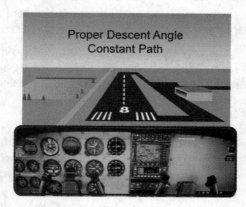

2)   If the aim point appears to move down your windshield or toward you, then you will overshoot the aim point and you need to pitch down.

a)   As you pitch down, reduce power to maintain approach speed.

3)   If the aim point appears to move up your windshield or away from you, then you will undershoot the aim point and you need to pitch up.

a)   As you pitch up, increase power to maintain approach speed.

e.   During the approach to a landing, power is at a considerably lower-than-cruise setting, and the airplane is flying at a relatively slower airspeed. Thus, you must trim your airplane to compensate for the change in aerodynamic forces.

6. **The applicant demonstrates the ability to maintain a stabilized approach and recommended airspeed, or in its absence, not more than 1.3 V_{SO}, with wind gust factor applied +10/-5 knots, or as recommended by the aircraft manufacturer for the aircraft type and gust velocity.**

   a. Airspeed control is the most important factor in achieving landing precision. A well-executed landing begins in the traffic pattern with the proper setup and a stabilized approach.

      1) Once on final approach, slight adjustments in pitch and power may be necessary to maintain the descent attitude and the desired airspeed.

      2) On final approach, you should use the airspeed in your POH/AFM. In the absence of the manufacturer's recommended airspeed, a speed equal to 1.3 V_{S0} should be used.

         a) EXAMPLE: If V_{S0} in your airplane is 60 kt., the airspeed on final approach should be 78 kt. (1.3 × 60).

   In your airplane, final approach speed (POH/AFM) _____, or 1.3 V_{S0} _____.

         b) Make necessary adjustments to that speed if you are in turbulent air or strong, gusty winds.

         c) Inform your evaluator of your final approach airspeed.

   b. The term **stabilized approach** means that your airplane is in a position where minimum input of all controls will result in a safe landing.

      1) Excessive control input at any juncture could be an indication of improper planning.

7. **The applicant demonstrates the ability to make smooth, timely, and correct control application during the round out and touchdown.**

   a. The roundout (flare) is a slow, smooth transition from a normal approach attitude to a landing attitude. When your airplane, in a normal descent, approaches what appears to be about 10 to 20 ft. above the ground, the roundout should be started, and, once started, should be a continuous process until the airplane touches down on the ground.

      1) To start the roundout, reduce power to idle and gradually apply back elevator pressure to increase the pitch attitude and angle of attack slowly. This will cause your airplane's nose to rise gradually toward the desired landing attitude.

         a) The angle of attack should be increased at a rate that will allow your airplane to continue settling slowly as forward speed decreases.

      2) When the angle of attack is increased, the lift is momentarily increased, thereby decreasing the rate of descent.

         a) Since power is normally reduced to idle during the roundout, the airspeed will gradually decrease. Decreasing airspeed, in turn, causes lift to decrease again, which must be controlled by raising the nose and further increasing the angle of attack.

         b) During the roundout, the airspeed is being decreased to touchdown speed while the lift is being controlled so your airplane will settle gently onto the runway.

      3) The rate at which the roundout is executed depends on your height above the ground, rate of descent, and the pitch attitude.

         a) A roundout started excessively high must be executed more slowly than one from a lower height to allow your airplane to descend to the ground while the proper landing attitude is being established.

          b)   The rate of rounding out must also be proportionate to the rate of closure with the ground. When your airplane appears to be descending slowly, the increase in pitch attitude must be made at a correspondingly slow rate.

    4)   Once the actual process of rounding out is started, the elevator control should not be pushed forward. If too much back pressure has been exerted, this pressure should be either slightly relaxed or held constant, depending on the degree of error.

          a)   In some cases, you may find it necessary to add power slightly to prevent an excessive rate of sink or a stall, both of which would result in a hard, drop-in landing.

    5)   You must be in the habit of keeping one hand on the throttle control throughout the approach and landing should a sudden and unexpected hazardous situation require an immediate application of power.

b.   The touchdown is the gentle settling of your airplane onto the runway. The touchdown should be made so that your airplane will touch down on the main gear at approximately stalling speed.

    1)   As your airplane settles, the proper landing attitude must be attained by application of remaining back elevator pressure.

    2)   It seems contradictory that the way to make a good landing is to try to hold your airplane's wheels a few inches off the ground as long as possible with the elevator.

          a)   Normally, when the wheels are about 2 or 3 ft. off the ground, the airplane will still be settling too fast for a gentle touchdown. Thus, this descent must be retarded by further back pressure on the elevator.

          b)   Since your airplane is already close to its stalling speed and is settling, this added back pressure will only slow the settling instead of stopping it. At the same time, it will result in your airplane's touching the ground in the proper nose-high landing attitude.

c.   During a normal landing, a nosewheel-type airplane should contact the ground in a tail-low attitude, with the main wheels touching down first so that no weight is on the nose wheel.

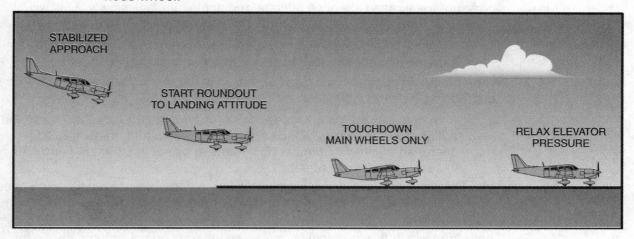

STABILIZED APPROACH

START ROUNDOUT TO LANDING ATTITUDE

TOUCHDOWN MAIN WHEELS ONLY

RELAX ELEVATOR PRESSURE

    1)   After the main wheels make initial contact with the ground, back pressure on the elevator control should be held to maintain a positive angle of attack for aerodynamic braking and to hold the nosewheel off the ground until the airplane decelerates.

2) As the airplane's momentum decreases, back pressure may be gradually relaxed to allow the nosewheel to settle gently onto the runway.

    a) This will permit prompt steering with the nosewheel, if it is of the steerable type.

    b) At the same time, it will cause a low angle of attack and negative lift on the wings to prevent floating or skipping and will allow the full weight of the airplane to rest on the wheels for better braking action.

d. During a normal landing in a tailwheel-type airplane, the roundout and touchdown should be timed so that the wheels of the main landing gear and tailwheel touch down simultaneously (i.e., a 3-point landing). This requires fine timing, technique, and judgment of distance and altitude.

1) When the wheels make contact with the ground, the elevator control should be carefully held fully back to hold the tail down and the tailwheel on the ground.

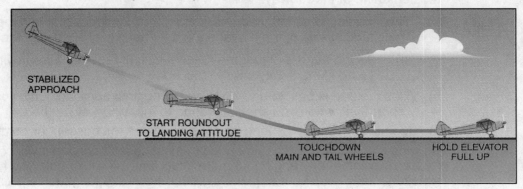

STABILIZED APPROACH

START ROUNDOUT TO LANDING ATTITUDE

TOUCHDOWN MAIN AND TAIL WHEELS

HOLD ELEVATOR FULL UP

    a) For the airplane equipped with a steerable tailwheel, holding the tailwheel on the ground provides more positive directional control and prevents any tendency for the airplane to nose over.

    b) If the tailwheel is not on the ground, easing back on the elevator control may cause the airplane to become airborne again because the change in attitude will increase the angle of attack and produce enough lift for the airplane to fly.

8. **The applicant demonstrates the ability to confirm touch down smoothly at a speed that provides little or no aerodynamic lift.**

a. At the point of touchdown, the airplane should be at a speed that is no longer capable of generating aerodynamic lift.

b. Touch down smoothly at the approximate stalling speed in the landing configuration.

1) However, due to ground effect and the operating weight of the airplane, the speed at touchdown may actually be slightly lower than the stall speed marked on the airspeed indicator.

2) You may hear the stall warning horn before touchdown, which is normal as the airplane is flying at a high angle of attack.

9. **The applicant demonstrates the ability to touch down within the available runway, within 400 feet beyond a specified point with no drift, and with the airplane's longitudinal axis aligned with and over the runway centerline.**

a. The evaluator may specify a point at which you are required to land. You will be expected to touch down within 400 ft. of this point.

b. You will demonstrate your proficiency and technique for judging distance and altitude.

1) Do not force the airplane onto the runway if you are not ready to land.

2) If you feel like you are not able to safely and smoothly land in the specified area, perform a go-around and attempt the landing again.

10. **The applicant demonstrates the ability to maintain crosswind correction and directional control throughout the approach and landing sequence.**

    a.   Immediately after the base-to-final approach turn is completed, the longitudinal axis of your airplane should be aligned with the centerline of the runway so that drift (if any) will be recognized immediately.

    b.   On a normal approach, with no wind drift, the longitudinal axis should be kept aligned with the runway centerline throughout the approach and landing.

        1)   Any corrections should be made with coordinated aileron and rudder pressure.

    c.   On a crosswind approach, there are two usual methods of maintaining the proper ground track on final approach. These are the crab method and the wing-low method.

        1)   The crab method is used first by establishing a heading (crab) toward the wind with the wings level so that your airplane's ground track remains aligned with the centerline of the runway.

            a)   This heading is maintained until just prior to touchdown, when the longitudinal axis of the airplane must be quickly aligned with the runway.

                i)   A high degree of judgment and timing is required in removing the crab immediately prior to touchdown.

            b)   This method is best to use while on a long final approach until you are on a short final, when you should change to the wing-low method.

            c)   Maintaining a crab as long as possible increases passenger comfort.

        2)   The wing-low method is recommended in most cases because it will compensate for a crosswind at any angle, but more importantly, it will enable you to simultaneously keep your airplane's ground track and longitudinal axis aligned with the runway centerline throughout the approach and landing.

            a)   To use this method, align your airplane's heading with the centerline of the runway, note the rate and direction of drift, and then promptly apply drift correction by lowering the upwind wing.

                i)   The amount the wing must be lowered depends on the rate of drift.

            b)   When you lower the wing, the airplane will tend to turn in that direction. Thus, it is necessary to simultaneously apply sufficient opposite rudder pressure to prevent the turn and keep the airplane's longitudinal axis aligned with the runway.

                i)   Drift is controlled with aileron, and the heading with rudder.

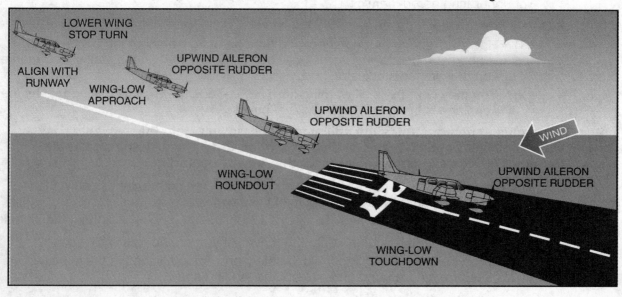

    c) Your airplane will now be slipping into the wind just enough that both the resultant flight path and the ground track are aligned with the runway.

    d) In a very strong crosswind, the required bank may be so steep that full opposite rudder will not prevent a turn. The wind is too strong to land safely on that particular runway with those wind conditions.

        i) Because the airplane's capabilities would be exceeded, it is imperative that the landing be made on a more favorable runway either at that airport or at an alternate airport.

d. The roundout during a crosswind landing approach can be made as in a normal landing approach, but the application of a crosswind correction must be continued as necessary to prevent drifting.

    1) Since the airspeed decreases as the roundout progresses, the flight controls gradually become less effective. Thus, the crosswind correction being held would become inadequate.

        a) It is therefore necessary to increase the deflection of the rudder and ailerons gradually to maintain the proper amount of drift correction.

    2) Do not level the wings. Keep the upwind wing down throughout the crosswind roundout.

        a) If the wings are leveled, your airplane will begin drifting, and the touchdown will occur while drifting, which imposes severe side stresses (loads) on the landing gear.

e. During a crosswind touchdown, you must make prompt adjustments to the crosswind correction to ensure that your airplane does not drift as it touches down.

    1) The crosswind correction should be maintained throughout the roundout, and the touchdown made on the upwind main wheel.

        a) As the forward momentum decreases after initial contact, the weight of the airplane will cause the downwind main wheel to settle gradually onto the runway.

    2)   In those airplanes having nosewheel steering interconnected with the rudder, the nosewheel may not be aligned with the runway as the wheels touch down because opposite rudder is being held in the crosswind correction.

        a)   This is the case in airplanes that have no centering cam built into the nose gear strut to keep the nosewheel straight until the strut is compressed.

        b)   To prevent swerving in the direction the nosewheel is offset, the corrective rudder pressure must be promptly relaxed just as the nosewheel touches down.

f.   Maintain directional control during the after-landing rollout on the runway.

    1)   The landing process must never be considered complete until your airplane decelerates to normal taxi speed during the landing roll or has been brought to a complete stop when clear of the runway.

        a)   Accidents have occurred as the result of pilots abandoning their vigilance and positive control after getting the airplane on the ground.

    2)   You must be alert for directional control problems immediately upon and after touchdown due to the ground friction on the wheels. The friction creates a pivot point on which a moment arm can act.

        a)   This is especially true in tailwheel-type airplanes because, unlike nosewheel-type airplanes, the CG is *behind* the main wheels.

            i)   Any difference between the direction in which the airplane is traveling and the direction in which it is headed will produce a moment about the pivot point of the wheels, and the airplane will tend to swerve.

        b)   Nosewheel-type airplanes make the task of directional control easier because the CG, being *ahead* of the main landing wheels, presents a moment arm that tends to straighten the airplane's path during the touchdown and after-landing roll.

            i)   This should not lull you into a false sense of security.

    3)   Another directional control problem in crosswind landings is due to the weathervaning tendency of your airplane. Characteristically, an airplane has a greater profile or side area behind the main landing gear than forward of it.

        a)   With the main landing wheels acting as a pivot point and the greater surface area exposed to a crosswind behind the pivot point, the airplane will tend to turn or weathervane into the wind.

        b)   This is characteristic of all airplanes, but it is more prevalent in the tailwheel type because the airplane's surface area behind the main landing gear is greater than in nosewheel-type airplanes.

    4)   Loss of directional control may lead to an aggravated, uncontrolled, tight turn on the ground (i.e., a ground loop).

        a)   The combination of centrifugal force acting on the CG and ground friction on the main wheels resisting it during the ground loop may cause the airplane to tip, or lean, enough for the outside wingtip to contact the ground.

            i)   This may impose a great enough sideward force to collapse the landing gear.

        b)   Tailwheel-type airplanes are most susceptible to ground loops late in the after-landing roll because rudder effectiveness decreases with the decreasing airflow along the rudder surface as the airplane slows.

    g.   The ailerons serve the same purpose on the ground as they do in the air; they change the lift and drag components of the wings.

        1)   While your airplane is decelerating during the after-landing roll, more and more aileron must be applied to keep the upwind wing from rising.

        2)   Since your airplane is slowing down and there is less airflow around the ailerons, they become less effective. At the same time, the relative wind is becoming more of a crosswind and exerting a greater lifting force on the upwind wing.

            a)   Consequently, when the airplane is coming to a full stop, the aileron control must be held FULLY toward the wind.

    h.   If available runway permits, the speed of the airplane should be allowed to dissipate in a normal manner by the friction and drag of the wheels on the ground.

        1)   Brakes may be used if needed to slow the airplane. This is normally done near the end of the after-landing roll to ensure the airplane is moving slowly enough to exit the runway in a controlled manner.

11.   **The applicant demonstrates the ability to execute a timely go-around decision when the approach cannot be made within the tolerances specified above or for any other condition that may result in an unsafe approach or landing.**

    a.   Establish a decision point on your final approach where, if you are not completely established and ready to land, you will execute a go-around.

        1)   It is important to remember that going around from a bad approach will not necessarily result in a failure. On the contrary, it shows the evaluator that you can make good decisions and that you are interested in safety.

            a)   You obviously cannot go-around repeatedly. At some point, you have to land the aircraft within the established tolerances.

    b.   For additional information on go-arounds, see Study Unit 32, "Go-Around/Rejected Landing," beginning on page 407.

12.   **The applicant demonstrates the ability to utilize after landing runway incursion avoidance procedures.**

    a.   After landing, be sure to clear the runway in a timely fashion.

        1)   Do not exit the runway above a safe taxi speed, and be sure to stop once the aircraft is clear of the runway area (i.e., fully across the hold short markings) and before crossing onto an intersecting taxiway or parallel runway.

        2)   In the case of ATC instructions to expedite your taxi, only accept them if you feel you can accommodate their request.

    b.   Visually clear intersecting taxiways/runways before crossing them, even if ATC has cleared you across.

    c.   Read back and confirm all ATC holding/crossing instructions/clearances.

END OF SKILLS ELEMENT

26.4 COMMON ERRORS

A.   Common Errors during a Normal Approach and Landing

1.   **Improper use of landing performance data and limitations**

a.   Use your POH/AFM to determine the appropriate airspeeds for a normal and crosswind approach and landing.

b.   In gusty and/or strong crosswinds, use the crosswind component chart to determine that you are not exceeding your airplane's crosswind limitations.

c.   Use your POH/AFM to determine data and limitations, and do not attempt to do better than the data.

2.   **Failure to establish approach and landing configuration at appropriate time or in proper sequence**

a.   Use the before-landing checklist in your POH/AFM to ensure that you follow the proper sequence in establishing the correct approach and landing configuration for your airplane.

b.   You should initially start the checklist at midpoint on the downwind leg with the power reduction beginning once you are abeam your intended point of landing.

1)   By the time you turn on final and align your airplane with the runway centerline, you should be in the final landing configuration. Confirm this by completing your checklist once again.

3.   **Failure to establish and maintain a stabilized approach**

a.   Once you are on final and aligned with the runway centerline, you should make small adjustments to pitch and power to establish the correct descent angle (i.e., glide path) and airspeed.

1)   Remember, you must make simultaneous adjustments to both pitch and power.
2)   Large adjustments will result in a roller coaster ride.

b.   Lock in your airspeed and glide path as soon as possible.

1)   Never let your airspeed go below your approach speed.
2)   Never let your airplane sink below your selected glide path or the glide path of a visual approach slope indicator (i.e., VASI or PAPI).

4.   **Inappropriate removal of hand from throttle**

a.   One hand should remain on the control yoke at all times.

b.   The other hand should remain on the throttle unless operating the microphone or making an adjustment, such as trim or flaps.

1)   Once you are on short final, your hand should remain on the throttle, even if ATC gives you instruction (e.g., cleared to land).

a)   Your first priority is to fly your airplane and avoid doing tasks that may distract you from maintaining control.

b)   Fly first; talk later.

c.   You must be in the habit of keeping one hand on the throttle in case a sudden and unexpected hazardous situation should require an immediate application of power.

5. **Improper technique during roundout and touchdown**

    a. High roundout

    1) This error occurs when you make the roundout too rapidly and your airplane is flying level too high above the runway.

       a) If you continue the roundout, you will increase the wings' angle of attack to the critical angle while reducing the airspeed. Thus, you will stall your airplane and drop hard onto the runway.

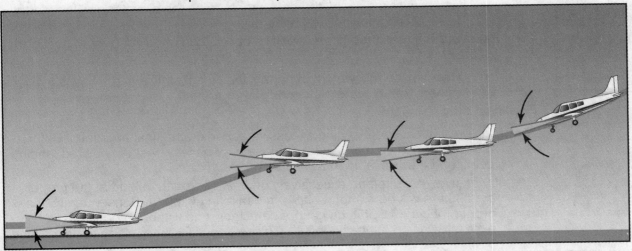

    2) To correct this, the pitch attitude should be held constant until the airplane decelerates enough to again start descending. Then the roundout can be continued to establish the proper landing attitude.

       a) Use this technique only when you have an adequate amount of airspeed. It may be necessary to add a slight amount of power to prevent the airspeed from decreasing excessively and to avoid losing lift too rapidly.

    3) Although back pressure on the elevator control may be relaxed slightly, the nose should not be lowered any perceptible amount to make the airplane descend when relatively close to the runway.

       a) The momentary decrease in lift resulting from lowering the nose (i.e., decreasing angle of attack) may be so great that a nosewheel-type airplane may contact the ground with the nosewheel, which can then collapse.

       b) Execute a go-around (see Study Unit 32, "Go-Around/Rejected Landing," beginning on page 407) anytime it appears that the nose should be lowered significantly.

b.   Late or rapid roundout

1)   Starting the roundout too late or pulling the elevator control back too rapidly to prevent your airplane from touching down prematurely can impose a heavy load factor on the wing and cause an accelerated stall.

a)   This is dangerous because it may cause your airplane to land extremely hard on the main landing wheels and then bounce back into the air.

i)   As your airplane contacts the ground, the tail will be forced down very rapidly by the back pressure on the elevator and the inertia acting downward on the tail.

2)   Recovery requires prompt and positive application of power prior to occurrence of the stall.

a)   This may be followed by a normal landing, if sufficient runway is available; otherwise, execute an immediate go-around.

c.   Floating during roundout

1)   This error is caused by using excessive speed on the final approach. Before touchdown can be made, your airplane may be well past the desired landing point, and the available runway may be insufficient.

2)   If you dive your airplane excessively on final approach to land at the proper point, there will be an appreciable increase in airspeed. Consequently, the proper touchdown attitude cannot be established without producing an excessive angle of attack and lift. This will cause your airplane to gain altitude.

3)   Failure to anticipate ground effect may also result in floating.

4)   The recovery will depend on the amount of floating, the effect of a crosswind (if any), and the amount of runway remaining.

a)   You must smoothly and gradually adjust the pitch attitude as your airplane decelerates to touchdown speed and starts to settle so that the proper landing attitude is attained at the moment of touchdown.

i)   The slightest error in judgment will result in either ballooning or bouncing.

b)   If a landing cannot be completed within 400 ft. of a specified point, you should immediately execute a go-around.

d. Ballooning during roundout

    1) If you misjudge the rate of sink during a landing and think your airplane is descending faster than it should, there is a tendency to increase the pitch attitude and angle of attack too rapidly.

        a) This not only stops the descent, but actually starts your airplane climbing (i.e., ballooning).

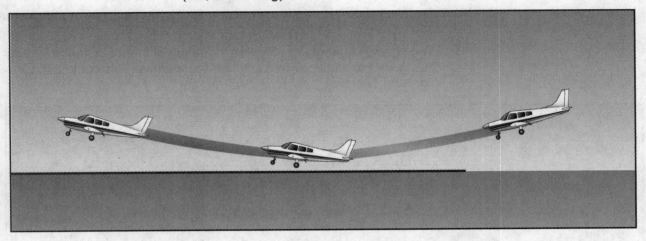

        b) Ballooning can be dangerous because the height above the ground is increasing and your airplane may be rapidly approaching a stalled condition.

    2) When ballooning is slight, a constant landing attitude may be held and the airplane allowed to settle onto the runway.

        a) You must be extremely cautious of ballooning when there is a crosswind present because the crosswind correction may be inadvertently released or it may become inadequate.

        b) Due to the lower airspeed after ballooning, the crosswind affects your airplane more. Consequently, the wing will have to be lowered even farther to compensate for the increased drift.

            i) You must ensure that the upwind wing is down and that directional control is maintained with opposite rudder.

    3) Depending on the severity of ballooning, the use of power may be helpful in cushioning the landing.

        a) By adding power, thrust can be increased to keep the airspeed from decelerating too rapidly and the wings from suddenly losing lift, but the throttle must be closed immediately after touchdown.

        b) Remember that torque will have been created as power was applied; thus, it will be necessary to use rudder pressure to counteract this effect.

    4) When ballooning is excessive, or if you have any doubts, you should immediately execute a go-around.

e. Bouncing during touchdown

1) When your airplane contacts the ground with a sharp impact as the result of an improper attitude or an excessive rate of sink, it tends to bounce back into the air.

a) Though your airplane's tires and shock struts provide some springing action, the airplane does not bounce as does a rubber ball.

b) Your airplane rebounds into the air because the wing's angle of attack was abruptly increased, producing a sudden addition of lift.

i) The change in angle of attack is the result of inertia instantly forcing the airplane's tail downward when the main wheels contact the ground sharply.

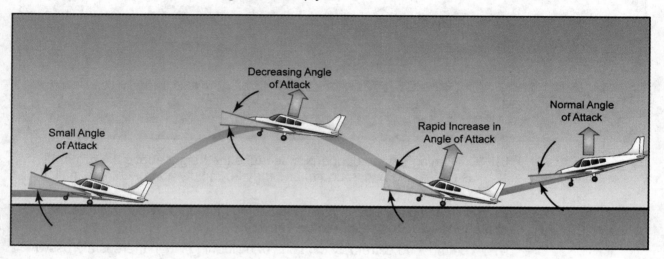

c) The severity of the bounce depends on the airspeed at the moment of contact and the degree to which the angle of attack, or pitch attitude, was increased.

2) The corrective action for a bounce is the same as for ballooning and similarly depends on its severity.

a) When it is very slight and there is not extreme change in your airplane's pitch attitude, a follow-up landing may be executed by applying sufficient power to cushion the subsequent touchdown and smoothly adjusting the pitch to the proper touchdown attitude.

3) Extreme caution and alertness must be exercised, especially when there is a crosswind. The crosswind correction will normally be released by inexperienced pilots when the airplane bounces.

a) When one main wheel of the airplane strikes the runway, the other wheel will touch down immediately afterward, and the wings will become level.

b) Then, with no crosswind correction as the airplane bounces, the wind will cause the airplane to roll with the wind, thus exposing even more surface to the crosswind and drifting the airplane more rapidly.

c) Remember, the upwind wing will have to be lowered even farther to compensate for the increased drift due to the slower airspeed.

f. Hard landing

1) When your airplane contacts the ground during landings, its vertical speed is instantly reduced to zero. Unless provision is made to slow this vertical speed and cushion the impact of touchdown, the force of contact with the ground may be so great as to cause structural damage to the airplane.

2) The purpose of pneumatic tires, rubber or oleo shock absorbers, and other such devices is, in part, to cushion the impact and to increase the time in which the airplane's vertical descent is stopped.

   a) The importance of this cushion may be understood from the computation that a 6-in. free fall on landing is roughly equivalent to a 340-fpm descent.

   b) Within a fraction of a second, your airplane must be slowed from this rate of vertical descent to zero, without damage.

      i) During this time, the landing gear together with some aid from the lift of the wings must supply the necessary force to counteract the force of the airplane's inertia and weight.

3) The lift decreases rapidly as the airplane's forward speed is decreased, and the force on the landing gear increases as the shock struts and tires are compressed by the impact of touchdown.

   a) When the descent stops, the lift will practically be zero, leaving the landing gear alone to carry both the airplane's weight and inertial forces.

   b) The load imposed at the instant of touchdown may easily be three or four times the actual weight of the airplane, depending on the severity of contact.

g. Touchdown in a drift or crab

1) If you have not taken adequate corrective action to avoid drift during a crosswind landing, the main wheels' tire treads offer resistance to the airplane's sideward movement in respect to the ground. Consequently, any sideward velocity of the airplane is abruptly decelerated, as shown in the figure below.

   a) This creates a moment around the main wheel when it contacts the ground, tending to overturn or tip the airplane.

   b) If the windward tip is raised by the action of this moment, all of the weight and shock of landing will be borne by one main wheel. This may cause structural damage.

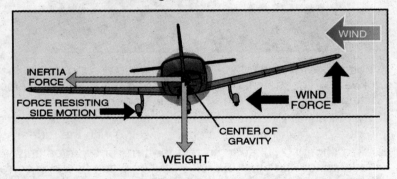

2) It is vital to prevent drift and keep the longitudinal axis of the airplane aligned with the runway during the roundout and touchdown.

6.   **Poor directional control after touchdown**

a.   Ground loop

1)   A ground loop is an uncontrolled turn during ground operation that may occur while taxiing or taking off, but especially during the after-landing roll.

a)   It is not always caused by drift or weathervaning, although these may cause the initial swerve. Other reasons may include careless use of rudder, an uneven ground surface, or a soft spot that retards one main wheel of the airplane.

2)   Due to the characteristics of an airplane equipped with a tailwheel, the forces that cause a ground loop increase as the swerve increases.

a)   The initial swerve develops centrifugal force and this, acting at the CG (located behind the main wheels), swerves the airplane even more.

b)   If allowed to develop, the centrifugal force produced may become great enough to tip the airplane until one wing strikes the ground.

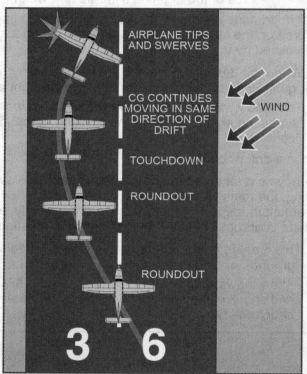

3)   A nosewheel-type airplane is less prone to ground loop. Since the CG is located forward of the main landing gear, anytime a swerve develops, centrifugal force acting on the CG will tend to stop the swerving action.

4)   If your airplane touches down while drifting or in a crab, you should apply aileron toward the high wing and stop the swerve with the rudder.

5)   Brakes should be used to correct for turns or swerves only when the rudder is inadequate. You must exercise caution when applying corrective brake action because it is very easy to over-control and aggravate the situation.

a)   If brakes are used, sufficient brake should be applied on the low wing (outside of the turn) to stop the swerve.

b)   When the wings are approximately level, the new direction must be maintained until the airplane has slowed to taxi speed or has stopped.

    b. Wing rising after touchdown

        1) When landing in a crosswind, there may be instances in which a wing will rise during the after-landing roll.

        2) Anytime an airplane is rolling on the ground in a crosswind condition, the upwind wing is receiving a greater force from the wind than is the downwind wing. This causes a lift differential.

            a) Also, the wind striking the fuselage on the upwind side may further raise the wing by tending to tip or roll the fuselage.

        3) The corrective action is for you immediately to apply more aileron pressure toward the high wing and maintain directional control.

            a) The sooner the aileron is applied, the more effective it will be.

            b) The farther a wing is allowed to rise before taking corrective action, the more airplane surface is exposed to the force of the crosswind. This reduces the effectiveness of the aileron.

7. **Improper use of brakes**

    a. Use the minimum amount of braking required, and let your airplane slow by the friction and drag of the wheels on the ground, if runway length permits.

    b. Never attempt to apply brakes until your airplane is firmly on the runway under complete control.

    c. Use equal pressure on both brakes to help prevent swerving and/or loss of directional control.

    d. Avoid locking the brakes at rollout speeds because this will cause the airplane to slide. This will result in excessive tire wear and possibly a blowout.

END OF COMMON ERRORS

STUDY UNIT TWENTY-SEVEN
SOFT-FIELD TAKEOFF AND CLIMB

Task	Task C. Soft-Field Takeoff and Climb
References	FAA-H-8083-2, FAA-H-8083-3; POH/AFM
Objective	To determine that the applicant exhibits satisfactory knowledge, risk management, and skills associated with a soft-field takeoff, climb operations, and rejected takeoff procedures.
Knowledge	The applicant demonstrates understanding of:
PA.IV.C.K1	1. The importance of weight transfer from wheels to wings.
PA.IV.C.K2	2. P factor in turning tendencies.
PA.IV.C.K3	3. The effects of aircraft configuration.
PA.IV.C.K4	4. The effects of runway surface.
PA.IV.C.K5	5. Takeoff distance.
PA.IV.C.K6	6. Takeoff power.
PA.IV.C.K7	7. Wind conditions and effects.
PA.IV.C.K8	8. Density altitude.
PA.IV.C.K9	9. Application of V_X or V_Y.
PA.IV.C.K10	10. Emergency procedures during takeoff and climb.
PA.IV.C.K11	11. Hazards of other than a hard surfaced runway.
Risk Management	The applicant demonstrates the ability to identify, assess and mitigate risks, encompassing:
PA.IV.C.R1	1. Failure to select the appropriate runway based on wind, pilot capability, and aircraft limitations.
PA.IV.C.R2	2. Exceeding the manufacturer's maximum demonstrated crosswind component.
PA.IV.C.R3	3. Operating from other than a hard surfaced runway.
PA.IV.C.R4	4. Windshear.
PA.IV.C.R5	5. Tailwind.
PA.IV.C.R6	6. Wake turbulence.
PA.IV.C.R7	7. Failure to recognize the need to perform a go-around/rejected landing.
PA.IV.C.R8	8. Task management.
PA.IV.C.R9	9. Low altitude maneuvering.
PA.IV.C.R10	10. Wire strikes.
PA.IV.C.R11	11. Obstacles on the departure path.
PA.IV.C.R12	12. Rejected takeoffs and failure to identify a takeoff abort point.
PA.IV.C.R13	13. An engine failure during takeoff and climb.
PA.IV.C.R14	14. Failure to use a soft-field takeoff technique on an other than hard surfaced runway.
PA.IV.C.R15	15. Takeoff distance available.
PA.IV.C.R16	16. Failure to adhere to sterile cockpit requirement.

Skills	The applicant demonstrates the ability to:
PA.IV.C.S1	1. Verify ATC clearance and no aircraft is on final before crossing the hold line.
PA.IV.C.S2	2. Ensure the aircraft is properly configured.
PA.IV.C.S3	3. Ensure the aircraft is on the correct takeoff runway.
PA.IV.C.S4	4. Ascertain wind direction with or without visible wind direction indicators.
PA.IV.C.S5	5. Calculate the crosswind component and determine if it is beyond the pilot ability or aircraft capability.
PA.IV.C.S6	6. Position the flight controls for the existing wind conditions to maximize lift as quickly as possible.
PA.IV.C.S7	7. Clear the area, taxi into the takeoff position and align the airplane on the runway center line without stopping while advancing the throttle smoothly to takeoff power.
PA.IV.C.S8	8. Confirm takeoff power, and proper engine and flight instrument indications prior to rotation.
PA.IV.C.S9	9. Establish and maintain a pitch attitude that will transfer the weight of the airplane from the wheels to the wings as rapidly as possible.
PA.IV.C.S10	10. Lift-off at the lowest possible airspeed consistent with safety and remain in ground effect while accelerating to V_X or V_Y, as appropriate.
PA.IV.C.S11	11. Establish a pitch attitude for V_X or V_Y, as appropriate, and maintain selected airspeed +10/-5 knots during the climb.
PA.IV.C.S12	12. Retract landing gear and flaps after a positive rate of climb has been verified or in accordance with aircraft manufacturer's guidance.
PA.IV.C.S13	13. Maintain takeoff power and V_Y +10/-5 knots to a safe maneuvering altitude.
PA.IV.C.S14	14. Maintain directional control and proper wind drift correction throughout the takeoff and climb.
PA.IV.C.S15	15. Comply with noise abatement and published departure procedures.
PA.IV.C.S16	16. Complete the appropriate checklist.
PA.IV.C.S17	17. Comply with manufacturer's recommended emergency procedures related to the takeoff sequence.

A.   General Information

   1.   The objective of this task is for you to demonstrate your knowledge, skills, and risk management related to soft-field takeoffs, climb operations, and rejected takeoff procedures.

   2.   In Study Unit 1, "Airplanes and Aerodynamics," of *Pilot Handbook*, see Subunit 8, "Ground Effect," for a discussion of the aerodynamic effects when flying just above the ground.

B.   Much of the content of Subunits 27.1 and 27.2 is abbreviated based on the assumption that you have thoroughly read and understood pages 287 through 304 and the additional common task topics found in Part II. The task objectives and specific references are provided here for your convenience.

27.1 KNOWLEDGE

A.   Task Objectives

   1.   **The applicant demonstrates understanding of the importance of weight transfer from wheels to wings.**

      a.   The goals of a soft-field takeoff are

         1)   To get the airplane airborne as soon as possible

         2)   To transfer as much weight as possible to the wings to minimize wheel friction with the soft surface

            a)   The combination of considerable back pressure on the yoke or stick and the manufacturer's recommended flap setting is the best means of achieving a soft-field takeoff.

            b)   Weight is transferred to the wings and away from the wheels because of the high angle of attack produced by the back elevator pressure.

2. **The applicant demonstrates understanding of P-factor in turning tendencies.**

    a.   P-factor is one of the four left-turning tendencies. It is caused by asymmetric load between the ascending and descending blades.

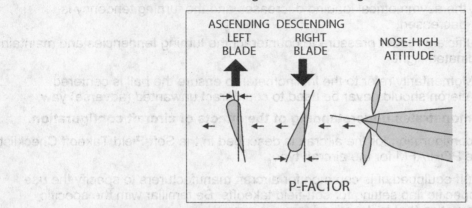

    b.   **Asymmetric Propeller Loading (P-Factor).** The effects of P-factor, or asymmetric propeller loading, usually occur when the airplane is flown at a high angle of attack.

        1)   Asymmetrical loading of the propeller simply means that the load on the upward-moving propeller blade is different from the load on the downward-moving propeller blade.

        2)   When an airplane is flying at a high angle of attack (i.e., with the propeller axis inclined upward), the bite (or load) of the downward-moving propeller blade is greater than the bite (load) of the upward-moving blade.

            a)   This is due to the downward-moving blade meeting the oncoming relative wind at a greater angle of attack and velocity than the upward-moving blade.

            b)   Since the propeller blade is an airfoil, increased angle of attack and velocity mean increased lift or, in the case of the propeller blade, more thrust.

                i)   Thus, the downward-moving blade on the right side (as viewed from the rear) has more thrust than the upward-moving blade, causing the airplane to yaw to the left.

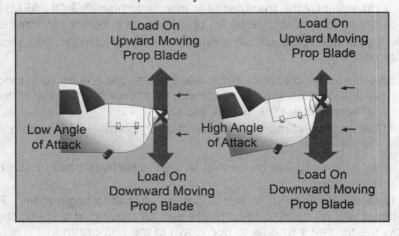

3) At low speeds, the yawing tendency caused by P-factor is greater because the airplane is at a high angle of attack.

    a) As the airspeed is increased and the airplane's angle of attack is reduced, the asymmetrical loading decreases and the turning tendency is decreased.

4) Use sufficient rudder pressure to counteract the turning tendencies and maintain coordinated flight.

    a) Momentarily refer to the inclinometer to ensure the ball is centered.
    b) Aileron should never be used to counteract unwanted (adverse) yaw.

3. **The applicant demonstrates understanding of the effects of aircraft configuration.**

a. The proper configuration for the aircraft is described in the Soft-Field Takeoff Checklist found in the POH/AFM for the aircraft type.

1) NOTE: If equipped, it is common for aircraft manufacturers to specify the use of a specific flap setting for soft-field takeoffs. Be familiar with the specific configuration that is described for your aircraft.

b. In general, the technique is to advance the power to takeoff power.

1) During a soft-field takeoff, you want to get the aircraft off the ground and into ground effect as soon as possible. In ground effect, you will level off and allow the aircraft to accelerate to V_Y. Then, pitch up to climb out normally once you accelerate to V_Y.

2) To accomplish this, hold the yoke (stick) back to get the nosewheel off the ground as soon as possible. This reduces friction and drag caused by the wheel rolling along the ground, lowers the chances of damaging the nosewheel as the aircraft accelerates, and increases lift due to the higher angle of attack.

3) If obstacles are present, climb at V_X until all obstacles are cleared, then accelerate to V_Y.

4. **The applicant demonstrates understanding of the effects of runway surface.**

a. Runway conditions affect takeoff and landing performance. Any surface that is not hard and smooth will increase the ground roll during takeoff. This is due to the inability of the tires to roll smoothly along the runway.

1) If the need arises to make a soft-field departure, consult the recommendations provided by the manufacturer in your airplane's POH/AFM. It will most likely have recommendations for operation on different runway surfaces.

b. Inspect your taxi route and your takeoff runway. Normally, you should walk the entire route carefully.

1) Note wet or soft spots and mark them as necessary (use pieces of cloth or paper tied to objects, e.g., fence posts, or anchor them to the ground at the side of the runway with stakes, sticks, etc.).

2) Determine and mark your takeoff abort point—exactly where you will cut power if not airborne.

    a) Seventy-five percent of V_R by the halfway point on the runway is a general rule.

c. It may take very near full power to get the aircraft to begin rolling. From that point, adjust power as needed to keep the aircraft moving at a speed that is safe, but do not allow the aircraft's wheels to bog down in the soft ground.

1) Do not come to a complete stop or let the power bleed off to the point that the aircraft bogs down in the soft ground. Keep the aircraft moving, but in a safe manner.

5. **The applicant demonstrates understanding of takeoff distance.**

   a. For information on takeoff distance, see Section IV Introduction, Knowledge, item A, beginning on page 289.

6. **The applicant demonstrates understanding of takeoff power.**

   a. For information on takeoff power, see Section IV Introduction, Knowledge, item C., beginning on page 291.

7. **The applicant demonstrates understanding of wind conditions and effects.**

   a. For information on wind conditions and effects, see Study Unit 9, Subunit 3, beginning on page 80.

8. **The applicant demonstrates understanding of density altitude.**

   a. For information on density altitude, see Study Unit 9, Subunit 1, beginning on page 77.

9. **The applicant demonstrates understanding of the application of V_X or V_Y.**

   a. For information on the application of V_X or V_Y, see Section IV Introduction, Knowledge, item E., beginning on page 295.

10. **The applicant demonstrates understanding of emergency procedures during takeoff and climb.**

    a. For information on emergency procedures during takeoff and climb, see Study Unit 8, Subunit 2, item D., beginning on page 74.

11. **The applicant demonstrates understanding of the hazards of other than a hard surfaced runway.**

    a. For information on the hazards of other than a hard surfaced runway, see Section IV Introduction, Knowledge, item G., beginning on page 298.

END OF KNOWLEDGE ELEMENT

27.2 RISK MANAGEMENT

A.   Task Objectives

1.   **The applicant demonstrates the ability to identify, assess, and mitigate risks encompassing failure to select the appropriate runway based on wind, pilot capability, and aircraft limitations.**

a.   For information on selecting the appropriate runway based on wind, pilot capability, and aircraft limitations, see Section IV Introduction, Risk Management, item A., beginning on page 299.

2.   **The applicant demonstrates the ability to identify, assess, and mitigate risks encompassing exceeding the manufacturer's maximum demonstrated crosswind component.**

a.   For information on crosswind component, see Study Unit 9, Subunit 3, item C., on page 80.

3.   **The applicant demonstrates the ability to identify, assess, and mitigate risks encompassing operating from other than a hard surfaced runway.**

a.   For information on operating from other than a hard surfaced runway, see Section IV Introduction, Risk Management, item K., beginning on page 303.

4.   **The applicant demonstrates the ability to identify, assess, and mitigate risks encompassing windshear.**

a.   For information on windshear, see Study Unit 9, Subunit 4, beginning on page 81.

5.   **The applicant demonstrates the ability to identify, assess, and mitigate risks encompassing tailwind.**

a.   For information on tailwind, see Study Unit 9, Subunit 3, beginning on page 80.

6.   **The applicant demonstrates the ability to identify, assess, and mitigate risks encompassing wake turbulence.**

a.   For information on wake turbulence, see Study Unit 7, Subunit 7, beginning on page 69.

7.   **The applicant demonstrates the ability to identify, assess, and mitigate risks encompassing failure to recognize the need to perform a go-around/rejected landing.**

a.   NOTE: We do not believe it is appropriate to discuss go-around rejected landings in a takeoff task as the FAA states in the ACS. We believe this item should be about go/no-go decision making.

b.   For information on go/no-go decision making, see Section IV Introduction, Risk Management, item B., beginning on page 299.

8.   **The applicant demonstrates the ability to identify, assess, and mitigate risks encompassing task management.**

a.   For information on task management, see Study Unit 6, Subunit 1, beginning on page 49.

9.   **The applicant demonstrates the ability to identify, assess, and mitigate risks encompassing low altitude maneuvering.**

a.   For information on low altitude maneuvering, see Section IV Introduction, Risk Management, item C., beginning on page 299.

10.   **The applicant demonstrates the ability to identify, assess, and mitigate risks, encompassing wire strikes.**

a.   For information on wire strikes, see Study Unit 7, Subunit 6, beginning on page 68.

11. **The applicant demonstrates the ability to identify, assess, and mitigate risks encompassing obstacles on the departure path.**

    a. For information on obstacles on the departure path, see Section IV Introduction, Risk Management, item D., beginning on page 300.

12. **The applicant demonstrates the ability to identify, assess, and mitigate risks encompassing rejected takeoff and failure to identify a takeoff abort point.**

    a. For information on rejected takeoff and identifying a takeoff abort point, see Section IV Introduction, Risk Management, item E., beginning on page 300.

13. **The applicant demonstrates the ability to identify, assess, and mitigate risks encompassing engine failure during takeoff and climb.**

    a. For information on engine failure during takeoff and climb, see Study Unit 8, Subunit 2, item E., on page 75.

14. **The applicant demonstrates the ability to identify, assess, and mitigate risks encompassing failure to use a soft-field takeoff technique on an other than hard surfaced runway.**

    a. Any surface that is not hard and smooth will increase the ground roll during takeoff. This is due to the inability of the tires to roll smoothly along the runway. Tires can sink into soft, grassy, or muddy runways.

        1) Soft surfaces or long, wet grass usually reduce the airplane's acceleration during the takeoff roll so much that adequate takeoff speed might not be attained if normal takeoff techniques are employed.

        2) These same techniques are also useful on a rough field where it is advisable to get the airplane off the ground as soon as possible to avoid damaging the landing gear.

    b. Therefore, a soft-field takeoff should be used whenever the surface is not smooth or dry. Typically, this is on grass runways after a rain shower or on dirt strips that are susceptible to having areas of loose dirt and/or mud.

    c. For more information on operating on other than a hard surfaced runway, see Section IV Introduction, Risk Management, item K., beginning on page 303.

15. **The applicant demonstrates the ability to identify, assess, and mitigate risks encompassing takeoff distance available.**

    a. For information on takeoff distance available, see Section IV Introduction, Risk Management, item I., beginning on page 302.

16. **The applicant demonstrates the ability to identify, assess, and mitigate risks, encompassing failure to adhere to sterile cockpit requirement.**

    a. For information on sterile cockpit, see Study Unit 6, Subunit 2, beginning on page 51.

END OF RISK MANAGEMENT ELEMENT

27.3 SKILLS

A.   Task Objectives

1.   **The applicant demonstrates the ability to verify ATC clearance and no aircraft is on final before crossing the hold line.**

a.   Use a standard clearing procedure before initiating movement on the surface.

1)   Look to your left, scan the area for other traffic, and announce "clear left" if it is in fact clear.

2)   Repeat this same procedure for both the front and right of the aircraft.

3)   Any time you stop moving, use this procedure (or one like it) before rolling again.

b.   Read back all ATC clearances. If any ATC takeoff instructions seem unclear or appear to conflict with other instructions that have been issued, stop and ask for clarification.

c.   At non-towered airports, visually check the runway and the approach path to ensure the area is clear before you taxi onto the runway for takeoff.

d.   Refer to the runway number and the magnetic heading of the aircraft as you taxi onto the runway and center the aircraft with the runway centerline to ensure you are using the correct/assigned runway.

2.   **The applicant demonstrates the ability to ensure the aircraft is properly configured.**

a.   If the use of flaps is recommended, the flaps must be extended prior to starting the takeoff roll.

1)   Always check your flap setting visually.

3.   **The applicant demonstrates the ability to ensure the aircraft is on the correct takeoff runway.**

a.   Thorough planning for taxi so you are on the correct runway is imperative.

1)   Have the current airport diagram readily available.

2)   Pay special attention to any complex intersections.

3)   Verify your assigned route once received from ATC.

4)   Minimize cockpit tasks, observe sterile cockpit, and practice "heads up, eyes out" mode while taxiing.

5)   When in doubt, stop and ask ATC for help.

b.   As you approach the hold short point, ensure the runway holding position sign confirms you are at the correct runway.

c.   Never cross a hold line without explicit ATC instructions. Controllers are required to issue explicit instructions to cross or hold short of each runway, including inactive and closed runways that intersect a taxi route.

d.   As you line up on the runway, confirm your compass and heading indicator agree you are on the correct runway.

4.   **The applicant demonstrates the ability to ascertain wind direction with or without visible wind direction indicators.**

a.   Make use of airport wind direction indicators if they are available and/or listen to automated weather broadcasts, where installed, to get timely wind information.

b.   If necessary, you can contact ATC for a wind check prior to takeoff at tower-controlled airports.

c.   If you have no ability to reference wind direction indicators, weather broadcasts, or ATC advisories, you can use various outside references, such as rising smoke, tree motion, or just the basic physical sensation of where the wind is blowing from.

d.   Always reverify wind direction as you taxi onto the runway by observing the windsock or other wind direction indicators, which may include grass or bushes.

5. **The applicant demonstrates the ability to calculate the crosswind component and determine if it is beyond the pilot ability or aircraft capability.**

   a. The aircraft's demonstrated crosswind component can be determined from Section 4, Normal Procedures, and/or Section 5, Performance, in your POH/AFM via a textual description in Section 4 and/or a graph in Section 5.

      1) Remember a numerical value for the crosswind component of the aircraft is likely the maximum demonstrated crosswind component for a direct 90° crosswind.
      2) The chart presented in Section 5 of the POH/AFM is the best way to determine the actual crosswind component that will be affecting the aircraft.

   b. Beyond what the aircraft is capable of, you have to be aware of what your skill level will allow.

      1) You should establish and follow personal minimums that are based on your comfort levels when dealing with crosswinds.
      2) You should regularly re-evaluate and update your personal minimums.
      3) Show the evaluator you are aware of your personal abilities by explaining your personal minimums when it comes to crosswind components.

6. **The applicant demonstrates the ability to position the flight controls for the existing wind conditions to maximize lift as quickly as possible.**

   a. Always reverify wind direction as you taxi onto the runway by observing the windsock or other wind direction indicator, which may include grass or bushes.
   b. For a crosswind, the ailerons should be fully deflected at the start of the takeoff roll.
   c. Use full or nearly full back pressure on the control yoke so as to maximize lift as quickly as possible during the takeoff roll.

      1) In a nosewheel airplane, this pressure helps remove some of the stress from the nosewheel and minimize rolling resistance during taxiing.

7. **The applicant demonstrates the ability to clear the area, taxi into the takeoff position, and align the airplane on the runway center line without stopping while advancing the throttle smoothly to takeoff power.**

   a. Before taxiing onto the runway, make certain that you have sufficient time to execute the takeoff before any aircraft in the traffic pattern turns onto the final approach.

      1) Check that the runway is clear of other aircraft, vehicles, persons, or hazards.

   b. Keep moving once your airplane is rolling. If your airplane becomes bogged down, there may be insufficient thrust available to pull out of the mud and/or ruts, and the only choice would be to shut down and move the airplane by hand or with equipment.

      1) Grass, sand, mud, and snow require more power than taxiing on a hard surface.
      2) Also, debris may be sucked up by the propeller, causing both propeller damage and/or wear and damage to your paint job when the debris strikes the airplane.
      3) You should taxi your airplane onto the takeoff surface as fast as possible, consistent with safety.

   c. Keep your airplane moving with sufficient power while lining up for the takeoff roll.

      1) Line up your airplane as done on a hard-surfaced runway with a centerline.
      2) Power must be applied smoothly and as rapidly as possible.

         a) Be aware that some engines will stumble or even fail if the throttle is advanced too rapidly.
         b) The point here is to accelerate as quickly as possible; open the throttle as appropriate for your engine.

8. **The applicant demonstrates the ability to confirm takeoff power and proper engine and flight instrument indications prior to rotation.**

   a. The engine instruments must be monitored during the entire maneuver.

      1) Monitoring enables you to notice immediately any malfunction or indication of insufficient power or other potential problems.

      2) Listen for any indication of power loss or engine roughness.

   b. Check your airspeed indicator for movement as you accelerate.

9. **The applicant demonstrates the ability to establish and maintain a pitch attitude that will transfer the weight of the airplane from the wheels to the wings as rapidly as possible.**

   a. Do not stop on a soft surface when transitioning from taxi to takeoff.

   b. Back elevator pressure should be applied to establish a positive angle of attack early in the takeoff run to reduce the weight supported by the nosewheel.

      1) The nose-high attitude will allow the weight to transfer from the wheels to the wings as lift is developed.

      2) In a tailwheel airplane, the tail should be kept low to maintain the inherent positive angle of attack and to avoid any tendency of the airplane to nose over as a result of soft spots, tall grass, or deep snow.

   c. Wingflaps may be lowered prior to starting the takeoff (if recommended by the manufacturer) to provide additional lift and transfer the airplane's weight from the wheels to the wings as early as possible.

   d. When the airplane is held at nose-high attitude throughout the takeoff run, the wings will, as speed increases and lift develops, progressively relieve the wheels of more and more of the airplane's weight, thereby minimizing the drag caused by surface irregularities or adhesion. If this attitude is accurately maintained, the airplane will virtually fly itself off the ground.

10. **The applicant demonstrates the ability to lift off at the lowest possible airspeed consistent with safety and remain in ground effect while accelerating to V_x or V_y, as appropriate.**

    a. If the pitch attitude is accurately maintained during the takeoff roll, the airplane should become airborne at an airspeed slower than a safe climb speed because of the action of ground effect.

    b. After your airplane becomes airborne, the nose must be lowered very gently with the wheels just clear of the surface to allow your airplane to accelerate in ground effect to V_x or V_y, as appropriate to the length of the takeoff surface and the presence of any obstacles.

       1) The leveling action should be accomplished by slightly relaxing back pressure on the control yoke.

       2) Failure to level off (i.e., maintain constant altitude) would mean the airplane would climb out of ground effect at too slow a speed and the increase in drag could reduce the lift sufficiently to cause the airplane to settle back onto the takeoff surface.

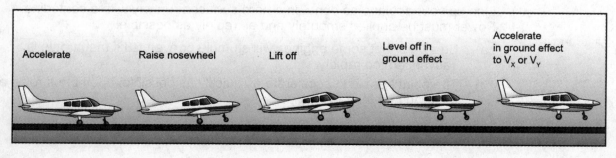

Accelerate   Raise nosewheel   Lift off   Level off in ground effect   Accelerate in ground effect to V_x or V_y

11. **The applicant demonstrates the ability to establish a pitch attitude for V$_X$ or V$_Y$, as appropriate, and maintain selected airspeed +10/-5 knots during the climb.**

    a. Once you have accelerated to V$_X$ or V$_Y$ in ground effect, you should establish the pitch attitude for V$_X$ or V$_Y$, as appropriate.

    b. If obstacles are present at the departure end of the takeoff area, accelerate to V$_X$ and climb at V$_X$ until clear of the obstacle(s).

12. **The applicant demonstrates the ability to retract the landing gear and flaps after a positive rate of climb has been verified or in accordance with aircraft manufacturer's guidance.**

    a. Before retracting the landing gear, apply the brakes momentarily to stop the rotation of the wheels to avoid excessive vibration of the gear mechanism.

        1) Centrifugal force caused by the rapidly rotating wheels expands the diameter of the tires, and if mud or other debris has accumulated in the wheel wells, the rotating wheels may rub as they enter.

    b. When to retract the landing gear varies among manufacturers. Thus, it is important that you know what procedure is prescribed by that airplane's POH/AFM.

        1) Normally, the landing gear will be retracted before the flaps.

        2) Make necessary pitch adjustments to maintain the appropriate airspeed.

    c. Flaps are normally retracted when you have established V$_X$ or V$_Y$, a positive rate of climb, and are clear of obstacles.

        1) Raise the flaps in increments (if appropriate) to avoid sudden loss of lift and settling of the airplane.

        2) Make needed pitch adjustment to maintain V$_X$ or V$_Y$.

13. **The applicant demonstrates the ability to maintain takeoff power and V$_Y$ +10/-5 knots to a safe maneuvering altitude.**

    a. After establishing V$_X$ or V$_Y$ and completing gear and flap retraction, maintain takeoff power to a safe maneuvering altitude, normally 500 to 1,000 ft. AGL.

        1) Then the power should be reduced to the normal cruise climb setting and the pitch adjusted for cruise climb airspeed.

    b. Most trainer-type airplane manufacturers recommend maintaining maximum power to your selected cruising altitude.

    c. Use the power setting recommended in your POH/AFM.

14. **The applicant demonstrates the ability to maintain directional control and proper wind drift correction throughout the takeoff and climb.**

    a. Crosswind takeoff techniques are consistent with a soft-field takeoff and should be employed simultaneously, as needed.

        1) A common error is to become preoccupied with the soft-field effort at the expense of neglecting crosswind correction. The results are directional stability problems.

    b. For additional information on maintaining directional control and proper wind-drift correction throughout the takeoff and climb, see Study Unit 25, Subunit 3, item A.12., beginning on page 313.

15. **The applicant demonstrates the ability to comply with noise abatement and published departure procedures.**

   a.   You must comply with any established noise abatement procedure.

   1)   A noise abatement policy is developed by the airport authority or city and is a local ordinance. Thus, you can be cited by the city for violation of the policy.

   b.   The Chart Supplement will list that an airport has a noise abatement procedure in effect under "airport remarks."

   1)   Other pilot guides may contain more detailed information on an airport's noise abatement procedures.

   c.   A key to complying with noise abatement is to put as much distance as possible between you and the ground, as quickly as possible.

   1)   Use the longest runway available.
   2)   Rotate at V_R and climb out at V_X or V_Y, as recommended in your POH/AFM.
   3)   Reduce power to climb power, and transition to a cruise climb as appropriate.

   a)   The reduction to climb power will reduce the noise of your engine, and the transition to cruise climb airspeed will reduce the time you are over the noise monitors and noise sensitive areas.

   d.   If you are flying from an unfamiliar airport that has a noise abatement policy, you should contact the airport's noise abatement office for details.

   e.   You should conduct your operations responsibly with respect to the environment.

   1)   When taking fuel samples during the preflight, do not dump fuel on the ground. Consider reusing the fuel if it is clean, or dispose of it properly. Your local FBO or airport manager can advise about proper disposal methods.

   2)   When taking off and climbing, follow published departure procedures.

   a)   Flying over towns and communities can create noise complaints.

   b)   Many airports have been forced to provide noise mitigation to properties in their surrounding communities. These can be very expensive resulting in higher fees for airports and aircraft operators.

   c)   For example, through 2006, the Hartsfield-Jackson Atlanta International Airport has provided sound insulation and/or relocated residents at a cost of $352.2 million.

16. **The applicant demonstrates the ability to complete the appropriate checklist.**

   a.   In Section 4, Normal Procedures, of your POH/AFM, find the soft-field takeoff checklist and study it and any amplified procedures.

   b.   Complete the checklist for climb to ensure that your airplane is in the proper configuration for the continued climb to cruising altitude.

   c.   Follow the checklist(s) in your POH/AFM.

17. **The applicant demonstrates the ability to comply with manufacturer's recommended emergency procedures relating to the takeoff sequence.**

   a.   The key to successful management of an emergency situation and/or preventing a non-normal situation from progressing into a true emergency is a thorough familiarity with, and adherence to, the procedures developed by the airplane manufacturer and contained in the POH/AFM for the particular make and model airplane.

   1)   For example, one particular procedure could entail engine failures on takeoff. Before a safe maneuvering altitude is attained, it is usually inadvisable to attempt to turn back to the field from where the takeoff was made. Instead, it is safer to immediately establish the proper glide attitude and select a field directly ahead or slightly to either side of the takeoff path.

END OF SKILLS ELEMENT

27.4 COMMON ERRORS

A.   Common Errors during a Soft-Field Takeoff and Climb

1.   **Improper initial positioning of the flight controls or wing flaps**

    a.   The control yoke should be held in the full back position and turned into the crosswind (if appropriate).

    b.   If wing flaps are recommended by your POH/AFM, they should be lowered prior to your taxiing onto the takeoff surface.

2.   **Allowing the airplane to stop on the takeoff surface prior to initiating takeoff**

    a.   Once stopped, your airplane may become bogged down and may not have the power to begin rolling again.

3.   **Improper power application**

    a.   Power must be used throughout the entire ground operation in a positive and safe manner.

    b.   Power must be applied smoothly and as quickly as the engine will accept (without faltering).

    c.   Remember, the goal is to get your airplane airborne as quickly as possible.

4.   **Inappropriate removal of hand from throttle**

    a.   Keep your hand on the throttle at all times except during

        1)   Flap retraction
        2)   Gear retraction
        3)   Trim adjustment

5.   **Poor directional control**

    a.   Maintain the center of the takeoff surface by use of the rudder.
    b.   Divide your attention between the soft-field takeoff and directional control.

6.   **Improper use of brakes**

    a.   Brakes should never be used on a soft field to avoid bogging down.
    b.   Keep your feet off the brakes.

7.   **Improper pitch attitude during liftoff**

    a.   During the takeoff roll, excessive back elevator pressure may cause the angle of attack to exceed that required for a climb, which would generate more drag.

        1)   In a nosewheel-type airplane, excessive back elevator pressure may also cause the tail of your airplane to drag on the ground.

    b.   You must slowly lower the nose after liftoff to allow the airplane to accelerate in ground effect.

        1)   If done too quickly, you will settle back onto the takeoff surface.
        2)   Merely relax some back pressure on the control yoke to allow for acceleration.

    c.   Attempting to climb without the proper airspeed may cause you to settle back onto the runway due to the increase in drag.

8.   **Settling back to takeoff surface after becoming airborne, resulting in**

    a.   Reduction of takeoff performance
    b.   A wheel digging in, causing an upset of the airplane
    c.   Side loads on the landing gear if in a crosswind crab
    d.   A gear-up landing or a prop strike if the landing gear is retracted early

9. **Failure to establish and maintain proper climb configuration and airspeed**
    a. Follow the procedures in your POH/AFM.
    b. You must fly your airplane by the numbers. Failure to do so means reduced performance, which may be devastating on a short soft-field takeoff, especially if there is an obstacle to be cleared.

10. **Drift during climbout**
    a. Maintain the extended center of the takeoff surface to avoid other obstacles.
    b. Other pilots in the traffic pattern will be expecting you to maintain the centerline. If you drift, they may be forced to take measures to avoid a collision.

END OF COMMON ERRORS

STUDY UNIT TWENTY-EIGHT
SOFT-FIELD APPROACH AND LANDING

Task	Task D. Soft-Field Approach and Landing
References	FAA-H-8083-2, FAA-H-8083-3; POH/AFM
Objective	To determine that the applicant exhibits satisfactory knowledge, risk management, and skills associated with a soft-field approach and landing with emphasis on proper use and coordination of flight controls.
Knowledge	The applicant demonstrates understanding of:
PA.IV.D.K1	1. Landing distance.
PA.IV.D.K2	2. Hazards of other than hard surfaced runway.
PA.IV.D.K3	3. Stabilized approach.
PA.IV.D.K4	4. Energy management.
PA.IV.D.K5	5. Wind conditions and effects.
PA.IV.D.K6	6. Density altitude.
PA.IV.D.K7	7. Emergency procedures during approach and landing.
Risk Management	The applicant demonstrates the ability to identify, assess and mitigate risks, encompassing:
PA.IV.D.R1	1. Failure to select the appropriate runway based on wind, pilot capability, and aircraft limitations.
PA.IV.D.R2	2. Exceeding the manufacturer's maximum demonstrated crosswind component.
PA.IV.D.R3	3. Operating from other than a hard surfaced runway.
PA.IV.D.R4	4. Losing elevator control, sinking into the soft surface, or striking the prop if moving too slowly.
PA.IV.D.R5	5. Windshear avoidance.
PA.IV.D.R6	6. Tailwind.
PA.IV.D.R7	7. Wake turbulence.
PA.IV.D.R8	8. Task management.
PA.IV.D.R9	9. Low altitude maneuvering.
PA.IV.D.R10	10. Collision avoidance, scanning, obstacle and wire strike avoidance.
PA.IV.D.R11	11. Failure to follow the right-of-way rules.
PA.IV.D.R12	12. Obstacles on approach and landing paths.
PA.IV.D.R13	13. Failure to recognize the need for go-around/rejected landing.
PA.IV.D.R14	14. Low altitude stall/spin.
PA.IV.D.R15	15. Performing a soft-field landing after an engine failure.
PA.IV.D.R16	16. Failure to adhere to sterile cockpit requirement.
Skills	The applicant demonstrates the ability to:
PA.IV.D.S1	1. Ensure the aircraft is aligned with the correct/assigned runway.
PA.IV.D.S2	2. Scan the landing runway/area for possible obstructions for landing.
PA.IV.D.S3	3. Complete the appropriate approach and landing checklist.
PA.IV.D.S4	4. Consider the wind conditions, landing surface, and obstructions to select a suitable touchdown point.
PA.IV.D.S5	5. Establish the recommended approach and landing configuration and airspeed, and adjust pitch attitude and power as required.
PA.IV.D.S6	6. Maintain a stabilized approach and recommended airspeed, or in its absence, not more than 1.3 V_{SO}, with wind gust factor applied +10/-5 knots.
PA.IV.D.S7	7. Make smooth, timely, and correct control application during the round out and touchdown and, for tricycle gear airplanes, keep the nose wheel off the surface until loss of elevator effectiveness.
PA.IV.D.S8	8. Touch down softly with minimum sink rate and no drift, with the airplane's longitudinal axis aligned with the center of the runway.
PA.IV.D.S9	9. Maintain full up elevator during rollout and exit the "soft" area at a speed that would preclude sinking into the surface.
PA.IV.D.S10	10. Maintain crosswind correction and directional control throughout the approach and landing sequence, as required.
PA.IV.D.S11	11. Execute a timely go-around decision when the approach cannot be made within the tolerances specified above or for any other condition that may result in an unsafe approach or landing.
PA.IV.D.S12	12. Maintain proper position of the flight controls and sufficient speed to taxi on the soft surface.
PA.IV.D.S13	13. Utilize after landing runway incursion avoidance procedures.

A.   General Information

1.   The objective of this task is for you to demonstrate your knowledge, risk management, and skills related to a soft-field approach and landing with emphasis on proper use and coordination of flight controls.

2.   Much of the content of Subunits 28.1 and 28.2 is abbreviated based on the assumption that you have thoroughly read and understood pages 287-304 and the additional common task topics found in Part II. The task objectives and specific references are provided here for your convenience.

28.1 KNOWLEDGE

A.   Task Objectives

1.   **The applicant demonstrates understanding of landing distance.**

a.   For information on landing distance, see Section IV Introduction, Knowledge, item B., beginning on page 289.

2.   **The applicant demonstrates understanding of the hazards of other than hard surfaced runway.**

a.   Landing on fields that are rough or have soft surfaces (e.g., snow, mud, sand, or tall grass) requires special techniques.

1)   When landing on such surfaces, you must control your airplane in a manner such that the wings support the weight of the airplane as long as practicable.

a)   Supporting the airplane's weight with the wings minimizes drag and stress put on the landing gear from the rough or soft surfaces.

3.   **The applicant demonstrates understanding of stabilized approach.**

a.   For information on stabilized approach, see Section IV Introduction, Knowledge, item D., beginning on page 292.

4.   **The applicant demonstrates understanding of energy management.**

a.   For information on energy management, see Study Unit 8, Subunit 1, beginning on page 71.

5.   **The applicant demonstrates understanding of wind conditions and effects.**

a.   For information on wind conditions and effects, see Study Unit 9, Subunit 3, beginning on page 80.

6.   **The applicant demonstrates understanding of density altitude.**

a.   For information on density altitude, see Study Unit 9, Subunit 1, beginning on page 77.

7.   **The applicant demonstrates understanding of emergency procedures during approach and landing.**

a.   For information on emergency procedures during approach and landing, see Study Unit 8, Subunit 2, item G., on page 76.

END OF KNOWLEDGE ELEMENT

28.2 RISK MANAGEMENT

A.   Task Objectives

1.   **The applicant demonstrates the ability to identify, assess, and mitigate risks encompassing failure to select the appropriate runway based on wind, pilot capability, and aircraft limitations.**

   a.   For information on selecting a runway based on wind, pilot capability, and aircraft limitations, see Section IV Introduction, Risk Management, item A., beginning on page 299.

2.   **The applicant demonstrates the ability to identify, assess, and mitigate risks encompassing exceeding the manufacturer's maximum demonstrated crosswind component.**

   a.   For information on crosswind component, see Study Unit 9, Subunit 3, item C., on page 80.

3.   **The applicant demonstrates the ability to identify, assess, and mitigate risks encompassing operating from other than a hard surfaced runway.**

   a.   For information on operating from other than a hard surfaced runway, see Section IV Introduction, Risk Management, item K, beginning on page 303.

4.   **The applicant demonstrates the ability to identify, assess, and mitigate risks encompassing losing elevator control, sinking into the soft surface, or striking the prop if moving too slowly.**

   a.   Operations on soft field conditions require the use of full back elevator pressure to transfer some of the weight of the nose wheel. Losing elevator control on the surface requires immediate action to prevent aircraft from getting bogged down.

      1)   You may need to add additional power to carry the airplane's momentum.
      2)   A loss of elevator control is a very serious condition requiring immediate maintenance.

   b.   Soft field airport surfaces may have hidden hazards from erosion or burrowing animals.

   c.   Recent precipitation can exacerbate already soft conditions.

   d.   Losing elevator control, or not holding back elevator pressure may allow the nose to sink into the surface causing the propeller to strike the surface.

5.   **The applicant demonstrates the ability to identify, assess, and mitigate risks encompassing windshear avoidance.**

   a.   For information on windshear, see Study Unit 9, Subunit 4, beginning on page 81.

6.   **The applicant demonstrates the ability to identify, assess, and mitigate risks encompassing tailwind.**

   a.   For information on tailwind, see Study Unit 9, Subunit 3, beginning on page 80.

7.   **The applicant demonstrates the ability to identify, assess, and mitigate risks encompassing wake turbulence.**

   a.   For information on wake turbulence, see Study Unit 7, Subunit 7, beginning on page 69.

8.   **The applicant demonstrates the ability to identify, assess, and mitigate risks encompassing task management.**

   a.   For information on task management, see Study Unit 6, Subunit 1, beginning on page 49.

9. **The applicant demonstrates the ability to identify, assess, and mitigate risks encompassing low altitude maneuvering.**

   a.   For information on low altitude maneuvering, see Section IV Introduction, Risk Management, item C., beginning on page 299.

10. **The applicant demonstrates the ability to identify, assess, and mitigate risks encompassing collision avoidance, scanning, and obstacle and wire strike avoidance.**

    a.   For information on collision avoidance, scanning, and obstacle avoidance, see Study Unit 7, Subunit 4, beginning on page 66.

    b.   For information on wire strikes, see Study Unit 7, Subunit 6, beginning on page 68.

11. **The applicant demonstrates the ability to identify, assess, and mitigate risks encompassing failure to follow right-of-way rules.**

    a.   For information on right-of-way rules, see Section IV Introduction, Risk Management, item F., beginning on page 300.

12. **The applicant demonstrates the ability to identify, assess, and mitigate risks encompassing obstacles on the approach and landing paths.**

    a.   For information on obstacles on approach and landing paths, see Section IV Introduction, Risk Management, item D., beginning on page 300.

13. **The applicant demonstrates the ability to identify, assess, and mitigate risks encompassing failure to recognize the need for a go-around/rejected landing.**

    a.   For information on go-around/rejected landing, see Section IV Introduction, Risk Management, item G., beginning on page 301.

14. **The applicant demonstrates the ability to identify, assess, and mitigate risks encompassing low altitude stall/spin.**

    a.   For information on low altitude stall/spin, see Section IV Introduction, Risk Management, item H., beginning on page 301.

15. **The applicant demonstrates the ability to identify, assess, and mitigate risks encompassing performing a soft-field landing after an engine failure.**

    a.   Landing on a soft field following an engine failure carries a higher level of risk.

       1)   The combination of mechanical failure with unfamiliar operating conditions can cause even well-trained pilots to make mistakes.

       2)   You only get one shot! With an engine failure, once you have committed to a landing area, stick to the plan.

       3)   You should focus on your airmanship while continuing to fly the plane to the surface. Many accidents could have been avoided if the pilot simply continued flying the plane.

       4)   If distance allows, carry a little extra speed or land with partial or no flaps. This will keep the nose at a higher angle, reducing the risk of the nosewheel digging into the surface.

16. **The applicant demonstrates the ability to identify, assess, and mitigate risks encompassing failure to adhere to sterile cockpit requirement.**

    a.   For information on sterile cockpit, see Study Unit 6, Subunit 2, beginning on page 51.

END OF RISK MANAGEMENT ELEMENT

28.3 SKILLS

A. Task Objectives

1. **The applicant demonstrates the ability to ensure the aircraft is aligned with the correct/assigned runway.**

   a. At airports with operating control towers, pilots can ensure the aircraft is on the correct/assigned runway by

      1) Understanding and following ATC instructions and clearances;
      2) Using an airport diagram; and
      3) Knowing the meaning of the visual aids available at the airport, such as airfield markings, signs, and lighting.

   b. Confirm runway number with heading indicator during all traffic pattern legs.

   c. Maintain orientation with the runway in use.

      1) While conducting airport traffic pattern operations, you must remain oriented with the runway in use.
      2) Know which runway is in use, and plan to enter properly and remain in the correct traffic pattern.
      3) When approaching an airport, you should visualize your position from the airport and the relative direction of the runway. Use the airplane's heading indicator to assist you.

2. **The applicant demonstrates the ability to scan the landing/runway area for possible obstructions for landing.**

   a. During your approach, you must look for any hazards or obstructions and then evaluate how they may affect your approach and selection of a suitable touchdown point.

      1) Be aware of traffic, both in the air and on the ground.
      2) Prior to landing, you must scan to make certain that the landing area and path are clear of other aircraft, vehicles, persons, livestock, wildlife (including birds), etc.
      3) Check the approach area for any natural or man-made obstacles (e.g., trees, towers, or construction equipment).
      4) Your angle of descent on final approach may need to be steepened if obstacles are present.

3. **The applicant demonstrates the ability to complete the appropriate approach and landing checklist.**

   a. Use the before-landing checklist in your POH/AFM to ensure that you follow the proper sequence in establishing the correct approach and landing configuration for your airplane.

   b. You should initially start the checklist at midpoint on the downwind leg with the power reduction beginning once you are abeam your intended point of landing.

      1) By the time you turn on final and align your airplane with the runway centerline, you should be in the final landing configuration. Confirm this by completing your checklist once again.

   c. On a soft field, the after-landing checklist should normally be accomplished only after you have parked your airplane.

      1) Some items can be done while taxiing (e.g., turning the carburetor heat OFF if it was used).

4. **The applicant demonstrates the ability to consider the wind conditions, landing surface, and obstructions and select a suitable touchdown point.**

    a. You must know the wind conditions and the effect they will have upon your airplane's approach and landing performance. The effect of wind on the landing distance may be significant and deserves proper consideration.

        1) A headwind will decrease the landing distance, while a tailwind will greatly increase the landing distance.

        2) The wind's effect on landing distance is important if the landing area is short and/or in a confined area.

    b. A soft field is any surface other than a paved one. You must take into account a hard-packed turf or a wet, high grass turf. Know the condition of the landing surface you will be operating into.

        1) If a surface is soft or wet, consider what effect that will have if you perform a crosswind landing, when one main wheel touches down before the other main wheel.

    c. During your approach, you must look for any hazards or obstructions and then evaluate how they may affect your approach and selection of a suitable touchdown point.

    d. After considering the conditions, you should select the most suitable touchdown point.

    e. Once you have selected your touchdown point, you need to select your aim point. The aim point will be the point at the end of your selected glide path, not your touchdown point. Thus, your aim point will be short of your touchdown point.

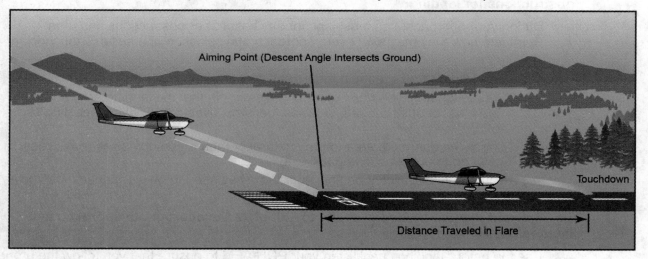

5. **The applicant demonstrates the ability to establish the recommended approach and landing configuration and airspeed, and adjust pitch attitude and power as required.**

    a. The approach for the soft-field landing is similar to the normal approach used for operating into long, firm landing areas.

        1) The major difference between the two is that, during the soft-field landing, the airplane is held 1 to 2 ft. off the surface as long as possible to dissipate the forward speed sufficiently to allow the wheels to touch down gently at minimum speed with a minimum sink rate.

    b.   Establish your airplane in the proper soft-field configuration as prescribed in your POH/AFM. This is usually similar to that used for a normal approach.

          1)   The use of flaps during soft-field landings will aid in touching down at minimum speed and is recommended whenever practical.

               a)   In low-wing airplanes, however, the flaps may suffer damage from mud, stones, or slush thrown up by the wheels. In such cases, it may be advisable not to use flaps.

    c.   For additional information on using pitch and power on the approach and landing, see Study Unit 26, Subunit 3, item A.5., beginning on page 325.

6.   **The applicant demonstrates the ability to maintain a stabilized approach and recommended airspeed, or in its absence, not more than 1.3 V_{SO}, with wind gust factor applied +10/-5 knots.**

    a.   Airspeed control is the most important factor in achieving landing precision. A well-executed landing begins in the traffic pattern with the proper setup and a stabilized approach.

          1)   Once on final approach, slight adjustments in pitch and power may be necessary to maintain the descent attitude and the desired airspeed.

          2)   On final approach, you should use the airspeed in your POH/AFM. In the absence of the manufacturer's recommended airspeed, a speed equal to 1.3 V_{S0} should be used.

               a)   EXAMPLE: If V_{S0} in your airplane is 60 kt., the airspeed on final approach should be 78 kt. (1.3 × 60).

In your airplane, final approach speed (POH/AFM) _____, or 1.3 V_{S0} _____.

               b)   Make necessary adjustments to that speed if you are in turbulent air or strong, gusty winds.

               c)   Inform your evaluator of your final approach airspeed.

    b.   The term **stabilized approach** means that your airplane is in a position where minimum input of all controls will result in a safe landing.

          1)   Excessive control input at any juncture could be an indication of improper planning.

7.   **The applicant demonstrates the ability to make smooth, timely, and correct control application during the round out and touchdown and, for tricycle gear airplanes, keep the nose wheel off the surface until loss of elevator effectiveness.**

    a.   Use a similar technique during the roundout and touchdown as discussed in Study Unit 26, Subunit 3, item A.7., beginning on page 327.

    b.   Do not misjudge the roundout too high, since this may cause you to stall above the surface and drop your airplane in too hard for a soft surface.

    c.   In a nosewheel-type or tricycle gear airplane, holding back elevator pressure will keep weight off the nosewheel, which otherwise could get bogged down, causing the gear to bend and/or nose over the airplane.

    d.   The use of a slight amount of power will help slow the sink rate.

          1)   Use caution to avoid excessive flooding.

8. **The applicant demonstrates the ability to touch down softly with minimum sink rate and no drift, with the airplane's longitudinal axis aligned with center of the runway.**

    a. Maintain slight power throughout the roundout (flare) to assist in producing as soft a touchdown (i.e., minimum sink rate) as possible.

        1) Attempt to hold your airplane about 1 to 2 ft. above the ground as long as possible to allow the touchdown to be made at the slowest possible airspeed with your airplane in a nose-high pitch attitude.

    b. In a tailwheel-type airplane, the tailwheel should touch down simultaneously with or just before the main wheels and then should be held down by maintaining firm back elevator pressure throughout the landing roll.

        1) This will minimize any tendency for your airplane to nose over and will provide aerodynamic braking.

    c. In nosewheel-type airplanes, after the main wheels touch the surface, you should hold sufficient back elevator pressure to keep the nosewheel off the ground until it can no longer aerodynamically be held off the surface.

        1) At this time you should let the nosewheel come down to the ground on its own. Maintain full back elevator pressure at all times on a soft surface.

            a) Maintaining slight power during and immediately after touchdown usually will aid in easing the nosewheel down.

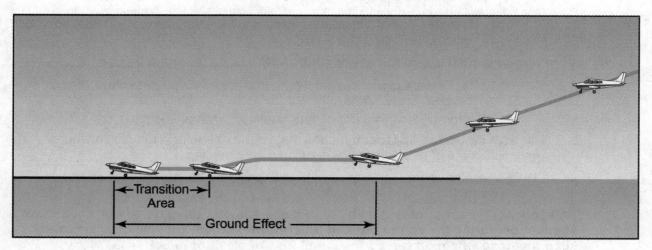

    d. Use the proper crosswind technique to ensure your airplane's longitudinal axis is aligned with the runway centerline.

9. **The applicant demonstrates the ability to maintain full up elevator during rollout and exit the "soft" area at a speed that would preclude sinking into the surface.**

    a. You must maintain full up elevator during rollout and exit with enough speed while taxiing to prevent becoming bogged down on the soft surface.

        1) You will often need to increase power after landing on a very soft surface to keep your airplane moving and prevent being stuck.

        2) Care must be taken not to taxi excessively fast because, if you taxi onto a very soft area, your airplane may bog down and bend the landing gear and/or nose over.

10. **The applicant demonstrates the ability to maintain crosswind correction and directional control throughout the approach and landing sequence, as required.**

    a.   If a crosswind is present, use the crosswind and directional control techniques described in Study Unit 26, Subunit 3, item A.10., beginning on page 330.

    b.   Maintain full back elevator pressure and the proper aileron deflection for a crosswind condition while on the ground.

11. **The applicant demonstrates the ability to execute a timely go-around decision when the approach cannot be made within the tolerances specified in items 6-10 or for any other condition that may result in an unsafe approach or landing.**

    a.   Establish a decision point on your final approach where, if you are not completely established and ready to land, you will execute a go-around.

    1)   It is important to remember that going around from a bad approach will not necessarily result in a failure. On the contrary, it shows the evaluator that you can make good decisions and that you are interested in safety.

    a)   You obviously cannot go-around repeatedly. At some point, you have to land the aircraft within the established tolerances.

    b.   For additional information on go-arounds, see Study Unit 32, "Go-Around/Rejected Landing," beginning on page 407.

12. **The applicant demonstrates the ability to maintain proper position of the flight controls and sufficient speed to taxi on the soft surface.**

    a.   Keep your airplane moving at all times until you are at the point where you will be parking your airplane.

    b.   Maintain full back elevator pressure and the proper aileron deflection for a crosswind condition while on the ground.

    c.   Brakes are not needed on a soft surface. Avoid using the brakes because their use may impose a heavy load on the nosegear due to premature or hard contact with the landing surface, causing the nosewheel to dig in.

    1)   On a tailwheel-type airplane, the application of brakes may cause the main wheels to dig in, causing the airplane to nose over.

13. **The applicant demonstrates the ability to utilize after landing runway incursion avoidance procedures.**

    a.   After landing, be sure to clear the runway in a timely fashion.

    1)   Do not exit the runway above a safe taxi speed; however, allow enough forward momentum to prevent the aircraft from getting stuck in other than hard surface areas and before crossing onto an intersecting taxiway or parallel runway.

    2)   In the case of ATC instructions to expedite your taxi, only accept them if you feel you can accommodate their request.

    b.   Visually clear intersecting taxiways/runways before crossing them, even if ATC has cleared you across.

    c.   Read back and confirm all ATC holding/crossing instructions/clearances.

END OF SKILLS ELEMENT

28.4 COMMON ERRORS

A.   Common Errors during a Soft-Field Approach and Landing

1.   **Improper use of landing performance data and limitations**

   a.   Use your POH/AFM to determine the appropriate airspeeds and performance for a soft-field approach and landing.

   b.   The most common error, as well as the easiest to avoid, is to attempt a landing that is beyond the capabilities of your airplane and/or your flying skills. Be sure that the surface of the field you plan to use is suitable for landing. Plan ahead!

2.   **Failure to establish approach and landing configuration at appropriate time or in proper sequence**

   a.   Use the before-landing checklist in your POH/AFM to ensure that you follow the proper sequence in establishing the correct approach and landing configuration for your airplane.

   b.   You should initially start the checklist at midpoint on the downwind leg with the power reduction beginning once you are abeam your intended point of landing.

      1)   By the time you turn on final and align your airplane with the runway centerline, you should be in the proper configuration. Confirm this by completing your checklist once again.

3.   **Failure to establish and maintain a stabilized approach**

   a.   Once you are on final and aligned with the runway centerline, you should make small adjustments to pitch and power to establish the correct descent angle (i.e., glide path) and airspeed.

      1)   Remember, you must make simultaneous adjustments to both pitch and power.

4.   **Failure to consider the effect of wind and landing surface**

   a.   Proper planning will ensure knowledge of the landing surface condition, e.g., wet, dry, loose, hard packed.

   b.   Understand how the wind affects the landing distance required on a soft field.

5.   **Improper technique in use of power, wing flaps, and trim**

   a.   Use power and pitch adjustments simultaneously to maintain the proper descent angle and airspeed.

   b.   Wing flaps should be used in accordance with your POH/AFM.

   c.   Trim to relieve control pressures to help in stabilizing the final approach.

   d.   Remember to maintain power throughout the roundout, touchdown, and after-landing roll.

6.   **Inappropriate removal of hand from throttle**

   a.   One hand should remain on the control yoke at all times.

   b.   The other hand should remain on the throttle unless you are operating the microphone or making an adjustment, such as trim or flaps.

      1)   Your first priority is to fly your airplane and avoid doing tasks that may distract you from maintaining control.

   c.   You must be in the habit of keeping one hand on the throttle in case a sudden and unexpected hazardous situation should require an immediate application of power.

7. **Improper technique during roundout and touchdown**

   a. Maintain a little power and hold the airplane off the ground as long as possible.

   b. See Study Unit 26, Subunit 4, beginning on page 334, for a detailed discussion of general landing errors.

   c. Remember, if you have any doubts about the suitability of the field, go around.

8. **Failure to hold back elevator pressure after touchdown**

   a. In a nosewheel-type airplane, holding back elevator pressure will keep weight off the nosewheel, which otherwise could get bogged down causing the gear to bend and/or nose over the airplane.

   b. In a tailwheel-type airplane, back elevator pressure keeps the tailwheel firmly on the surface to prevent the tendency to nose over.

9. **Closing the throttle too soon after touchdown**

   a. On a soft field, you must keep your airplane moving at all times.

10. **Poor directional control after touchdown**

    a. Use rudder to steer your airplane on the landing surface, and increase aileron deflection into the wind as airspeed decreases.

    b. See Study Unit 26, Subunit 4, item A.6., beginning on page 340 for a discussion of ground loops and other directional control problems after touchdown.

11. **Improper use of brakes**

    a. Brakes are not needed on a soft field and should be avoided.

    b. On a very soft surface, you may even need full power to avoid stopping and/or becoming bogged down on the landing surface.

END OF COMMON ERRORS

STUDY UNIT TWENTY-NINE
SHORT-FIELD TAKEOFF AND
MAXIMUM PERFORMANCE CLIMB

Task	Task E. Short-Field Takeoff and Maximum Performance Climb
References	FAA-H-8083-2, FAA-H-8083-3; POH/AFM
Objective	To determine that the applicant exhibits satisfactory knowledge, risk management, and skills associated with a short-field takeoff, maximum performance climb operations, and rejected takeoff procedures.
Knowledge	The applicant demonstrates understanding of:
PA.IV.E.K1	1. The effects of aircraft configuration.
PA.IV.E.K2	2. The effects of runway surface.
PA.IV.E.K3	3. Takeoff distance.
PA.IV.E.K4	4. Takeoff power.
PA.IV.E.K5	5. Obstruction clearance.
PA.IV.E.K6	6. Wind conditions and effects.
PA.IV.E.K7	7. Minimum safe altitude.
PA.IV.E.K8	8. Density altitude.
PA.IV.E.K9	9. Application of V_X or V_Y.
PA.IV.E.K10	10. Emergency procedures during takeoff and climb.
Risk Management	The applicant demonstrates the ability to identify, assess and mitigate risks, encompassing:
PA.IV.E.R1	1. Failure to select the appropriate runway based on wind, pilot capability, and aircraft limitations.
PA.IV.E.R2	2. Exceeding the manufacturer's maximum demonstrated crosswind component.
PA.IV.E.R3	3. Operating from other than a hard surfaced runway.
PA.IV.E.R4	4. Obstruction clearance.
PA.IV.E.R5	5. Climb attitude and stall awareness.
PA.IV.E.R6	6. Windshear.
PA.IV.E.R7	7. Tailwind.
PA.IV.E.R8	8. Wake turbulence.
PA.IV.E.R9	9. Failure to recognize the need to perform a go-around/rejected landing.
PA.IV.E.R10	10. Task management.
PA.IV.E.R11	11. Low altitude maneuvering.
PA.IV.E.R12	12. Wire strikes.
PA.IV.E.R13	13. Obstacles on the departure paths.
PA.IV.E.R14	14. Recognition of need for rejected takeoff and identification of takeoff abort criteria.
PA.IV.E.R15	15. Strategies for handling engine failure during takeoff and climb, including recognition that climb at V_X (versus V_{XSE}) may result in loss of directional control if an engine fails.
PA.IV.E.R16	16. Criticality of takeoff distance available.
PA.IV.E.R17	17. An engine failure after takeoff.
PA.IV.E.R18	18. Failure to adhere to sterile cockpit requirement.

Skills	The applicant demonstrates the ability to:
PA.IV.E.S1	1. Verify proper aircraft configuration.
PA.IV.E.S2	2. Verify ATC clearance and no aircraft is on final before crossing the hold line.
PA.IV.E.S3	3. Ensure the aircraft is on the correct takeoff runway.
PA.IV.E.S4	4. Determine wind direction with or without visible wind direction indicators.
PA.IV.E.S5	5. Calculate the crosswind component and determine if it is beyond the pilot ability or aircraft capability.
PA.IV.E.S6	6. Position the flight controls for the existing wind conditions.
PA.IV.E.S7	7. Clear the area, taxi into the takeoff position utilizing maximum available takeoff area and align the airplane on the runway center line.
PA.IV.E.S8	8. Apply brakes (if appropriate), while configuring aircraft power setting to achieve maximum performance.
PA.IV.E.S9	9. Confirm takeoff power prior to brake release (if appropriate) and proper engine and flight instrument indications prior to rotation.
PA.IV.E.S10	10. Rotate and lift-off at the recommended airspeed, and accelerate to the recommended obstacle clearance airspeed or V_x.
PA.IV.E.S11	11. Establish a pitch attitude that will maintain the recommended obstacle clearance airspeed, or V_x, +10/-5 knots, until the obstacle is cleared, or until the airplane is 50 feet above the surface.
PA.IV.E.S12	12. After clearing the obstacle, establish the pitch attitude for V_Y, accelerate to V_Y, and maintain V_Y, +10/-5 knots, during the climb.
PA.IV.E.S13	13. Retract landing gear and flaps after a positive rate of climb has been verified or in accordance with aircraft manufacturer's guidance.
PA.IV.E.S14	14. Maintain takeoff power and V_Y +10/-5 knots to a safe maneuvering altitude.
PA.IV.E.S15	15. Maintain directional control and proper wind drift correction throughout the takeoff and climb.
PA.IV.E.S16	16. Comply with noise abatement and published departure procedures.
PA.IV.E.S17	17. Complete the appropriate checklist.
PA.IV.E.S18	18. Comply with manufacturer's recommended emergency procedures related to the takeoff sequence.
PA.IV.E.S19	19. Utilize runway incursion avoidance procedures.

A. General Information

1. The objective of this task is for you to demonstrate your knowledge, risk management, and skills related to short-field takeoffs, maximum performance climb operations, and rejected takeoff procedures.

2. Some of the content of Subunits 29.1 and 29.2 is abbreviated based on the assumption that you have thoroughly read and understood pages 287 through 304 and the additional common task topics found in Part II. The task objectives and specific references are provided here for your convenience.

29.1 KNOWLEDGE

A. Task Objectives

1. **The applicant demonstrates understanding of the effects of aircraft configuration.**

   a. Aircraft configuration refers to the position of the landing gear and flaps.

      1) Follow the gear and flap settings prescribed by the airplane's manufacturer.

         a) If the use of flaps is recommended, they should be extended prior to starting the takeoff roll.

         b) Always check your flap setting visually.

2. **The applicant demonstrates understanding of the effects of runway surface.**

   a. For information on the effects of runway surface, see Section IV Introduction, Knowledge, item G., on page 298.

3. **The applicant demonstrates understanding of takeoff distance.**

   a. For general information on takeoff distance, see Section IV Introduction, Knowledge, item A., on page 289.

   b. Positive and accurate control of your airplane attitude and airspeed is required to obtain the shortest ground roll and the steepest angle of climb.

   c. Section 5, Performance, in your POH/AFM will provide you with the performance charts and/or graphs necessary to calculate takeoff distance.

      1) Pay attention to any notes on the charts specifying required aircraft configuration, including power settings, RPM, use of flaps, cowl flaps, and landing gear retraction.

   d. Section 4, Normal Procedures, in your POH/AFM will provide you with the proper airspeeds, e.g., V_R, V_X, V_Y, and also the proper configurations.

      1) Best angle of climb, V_X, is the speed that will result in the greatest gain of altitude for a given distance over the ground.

         a) In some airplanes, a deviation of 5 kt. from V_X can result in a significant reduction in climb performance.

4. **The applicant demonstrates understanding of takeoff power.**

   a. For general information on takeoff power, see Section IV Introduction, Knowledge, item C., on page 291.

   b. Apply brakes (if appropriate) while advancing the throttle smoothly to takeoff power.

      1) Apply and hold brake pressure, add takeoff (i.e., full) power, and then release the brakes smoothly. Confirm that the engine is developing takeoff power under prevailing conditions before releasing the brakes.

      2) Engine instruments must be monitored during the entire maneuver.

         a) Monitoring enables you to notice immediately any malfunctions or indication of insufficient power or other potential problems.

         b) Listen for any indication of power loss or engine roughness.

         c) Do not hesitate to abort the takeoff if all engine indications are not normal.

      3) Check your airspeed indicator for movement as you accelerate.

         a) Call out your airspeed as you accelerate to V_R, e.g., "40, 60, 80."

5. **The applicant demonstrates understanding of obstruction clearance.**

    a. When taking off from a field where the available runway is short and/or where obstacles must be cleared, you must operate your airplane to its maximum capability.

    b. Always climb above the altitude of obstacles (usually powerlines or treelines) before accelerating to V_Y. This acceleration involves a reduction in pitch.

    c. Establish a pitch attitude that will maintain the recommended obstacle clearance airspeed, or V_X, +10/–5 kt., until the obstacle is cleared or until your airplane is 50 ft. above the surface.

        1) While you are practicing short-field takeoffs, you should learn the pitch attitude required to maintain V_X.

            a) Observe the position of the airplane's nose on the horizon.
            b) Note the position of the aircraft bar on the attitude indicator.

        2) You should rotate to this predetermined pitch angle as soon as you reach V_R. As you climb out at V_X, maintain visual references, but occasionally glance at the attitude indicator and airspeed indicator to check the pitch angle and airspeed.

        3) If not enough back pressure is held to maintain the correct takeoff attitude or the nose is allowed to lower excessively, your airplane may settle back to the runway. This problem occurs because the angle of attack is decreased and lift is diminished to the point at which it will not support the airplane.

            a) Too much back elevator pressure will result in too low of an airspeed, which will decrease climb performance and possibly result in a stall.

        4) Maintain V_X, +10/–5 kt., until the obstacle is cleared, or to at least 50 ft. AGL.

            Your airplane's V_X _____.

    d. After clearing the obstacle, establish the pitch attitude for V_Y, accelerate to V_Y, and maintain V_Y, +10/–5 kt., during the climb.

        1) Release back pressure to allow the nose to lower slightly to the approximate attitude for a V_Y climb.

        2) Maintain V_Y by adjusting pitch attitude as necessary.

        3) Trim away control pressure.

6. **The applicant demonstrates understanding of wind conditions and effects.**

    a. For information on wind conditions and effects, see Study Unit 9, Subunit 3, beginning on page 80.

7. **The applicant demonstrates understanding of minimum safe altitude.**

    a. 14 CFR 91.119 states that, except when necessary for takeoff and landing, the following altitudes are required:

        1) You must have sufficient altitude for an emergency landing without undue hazard to persons or property on the surface if your engine fails.

        2) Over congested areas of a city, town, or settlement, or over an open-air assembly of persons, you must have 1,000 ft. of clearance over the highest obstacle within a 2,000-ft. radius of your airplane.

        3) Over other than congested areas, you must have an altitude of 500 ft. above the surface.

        4) Over open water or sparsely populated areas, you must remain at least 500 ft. from any person, vessel, vehicle, or structure.

    b. You can use the maximum elevation figures (MEF) on your sectional chart to determine minimum safe altitude.

8. **The applicant demonstrates understanding of density altitude.**

    a. For general information on density altitude, see Study Unit 9, Subunit 1, beginning on page 77.

    b. Consult Section 5, Performance, of your POH/AFM before attempting a short-field takeoff, specifically taking into account the existing temperature, barometric pressure, field length, wind, type of runway surface, and airplane operating condition and weight.

        1) Since the performance charts assume good pilot technique, consider your short-field takeoff proficiency.

        2) Recognize that, in some situations, you should decide NOT to attempt to take off because the margin of safety is too small. You may have to

            a) Remove fuel, people, or baggage.
            b) Wait for different wind and/or temperature conditions.
            c) Retain a more experienced pilot to make the flight.
            d) Have the airplane moved to a safer takeoff location.

9. **The applicant demonstrates understanding of the application of V_X or V_Y.**

    a. For information on the application of V_X or V_Y, see Section IV Introduction, Knowledge, item E., beginning on page 295.

10. **The applicant demonstrates understanding of emergency procedures during takeoff and climb.**

    a. For information on emergency procedures during takeoff and climb, see Study Unit 8, Subunit 2, Item D., on page 74.

END OF KNOWLEDGE ELEMENT

29.2 RISK MANAGEMENT

A.   Task Objectives

1.   **The applicant demonstrates the ability to identify, assess, and mitigate risks encompassing failure to select the appropriate runway based on wind, pilot capability, and aircraft limitations.**

a.   For information on selection of runway based on wind, pilot capability, and aircraft limitations, see Section IV Introduction, Risk Management, item A., on page 299.

2.   **The applicant demonstrates the ability to identify, assess, and mitigate risks encompassing exceeding the manufacturer's maximum demonstrated crosswind component.**

a.   For information on crosswind component, see Study Unit 9, Subunit 3, item C., on page 80.

3.   **The applicant demonstrates the ability to identify, assess, and mitigate risks encompassing operating from other than a hard surfaced runway.**

a.   For information on operating from other than a hard surfaced runway, see Section IV Introduction, Risk Management, item K., beginning on page 303.

4.   **The applicant demonstrates the ability to identify, assess, and mitigate risks encompassing obstruction clearance.**

a.   For information on obstruction clearance, see Subunit 29.1, item A.5., on page 372.

5.   **The applicant demonstrates the ability to identify, assess, and mitigate risks encompassing climb attitude and stall awareness.**

a.   For information on climb attitude, see Subunit 29.1, item A.5., on page 372.

b.   For information on stall awareness, see Section IV Introduction, Risk Management, item H., beginning on page 301.

6.   **The applicant demonstrates the ability to identify, assess, and mitigate risks encompassing windshear.**

a.   For information on windshear, see Study Unit 9, Subunit 4, beginning on page 81.

7.   **The applicant demonstrates the ability to identify, assess, and mitigate risks encompassing tailwind.**

a.   For information on tailwind, see Study Unit 9, Subunit 3, beginning on page 80.

8.   **The applicant demonstrates the ability to identify, assess, and mitigate risks encompassing wake turbulence.**

a.   For information on wake turbulence, see Study Unit 7, Subunit 7, beginning on page 69.

9.   **The applicant demonstrates the ability to identify, assess, and mitigate risks encompassing failure to recognize the need to perform a go-around/rejected landing.**

a.   NOTE: We do not believe it is appropriate to discuss go-around rejected landings in a takeoff task as the FAA states in the ACS. We believe this item should be about go/no-go decision making.

b.   For information on go/no-go decision making, see Section IV Introduction, Risk Management, item B., on page 299.

10.   **The applicant demonstrates the ability to identify, assess, and mitigate risks encompassing task management.**

a.   For information on task management, see Study Unit 6, Subunit 1, beginning on page 49.

11. **The applicant demonstrates the ability to identify, assess, and mitigate risks encompassing low altitude maneuvering.**

    a.   For information on low altitude maneuvering, see Section IV Introduction, Risk Management, item C., on page 299.

12. **The applicant demonstrates the ability to identify, assess, and mitigate risks encompassing wire strikes.**

    a.   For information on wire strikes, see Study Unit 7, Subunit 6, beginning on page 68.

13. **The applicant demonstrates the ability to identify, assess, and mitigate risks encompassing obstacles on the departure paths.**

    a.   For information on obstacles on the departure paths, see Section IV Introduction, Risk Management, item D., on page 300.

14. **The applicant demonstrates the ability to identify, assess, and mitigate risks encompassing recognition of the need for rejected takeoff and identification of takeoff abort criteria.**

    a.   For information on recognition of the need for rejected takeoff and identification of takeoff abort criteria, see Section IV Introduction, Risk Management, item E., on page 300.

15. **The applicant demonstrates the ability to identify, assess, and mitigate risks encompassing strategies for handling engine failure during takeoff and climb.**

    a.   For information on strategies for handling engine failure during takeoff and climb, see Study Unit 8, Subunit 2, item E., on page 75.

16. **The applicant demonstrates the ability to identify, assess, and mitigate risks encompassing criticality of takeoff distance available.**

    a.   For information on criticality of takeoff distance available, see Section IV Introduction, Risk Management, item I., beginning on page 302.

17. **The applicant demonstrates the ability to identify, assess, and mitigate risks encompassing an engine failure after takeoff.**

    a.   For information on engine failure after takeoff, see Study Unit 8, Subunit 2, item F., beginning on page 75.

18. **The applicant demonstrates the ability to identify, assess, and mitigate risks encompassing failure to adhere sterile cockpit requirement.**

    a.   For information on sterile cockpit, see Study Unit 6, Subunit 2, beginning on page 51.

END OF RISK MANAGEMENT ELEMENT

29.3 SKILLS

A.   Task Objectives

1.   **The applicant demonstrates the ability to verify aircraft configuration.**

   a.   The correct configuration in included in the short-field takeoff checklist in the POH/AFM for the aircraft.

   1)   NOTE: Be prepared to discuss with your evaluator the specific flap position, if installed, and configuration considerations for your type of aircraft.

   b.   If the use of flaps is recommended, position the flaps prior to taxiing onto the active runway.

   1)   Always check your flap setting visually.

2.   **The applicant demonstrates the ability to verify ATC clearance and no aircraft is on final before crossing the hold line.**

   a.   Use a standard clearing procedure before initiating movement on the surface.

   1)   Look to your left, scan the area for other traffic, and announce "clear left" if it is in fact clear.

   2)   Repeat this same procedure for both the front and right of the aircraft.

   3)   Any time you stop moving, use this procedure (or one like it) before rolling again.

   b.   Read back all ATC clearances. If any ATC takeoff instructions seem unclear or appear to conflict with other instructions that have been issued, stop and ask for clarification.

   c.   At non-towered airports, visually check the runway and the approach path to ensure the area is clear before you taxi onto the runway for takeoff.

   d.   Refer to the runway number and the magnetic heading of the aircraft as you taxi onto the runway and center the aircraft with the runway centerline to ensure you are using the correct/assigned runway.

   e.   Before taxiing onto the runway, you must make certain that you have sufficient time to execute the takeoff before any aircraft in the traffic pattern turns onto the final approach.

   1)   Check that the runway is clear of other aircraft, vehicles, persons, or other hazards.

   2)   This check should be done at airports both with and without an operating control tower.

3.   **The applicant demonstrates the ability to ensure the aircraft is on the correct takeoff runway.**

   a.   Runway safety is a significant challenge and a top priority for everyone in aviation. In the U.S., an average of three runway incursions occur daily.

   b.   A runway incursion is any occurrence at an aerodrome involving the incorrect presence of an aircraft, vehicle, or person on the protected area of a surface designated for the landing and takeoff of aircraft.

   c.   Thorough planning for taxi so you are on the correct runway is imperative.

   1)   Have the current airport diagram readily available.

   2)   Pay special attention to any complex intersections.

   3)   Verify your assigned route once received from ATC.

   4)   Minimize cockpit tasks, observe sterile cockpit, and practice "heads up, eyes out" mode while taxiing.

   5)   When in doubt, stop and ask ATC for help.

   d.   As you approach the hold short point, ensure the runway holding position sign confirm you are at the correct runway.

e. Never cross a hold line without explicit ATC instructions. Controllers are required to issue explicit instructions to cross or hold short of each runway, including inactive and closed runways that intersect a taxi route.

f. As you line up on the runway, confirm your compass and heading indicator agree you are on the correct runway.

4. **The applicant demonstrates the ability to determine wind direction with or without visible wind direction indicators.**

a. Make use of airport wind direction indicators if they are available and/or listen to automated weather broadcasts, where installed, to get timely wind information.

b. If necessary, you can contact ATC for a wind check prior to takeoff at tower-controlled airports.

c. If you have no ability to reference wind direction indicators, weather broadcasts, or ATC advisories, you can use various outside references, such as rising smoke, tree motion, or just the basic physical sensation of where the wind is blowing from.

d. Always reverify wind direction as you taxi onto the runway by observing the windsock or other wind direction indicators, which may include grass or bushes.

5. **The applicant demonstrates the ability to calculate the crosswind component and determine if it is beyond the pilot ability or aircraft capability.**

a. The aircraft's demonstrated crosswind component can be determined from Section 4, Normal Procedures, and/or Section 5, Performance, in your POH/AFM via a textual description in Section 4 and/or a graph in Section 5.

1) Bear in mind that a numerical value for the crosswind component of the aircraft is likely the maximum demonstrated crosswind component for a direct 90° crosswind.

2) The chart presented in Section 5 of the POH/AFM is the best way to determine the actual crosswind component that will be affecting the aircraft during your takeoff.

b. Beyond what the aircraft is capable of, you have to be aware of what your skill level will allow.

1) You should establish and follow personal minimums that are based on your comfort levels when dealing with crosswinds.

2) You should regularly re-evaluate your personal minimums and determine if they need to be updated.

6. **The applicant demonstrates the ability to position the flight controls for the existing wind conditions.**

a. Always reverify wind direction as you taxi onto the runway by observing the windsock or other wind direction indicator, which may include grass or bushes.

b. For a crosswind takeoff, the ailerons should be fully deflected at the start of the takeoff roll.

1) The aileron should be up on the upwind side of the airplane (i.e., the control yoke turned toward the wind).

2) This will impose a downward force on the upwind wing to counteract the lifting force of the crosswind and prevent that wing from rising prematurely.

3) Aileron deflection should be gradually reduced as you accelerate during the takeoff roll.

c. For a takeoff with a headwind or nearly so, ailerons should be in the neutral position.

7. **The applicant demonstrates the ability to clear the area, taxi into the takeoff position utilizing maximum available takeoff area, and align the airplane on the runway center line.**

    a. You should taxi to the very beginning of the takeoff runway (i.e., threshold) and come to a complete stop, thus making full use of the runway.

        1) This position may require a back taxi, announce your intentions on the CTAF or request permission from the tower.

    b. Before taxiing onto the runway, make certain that you have sufficient time to execute the takeoff before any aircraft in the traffic pattern turns onto the final approach.

        1) Check that the runway is clear of other aircraft, vehicles, persons, or other hazards.
        2) This should be done at both airports with and without an operating control tower.

    c. Before beginning your takeoff roll, study the runway and related ground reference points, such as nearby buildings, trees, runway lights (at night), etc.

        1) This will give you a frame of reference for directional control during takeoff.
        2) You will feel more confident about having everything under control.

    d. After taxiing onto the runway, your airplane should be aligned with the runway centerline, and the nosewheel (or tailwheel) should be straight (or centered).

8. **The applicant demonstrates the ability to apply brakes (if appropriate) while configuring aircraft power setting to achieve maximum performance.**

    a. Apply and hold brake pressure.
    b. Recheck that the mixture is set in accordance with your POH/AFM.
    c. Use the power setting that is recommended in your POH/AFM, usually full power with the throttle fully open.

9. **The applicant demonstrates the ability to confirm takeoff power prior to brake release (if appropriate) and proper engine and flight instrument indications prior to rotation.**

    a. Confirm that the engine is developing takeoff power under prevailing conditions before releasing the brakes.
    b. Engine instruments must be monitored during the entire maneuver.

        1) Monitoring enables you to notice immediately any malfunctions or indication of insufficient power or other potential problems.
        2) Listen for any indication of power loss or engine roughness.
        3) Do not hesitate to abort the takeoff if all engine indications are not normal.

    c. You should not release the brakes until the engine is producing full power and you have checked that the engine instruments are operating normally.
    d. When the brakes are released, ensure that your feet move to the bottom of the rudder pedal and are not on the brakes so that no further braking can take place.

        1) Any use of brakes will increase the takeoff distance.

10. **The applicant demonstrates the ability to rotate and lift off at the recommended airspeed, and accelerate to the recommended obstacle clearance airspeed or V_X.**

    a. At the recommended rotation speed (V_R) specified in your POH/AFM, you should smoothly raise the nose of your airplane to the attitude that will deliver the best angle-of-climb airspeed, V_X.

        1) If no rotation airspeed is recommended, accelerate to V_X minus 5 kt. and rotate to V_X attitude.

   b.   DO NOT attempt to raise the nose until V_R because doing so will create unnecessary drag and prolong the takeoff roll.

   1)   In a nosewheel-type airplane, keep the elevator in a neutral position to maintain a low drag attitude until rotation.

   2)   In a tailwheel-type airplane, the tail should be allowed to rise off the ground slightly and then be held in this tail-low flight attitude until the proper liftoff or rotation airspeed is attained.

Your airplane's V_R _____.

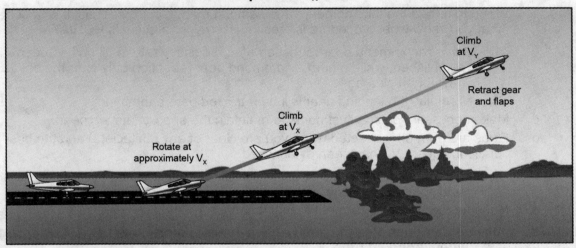

11.   **The applicant demonstrates the ability to establish a pitch attitude that will maintain the recommended obstacle clearance airspeed, or V_X, +10/-5 knots, until the obstacle is cleared or until the airplane is 50 feet above the surface.**

   a.   While you are practicing short-field takeoffs, you should learn the pitch attitude required to maintain V_X.

   1)   Observe the position of the airplane's nose on the horizon.
   2)   Note the position of the aircraft bar on the attitude indicator.

   b.   You should rotate to this predetermined pitch angle as soon as you reach V_R. As you climb out at V_X, maintain visual references, but occasionally glance at the attitude indicator and airspeed indicator to check the pitch angle and airspeed.

   c.   If not enough back pressure is held to maintain the correct takeoff attitude or the nose is allowed to lower excessively, your airplane may settle back to the runway. This problem occurs because the angle of attack is decreased and lift is diminished to the point at which it will not support the airplane.

   1)   Too much back elevator pressure will result in too low of an airspeed, which will decrease climb performance and possibly result in a stall.

   d.   Maintain V_X, +10/–5 kt., until the obstacle is cleared, or to at least 50 ft. AGL.

Your airplane's V_X _____.

12.   **The applicant demonstrates the ability, after clearing the obstacle, to establish the pitch attitude for V_Y, accelerate to V_Y, and maintain V_Y, +10/-5 knots, during the climb.**

   a.   Release back pressure to allow the nose to lower slightly to the approximate attitude for a V_Y climb.

   b.   Maintain V_Y by adjusting pitch attitude as necessary.

   c.   Trim away control pressure.

Your airplane's V_Y _____.

13. **The applicant demonstrates the ability to retract landing gear and flaps after a positive rate of climb has been verified or in accordance with aircraft manufacturer's guidance.**

    a.   Before retracting the landing gear, apply the brakes momentarily to stop the rotation of the wheels to avoid excessive vibration of the gear mechanism.

        1)   Centrifugal force caused by the rapidly rotating wheels expands the diameter of the tires, and if mud or other debris has accumulated in the wheel wells, the rotating wheels may rub as they enter.

    b.   When to retract the landing gear varies among manufacturers. Thus, it is important that you know what procedure is prescribed by your airplane's POH/AFM.

        1)   Some recommend gear retraction after a positive rate of climb has been established, while others recommend gear retraction only after the obstacles have been cleared.

        2)   Normally, the landing gear will be retracted before the flaps.

    c.   Make necessary pitch adjustments to maintain the appropriate airspeed.

    d.   Flaps are normally retracted when you are clear of any obstacle(s) and the best rate-of-climb speed, V_Y, has been established.

        1)   Raise the flaps in increments (if appropriate) to avoid sudden loss of lift and settling of the airplane.

    e.   Make needed pitch adjustment to maintain V_Y.

14. **The applicant demonstrates the ability to maintain takeoff power and V_Y +10/-5 knots to a safe maneuvering altitude.**

    a.   After establishing, V_Y, completing gear and flap retraction, and reaching a safe maneuvering altitude (normally 500 to 1,000 ft. AGL), reduce the power to the normal cruise climb setting and adjust pitch for cruise climb airspeed.

        1)   Most trainer-type airplane manufacturers recommend maintaining maximum power to your selected cruising altitude.

        2)   Due to higher operating temperatures in a climb, some manufacturers recommend reducing power during the climb to your selected cruising altitude.

    b.   Use the power setting recommended in your POH/AFM.

15. **The applicant demonstrates the ability to maintain directional control and proper wind drift correction throughout the takeoff and climb.**

    a.   Crosswind takeoff techniques are consistent with a short-field takeoff and should be employed simultaneously, as needed.

        1)   A common error is to become preoccupied with the short-field effort at the expense of neglecting crosswind correction. The results are directional stability problems.

    b.   For additional information on maintaining directional control and proper wind drift correction throughout the takeoff and climb, see Study Unit 25, Subunit 3, item A.12., beginning on page 313.

16. **The applicant demonstrates the ability to comply with noise abatement and published departure procedures.**

    a.   When taking off and climbing, follow published departure procedures, including any established noise abatement procedure.

        1)   You must comply with any established noise abatement procedure.

            a)   A noise abatement policy is developed by the airport authority or city and is a local ordinance. Thus, you can be cited by the city for violation of the policy.

     2)   Flying over towns and communities can create noise complaints.

     3)   Many airports have been forced to provide noise mitigation to properties in their surrounding communities. These can be very expensive resulting in higher fees for airports and aircraft operators.

     4)   For example, the Hartsfield-Jackson Atlanta International Airport has provided sound insulation and/or relocated residents at a cost.

  b.   The Chart Supplement will list that an airport has a noise abatement procedure in effect under "airport remarks."

     1)   Other pilot guides may contain more detailed information on an airport's noise abatement procedures.

  c.   A key to complying with noise abatement is to put as much distance as possible between you and the ground, as quickly as possible.

     1)   Use the longest runway available.

     2)   Rotate at V_R and climb out at V_X or V_Y, as recommended in your POH/AFM.

     3)   Reduce power to climb power, and transition to a cruise climb as appropriate.

        a)   The reduction to climb power will reduce the noise of your engine, and the transition to cruise climb airspeed will reduce the time you are over the noise monitors and noise sensitive areas.

  d.   If you are flying from an unfamiliar airport that has a noise abatement policy, you should contact the airport's noise abatement office for details.

17. **The applicant demonstrates the ability to complete the appropriate checklist.**

  a.   Follow the short-field takeoff checklist in your POH/AFM.

  b.   Complete the checklist for climb to ensure that your airplane is in the proper configuration for the continued climb to cruising altitude.

18. **The applicant demonstrates the ability to comply with manufacturer's recommended emergency procedures related to the takeoff sequence.**

  a.   The key to successful management of an emergency situation and/or preventing a non-normal situation from progressing into a true emergency is a thorough familiarity with, and adherence to, the procedures developed by the airplane manufacturer and contained in the POH/AFM for the particular make and model airplane.

     1)   For example, one particular procedure could entail engine failures on takeoff. Before a safe maneuvering altitude is attained, it is usually inadvisable to attempt to turn back to the field from where the takeoff was made. Instead, it is safer to immediately establish the proper glide attitude and select a field directly ahead or slightly to either side of the takeoff path.

19. **The applicant demonstrates the ability to utilize runway incursion avoidance procedures.**

  a.   Prior to taxiing onto the runway, you must make certain that the takeoff area and path are clear of other aircraft, vehicles, persons, livestock, wildlife (including birds), etc.

  b.   At controlled airports, this is a function of ATC, but you must also check for conflicts with other aircraft or other hazards.

  c.   At uncontrolled airports, you should announce your intentions on the appropriate CTAF, and if possible, make a 360° turn on the taxiway in the direction of the runway traffic pattern to look for other aircraft.

END OF SKILLS ELEMENT

29.4 COMMON ERRORS

A.   Common Errors during a Short-Field Takeoff and Maximum Performance Climb

1.   **Failure to use the maximum amount of runway available for the takeoff**

a.   Instead of making a wide turn onto the runway, you should taxi to the beginning of the usable portion of the runway for takeoff. The usable portion includes any runway before a displaced threshold.

1)   Paved areas that are marked with arrows pointing toward the beginning of the runway for landings may be used for takeoff. Chevron-marked areas are to be used only in an emergency.

2.   **Improper positioning of flight controls and wing flaps**

a.   If a crosswind is present, full aileron should be held into the wind initially to prevent the crosswind from raising the upwind wing.

b.   Flaps should be visually checked to ensure that they are in the proper position recommended by the POH/AFM.

1)   The short-field takeoff performance chart in your POH/AFM will also list the flap setting used to attain the chart performance.

2)   Position the flaps prior to taxiing onto the active runway.

3.   **Improper engine operation during short-field takeoff and climbout**

a.   In an attempt to gain the most performance, some pilots use very rapid throttle movements, overboost the engine, and use improper power settings.

1)   Operating the engine in this manner can degrade engine performance, cause long-term engine wear, and add to the risk of engine failure.

b.   The performance for short-field takeoffs should be obtained by flap settings, runway selection, rotation speed, climbout attitude, and climbout airspeed indicated in the POH/AFM, not by misusing the engine.

4.   **Inappropriate removal of hand from throttle**

a.   Throughout this maneuver, your hand should remain on the throttle.

b.   Exceptions are when you are raising the flaps, raising the landing gear, and/or adjusting the trim during the climb. After you complete these tasks, your hand should return to the throttle.

5.   **Poor directional control**

a.   Maintain the runway centerline throughout the takeoff roll by use of the rudder.

b.   Poor directional control can lead to a longer takeoff roll and control problems at liftoff.

c.   Positive and accurate control of your airplane is required to obtain the shortest ground roll and the steepest angle of climb (V_X).

d.   The higher pitch attitude required for V_X will result in increased torque effects; thus, more right rudder will be required than during a climb at V_Y.

1)   Slipping will degrade your airplane's climb performance.

6.   **Improper use of brakes**

a.   You should not release the brakes until the engine is producing full power and you have checked that the engine instruments are operating normally.

b.   When the brakes are released, ensure that your feet move to the bottom of the rudder pedal and are not on the brakes so that no further braking can take place.

1)   Any use of brakes will increase the takeoff distance.

7. **Improper pitch attitude during liftoff**

    a. The attitude to maintain V_X will be significantly higher than that to maintain V_Y; thus, a pilot not completely comfortable with his or her airplane may find it difficult to pull the airplane into a high pitch angle.

    b. Have confidence in your airplane's abilities, and fly it by the numbers.

8. **Failure to establish and maintain proper climb configuration and airspeed**

    a. Follow the recommended procedures in your POH/AFM.

    b. Maintain V_X because a 5-kt. deviation can result in a reduction of climb performance.

9. **Drift during climbout**

    a. Maintain the extended runway centerline until a turn is required.

    b. Remember an airport traffic pattern can be a very busy area, and collision avoidance and awareness are of extreme importance.

        1) Your fellow pilots will be expecting you to maintain the extended runway centerline during your initial climb.

END OF COMMON ERRORS

STUDY UNIT THIRTY
SHORT-FIELD APPROACH AND LANDING

Task	Task F. Short-Field Approach and Landing
References	FAA-H-8083-2, FAA-H-8083-3; POH/AFM
Objective	To determine that the applicant exhibits satisfactory knowledge, risk management, and skills associated with a short-field approach and landing with emphasis on proper use and coordination of flight controls.
Knowledge	The applicant demonstrates understanding of:
PA.IV.F.K1	1. Landing distance.
PA.IV.F.K2	2. Hazards of other than a hard surfaced runway.
PA.IV.F.K3	3. Obstruction clearance.
PA.IV.F.K4	4. Stabilized approach.
PA.IV.F.K5	5. Energy management.
PA.IV.F.K6	6. Wind conditions and effects.
PA.IV.F.K7	7. Density altitude.
PA.IV.F.K8	8. Emergency procedures during approach and landing.
PA.IV.F.K9	9. Land and hold short operations.
Risk Management	The applicant demonstrates the ability to identify, assess and mitigate risks, encompassing:
PA.IV.F.R1	1. Failure to select the appropriate runway based on wind, pilot capability, and aircraft limitations.
PA.IV.F.R2	2. Exceeding the manufacturer's maximum demonstrated crosswind component.
PA.IV.F.R3	3. Operating from other than a hard surfaced runway.
PA.IV.F.R4	4. Obstruction clearance.
PA.IV.F.R5	5. Climb attitude and stall awareness.
PA.IV.F.R6	6. Wind shear avoidance.
PA.IV.F.R7	7. Tailwind.
PA.IV.F.R8	8. Wake turbulence.
PA.IV.F.R9	9. Task management.
PA.IV.F.R10	10. Low altitude maneuvering.
PA.IV.F.R11	11. Collision avoidance, scanning, obstacle and wire strike avoidance.
PA.IV.F.R12	12. Failure to follow the right-of-way rules.
PA.IV.F.R13	13. Obstacles on approach and landing paths.
PA.IV.F.R14	14. Failure to recognize the need for a go-around/rejected landing.
PA.IV.F.R15	15. Low altitude stall/spin.
PA.IV.F.R15	16. Land and hold short operations (LAHSO).
PA.IV.F.R17	17. Failure to adhere to sterile cockpit requirement.

Skills	The applicant demonstrates the ability to:
PA.IV.F.S1	1. Ensure the aircraft is aligned with the correct/assigned runway.
PA.IV.F.S2	2. Scan the landing runway/area for possible obstructions for landing.
PA.IV.F.S3	3. Complete the appropriate approach and landing checklist.
PA.IV.F.S4	4. Consider the wind conditions, landing surface and obstructions to select a suitable touchdown point.
PA.IV.F.S5	5. Establish the recommended approach and landing configuration and airspeed, and adjust pitch attitude and power as required.
PA.IV.F.S6	6. Maintain a stabilized approach and recommended airspeed, or in its absence, not more than 1.3 V_{so}, with wind gust factor applied +10/-5 knots or as recommended by aircraft manufacturer to a safe maneuvering altitude.
PA.IV.F.S7	7. Make smooth, timely, and correct control application during the round out and touchdown.
PA.IV.F.S8	8. Touch down smoothly at an appropriate airspeed.
PA.IV.F.S9	9. Touch down within the available runway, at or within 200 feet beyond the specified point, threshold markings or runway numbers, with no side drift, minimum float, and with the airplane's longitudinal axis aligned with and over the runway center line/landing path.
PA.IV.F.S10	10. Maintain crosswind correction and directional control throughout the approach and landing sequence, as required.
PA.IV.F.S11	11. Execute a safe and timely go-around decision when the approach cannot be made within the tolerances specified above or for any other condition that may result in an unsafe approach or landing.
PA.IV.F.S12	12. Apply brakes, as necessary, to stop in the shortest distance consistent with safety.
PA.IV.F.S13	13. Utilize after landing runway incursion avoidance procedures.

A.   General Information

1.   The objective of this task is for you to demonstrate your knowledge, risk management, and skills related to a short-field approach and landing with emphasis on proper use and coordination of flight controls.

2.   Much of the content of Subunits 30.1 and 30.2 is abbreviated based on the assumption that you have thoroughly read and understood pages 287 through 304 and the additional common task topics found in Part II. The task objectives and specific references are provided here for your convenience.

30.1 KNOWLEDGE

A. Task Objectives

1. **The applicant demonstrates understanding of landing distance.**

   a. For information on landing distance, see Section IV Introduction, Knowledge, item B., beginning on page 289.

2. **The applicant demonstrates understanding of the hazards of other than a hard surfaced runway.**

   a. For information on other than a hard surfaced runway, see Section IV Introduction, Knowledge, item K., beginning on page 303.

3. **The applicant demonstrates understanding of obstruction clearance.**

   a. For information on obstruction clearance, see Study Unit 29, Subunit 1, item A.5., on page 372.

4. **The applicant demonstrates understanding of stabilized approach.**

   a. For information on stabilized approach, see Section IV Introduction, Knowledge, item D., beginning on page 292.

5. **The applicant demonstrates understanding of energy management.**

   a. For information on energy management, see Study Unit 8, Subunit 1, beginning on page 71.

6. **The applicant demonstrates understanding of wind conditions and effects.**

   a. For information on wind conditions and effects, see Study Unit 9, Subunit 3, beginning on page 80.

7. **The applicant demonstrates understanding of density altitude.**

   a. For information on density altitude, see Study Unit 9, Subunit 1, beginning on page 77.

8. **The applicant demonstrates understanding of emergency procedures during approach and landing.**

   a. For information on emergency procedures during approach and landing, see Study Unit 8, Subunit 2, item G., beginning on page 76.

9. **The applicant demonstrates understanding of land and hold short operations.**

   a. For information on land and hold short operations, see Section IV Introduction, Knowledge, item F., on page 297.

END OF KNOWLEDGE ELEMENT

30.2 RISK MANAGEMENT

A. Task Objectives

1. **The applicant demonstrates the ability to identify, assess, and mitigate risks encompassing failure to select the appropriate runway based on wind, pilot capability, and aircraft limitations.**

    a. For information on selecting the appropriate runway based on wind, pilot capability, and aircraft limitations, see Section IV Introduction, Risk Management, item A., on page 299.

    b. Operating into a short-field that you are not used to requires extra vigilance to ensure your are not using the wrong runway.

        1) A short-field has less margin of safety should you select the wrong runway.

        2) Double-check the wind direction indicators and weather broadcasts to ensure proper runway use.

        3) Accidentally landing with a tailwind can dramatically increase the required landing distance.

    c. Consider your own capabilities. If you do not regularly operate on short fields, practice short-field takeoff and landing techniques at a longer runway before attempting the procedure in an actual situation.

        1) Recurrent training with a CFI is welcome and encouraged.

    d. Consider the performance charts for your airplane and know the limitations.

        1) Since performance charts are based on a new airplane with a highly skilled test pilots, assume your aircraft might not perform as well as the charts indicate.

        2) While technically not a limitation, applying the maximum demonstrated crosswind component to your personal minimums is recommended.

2. **The applicant demonstrates the ability to identify, assess, and mitigate risks encompassing exceeding the manufacturer's maximum demonstrated crosswind component.**

    a. For information on crosswind component, see Study Unit 9, Subunit 3, item C., on page 80.

3. **The applicant demonstrates the ability to identify, assess, and mitigate risks encompassing operating from other than a hard surfaced runway.**

    a. For information on operating from other than a hard surfaced runway, see Section IV Introduction, Risk Management, item K., beginning on page 303.

4. **The applicant demonstrates the ability to identify, assess, and mitigate risks encompassing obstruction clearance.**

    a. The height of obstructions will dictate how steep the approach will have to be. Know the type and height of the obstructions.

    b. Your POH/AFM has performance charts on landing distances required to clear a 50-ft. obstacle under the conditions specified on the chart. During your preflight preparation, you need to ensure that you can land in a confined area or short field before attempting to do so.

    c. Select a touchdown aim point that allows you to clear any obstacles and land with the greatest amount of runway available.

        1) Your descent angle (glide path) may be steeper than the one used on a normal approach.

            a) This steeper descent angle helps you pick a touchdown aim point closer to the base of any obstacle, which means a shorter landing distance.

  d. You should also select points along the approach path at which you will decide between continuing the approach or executing a go-around.

    1) A go-around may be necessary if you are too low and will not have obstruction clearance.

5. **The applicant demonstrates the ability to identify, assess, and mitigate risks encompassing climb attitude and stall awareness.**

  a. If you have to make a go-around, consider obstructions at both ends of the runway. Deciding to go-around too late could increase the risk of impact with obstructions on the departure end of the runway.

    1) A common error is climbing at too steep of a climb attitude instead of flying the appropriate best angle of climb (V_X) speed.

    2) At any speed other than V_X, the aircraft will not achieve the best gain in altitude for the forward distance traveled.

    3) Climbing at an excessive angle of attack can also lead to a low level stall, which may not be recoverable.

  b. For information on stall awareness, see Section IV Introduction, Risk Management, item H., beginning on page 301.

6. **The applicant demonstrates the ability to identify, assess, and mitigate risks encompassing wind shear avoidance.**

  a. For information on wind shear, see Study Unit 9, Subunit 4, beginning on page 81.

7. **The applicant demonstrates the ability to identify, assess, and mitigate risks encompassing tailwind.**

  a. For information on tailwind, see Study Unit 9, Subunit 3, beginning on page 80.

8. **The applicant demonstrates the ability to identify, assess, and mitigate risks encompassing wake turbulence.**

  a. For information on wake turbulence, see Study Unit 7, Subunit 7, beginning on page 69.

9. **The applicant demonstrates the ability to identify, assess, and mitigate risks encompassing task management.**

  a. For information on task management, see Study Unit 6, Subunit 1, beginning on page 49.

10. **The applicant demonstrates the ability to identify, assess, and mitigate risks encompassing low altitude maneuvering.**

  a. For information on low altitude maneuvering, see Section IV Introduction, Risk Management, item C., on page 299.

11. **The applicant demonstrates the ability to identify, assess, and mitigate risks encompassing collision avoidance, scanning, and obstacle and wire strike avoidance.**

  a. For information on collision avoidance, scanning, and obstacle avoidance, see Study Unit 7, Subunit 4, beginning on page 66.

  b. For information on wire strikes, see Study Unit 7 Subunit 6, beginning on page 68.

12. **The applicant demonstrates the ability to identify, assess, and mitigate risks encompassing failure to follow right-of-way rules.**

  a. For information on right-of-way rules, see Section IV Introduction, Risk Management, item F., on page 300.

13. **The applicant demonstrates the ability to identify, assess, and mitigate risks encompassing obstacles on approach and landing paths.**

    a.   For information on obstacles on approach and landing paths, see Section IV Introduction, Risk Management, item D., on page 300.

14. **The applicant demonstrates the ability to identify, assess, and mitigate risks encompassing failure to recognize the need for go-around/rejected landing.**

    a.   For information on recognizing the need for go-around/rejected landing, see Section IV Introduction, Risk Management, item G., on page 301.

15. **The applicant demonstrates the ability to identify, assess, and mitigate risks encompassing low altitude stall/spin.**

    a.   For information on low altitude stall/spin, see Section IV Introduction, Risk Management, item H., beginning on page 301.

16. **The applicant demonstrates the ability to identify, assess, and mitigate risks encompassing land and hold short operations (LAHSO).**

    a.   For information on LAHSO, see Section IV Introduction, Risk Management, item J., on page 303.

17. **The applicant demonstrates the ability to identify, assess, and mitigate risks encompassing failure to adhere to sterile cockpit requirement.**

    a.   For information on sterile cockpit, see Study Unit 6, Subunit 2, on page 51.

END OF RISK MANAGEMENT ELEMENT

30.3 SKILLS

A. Task Objectives

1. **The applicant demonstrates the ability to ensure the aircraft is aligned with the correct/assigned runway.**

    a. When you arrive at the airport to enter the traffic pattern and land, it is important that you identify the correct runway as early as possible. Familiarize yourself with the airport diagram and from which direction you expect to enter ahead of time.

    b. Confirm that you are entering the pattern for the proper runway by comparing the direction of intended landing to your heading indicator. The downwind leg is a course flown parallel to the intended landing runway, but in a direction opposite to the direction.

    c. Use visual markings indicating traffic pattern direction of turns to help orient you.

    d. After turning onto final approach, confirm runway direction with your heading indicator and magnetic compass.

2. **The applicant demonstrates the ability to scan the landing/runway area for possible obstructions for landing.**

    a. During your approach, you must look for any hazards or obstructions and then evaluate how they may affect your approach and selection of a suitable touchdown point.

        1) Be aware of traffic, both in the air and on the ground.

        2) Prior to landing, you must scan to make certain that the landing area and path are clear of other aircraft, vehicles, persons, livestock, wildlife (including birds), etc.

        3) Check the approach area for any natural or man-made obstacles (e.g., trees, towers, or construction equipment).

        4) Your angle of descent on final approach may need to be steepened if obstacles are present.

            a) The height of obstructions will dictate how steep the approach will have to be. Know the type and height of the obstructions.

            b) Select a touchdown aim point that allows you to clear any obstacles and land with the greatest amount of runway available.

                i) Your descent angle (glide path) may be steeper than the one used on a normal approach.

                    • This steeper descent angle helps you pick a touchdown aim point closer to the base of any obstacle, which means a shorter landing distance.

3. **The applicant demonstrates the ability to complete the appropriate approach and landing checklist.**

    a. Use the before-landing checklist in your POH/AFM to ensure that you follow the proper sequence in establishing the correct approach and landing configuration for your airplane.

    b. The before-landing checklist should be completed on or before entering the downwind leg of the traffic pattern.

    c. Remember, if you realize you have missed an important step (e.g., checklist, not extending the landing gear, etc.), you should do whatever is necessary to accomplish that step, including breaking off a landing approach and executing a go-around.

        1) Do not try to rush through such items.

4. **The applicant demonstrates the ability to consider the wind conditions, landing surface, and obstructions to select a suitable touchdown point.**

    a. The height of obstructions will dictate how steep the approach will have to be. Know the type and height of the obstructions.

    b. The landing surface will affect your airplane's braking/stopping distance. A headwind may shorten the distance, while a tailwind will significantly lengthen the landing distance.

    c. Your POH/AFM has performance charts on landing distances required to clear a 50-ft. obstacle under the conditions specified on the chart. During your preflight preparation, you need to ensure that you can land in a confined area or short field before attempting to do so.

    d. Select a touchdown aim point that allows you to clear any obstacles and land with the greatest amount of runway available.

        1) Your descent angle (glide path) may be steeper than the one used on a normal approach.

            a) This steeper descent angle helps you pick a touchdown aim point closer to the base of any obstacle, which means a shorter landing distance.

    e. You should also select points along the approach path at which you will decide between continuing the approach or executing a go-around.

        1) A go-around may be necessary if you are too low, too high, too slow, or too fast, and/or if you are not stabilized on the final approach.

    f. Once you have selected a touchdown point, select an aim point. Remember, your aim point will be the point at the end of your selected glide path, not your touchdown point. Thus, your aim point will be short of your touchdown point.

        1) See Study Unit 26, Subunit 3, beginning on page 326, for a discussion of the use of the aim point.

    g. After you select your point, you should identify it to your evaluator.

5. **The applicant demonstrates the ability to establish the recommended approach and landing configuration and airspeed, and adjust pitch attitude and power as required.**

    a. Follow the procedures in your POH/AFM to establish the proper short-field approach and landing configuration.

    b. After the landing gear (if retractable) and full flaps have been extended, you should simultaneously adjust the pitch attitude and power to establish and maintain the proper descent angle and airspeed.

        1) Since short-field approaches are power-on approaches, the pitch attitude is adjusted as necessary to establish and maintain the desired rate or angle of descent, and power is adjusted to maintain the desired airspeed.

            a) However, a coordinated combination of both pitch and power adjustments is required.

            b) When the proper adjustments are made, and the final approach is stabilized, very little change in your airplane's pitch attitude and power will be necessary to make corrections in the angle of descent and airspeed.

        2) If it appears that the obstacle clearance is excessive and touchdown will occur well beyond the desired spot, leaving insufficient room to stop, power may be reduced while lowering the pitch attitude to increase the rate of descent while maintaining the proper airspeed.

        3) If it appears that the descent angle will not ensure safe clearance of obstacles, power should be increased while simultaneously raising the pitch attitude to decrease the rate of descent and maintain the proper airspeed.

        4)   Care must be taken to avoid excessively low airspeed.

            a)   If the speed is allowed to become too slow, an increase in pitch and application of full power may only result in a further rate of descent.

                i)   The rate of descent increases when the angle of attack is so great and creates so much drag that the maximum available power is insufficient to overcome it.

   c.   The final approach is normally started from an altitude of at least 500 ft. higher than the touchdown area, when you are approximately 3/4 to 1 SM from the runway threshold.

        1)   The steeper descent angle means more altitude for a longer period of time, which can be converted to airspeed if needed by lowering the nose. This is good for safety because it prevents an approach that is simultaneously too low and too slow.

6.   **The applicant demonstrates the ability to maintain a stabilized approach and recommended airspeed, or in its absence, not more than 1.3 V_{SO}, with wind gust factor applied +10/-5 knots or as recommended by aircraft manufacturer to a safe maneuvering altitude.**

   a.   A stabilized approach and controlled rate of descent can be accomplished only by making minor adjustments to pitch and power while on final approach.

        1)   To do this you must maintain your selected glide path and airspeed.

   b.   An excessive amount of airspeed may result in touchdown too far from the runway threshold or an after-landing roll that exceeds the available landing area.

7.   **The applicant demonstrates the ability to make smooth, timely, and correct control application during the round out and touchdown.**

   a.   Use the same technique during the roundout and touchdown as discussed in Study Unit 26, Subunit 3, item A.7., beginning on page 327.

8.   **The applicant demonstrates the ability to touch down smoothly at an appropriate airspeed.**

   a.   Since the final approach over obstacles is made at a steep approach angle and close to the stalling speed, the initiation of the roundout (flare) must be judged accurately to avoid flying into the ground or stalling prematurely and sinking rapidly.

        1)   Smoothly close the throttle during the roundout.

        2)   Touchdown should occur at the minimum controllable airspeed at a pitch attitude that will produce a power-off stall.

   b.   Use the same technique during the roundout and touchdown as discussed in Study Unit 26, Subunit 3, on page 327.

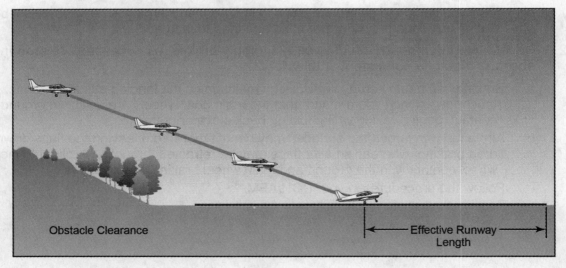

Obstacle Clearance

Effective Runway Length

9. **The applicant demonstrates the ability to touch down within the available runway, at or within 200 feet beyond the specified point, threshold markings or runway numbers, with no side drift, minimum float, and with the airplane's longitudinal axis aligned with and over the runway center line/landing path.**

   a. You must touch down at or within 200 ft. beyond a specified point.

      1) Upon touchdown, nosewheel-type airplanes should be held in a nose-high pitch attitude as long as the elevator/stabilator remains effective, and tailwheel-type airplanes should be firmly held in a three-point attitude to provide aerodynamic braking.

      2) A lack of floating during the roundout, with sufficient control to touch down properly, is one verification that the approach speed was correct.

   b. Use proper crosswind technique to ensure that your airplane's longitudinal axis is aligned with and over the runway centerline.

10. **The applicant demonstrates the ability to maintain crosswind correction and directional control throughout the approach and landing sequence, as required.**

    a. Use the crosswind and directional control techniques described in Study Unit 26, Subunit 3, beginning on page 330.

11. **The applicant demonstrates the ability to execute a safe and timely go-around decision when the approach cannot be made within the tolerances specified above or for any other condition that may result in an unsafe approach or landing.**

    a. The need to discontinue a landing may arise at any point in the landing process, but the most critical go-around is one started when very close to the ground. A timely decision must be made.

       1) A go-around must be made when the approach cannot be made within the required tolerances.

       2) The earlier you recognize a dangerous situation, the sooner you can decide to reject the landing and start the go-around, and the safer this maneuver will be.

       3) Never wait until the last possible moment to make a decision.

    b. Official reports concerning go-around accidents frequently cite "pilot indecision" as a cause. This happens when a pilot fixates on trying to make a bad landing good, resulting in a late decision to go around.

       1) This is natural, since the purpose of an approach is a landing.

       2) Delays in deciding what to do costs valuable runway stopping distance. They also cause loss of valuable altitude as the approach continues.

       3) If there is any question about making a safe touchdown and rollout, execute a go-around immediately.

    c. Once you decide to go around, stick to it! Too many airplanes have been lost because a pilot has changed his or her mind and tried to land after all.

12. **The applicant demonstrates the ability to apply brakes, as necessary, to stop in the shortest distance consistent with safety.**

    a. Braking can begin aerodynamically by maintaining the landing attitude after touchdown. Once you are sure that the main gear wheels are solidly in ground contact, begin braking while holding back elevator pressure.

    b. Airplanes with larger flap surfaces may benefit more from leaving the flaps down for drag braking, whereas smaller flaps may be retracted through the rollout to increase wheel contact with the ground and main wheel braking effectiveness.

    c. Follow the procedures in your POH/AFM.

13. **The applicant demonstrates the ability to utilize after landing runway incursion avoidance procedures.**

   a. After landing, be sure to clear the runway in a timely fashion.

      1) Do not exit the runway above a safe taxi speed, and be sure to stop once the aircraft is clear of the runway area (i.e., fully across the hold short markings) and before crossing onto an intersecting taxiway or parallel runway.

      2) In the case of ATC instructions to expedite your taxi, only accept them if you feel you can accommodate their request.

   b. Visually clear intersecting taxiways/runways before crossing them, even if ATC has cleared you across.

   c. Read back and confirm all ATC holding/crossing instructions/clearances.

END OF SKILLS ELEMENT

30.4 COMMON ERRORS

A. Common Errors during a Short-Field Approach and Landing

   1. **Improper use of landing performance data and limitations**

      a. Use your POH/AFM to determine the appropriate airspeeds for a short-field approach and landing.

      b. In gusty and/or strong crosswinds, use the crosswind component chart to determine that you are not exceeding your airplane's crosswind limitations.

      c. Use your POH/AFM to determine minimum landing distances, and do not attempt to do better than the data.

      d. The most common error, as well as the easiest to avoid, is to attempt a landing that is beyond the capabilities of your airplane and/or your flying skills. You need to remember that the distance needed for a safe landing is normally less than is needed for a safe takeoff. Plan ahead!

   2. **Failure to establish approach and landing configuration at appropriate time or in proper sequence**

      a. Use the before-landing checklist in your POH/AFM to ensure that you follow the proper sequence in establishing the correct approach and landing configuration for your airplane.

      b. You should initially start the checklist at midpoint on the downwind leg with the power reduction beginning once you are abeam your intended point of landing.

         1) By the time you turn on final and align your airplane with the runway centerline, you should be in the final landing configuration. Confirm this by completing your checklist once again.

   3. **Failure to establish and maintain a stabilized approach**

      a. Once you are on final and aligned with the runway centerline, you should make small adjustments to pitch and power to establish the correct descent angle (i.e., glide path) and airspeed.

         1) Remember, you must make simultaneous adjustments to both pitch and power.

         2) Large adjustments will result in a roller coaster ride.

4. **Improper technique in use of power, wing flaps, and trim**

    a. Use power and pitch adjustments simultaneously to maintain the proper descent angle and airspeed.

    b. Wing flaps should be used in accordance with your POH/AFM.

    c. Trim to relieve control pressures to help in stabilizing the final approach.

5. **Inappropriate removal of hand from throttle**

    a. One hand should remain on the control yoke at all times.

    b. The other hand should remain on the throttle unless you are operating the microphone or making an adjustment, such as trim or flaps.

        1) Once you are on short final, your hand should remain on the throttle, even if ATC gives you instruction (e.g., cleared to land).

            a) Your first priority is to fly your airplane and avoid doing tasks that may distract you from maintaining control.

            b) Fly first; talk later.

    c. You must be in the habit of keeping one hand on the throttle in case a sudden and unexpected hazardous situation should require an immediate application of power.

6. **Improper technique during roundout and touchdown**

    a. Do not attempt to hold the airplane off the ground.

    b. See Study Unit 26, Subunit 4, beginning on page 334, for a detailed discussion of general landing errors.

    c. Remember, you have limited runway, so when in doubt, go around.

7. **Poor directional control after touchdown**

    a. Use rudder to steer your airplane on the runway, and increase aileron deflection into the wind as airspeed decreases.

    b. See Study Unit 26, Subunit 4, item A.6., beginning on page 340, for a discussion of ground loops and other directional control problems after touchdown.

8. **Improper use of brakes**

    a. Never attempt to apply the brakes until your airplane is firmly on the runway under complete control.

    b. Use equal pressure on both brakes to prevent swerving and/or loss of directional control.

    c. Follow the braking procedures described in your POH/AFM.

END OF COMMON ERRORS

STUDY UNIT THIRTY-ONE
FORWARD SLIP TO A LANDING

Task	*Task M. Forward Slip to a Landing*
References	FAA-H-8083-2, FAA-H-8083-3; POH/AFM
Objective	To determine that the applicant exhibits satisfactory knowledge, risk management, and skills associated with a forward slip to a landing.
Knowledge	The applicant demonstrates understanding of:
PA.IV.M.K1	1. When and why forward slips are used and differences between side and forward slips.
PA.IV.M.K2	2. How forward slips are executed.
PA.IV.M.K3	3. Landing distance.
PA.IV.M.K4	4. Stabilized approach.
PA.IV.M.K5	5. Energy management.
PA.IV.M.K6	6. The effects of forward slips affecting indicated airspeed versus true airspeed.
PA.IV.M.K7	7. Wind conditions and effects.
PA.IV.M.K8	8. Density altitude.
PA.IV.M.K9	9. Emergency procedures during approach and landing.
PA.IV.M.K10	10. Land and hold short operations.
Risk Management	The applicant demonstrates the ability to identify, assess and mitigate risks, encompassing:
PA.IV.M.R1	1. Failure to recognize the need to perform a go-around/rejected landing.
PA.IV.M.R2	2. Failure to correlate any crosswind effects with direction of forward slip.
PA.IV.M.R3	3. Failure to transition to a side slip for landing.
PA.IV.M.R4	4. Low altitude stall/spin.
PA.IV.M.R5	5. Windshear.
PA.IV.M.R6	6. Land and hold short operations (LAHSO).
PA.IV.M.R7	7. Tailwind.
PA.IV.M.R8	8. Wake turbulence.
PA.IV.M.R9	9. Task management.
PA.IV.M.R10	10. Low altitude maneuvering.
PA.IV.M.R11	11. Failure to confirm your gear position in an amphibious aircraft.
PA.IV.M.R12	12. Collision avoidance, scanning, obstacle and wire strike avoidance.
PA.IV.M.R13	13. Failure to follow the right-of-way rules.
PA.IV.M.R14	14. Obstacles on approach and landing paths.
PA.IV.M.R15	15. Aircraft systems affected by performing a forward slip to include airspeed indications and fuel flow.
PA.IV.M.R16	16. Failure to adhere to sterile cockpit requirement.
Skills	The applicant demonstrates the ability to:
PA.IV.M.S1	1. Select runway/landing area based on wind, landing surface and obstructions, pilot capability and aircraft limitations.
PA.IV.M.S2	2. Calculate the crosswind component and determine if it is beyond the pilot's ability or aircraft capability.
PA.IV.M.S3	3. Select the most suitable touchdown point.
PA.IV.M.S4	4. Establish the slipping attitude at the point from which a landing can be made using the recommended approach and landing configuration and airspeed; adjust pitch attitude as required.
PA.IV.M.S5	5. Maintain a ground track aligned with the runway/landing path centerline and an airspeed, which results in minimum float during the round out.
PA.IV.M.S6	6. Make smooth, timely, and correct control application during the recovery from the slip, the round out, and the touchdown.
PA.IV.M.S7	7. Touch down within 400 feet beyond a specified point with no drift, and with the airplane's longitudinal axis aligned with and over the runway centerline.
PA.IV.M.S8	8. Maintain crosswind correction and directional control throughout the approach and landing sequence.
PA.IV.M.S9	9. Complete the appropriate checklist.
PA.IV.M.S10	10. Execute a timely go-around decision when the approach cannot be made within the tolerances specified above.

A.   General Information

   1.   The objective of this task is for you to demonstrate your knowledge, risk management, and skills related to a forward slip to a landing.

   2.   Much of the content of Subunits 31.1 and 31.2 is abbreviated based on the assumption that you have thoroughly read and understood pages 287 through 304 and the additional common task topics found in Part II. The task objectives and specific references are provided here for your convenience.

31.1 KNOWLEDGE

A.   Task Objectives

   1.   **The applicant demonstrates understanding of when and why forward slips are used and the differences between side and forward slips.**

      a.   A slip occurs when the bank angle of an airplane is too steep for the existing rate of turn. In other words, inadequate rudder is used for the amount of bank angle, resulting in an uncoordinated turn.

      b.   Unintentional slips are most often the result of uncoordinated rudder/aileron application.

      c.   Intentional slips, however, have various useful circumstances. There are two types of intentional slips:

         1)   Side slip:

            a)   In a side slip, the airplane's longitudinal axis remains parallel to the original flightpath, but the airplane no longer flies straight ahead.

               i)   Instead, the horizontal component of wing lift forces the airplane also to move somewhat sideways towards the low wing.

            b)   Use of a side slip: to adjust airplane ground track during a crosswind.

         2)   Forward slip:

            a)   The forward slip is a descent with one wing lowered and the airplane's longitudinal axis at an angle to the flight path. The flight path remains the same as before the slip was begun.

            b)   The primary purpose of a forward slip is to dissipate altitude without increasing your airplane's speed, particularly in airplanes not equipped with flaps.

            c)   Altitude is lost in a slip by increasing drag caused by the air flow striking the wing-low side of the airplane, which causes the rate of descent to increase.

            d)   Uses of a forward slip:

               i)   A forward slip can be used as an emergency means of rapidly reducing airspeed in situations where wing flaps are inoperative or not installed.

               ii)   In situations where obstacles must be cleared during approaches to confined areas.

               iii)   In a forced landing, when it is always wise to allow an extra margin of altitude for safety in the original estimate of the approach.

   2.   **The applicant demonstrates understanding of how forward slips are executed.**

      a.   For information on executing forward slips, see Subunit 31.3, items A.4.-5. beginning on page 403.

3.   **The applicant demonstrates understanding of landing distance.**

   a.   For information on landing distance, see Section IV Introduction, Knowledge, item B. beginning on page 289.

4.   **The applicant demonstrates understanding of stabilized approach.**

   a.   Once you decide to use a slip, you must use the proper flight control application and power to establish the slip.

   b.   Stabilize the slip as soon as possible. Avoid large corrections, as they will prevent you from maintaining a stabilized slip.

   c.   For more information on stabilized approach, see Section IV Introduction, Knowledge, item D., beginning on page 292.

5.   **The applicant demonstrates understanding of energy management.**

   a.   For information on energy management, see Study Unit 8, Subunit 1, beginning on page 71.

6.   **The applicant demonstrates understanding of the effects of forward slips affecting indicated airspeed vs. true airspeed.**

   a.   Because of the location of the pitot tube and static vent(s) in some airplanes, the airspeed indicator may have a considerable degree of error when the airplane is in a slip.

   1)   If your airplane has only one static vent (normally on the left side of the fuselage), airspeed indications may be in error during a slip.

   a)   In a slip to the left (i.e., left-wing down), ram air pressure will be entering the static tube, and the pressure in the airspeed indicator will be higher than normal.

   i)   Thus, the airspeed indication will be **lower** than the true airspeed.

   b)   In a slip to the right, a low pressure area tends to form on the left side of the airplane, thus lowering the pressure in the static vent and the airspeed indicator.

   i)   Thus, the airspeed indication will be **higher** than the true airspeed.

   2)   If your airplane has a static vent on each side of the fuselage, these errors tend to cancel each other out.

   3)   You must recognize a properly performed slip by the attitude of your airplane, the sound of the airflow, and the feel of the flight controls.

7.   **The applicant demonstrates understanding of wind conditions and effects.**

   a.   For information on wind conditions and effects, see Study Unit 9, Subunit 3, beginning on page 80.

8.   **The applicant demonstrates understanding of density altitude.**

   a.   For information on density altitude, see Study Unit 9, Subunit 1, beginning on page 77.

9.   **The applicant demonstrates understanding of emergency procedures during approach and landing.**

   a.   For information on emergency procedures during approach and landing, see Study Unit 8, Subunit 2, item G., on page 76.

10.   **The applicant demonstrates understanding of land and hold short operations.**

   a.   For information on land and hold short operations, see Section IV Introduction, Knowledge, item F., on page 297.

END OF KNOWLEDGE ELEMENT

31.2 RISK MANAGEMENT

A.   Task Objectives

1.   **The applicant demonstrates the ability to identify, assess, and mitigate risks encompassing failure to recognize the need to perform a go-around/rejected landing.**

   a.   For information on recognizing the need for go-around/rejected landing, see Section IV Introduction, Risk Management, item G., on page 301.

   b.   For information on how to perform a go-around/rejected landing, see Study Unit 32.

2.   **The applicant demonstrates the ability to identify, assess, and mitigate risks encompassing failure to correlate any crosswind effects with direction of forward slip.**

   a.   A crosswind takeoff and climb is one in which your airplane is NOT headed directly into the wind.

   b.   If there is any crosswind, the slip will be more effective and easier to recover if made toward the wind.

   c.   If a crosswind condition is present, you should make the adjustment from a forward slip to a side slip (i.e., the wing-low method) to counteract any drift.

   d.   Use the proper crosswind technique to ensure that your airplane's longitudinal axis is aligned with and over the runway centerline.

3.   **The applicant demonstrates the ability to identify, assess, and mitigate risks encompassing failure to transition to a side slip for landing.**

   a.   Failing to transition to the side slip for landing could result in overshooting and overrunning the landing area.

      1)   If a short-field landing is necessary and obstacle clearance is also an issue, a forward slip may be the only way to safely land your airplane.

      2)   In an emergency, such as an engine failure, your options may be limited. Failure to perform a side-slip could prevent you from touching down safely in a suitable landing area.

4.   **The applicant demonstrates the ability to identify, assess, and mitigate risks encompassing low altitude stall/spin.**

   a.   For information on low altitude stall/spin, see Section IV Introduction, Risk Management, item H., beginning on page 301.

5.   **The applicant demonstrates the ability to identify, assess, and mitigate risks encompassing windshear.**

   a.   For information on wind shear, see Study Unit 9, Subunit 4, beginning on page 81.

6.   **The applicant demonstrates the ability to identify, assess, and mitigate risks encompassing land and hold short operations (LAHSO).**

   a.   For information on LAHSO, see Section IV Introduction, Risk Management, item J., on page 303.

7.   **The applicant demonstrates the ability to identify, assess, and mitigate risks encompassing tailwind.**

   a.   For information on tailwind, see Study Unit 9, Subunit 3, beginning on page 80.

8.   **The applicant demonstrates the ability to identify, assess, and mitigate risks encompassing wake turbulence.**

   a.   For information on wake turbulence, see Study Unit 7, Subunit 7, beginning on page 69.

9. **The applicant demonstrates the ability to identify, assess, and mitigate risks encompassing task management.**

    a. For information on task management, see Study Unit 6, Subunit 1, beginning on page 49.

10. **The applicant demonstrates the ability to identify, assess, and mitigate risks encompassing low altitude maneuvering.**

    a. For information on low altitude maneuvering, see Section IV Introduction, Risk Management, item C., on page 299.

11. **The applicant demonstrates the ability to identify, assess, and mitigate risks encompassing failure to confirm your gear position in an amphibious aircraft.**

    a. If conducting your practical test in an amphibious aircraft on land, ensure your gear position has been lowered for landing.

12. **The applicant demonstrates the ability to identify, assess, and mitigate risks encompassing collision avoidance, scanning, and obstacle and wire strike avoidance.**

    a. For information on collision avoidance, scanning, and obstacle avoidance, see Study Unit 7, Subunit 4, beginning on page 66.

    b. For information on wire strikes, see Study Unit 7, Subunit 6, beginning on page 68.

13. **The applicant demonstrates the ability to identify, assess, and mitigate risks encompassing failure to follow the right-of-way rules.**

    a. For information on right-of-way rules, see Section IV Introduction, Risk Management, item F., on page 300.

14. **The applicant demonstrates the ability to identify, assess, and mitigate risks encompassing obstacles on approach and landing paths.**

    a. For information on obstacles on approach and landing paths, see Section IV Introduction, Risk Management, item D., on page 300.

15. **The applicant demonstrates the ability to identify, assess, and mitigate risks encompassing aircraft systems affected by performing a forward slip to include airspeed indications and fuel flow.**

    a. The pilot must check the POH/AFM for any limitations on the use of a forward slip.

        1) Some airplanes may be prohibited from performing a forward slip with the wing flaps extended or with minimum fuel in one or more tanks.

        2) Other airplanes may have a time limitation (i.e., slip can be used no more than 30 sec.)

    b. The pilot must realize that airspeed control is critical because the controls are crossed. A stall with crossed controls could be disastrous, so be sure to maintain an airspeed at or slightly above the usual approach speed while slipping.

    c. The pilot must consider that some aircraft may have an issue with the flaps affecting airflow over the tail, or aileron control may be limited allowing only a certain amount of bank, or the placement of fuel tanks may limit the duration that a slip is allowed before fuel flow is interrupted.

16. **The applicant demonstrates the ability to identify, assess, and mitigate risks encompassing a failure to adhere to sterile cockpit requirement.**

    a. For information on sterile cockpit, see Study Unit 6, Subunit 2, beginning on page 51.

END OF RISK MANAGEMENT ELEMENT

31.3 SKILLS

A. Task Objectives

1. **The applicant demonstrates the ability to select runway/landing area based on wind, landing surface and obstructions, pilot capability, and aircraft limitations.**

   a. Depending on the wind conditions, landing surface (i.e., hard surface or soft surface), and any obstructions, you should select the touchdown point as you would for a normal, soft, or short field.

   b. Advise your evaluator if your personal minimums would prevent you from attempting a landing on a runway that requires skills beyond your experience.

   c. Advise the evaluator of any aircraft limitations that may prevent or limit a forward slip.

      1) Calculate the wind component and landing distance required at the destination airport.

      2) Explain that the maximum demonstrated crosswind component is not necessarily a limitation. However, explain that you may use it as a guideline so as not to exceed your or the aircraft's capabilities.

2. **The applicant demonstrates the ability to calculate the crosswind component and determine if it is beyond the pilot's ability or aircraft capability.**

   a. Use the Crosswind Component chart of the front of the Gleim E6B flight computer to calculate the crosswind component based on the current wind conditions and runway configuration.

      1) For a detailed discussion explaining how to calculate the crosswind component using this chart, refer to the Gleim *Pilot Handbook*, Study Unit 9, Subunit 25.

   b. Takeoffs and landings in certain crosswind conditions are inadvisable or even dangerous. If the crosswind is strong enough that the airplane is incapable of preventing a sideways drift, a hazardous landing condition may result.

      1) Always consider the takeoff or landing capabilities with respect to the reported surface wind conditions and the available landing directions.

      2) The airplane's POH/AFM indicates the maximum demonstrated crosswind component of the airplane.

      3) Some POH/AFMs have a chart so the pilot can determine the crosswind component.

   c. Many airplanes have an upper limit to the amount of direct crosswind in which they can land (usually about 20% of stall speed). Crosswinds of less than 90° are converted into a 90° component on graphs.

   d. Consider that your aircraft may need to decrease the wind components further than the suggested POH/AFM.

      1) Do you have a Supplemental Type Certificate (STC) for your airplane, such as tip tanks or vortex generators?

         a) Refer to supplemental instructions in the POH/AFM if your aircraft has approved modifications affecting handling characteristics.

      2) Are you comfortable with crosswind landings when the airplane is half full of fuel?

         a) Landing on minimum fuel reserves mans the airplane is light and more susceptible to crosswinds than when the airplane is heavier.

3. **The applicant demonstrates the ability to select the most suitable touchdown point.**

   a. For information on selecting the most suitable touchdown point, refer to item A.1.

   b. After you select your touchdown point, you should identify it to your evaluator.

4. **The applicant demonstrates the ability to establish the slipping attitude at the point from which a landing can be made using the recommended approach and landing configuration and airspeed; adjust pitch attitude as required.**

    a. Once you are assured that you can safely land in the desired area, you should establish a forward slip.

        1) You will need to establish your airplane higher on final, since the slip will result in a steeper than normal descent.

    b. Apply carburetor heat (if applicable) and reduce power to idle.

        1) Extend the flaps, unless your POH/AFM prohibits slips with flaps extended.

        2) Establish a pitch attitude that will maintain a normal final approach speed.

    c. Assuming that your airplane is originally in straight flight, you should lower the wing on the side toward which the slip is to be made by use of the ailerons (wing down into crosswind, if one exists).

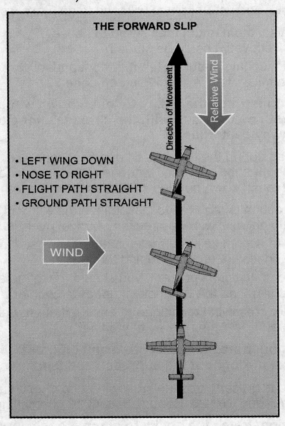

THE FORWARD SLIP

Direction of Movement

Relative Wind

• LEFT WING DOWN
• NOSE TO RIGHT
• FLIGHT PATH STRAIGHT
• GROUND PATH STRAIGHT

WIND

        1) Simultaneously, your airplane's nose must be yawed in the opposite direction with the rudder so that the airplane's longitudinal axis is at an angle to its flight path.

            a) If rudder application is delayed, the airplane will turn in the direction of the lowered wing.

        2) The nose of the airplane should also be raised as necessary to prevent the airspeed from increasing.

            a) Remember, if your airspeed indicator is subject to errors in slips, you should understand those errors.

                i) Maintain the proper pitch attitude by sight and feel.

5.   **The applicant demonstrates the ability to maintain a ground track aligned with the runway/landing path centerline and an airspeed, which results in minimum float during the round out.**

   a.   The degree to which the nose is yawed in the opposite direction from the bank should be such that your airplane maintains a ground track over the extended centerline of the runway.

   b.   You should maintain no more than the approach speed specified in your POH/AFM.

6.   **The applicant demonstrates the ability to make smooth, timely, and correct control application during the recovery from the slip, the round out, and the touchdown.**

   a.   Discontinuing the slip is accomplished by leveling the wings and simultaneously releasing the rudder pressure while readjusting the pitch attitude to the normal glide attitude.

      1)   If the pressure on the rudder is released abruptly, the nose will swing too quickly into line, and your airplane will tend to gain excess speed.

         a)   Also, momentum may swing the nose of your airplane past straight ahead. Recovery should be smooth.

   b.   Use the same technique during the roundout and touchdown as discussed in Study Unit 26, Subunit 3, item 7., beginning on page 327.

7.   **The applicant demonstrates the ability to touch down within 400 feet beyond a specified point with no drift, and with the airplane's longitudinal axis aligned with and over the runway centerline.**

   a.   If a slip is used during the last portion of a final approach, the longitudinal axis of your airplane must be realigned with the runway just prior to touchdown so that your airplane will touch down headed in the direction in which it is moving over the runway.

      1)   Timely action is required to discontinue the slip and realign your airplane's longitudinal axis with its direction of travel over the ground before touchdown.

      2)   Failure to accomplish the realignment causes severe sideloads on the landing gear and violent ground looping tendencies.

   b.   If a crosswind condition is present, you should make the adjustment from a forward slip to a side slip (i.e., the wing-low method) to counteract any drift.

   c.   Use the proper crosswind technique to ensure that your airplane's longitudinal axis is aligned with and over the runway centerline.

8.   **The applicant demonstrates the ability to maintain crosswind correction and directional control throughout the approach and landing sequence.**

   a.   If a crosswind is present, use the crosswind and directional control techniques described in Study Unit 26, Subunit 3, item 10., beginning on page 330.

9.   **The applicant demonstrates the ability to complete the appropriate checklist.**

   a.   The before-landing checklist should be completed on the downwind leg.

      1)   Remember that, if your airplane has an operating limitation on the use of flaps during a slip, you must comply with the limitation.

   b.   After your airplane is clear of the runway, you should stop and complete the after-landing checklist.

10. **The applicant demonstrates the ability to execute a timely go-around decision when the approach cannot be made within the tolerances specified above.**

   a. The need to discontinue a landing may arise at any point in the landing process, but the most critical go-around is one started when very close to the ground. A timely decision must be made.

      1) If you cannot execute the approach and landing within the specified tolerance, you should go-around.

      2) If you need to go around because of a dangerous situation, the sooner you can decide to reject the landing and start the go-around, the safer this maneuver will be.

      3) Never wait until the last possible moment to make a decision.

   b. Official reports concerning go-around accidents frequently cite "pilot indecision" as a cause. This happens when a pilot fixates on trying to make a bad landing good, resulting in a late decision to go around.

      1) This is natural, since the purpose of an approach is a landing.

      2) Delays in deciding what to do cost valuable runway stopping distance. They also cause loss of valuable altitude as the approach continues.

      3) If there is any question about making a safe touchdown and rollout, execute a go-around immediately.

   c. Once you decide to go around, stick to it! Too many airplanes have been lost because a pilot has changed his or her mind and tried to land after all.

END OF SKILLS ELEMENT

31.4 COMMON ERRORS

A. Common Errors during Forward Slip to a Landing

   1. **Improper use of landing performance data and limitations**

      a. Use your POH/AFM to determine the appropriate airspeeds for a normal and crosswind approach and landing.

      b. In gusty and/or strong crosswinds, use the crosswind component chart to determine that you are not exceeding your airplane's crosswind limitations.

      c. Use your POH/AFM to determine data and limitations, and do not attempt to do better than the data.

   2. **Failure to establish approach and landing configuration at appropriate time or in proper sequence**

      a. Use the before-landing checklist in your POH/AFM to ensure that you follow the proper sequence in establishing the correct approach and landing configuration for your airplane.

      b. You should be in your final landing configuration, if possible, before entering the slip.

   3. **Failure to stabilize the slip**

      a. Once you decide to use a slip, you must use the proper flight control application and power to establish the slip.

      b. Stabilize the slip as soon as possible. Avoid large corrections, as this will prevent you from maintaining a stabilized slip.

4.   **Inappropriate removal of hand from throttle**

   a.   One hand should remain on the control yoke at all times.

   b.   The other hand should remain on the throttle unless you are operating the microphone or making an adjustment, such as trim or flaps.

      1)   Once you are on short final, your hand should remain on the throttle, even if ATC gives you instruction (e.g., cleared to land).

         a)   Your first priority is to fly your airplane and avoid doing tasks that may distract you from maintaining control.

         b)   Fly first; talk later.

   c.   You must be in the habit of keeping one hand on the throttle in case a sudden and unexpected hazardous situation should require an immediate application of power.

5.   **Improper technique during transition from the slip to touchdown**

   a.   You should smoothly straighten the nose with the rudder and use ailerons as necessary to correct for any crosswind.

   b.   If you release the pressure on the rudder too abruptly, the nose will swing too quickly into line, and your airplane's airspeed will increase.

      1)   An abrupt release may also cause the nose to swing past straight ahead.

   c.   Failure to realign the airplane's longitudinal axis with the runway centerline will cause severe sideloads on the landing gear.

6.   **Poor directional control after touchdown**

   a.   Use rudder to steer your airplane on the runway, and increase aileron deflection into the wind as airspeed decreases.

   b.   See Study Unit 26, Subunit 4, beginning on page 334, for a discussion of ground loops and other directional control problems after touchdown.

7.   **Improper use of brakes**

   a.   Use the minimum amount of braking required, and let your airplane slow by the friction and drag of the wheels on the ground, if runway length permits.

   b.   Never attempt to apply brakes until your airplane is firmly on the runway under complete control.

   c.   Use equal pressure on both brakes to help prevent swerving and/or loss of directional control.

END OF COMMON ERRORS

STUDY UNIT THIRTY-TWO
GO-AROUND/REJECTED LANDING

Task	Task N. Go-Around/Rejected Landing
References	FAA-H-8083-3, FAA-H-8083-23; POH/AFM
Objective	To determine that the applicant exhibits satisfactory knowledge, risk management, and skills associated with a go-around/rejected landing with emphasis on factors that contribute to landing conditions that may require a go-around.
Knowledge	The applicant demonstrates understanding of:
PA.IV.N.K1	1. Landing distance.
PA.IV.N.K2	2. Stabilized approach.
PA.IV.N.K3	3. Energy management.
PA.IV.N.K4	4. Wind conditions and effects.
PA.IV.N.K5	5. Communication procedures.
Risk Management	The applicant demonstrates the ability to identify, assess and mitigate risks, encompassing:
PA.IV.N.R1	1. Failure to make a timely go-around/rejected landing decision.
PA.IV.N.R2	2. Task management.
PA.IV.N.R3	3. Low altitude maneuvering.
PA.IV.N.R4	4. Slow flight.
PA.IV.N.R5	5. Collision avoidance, scanning, obstacle and wire strike avoidance.
PA.IV.N.R6	6. Failure to follow the right-of-way rules.
PA.IV.N.R7	7. Obstacles on approach and departure paths.
PA.IV.N.R8	8. Low altitude stall/spin.
PA.IV.N.R9	9. Elevator trim stalls.
PA.IV.N.R10	10. Indecision or changing the go-around/rejected landing decision.
PA.IV.N.R11	11. Failure to adhere to sterile cockpit requirement.
Skills	The applicant demonstrates the ability to:
PA.IV.N.S1	1. Make a timely decision to discontinue the approach to landing.
PA.IV.N.S2	2. Apply takeoff power immediately and transition to climb pitch attitude for V_X or V_Y as appropriate +10/−5 knots.
PA.IV.N.S3	3. Retract the flaps, as appropriate.
PA.IV.N.S4	4. Retract the landing gear after establishing a positive rate of climb and in accordance with manufacturer's guidance.
PA.IV.N.S5	5. Maneuver to the side of the runway/landing area when necessary to clear and avoid conflicting traffic.
PA.IV.N.S6	6. Maintain takeoff power V_Y +10/−5 knots or to a safe maneuvering altitude.
PA.IV.N.S7	7. Maintain directional control and proper wind-drift correction throughout the climb.
PA.IV.N.S8	8. Complete the appropriate checklist.

A.   General Information

1.   The objective of this task is for you to demonstrate your knowledge, risk management, and skills related to a go-around/rejected landing with emphasis on factors that contribute to landing conditions that may require a go-around.

2. For safety reasons, it may be necessary for you to discontinue your approach and attempt another approach under more favorable conditions.

    a. This is called a go-around from a rejected (balked) landing.

3. Much of the content of Subunits 32.1 and 32.2 is abbreviated, based on the assumption that you have thoroughly read and understood pages 287 through 304 and the additional common task topics found in Part II. The task objectives and specific references are provided here for your convenience.

32.1 KNOWLEDGE

A. Task Objectives

1. **The applicant demonstrates understanding of landing distance.**

    a. For information on landing distance, see Section IV Introduction, Knowledge, item B., beginning on page 289.

2. **The applicant demonstrates understanding of stabilized approach.**

    a. For information on stabilized approach, see Section IV Introduction, Knowledge, item D., beginning on page 292.

3. **The applicant demonstrates understanding of energy management.**

    a. For information on energy management, see Study Unit 8, Subunit 1, beginning on page 71.

4. **The applicant demonstrates understanding of wind conditions and effects.**

    a. For information on wind conditions and effects, see Study Unit 9, Subunit 3, beginning on page 80.

5. **The applicant demonstrates understanding of communication procedures.**

    a. At a towered airport, announce that you are going around so that the tower controller and any other traffic in the area is aware that you are no longer committed to landing, and that you will be climbing and reentering the traffic pattern.

    b. The go-around is a normal procedure, so it is perfectly acceptable to remain in the traffic pattern.

        1) At an airport with an operating control tower, the controller will advise the next steps for the traffic pattern, i.e., left or right traffic.

        2) At an airport without an operating control tower, make radio calls on the CTAF as appropriate to each leg of the pattern, and make your intentions clear so other traffic in the pattern knows what to expect from you.

    c. Remember that your first priority is to maintain positive control of your airplane.

        1) Always fly the airplane first.
        2) Communications are secondary.

END OF KNOWLEDGE ELEMENT

32.2 RISK MANAGEMENT

A. Task Objectives

1. **The applicant demonstrates the ability to identify, assess, and mitigate risks encompassing failure to make a timely go-around/rejected landing decision.**

   a. The pilot must realize that when there is any doubt of the safe outcome of a landing, the go-around should be initiated immediately.

   b. Do not attempt to salvage a possible bad landing.

   c. The pilot must consider the hazards of delaying a decision to go around.

      1) Delay can lead to an accident because the remaining runway may be insufficient for landing or because delay can prevent the clearing of obstacles on the departure end of the runway.

   d. For more information on making go-around/rejected landing decisions, see Section IV Introduction, Risk Management, item G., on page 301.

2. **The applicant demonstrates the ability to identify, assess, and mitigate risks encompassing task management.**

   a. For information on task management, see Study Unit 6, Subunit 1, beginning on page 49.

3. **The applicant demonstrates the ability to identify, assess, and mitigate risks encompassing low altitude maneuvering.**

   a. For information on low altitude maneuvering, see Section IV Introduction, Risk Management, item C., on page 299.

4. **The applicant demonstrates the ability to identify, assess, and mitigate risks encompassing slow flight.**

   a. In a go-around, you must consider that you are in a slow-flight situation and be prepared for the flight characteristics and degree of controllability of your airplane in slow flight.

      1) It is of great importance that you know the characteristic control responses of your airplane during slow flight.

      2) You must develop this awareness in order to avoid stalls in your (or any) airplane that you may fly at the slower airspeeds that are characteristic of takeoffs, climbs, and landing approaches.

      3) In a go-around, you will be flying the aircraft at a slow enough speed that an increase in angle of attack or power reduction could result in a stall.

   b. The flight controls in slow flight are less effective than at normal cruise due to the reduced airflow over them.

      1) Anticipate the need of right rudder to counteract the torque effect in a low airspeed, high power setting condition.

      2) Large control movements may be required, but this does not mean rough or jerky movements.

   c. It is important to know the relationship among parasite drag, induced drag, and the power needed to maintain a given altitude (or climb angle or glide slope) at a selected airspeed.

5. **The applicant demonstrates the ability to identify, assess, and mitigate risks encompassing collision avoidance, scanning, and obstacle and wire strike avoidance.**

   a. For information on collision avoidance, scanning, and obstacle avoidance, see Study Unit 7, Subunit 4, beginning on page 66.

   b. For information on wire strikes, see Study Unit 7, Subunit 6, beginning on page 68.

6. **The applicant demonstrates the ability to identify, assess, and mitigate risks encompassing failure to follow right-of-way rules.**

    a. For information on right-of-way rules, see Section IV Introduction, Risk Management, item F., on page 300.

7. **The applicant demonstrates the ability to identify, assess, and mitigate risks encompassing obstacles on approach and departure paths.**

    a. For information on obstacles on approach and departure paths, see Section IV Introduction, Risk Management, item D., on page 300.

8. **The applicant demonstrates the ability to identify, assess, and mitigate risks encompassing low altitude stall/spin.**

    a. Many stall/spin accidents have occurred during go-arounds.

        1) A causal factor in go-arounds has been pilot failure to maintain positive control due to a nose-high trim setting or premature flap retraction.

    b. For more information on low altitude stall/spin, see Section IV Introduction, Risk Management, item H., beginning on page 301.

9. **The applicant demonstrates the ability to identify, assess, and mitigate risks encompassing elevator trim stalls.**

    a. The pilot must consider the possibility of an elevator trim stall situation during a go-around maneuver.

        1) A causal factor of elevator trim stalls during go-arounds has been pilot failure to maintain positive control due to a nose-height trim setting.

    b. When takeoff power is applied in the go-around, you must cope with undesirable pitch.

        1) Since you have trimmed your airplane for the approach (i.e., nose-up trim), the nose may rise sharply.

            a) Proper elevator pressure must be applied to maintain a safe climbing pitch attitude.

            b) Retrim the aircraft for neutral trim pressure for the desired climb pitch altitude.

        2) Using excessive up elevator trim during a go-around maneuver could make recovery from an elevator trim stall difficult (e.g., it will be more difficult to lower the nose).

10. **The applicant demonstrates the ability to identify, assess, and mitigate risks encompassing indecision or changing the go-around/rejected landing decision.**

    a. Official reports concerning go-around accidents frequently cite "pilot indecision" as a cause. This happens when a pilot fixates on trying to make a bad landing good, resulting in a late decision to go around.

        1) This is natural, since the purpose of an approach is a landing.

        2) Delays in deciding what to do cost valuable runway stopping distance. They also cause loss of valuable altitude as the approach continues.

        3) If there is any question about making a safe touchdown and rollout, execute a go-around immediately.

    b. Once you decide to go around, stick to it! Too many airplanes have been lost because a pilot has changed his or her mind and tried to land after all.

11. **The applicant demonstrates the ability to identify, assess, and mitigate risks encompassing failure to adhere to sterile cockpit requirement.**

    a. For information on sterile cockpit, see Study Unit 6, Subunit 2, on page 51.

END OF RISK MANAGEMENT ELEMENT

32.3 SKILLS

A.   Task Objectives

1.   **The applicant demonstrates the ability to make a timely decision to discontinue the approach to landing.**

   a.   The need to discontinue a landing may arise at any point in the landing process, but the most critical go-around is one started when very close to the ground. A timely decision must be made.

   1)   The earlier you recognize a dangerous situation, the sooner you can decide to reject the landing and start the go-around, and the safer this maneuver will be.

   2)   Never wait until the last possible moment to make a decision.

   b.   Official reports concerning go-around accidents frequently cite "pilot indecision" as a cause. This happens when a pilot fixates on trying to make a bad landing good, resulting in a late decision to go around.

   1)   This is natural, since the purpose of an approach is a landing.

   2)   Delays in deciding what to do cost valuable runway stopping distance. They also cause loss of valuable altitude as the approach continues.

   3)   If there is any question about making a safe touchdown and rollout, execute a go-around immediately.

   c.   Once you decide to go around, stick to it! Too many airplanes have been lost because a pilot has changed his or her mind and tried to land after all.

   d.   When there is any doubt of the safe outcome of a landing, the go-around should be initiated immediately.

   e.   Do not attempt to salvage a possible bad landing.

   f.   Delay can lead to an accident because the remaining runway may be insufficient for landing or because delay can prevent the clearing of obstacles on the departure end of the runway.

2.   **The applicant demonstrates the ability to apply takeoff power immediately and transition to climb pitch attitude for V_X or V_Y as appropriate +10/–5 knots.**

   a.   Once you decide to go around, takeoff power should be applied immediately and your airplane's pitch attitude changed so as to slow or stop the descent.

   b.   You should level the wings and simultaneously release the rudder pressure while readjusting the pitch attitude to the normal glide attitude. If the pressure on the rudder is released abruptly, the nose will swing too quickly into line and the airplane will tend to acquire excess speed.

   c.   Power is the single most essential ingredient. Every precaution must be taken (i.e., completion of the before-landing checklist) to assure that power is available when you need it.

   1)   Adjust carburetor heat to OFF (cold) position, if appropriate.

   2)   If a mixture control is available, check that the mixture is full rich or appropriately leaned for high-density altitude airport operations. This should have been accomplished during the before-landing checklist.

   1)   You should establish the pitch attitude to maintain V_Y.

   NOTE: You should climb at V_X initially if you need to clear any obstacles.

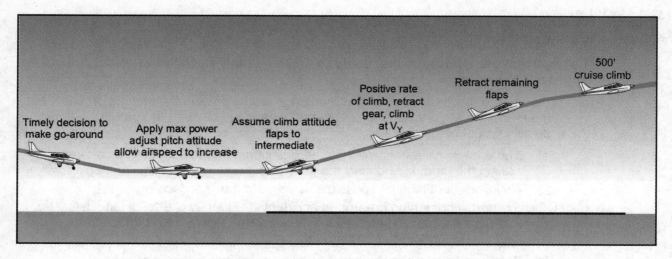

d.   As discussed earlier, you may have to cope with undesirable pitch and yaw due to the addition of full power in a nose-up trim configuration.

   1)   You must use whatever control pressure is required to maintain the proper pitch attitude and to keep your airplane straight. This may require considerable pressure.

   2)   While holding your airplane straight and in a safe climbing attitude, you should retrim your airplane to relieve any heavy control pressures.

      a)   Since the airspeed will build up rapidly with the application of takeoff power and the controls will become more effective, this initial trim is to relieve the heavy pressures until a more precise trim can be made for the lighter pressures.

   3)   If the pitch attitude is increased excessively in an effort to prevent your airplane from mushing onto the runway, the airplane may stall.

      a)   A stall is especially likely if no trim correction is made and the flaps remain fully extended.

e.   During the initial part of an extremely low go-around, your airplane may "mush" onto the runway and bounce. This situation is not particularly dangerous if the airplane is kept straight and a constant, safe pitch attitude is maintained.

   1)   Your airplane will be approaching safe flying speed rapidly, and the advanced power will cushion any secondary touchdown.

f.   Establish a climb pitch attitude by use of outside visual references. From your training you should have a knowledge of the visual clues to attain the attitude.

3.   **The applicant demonstrates the ability to retract the flaps, as appropriate.**

   a.   Unless otherwise noted in your POH/AFM, the flaps are normally retracted (at least partially) before retracting the landing gear.

   1)   On most airplanes, full flaps create more drag than the landing gear.

4.   **The applicant demonstrates the ability to retract the landing gear after establishing a positive rate of climb and in accordance with manufacturer's guidance.**

   a.   In case your airplane should inadvertently touch down as the go-around is initiated, it is desirable to have the landing gear in the down-and-locked position.

   b.   Never attempt to retract the landing gear until after a rough trim is accomplished and a positive rate of climb is established.

5. **The applicant demonstrates the ability to maneuver to the side of the runway/landing area when necessary to clear and avoid conflicting traffic.**

   a. After establishing a positive rate of climb and ensuring that you are clear of all obstacles, move to the side of the runway.

      1) This is done so that you can see other traffic that may be on the runway.

6. **The applicant demonstrates the ability to maintain takeoff power V$_Y$ +10/–5 knots or to a safe maneuvering altitude.**

   a. After a safe maneuvering altitude has been reached (normally 500 to 1,000 ft. AGL), the power should be set to an appropriate setting to transition to an appropriate airspeed for the traffic pattern.

      1) Most trainer-type airplane manufacturers recommend maintaining maximum power until reaching traffic pattern altitude.

7. **The applicant demonstrates the ability to maintain directional control and proper wind-drift correction throughout the climb.**

   a. Maintain a ground track parallel to the runway centerline and in a position where you can see the runway.

   b. Now that you have your airplane under control, you can communicate with the tower or the appropriate ground station to advise that you are going around.

8. **The applicant demonstrates the ability to complete the appropriate checklist.**

   a. Consult your POH/AFM for the proper procedure to follow for your airplane.

   b. A go-around checklist is an excellent example of a checklist that you will "do and then review." When you execute a go-around, you will do it from memory and then review your checklist after you have initiated and stabilized your go-around.

END OF SKILLS ELEMENT

32.4 COMMON ERRORS

A. Common Errors during a Go-Around/Rejected Landing

1. **Failure to recognize a situation in which a go-around is necessary**

   a. When there is any doubt of the safe outcome of a landing, the go-around should be initiated immediately.

   b. Do not attempt to salvage a possible bad landing.

2. **Hazards of delaying a decision to go around**

   a. Delay can lead to an accident because the remaining runway may be insufficient for landing or because delay can prevent the clearing of obstacles on the departure end of the runway.

3. **Improper power application**

   a. Power should be added smoothly and continuously.

   b. Ensure that you have maximum power available at all times during the final approach by completing your before-landing checklist.

4. **Failure to control pitch attitude**

   a. You must be able to divide your attention to accomplish this procedure and maintain control of your airplane.

   b. Learn the visual clues as to climb (V_Y) pitch attitudes, and then cross-check with the airspeed indicator.

5. **Failure to compensate for torque effect**

   a. In a high-power, low airspeed configuration, right rudder pressure must be increased to counteract torque and to keep the airplane's nose straight.

      1) Center the ball in the inclinometer.

6. **Improper trim technique**

   a. Initial trim is important to relieve the heavy control pressures.

   b. Since your airplane may be in a nose-up trim configuration, the application of full power may cause the nose to rise sharply.

      1) Then a considerable amount of forward elevator pressure would be required to maintain the proper pitch attitude and to prevent a stall/spin situation. The use of trim will decrease the pressure you will have to hold.

7. **Failure to maintain recommended airspeeds**

   a. This error will reduce the climb performance of your airplane and may create unsafe conditions due to obstructions or, if the airspeed is too slow, a stall/spin situation.

8. **Improper wing flap or landing gear retraction procedure**

   a. Follow the procedures in your POH/AFM.

   b. On most airplanes, the flaps create more drag than the landing gear; thus, you should raise (at least partially) the flaps before the landing gear, if retractable.

   c. Retract the landing gear only after a positive rate of climb is established, as indicated on the vertical speed indicator.

9. **Failure to maintain proper ground track during climbout**

   a. Not maintaining the proper ground track may cause possible conflicts with other traffic and/or obstructions.

   b. You are expected by other traffic and/or ATC to maintain a ground track parallel to the runway centerline until at the proper position to turn crosswind.

10. **Failure to remain well clear of obstructions and other traffic**

    a. Climb at V_X if necessary to clear any obstructions.

    b. Maintain visual contact with other traffic, especially if the go-around was due to departing traffic.

END OF COMMON ERRORS

PART III
SECTION V:
PERFORMANCE MANEUVERS

Study Units 33 and 34 of Section V explain the two FAA ACS tasks (A-B) of Performance Maneuvers. These tasks include knowledge, risk management, and skill. Your evaluator is required to test you on both of these tasks.

STUDY UNIT THIRTY-THREE
STEEP TURNS

Task	Task A. Steep Turns
References	FAA-H-8083-2, FAA-H-8083-3; POH/AFM
Objective	To determine that the applicant exhibits satisfactory knowledge, risk management, and skills associated with steep turns.
Knowledge	The applicant demonstrates understanding of:
PA.V.A.K1	1. Coordinated flight.
PA.V.A.K2	2. Attitude control at various airspeeds.
PA.V.A.K3	3. Maneuvering speed, including changes in weight.
PA.V.A.K4	4. Controlling rate and radius of turn.
PA.V.A.K5	5. Accelerated stalls.
PA.V.A.K6	6. Overbanking tendencies.
PA.V.A.K6	7. Use of trim in a turn.
PA.V.A.K6	8. Aerodynamics associated with steep turns.
PA.V.A.K6	9. Aerobatic requirements and limitations.
Risk Management	The applicant demonstrates the ability to identify, assess and mitigate risks, encompassing:
PA.V.A.R1	1. Failure to divide the attention between airplane control and orientation.
PA.V.A.R2	2. Task management.
PA.V.A.R3	3. Energy management.
PA.V.A.R4	4. Accelerated stalls.
PA.V.A.R5	5. Spins.
PA.V.A.R6	6. Failure to maintain situational awareness.
PA.V.A.R7	7. Collision avoidance, scanning, obstacle and wire strike avoidance.
PA.V.A.R8	8. Failure to maintain coordinated flight.
Skills	The applicant demonstrates the ability to:
PA.V.A.S1	1. Establish the manufacturer's recommended airspeed or if one is not stated, a safe airspeed not to exceed V_A.
PA.V.A.S2	2. Roll into a coordinated 360° steep turn with a 45° bank.
PA.V.A.S3	3. Perform the Task in the opposite direction, as specified by the evaluator.
PA.V.A.S4	4. Maintain the entry altitude ±100 feet, airspeed ±10 knots, bank ±5°; and roll out on the entry heading, ±10° or as recommended by aircraft manufacturer to a safe maneuvering altitude.

A.   General Information

1.   The objective of this task is for you to demonstrate your smoothness, coordination, orientation, division of attention, and control techniques in the performance of steep turns.

2.   Additional reading: In Study Unit 1, "Airplanes and Aerodynamics," of *Pilot Handbook*, see the following:

a.   Subunit 11, "Airplane Stability," for a discussion on lateral stability or instability in turns

b.   Subunit 12, "Loads and Load Factors," for a discussion on the effect of turns on load factors, the effect of load factor on the stalling speed, and design maneuvering speed (V_A)

33.1 KNOWLEDGE

A. Task Objectives

1. **The applicant demonstrates understanding of coordinated flight.**

    a. When applying aileron to bank the airplane, the lowered aileron (on the rising wing) produces a greater lift and a greater drag, than the raised aileron (on the lowering wing). This is commonly referred to as **adverse yaw**.

        1) This increased aileron drag tends to yaw the airplane toward the rising wing (i.e., opposite the direction of turn) while the banking action is taking effect.

    b. To counteract this adverse yaw, rudder pressure must be applied simultaneously with the ailerons in the desired direction of turn. This produces a coordinated turn.

    c. For the purposes of this discussion, an airplane is in coordinated flight when it flies straight ahead through the relative wind, i.e., not sideways (about its vertical axis). In other words, the airplane is always turning at a rate appropriate to its angle of bank.

    d. Once the airplane is at the desired bank, the pilot neutralizes the ailerons and the rudder.

2. **The applicant demonstrates understanding of attitude control at various airspeeds.**

    a. In this maneuver, a constant airspeed is required, so power is usually added as necessary.

        1) When back pressure is applied to increase lift in a steep bank, drag also increases. Thus, power may be required to maintain the entry altitude and airspeed.

3. **The applicant demonstrates understanding of maneuvering speed, including changes in weight.**

    a. Establish the manufacturer's recommended airspeed or, if one is not stated, a safe airspeed not to exceed V_A.

        1) V_A is the maximum speed at which the airplane will normally stall before the load limits are exceeded, avoiding structural damage.

            a) V_A is a function of the gross weight of your airplane.
            b) See your POH/AFM for the maneuvering speed at gross weight.
            c) At lower weights, the maneuvering speed also decreases.

            In your airplane, V_A _____ at _____ lb.

        2) Due to the increase in load factors during steep turns, you should not exceed V_A.

            a) At speeds above maneuvering speed, full deflection of any flight control surface could cause structural damage to the aircraft.

4. **The applicant demonstrates understanding of controlling rate and radius of turn.**

    a. The rate of turn at any given true airspeed depends on the horizontal lift component. The horizontal lift component varies in proportion to the amount of bank. Therefore, the rate of turn at a given true airspeed increases as the angle of bank is increased.

        1) A steeper bank angle will result in a higher rate of turn.
        2) The rate of turn will decrease if the bank angle decreases.

    b. When a turn is made at a higher true airspeed at a given bank angle, the inertia is greater and the horizontal life component required for the turn is greater, causing the turning rate to become slower. Therefore, at a given angle of bank, a higher true airspeed will make the radius of turn larger because the airplane will be turning at a slower rate.

5. **The applicant demonstrates understanding of accelerated stalls.**

    a. An airplane will stall during a coordinated steep turn exactly as it does from straight flight, except that the pitching and rolling actions tend to be more sudden.

        1) If the airplane is slipping toward the inside of the turn at the time the stall occurs, it tends to roll rapidly toward the outside of the turn as the nose pitches down because the outside wing stalls before the inside wing.

        2) If the airplane is skidding toward the outside of the turn, it will have a tendency to roll to the inside of the turn because the inside wing stalls first.

    b. If the coordination of the turn at the time of the stall is accurate, the airplane's nose will pitch away from the pilot just as it does in a straight flight stall, since both wings stall simultaneously.

6. **The applicant demonstrates understanding of overbanking tendencies.**

    a. The so-called **overbanking tendency** is the result of the airplane being banked steeply enough to reach a condition of negative static stability about the longitudinal axis.

        1) Static stability can be positive, neutral, or negative. It is the tendency of the airplane, once displaced, to try to return to a stable condition as it was before being disturbed.

            a) In a shallow turn, the airplane displays positive static stability and tries to return to a wings-level attitude.

            b) In a medium bank turn, the airplane shows neutral static stability and will tend to remain in the medium bank, assuming calm air.

            c) In a steep turn, the airplane demonstrates negative static stability and tries to steepen the bank rather than remain stable. This is the overbanking tendency.

        2) Why overbanking occurs: As the radius of the turn becomes smaller, a significant difference develops between the speed of the inside wing and the speed of the outside wing.

            a) The wing on the outside of the turn travels a longer circuit than the inside wing, yet both complete their respective circuits in the same length of time.

            b) Therefore, the outside wing must travel faster than the inside wing; as a result, it develops more lift. This creates a slight differential between the lift of the inside and outside wings and tends to further increase the bank.

            c) When changing from a shallow bank to a medium bank, the airspeed of the wing on the outside of the turn increases in relation to the inside wing as the radius of turn decreases, but the force created exactly balances the force of the inherent lateral stability of the airplane so that, at a given speed, no aileron pressure is required to maintain that bank.

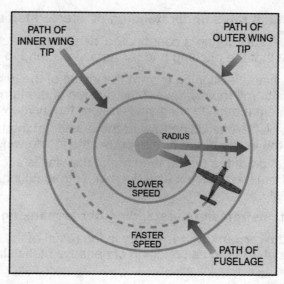

d) As the radius decreases further (i.e., when the bank progresses from a medium bank to a steep bank), the lift differential overbalances the lateral stability, and counteractive pressure on the ailerons is necessary to keep the bank from steepening.

7. **The applicant demonstrates understanding of use of trim in a turn.**

    a. Trim devices are commonly used to relieve you of the need to maintain continuous pressure on the primary controls. Thus, you can retrim at each power setting, airspeed, and/or flight attitude to neutralize control pressure.

    b. Trim tabs should not be used to position the primary control. Rather, control pressure should be used on the control yoke or rudder pedals to position the primary control; then the trim tab should be adjusted to relieve the control pressure.

8. **The applicant demonstrates understanding of aerodynamics associated with steep turns.**

    a. Your airplane's turning performance is limited by the amount of power the engine is developing, its limit load factor (structural strength), and its aerodynamic characteristics.

    b. In a constant altitude, coordinated turn in any aircraft, the load factor is the result of two forces: centrifugal force and gravity.

    c. For any given bank angle, the rate of turn (ROT) varies with the airspeed–the higher the speed, the slower the ROT. This compensates for added centrifugal force, allowing the load factor to remain the same.

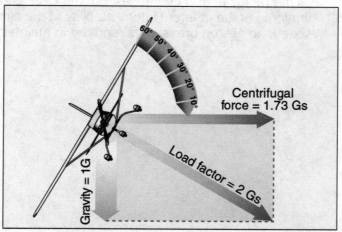

Two forces cause load factor during turns.

d. The figure below reveals an important fact about turns—the load factor increases at a terrific rate after a bank has reached 45° or 50°.

e. The load factor for any aircraft in a 60° bank is 2 Gs. The load factor in an 80° bank is 5.76 Gs.

    1) The wing must produce lift equal to these load factors if altitude is to be maintained.

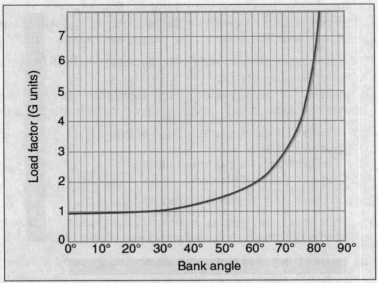

Angle of bank changes load factor.

9. **The applicant demonstrates understanding of aerobatic requirements and limitations.**

a. It should be noted how rapidly the line denoting load factor rises as it approaches the 90° bank line, which it never quite reaches because a 90° banked, constant altitude turn is not mathematically possible.

b. An aircraft may be banked to 90°, but not in a coordinated turn. An aircraft which can be held in a 90° banked slipping turn is capable of straight knife-edged flight.

c. At slightly more than 80°, the load factor exceeds the limit of 6 Gs, the limit load factor of an acrobatic aircraft

END OF KNOWLEDGE ELEMENT

33.2 RISK MANAGEMENT

A. Task Objectives

1. **The applicant demonstrates the ability to identify, assess, and mitigate risks encompassing failure to divide the attention between airplane control and orientation.**

    a. Do not stare at any one object during this maneuver.

    b. To maintain orientation as well as altitude requires an awareness of the relative position of the nose, the horizon, the wings, and the amount of turn.

        1) If you watch only the nose of your airplane, you will have trouble holding altitude constant and remaining oriented in the turn.

        2) By watching all available visual and instrument references, you will be able to hold a constant altitude and remain oriented throughout the maneuver.

            a) Keep attitude indicator at 45° of bank.
            b) Keep VSI at or near 0 fpm.
            c) Reference heading and altitude.
            d) Scan outside for traffic.

    c. Maintain control of your airplane throughout the turn.

        1) To recover from an excessive nose-low attitude, you should first slightly reduce the angle of bank with coordinated aileron and rudder pressure.

            a) Then back elevator pressure should be used to raise your airplane's nose to the desired pitch attitude.

            b) After completing this, reestablish the desired angle of bank.

            c) Attempting to raise the nose first will usually cause a tight descending spiral and could lead to overstressing the airplane.

        2) If your altitude increases, the bank should be increased to 45° by coordinated use of aileron and rudder.

2. **The applicant demonstrates the ability to identify, assess, and mitigate risks encompassing task management.**

    a. For information on task management, see Study Unit 6, Subunit 1, beginning on page 49.

3. **The applicant demonstrates the ability to identify, assess, and mitigate risks encompassing energy management.**

    a. For information on energy management, see Study Unit 8, Subunit 1, beginning on page 71.

4. **The applicant demonstrates the ability to identify, assess, and mitigate risks encompassing accelerated stalls.**

    a. The aerodynamics of steep turns outlined earlier discussed the implications of increased load factors and the greater possibility of uncoordinated flight.

        1) An increased load factor increases the stalling speed of the aircraft. Since the maneuver must be performed at a speed at or below maneuvering speed (V_A), there is a reduced margin between the true airspeed and the speed at which a critical angle of attack will be reached and subsequent stall.

5. **The applicant demonstrates the ability to identify, assess, and mitigate risks encompassing spins.**

    a. Should a stall occur while also improperly flying uncoordinated, there is an elevated risk of entering a spin, which must be avoided.

    b. For information on spins, see Section IV Introduction, Risk Management, item H., beginning on page 301.

6. **The applicant demonstrates the ability to identify, assess, and mitigate risks encompassing failure to maintain situational awareness.**

    a. The steep turn is performed at a high rate of turn. It is possible to lose situational awareness during the maneuver.

        1) Before starting the maneuver, note the entry heading and a reference point in front of the airplane.

        2) Divide your attention between outside the airplane and the flight instruments to avoid overshooting the turn.

        3) To maintain altitude, as well as orientation, an awareness of the relative position of the nose, the horizon, the wings, and the amount of bank is required.

    b. For more information on situational awareness, see Study Unit 7, Subunit 1, beginning on page 57.

7. **The applicant demonstrates the ability to identify, assess, and mitigate risks encompassing collision avoidance, scanning, and obstacle and wire strike avoidance.**

    a. Before starting the steep turn, the pilot should ensure that the area is clear of other air traffic since the rate of turn will be quite rapid.

    b. For more information on collision avoidance, scanning, and obstacle avoidance, see Study Unit 7, Subunit 4, beginning on page 66.

    c. For more information on wire strikes, see Study Unit 7, Subunit 6, beginning on page 68.

8. **The applicant demonstrates the ability to identify, assess, and mitigate risks encompassing failure to maintain coordinated flight.**

    a. All bank angle changes should be done with coordinated use of aileron and rudder.

    b. As discussed earlier, when performing steep turns, there is a smaller margin of safety due to the accelerated stall speed.

END OF RISK MANAGEMENT ELEMENT

33.3 SKILLS

A.   Task Objectives

1.   **The applicant demonstrates the ability to establish the manufacturer's recommended airspeed or, if one is not stated, a safe airspeed not to exceed V_A.**

   a.   Before starting the steep turn, you should perform **clearing turns** to ensure that the area is clear of other air traffic since the rate of turn will be relatively rapid.

   b.   Establish and use the recommended entry speed found in your POH/AFM. If none is listed, then use a safe airspeed assigned by your evaluator, not to exceed V_A (design maneuvering speed).

   c. V_A is the maximum speed at which the airplane will normally stall before the load limits are exceeded, avoiding structural damage.

      1) V_A is a function of the gross weight of your airplane.
      2)   See your POH/AFM.

   d.   Due to the increase in load factors during steep turns, you should not exceed V_A.

2.   **The applicant demonstrates the ability to roll into a coordinated 360° steep turn with a 45° bank.**

   a.   Note your heading toward your reference point and smoothly roll into a coordinated turn with a 45° angle of bank, ±5°.

      1)   As the turn is being established, back pressure on the elevator control should be smoothly increased to increase the angle of attack.

   b.   As the bank steepens beyond 30°, you may find it necessary to hold a considerable amount of back elevator control pressure to maintain a constant altitude.

      1)   Additional back elevator pressure increases the angle of attack, which increases drag.

         a)   Additional power may be required to maintain entry altitude and airspeed.

      2)   Retrim your airplane of excess control pressures, as appropriate.

         a)   This will help you to maintain a constant altitude.

3.   **The applicant demonstrates the ability to perform the task in the opposite direction, as specified by the evaluator.**

   a.   Perform the task in the opposite direction, as specified by your evaluator.

      1)   Your evaluator may have you roll out of a steep turn and then roll into a steep turn in the opposite direction.

         a)   Always look and say "clear (left or right)," and then roll into a 45° bank.

4.   **The applicant demonstrates the ability to maintain the entry altitude ±100 feet, airspeed ±10 knots, and bank ±5°; and roll out on the entry heading, ±10° or as recommended by aircraft manufacturer to a safe maneuvering altitude.**

   a.   You must maintain your entry altitude and airspeed throughout the entire maneuver.

      1)   The authors suggest performing this maneuver at an altitude that is easy to scan on your altimeter (e.g., 2,500 ft. instead of 2,700 ft.)

   b.   While the rollout is being made, back elevator pressure must be gradually released and power reduced as necessary to maintain the altitude and airspeed.

   c.   The rollout from the turn should be timed so that the wings reach level flight when your airplane is on the entry heading (i.e., toward your reference point).

      1)   Normally, you lead your desired heading by one-half of the number of degrees of bank, e.g., approximately a 22° lead in a 45° bank.

      2)   During your training, you should have developed your technique and knowledge of the lead required.

END OF SKILLS ELEMENT

33.4 COMMON ERRORS

A. Common Errors during Steep Turns

1. **Improper pitch, bank, and power coordination during entry and rollout**

    a. Do not overanticipate the amount of pitch change needed during entry and rollout.

      1) During entry, if the pitch is increased (nose up) before the bank is established, altitude will be gained.

      2) During recovery, if back pressure is not released, altitude will be gained.

    b. Power should be added as required during entry and then reduced during rollout.

      1) Do not adjust power during transition to turn in the opposite direction.

2. **Uncoordinated use of flight controls**

    a. This error is normally indicated by a slip, especially in right-hand turns.

      1) Check inclinometer (i.e., "the ball").

    b. If the airplane's nose starts to move before the bank starts, rudder is being applied too soon.

    c. If the bank starts before the nose starts turning, or the nose moves in the opposite direction, the rudder is being used too late.

    d. If the nose moves up or down when entering a bank, excessive or insufficient back elevator pressure is being applied.

3. **Inappropriate control applications**

    a. This error may be due to a lack of planning.

    b. Failure to plan may require you to make a large control movement to attain the desired result.

4. **Improper technique in correcting altitude deviations**

    a. When altitude is lost, you may attempt to raise the nose first by increasing back elevator pressure without shallowing the bank. This usually causes a tight descending spiral.

5. **Loss of orientation**

    a. This error can be caused by forgetting the heading or reference point from which this maneuver was started.

    b. Select a prominent checkpoint to be used in this maneuver.

6. **Excessive deviation from desired heading during rollout**

    a. This error is due to a lack of planning.

    b. The lead on the rollout should be one-half of the bank being used.

      1) With a 45° bank, approximately 22° is needed for the rollout lead.

      2) It is easier to work with 20°, and the same result will be achieved.

END OF COMMON ERRORS

STUDY UNIT THIRTY-FOUR
GROUND REFERENCE MANEUVERS

Task	Task B. Ground Reference Maneuvers
References	14 CFR part 61; FAA-H-8083-2, FAA-H-8083-3
Objective	To determine that the applicant exhibits satisfactory knowledge, risk management, and skills associated with ground reference maneuvering which may include a rectangular course, S-turns, or turns around a point.
Knowledge	The applicant demonstrates understanding of:
PA.V.B.K1	1. The effects of wind on ground track and relation to a ground reference point.
PA.V.B.K2	2. The effects of bank angle and groundspeed on rate and radius of turn.
PA.V.B.K3	3. The entry/exit requirements of maneuver.
PA.V.B.K4	4. The relationship of rectangular course to airport traffic pattern.
PA.V.B.K5	5. Emergency landing considerations while conducting a ground reference maneuver.
PA.V.B.K6	6. S-turns and how they can be performed to increase separation from other aircraft.
Risk Management	The applicant demonstrates the ability to identify, assess and mitigate risks, encompassing:
PA.V.B.R1	1. Collision avoidance, scanning, obstacle and wire strike avoidance.
PA.V.B.R2	2. Low altitude maneuvering.
PA.V.B.R3	3. Task management.
PA.V.B.R4	4. Failure to maintain aircraft control.
PA.V.B.R5	5. Failure to select a suitable emergency landing area.
Skills	The applicant demonstrates the ability to:
PA.V.B.S1	1. Determine the area is clear of terrain, obstacles, and other aircraft and the aircraft will remain in the appropriate airspace.
PA.V.B.S2	2. Select a suitable ground reference.
PA.V.B.S3	3. Identify a suitable emergency landing area.
PA.V.B.S4	4. Plan the maneuver: Note: The evaluator must select at least one maneuver for the applicant to demonstrate.
PA.V.B.S4a	a. Rectangular course: enter a left or right pattern, 600 to 1,000 feet above ground level (AGL) at an appropriate distance from the selected reference area, 45° to the downwind leg
PA.V.B.S4b	b. S-turns: enter perpendicular to the selected reference line, 600 to 1,000 feet AGL at an appropriate distance from the selected reference area
PA.V.B.S4c	c. Turns around a point: enter at an appropriate distance from the reference point, 600 to 1,000 feet AGL at an appropriate distance from the selected reference area
PA.V.B.S5	5. Apply adequate wind drift correction during straight and turning flight to maintain a constant ground track if around a rectangular reference area or to track a constant radius turn on each side of the selected reference line or a selected point.
PA.V.B.S6	6. If performing a pattern such as S-Turns, reverse the turn directly over the selected reference line; if performing turns around a point, complete turns in either direction around the selected reference point.
PA.V.E.S7	7. Divide attention between airplane control, traffic avoidance and the ground track while maintaining coordinated flight.
PA.V.E.S8	8. Maintain altitude ±100 feet; maintain airspeed ±10 knots or as recommended by aircraft manufacturer to a safe maneuvering altitude.

A. General Information

1. The objective of this task is for you to demonstrate your knowledge, risk management, and skills related to ground reference maneuvering, which may include a rectangular course, S-turns, or turns around a point.

2.   This study unit explains the three maneuvers of Ground Reference Maneuvers. These maneuvers include both knowledge and skill. Your evaluator is required to test you on at least one task; therefore, you should be prepared for all three tasks.

3.   The three ground reference maneuvers–rectangular course, S-turns, and turns around a point–are each designed to improve your proficiency in dividing your attention between airplane control and ground track.

4.   These maneuvers aid the pilot in analyzing the effect of wind and other forces acting on the airplane and in developing a fine control touch, coordination, and the division of attention necessary for accurate and safe maneuvering of the airplane.

5.   Before beginning any ground reference maneuver, you must determine the wind direction and estimate its speed.

   a.   You can determine the wind direction by observing the movement of smoke or dust, or the wave patterns on water or grain fields.

   b.   Another method is to make a 360° turn using a constant 30° angle of bank. By noting your ground track during the turn, you can determine wind direction and velocity.

      1)   Using a road intersection will provide you with a better starting point to begin the 360° turn.

6.   We have organized this study unit by color coding the three maneuvers. As you read through the material,

Maneuver	Color
Rectangular course	Orange
S-turns	Green
Turns around a point	Blue

34.1 KNOWLEDGE

A.   Task Objectives

1.   **The applicant demonstrates understanding of the effects of wind on ground track and relation to a ground reference point.**

   a.   As soon as your airplane becomes airborne, it is free of ground friction. Its path is then affected by the air mass (wind) and will not always track along the ground in the exact direction that it is headed.

      1)   When flying with the longitudinal axis of your airplane aligned with a road, you may notice that you move closer to or farther from the road without any turn having been made.

         a)   This would indicate that the wind is moving across your intended flight path.

No Wind - No Drift   With any wind, the airplane drifts downwind unless corrected.

b. In straight flight and following a selected ground track (e.g., a road), the preferred method of correcting for wind drift is to head (crab) your airplane into the wind to cause the airplane to move forward into the wind at the same rate that the wind is moving it sideways.

   1) Depending on the wind velocity, correcting for drift may require a large crab angle or one of only a few degrees.

   2) When the drift has been neutralized, the airplane will follow the desired ground track.

2. **The applicant demonstrates understanding of the effects of bank angle and groundspeed on rate and radius of turn.**

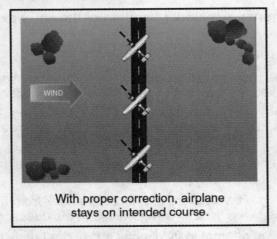

With proper correction, airplane
stays on intended course.

a. In turning flight, the wind will be acting on your airplane from constantly changing angles.

   1) The time it takes for the airplane to progress through any part of a turn is governed by the relative wing angle and speed.

   2) When your airplane is headed into the wind, the groundspeed is decreased; when headed downwind, the groundspeed is increased.

   3) For you to fly a specific ground track, your rate of turn must be proportional to the groundspeed.

      a) When groundspeed is higher (tailwind), the rate of turn must be greater. To get a faster rate of turn, use a steeper bank.

      b) Headwind results in a slower groundspeed, so use a lower rate of turn, i.e., less bank.

b. Two of the three ground reference maneuvers, S-turns and turns around a point, require a constantly changing angle of bank.

c. S-turns: Since turns to effect a constant radius on the ground track require a changing roll rate and angle of bank to establish the crab needed to compensate for the wind, both will increase or decrease as groundspeed increases or decreases.

   1) The bank must be steepest as the turn begins on the downwind side of the ground reference line and must be shallowed gradually as the turn progresses from a downwind heading to an upwind heading.

   2) On the upwind side, the turn should be started with a relatively shallow bank, which is gradually steepened as the airplane turns from an upwind heading to a downwind heading.

d.   Turns around a point: A constant radius around a point will, if any wind exists, require constantly changing the angle of bank and the angles of crab.

    1)   The closer your airplane is to a direct downwind heading where the groundspeed is greatest, the steeper the bank and the faster the rate of turn required to establish the proper crab.

    2)   The closer your airplane is to a direct upwind heading where the groundspeed is least, the shallower the bank and the slower the rate of turn required to establish the proper crab.

    3)   It follows then that, throughout the maneuver, the bank and rate of turn must be gradually varied in proportion to the groundspeed.

3.   **The applicant demonstrates understanding of the entry/exit requirements of the maneuver.**

a.   Rectangular course (see figure on page 436):

    1)   Enter the rectangular course 45° to, and at the midpoint of, the left or right downwind leg (i.e., the course will be to your left or right, respectively).

    2)   Your entry on the downwind leg should place your airplane parallel to, and at a uniform distance (one-fourth to one-half mile) away from, the field boundary.

        a)   You should be able to see the edges of the selected field while seated in a normal position and looking out the side of the airplane during either a left-hand or right-hand course.

            i)   The distance of the ground track from the edges of the field should be the same regardless of the direction in which the course is flown.

        b)   If you attempt to fly directly above the edges of the field, you will have no usable reference points to start and complete the turns.

        c)   The closer the track of your airplane is to the field boundaries, the steeper the bank is required at the turning points.

            i)   The maximum angle of bank is 45°.

    3)   Exit the maneuver on the downwind after completing an entire circuit.

b.   S-turns (see figure on page 438): The maneuver consists of crossing a reference line on the ground at a 90° angle and immediately beginning a series of 180° turns of uniform radius in opposite directions, recrossing the road at a 90° angle just as each 180° turn is completed.

    1)   Enter the maneuver with the wind behind the aircraft.

        a)   The groundspeed will be the fastest throughout the maneuver at entry.

    2)   Exit the maneuver after completing at least two successive 180° turns in opposite directions.

c.   Turns around a point (see figure on page 439): A turn around a point is a practice maneuver in which the airplane is flown in two or more complete circles of uniform radii or distance from a prominent ground reference point.

    1)   To enter a turn around a point, the airplane should be flown on a downwind heading to one side of the selected point at a distance equal to the desired radius of turn.

        a)   In a high-wing airplane, the distance from the point must permit the pilot to see the point throughout the maneuver even with the wing lowered in a bank.

        b)   If the radius is too large, the lowered wing will block the pilot's view of the point.

      2) When any significant wind exists, it will be necessary to roll into the initial bank at a rapid rate so that the steepest bank is attained abeam of the point when the airplane is headed directly downwind.

         a) By entering the maneuver while heading directly downwind, the steepest bank can be attained immediately.

      3) Thus, if maximum bank of 45° is desired, the initial bank will be 45° if the airplane is at the correct distance from the point.

         a) Thereafter, the bank is shallowed gradually until the point is reached where the airplane is headed directly upwind. At this point, the bank should be gradually steepened until the steepest bank is again attained when heading downwind at the initial point of entry.

      4) The groundspeed and bank angle will constantly change throughout the maneuver.

      5) Exit the maneuver after completing at least one 360° turn around the point.

4. **The applicant demonstrates understanding of the relationship of rectangular course to airport traffic pattern.**

   a. Rectangular course: The rectangular course is a practice maneuver in which the ground track of your airplane is equidistant from all sides of a rectangular area on the ground.

      1) An objective is to develop recognition of drift toward or away from a line parallel to the intended ground track.

         a) Development of this skill will assist you in recognizing drift toward or from an airport runway during the various legs of the airport traffic pattern.

      2) The rectangular course simulates a normal airport traffic pattern.

5. **The applicant demonstrates understanding of emergency landing considerations while conducting a ground reference maneuver.**

   a. When selecting a suitable reference area for all three of these maneuvers, you must consider possible emergency landing areas.

      1) There is little time available to search for a suitable field for landing in the event the need arises, e.g., during engine failure.

      2) Select an area that meets the needs of the maneuver as well as safe emergency landing areas within gliding distance.

6. **The applicant demonstrates understanding of S-turns and how they can be performed to increase separation from other aircraft.**

   a. S-turns may be used to increase the separation from slower aircraft ahead.

      1) This can be helpful when following another aircraft to increase spacing before entering the traffic pattern.

END OF KNOWLEDGE ELEMENT

34.2 RISK MANAGEMENT

A. Task Objectives

1. **The applicant demonstrates the ability to identify, assess, and mitigate risks encompassing collision avoidance, scanning, and obstacle and wire strike avoidance.**

    a. Check the area to ensure that no obstructions or other aircraft are in the immediate vicinity.

    b. Conduct two clearing turns while scanning for traffic and obstacles.

    c. Use the landing light to enhance the aircraft's visibility.

    d. For more information on collision avoidance, scanning, and obstacle avoidance, see Study Unit 7, Subunit 4, beginning on page 66.

    e. For more information on wire strikes, see Study Unit 7, Subunit 6, beginning on page 68.

2. **The applicant demonstrates the ability to identify, assess, and mitigate risks encompassing low altitude maneuvering.**

    a. For information on low altitude maneuvering, see Section IV Introduction, Risk Management, item C., on page 299.

    b. Without a clearly discernible horizon, even large deviations from a desired heading, attitude, altitude, or course may not be immediately obvious.

        1) Adequate flight visibility should be ensured to maintain visual separation from any obstacles.

        2) Ground reference maneuvers should be performed in an area well clear of towers and other obstructions.

3. **The applicant demonstrates the ability to identify, assess, and mitigate risks encompassing task management.**

    a. For information on task management, see Study Unit 6, Subunit 1, beginning on page 49.

4. **The applicant demonstrates the ability to identify, assess, and mitigate risks encompassing failure to maintain aircraft control.**

    a. In common terms, positive aircraft control means that you are always "in control" of the airplane.

        1) During all maneuvers, the aircraft should appropriately respond to all of your control inputs in a manner that ensures safe flight.

        2) You should always be trying to "lead the airplane," anticipating the outcome of your actions and planning ahead.

5. **The applicant demonstrates the ability to identify, assess, and mitigate risks encompassing failure to select a suitable emergency landing area.**

    a. Be aware of wind direction and velocity both for the desired emergency landing direction and for their effect on glide distance.

    b. You should always be aware of suitable forced-landing fields. The perfect field would be an established airport or a hard-packed, long, smooth field with no high obstacles on the approach end. You need to select the best field available.

    c. Ground reference maneuvers are performed at low altitudes, which creates additional risks by having less time to react in the event of an emergency.

END OF RISK MANAGEMENT ELEMENT

34.3 SKILLS

A.   Task Objectives

1.   **The applicant demonstrates the ability to determine the area is clear of terrain, obstacles, and other aircraft and the aircraft will remain in the appropriate airspace.**

   a.   Check the area to ensure that no obstructions or other aircraft are in the immediate vicinity.

   b.   Identify your rectangular course, reference line, or reference point and emergency landing area to your evaluator.

2.   **The applicant demonstrates the ability to select a suitable ground reference.**

   a.   Rectangular course: You need to select a rectangular field or an area bounded on four sides by section lines or roads.

      1)   The sides of the selected area should be approximately 1 mi. in length and well away from other air traffic.

      2)   The field should, however, be in an area away from communities, livestock, or groups of people on the ground to prevent possible annoyance or hazards to others.

   b.   S-turns: Before starting the maneuver, you must select a straight ground reference line.

      1)   This line may be a road, fence, railroad, or section line that is easily identifiable to you.

      2)   This line should be perpendicular (i.e., 90°) to the direction of the wind.

      3)   The line should be a sufficient length for making a series of turns.

      4)   The point should, however, be in an area away from communities, livestock, or groups of people on the ground to prevent possible annoyance or hazards to others.

   c.   Turns around a point: The point you select should be prominent, easily distinguished by you, and yet small enough to present a precise reference.

      1)   Isolated trees, crossroads, or other similar landmarks are usually suitable.

      2)   The point should, however, be in an area away from communities, livestock, or groups of people on the ground to prevent possible annoyance or hazards to others.

3.   **The applicant demonstrates the ability to identify a suitable emergency landing area.**

   a.   During these maneuvers, both the instructor and the student should be alert for available forced-landing fields.

      1)   The area chosen should be away from communities, livestock, or groups of people to prevent possible annoyance or hazards to others.

   b.   Due to the altitudes at which these maneuvers are performed, there is little time available to search for a suitable field for landing in the event the need arises.

   c.   Check the area to ensure that no obstructions or other aircraft are in the immediate vicinity.

   d.   Identify your reference point and emergency landing area to your evaluator.

      1)   Rectangular course: The field you use for a rectangular course should also be appropriate to use as an emergency landing area.

      2)   S-turns: Select an area that meets the requirements of both S-turns and safe emergency landing areas.

      3)   Turns around a point: Select an area that provides a usable ground reference point and the opportunity for a safe emergency landing.

4.   **The applicant demonstrates the ability to plan the maneuver:**

    a.   **Rectangular course: Enter a left or right pattern, 600 to 1,000 feet above ground level (AGL) at an appropriate distance from the selected reference area, 45° to the downwind to the downwind leg.**

        1)   Because this maneuver is used to improve your ability to fly a traffic pattern, it should be performed at a traffic pattern altitude appropriate to your area.

            a)   While most traffic patterns are flown between 600 to 1,000 ft. AGL, the recommended traffic pattern altitude is 1,000 ft. AGL.

                i)   When given an altitude window like this, you should always use the highest altitude, i.e., 1,000 ft. AGL.

    b.   **S-turns: Enter perpendicular to the selected reference line, 600 to 1,000 feet AGL at an appropriate distance from the selected reference area.**

        1)   When given an altitude window like this, you should always use the highest altitude, i.e., 1,000 ft. AGL.

            a)   A smart pilot is always prepared for an emergency and minimizes low altitude activity that reflects poorly on aviation.

        2)   Your airplane should be perpendicular to your ground reference line.

            a)   You should normally approach the reference line from the upwind side (i.e., so the airplane is heading downwind).

            b)   Your airplane should be in the normal cruise configuration.

        3)   When you are directly over the road, start the first turn immediately to the left or right, as directed by the evaluator.

            a)   This normally means that when your airplane's lateral axis (i.e., wingtip-to-wingtip) is over the reference line, the first turn is started.

    c.   **Turns around a point: Enter at an appropriate distance from the reference point, 600 to 1,000 feet AGL at an appropriate distance from the selected reference area.**

        1)   To enter turns around a point, you should normally fly your airplane on a downwind heading to one side of the selected point at a distance equal to the desired radius of turn.

            a)   To enter a left turn, keep the point to your left.

                i)   To enter a right turn, keep the point to your right.

            b)   In a high-wing airplane (e.g., Cessna-152, the distance from the point must permit you to see the point throughout the maneuver even with the wing lowered in a bank.

                i)   If the radius is too large, the lowered wing will block your view of the point.

        2)   Your airplane should be in the normal cruise configuration.

        3)   When given an altitude window like this, you should use the highest altitude, i.e., 1,000 ft. AGL.

            a)   A smart pilot is always prepared for an emergency and minimizes low altitude activity that reflects poorly on aviation.

        4)   When any significant wind exists, it will be necessary to roll your airplane into the initial bank at a rapid rate so that the steepest bank is attained abeam of the point when headed downwind.

            a)   Thus, if 45° of bank is desired, the initial bank will be 45° if your airplane is at the correct distance from the point.

5.   **The applicant demonstrates the ability to apply adequate wind drift correction during straight and turning flight to maintain a constant ground track if around a rectangular reference area or to track a constant radius turn on each side of the selected reference line or a selected point.**

   a.   Rectangular course:

   1)   All turns should be started when your airplane is abeam the corners of the field boundaries.

   2)   This discussion begins with a downwind entry.

   3)   While the airplane is on the downwind leg (similar to the downwind leg in a traffic pattern), observe the next field boundary as it approaches, to plan the turn onto the crosswind leg.

   a)   Maintain your desired distance from the edge of the course and maintain entry altitude, i.e., 1,000 ft. AGL.

   b)   Since you have a tailwind on this leg, your airplane has an increased groundspeed. During your turn to the next leg, the wind will tend to move your airplane away from the field.

   i)   Thus, the turn must be entered with a fairly fast rate of roll-in with a relatively steep bank.

   ii)   To compensate for the drift on the next leg, the amount of turn must be more than 90°.

   c)   As the turn progresses, the tailwind component decreases, resulting in a decreasing groundspeed.

   i)   Thus, the bank angle and rate of turn must be decreased gradually to ensure that, upon completion of the turn, you will continue the crosswind ground track at the same distance from the field.

   4)   The rollout onto this next leg (similar to the base leg in a traffic pattern) is such that, as the wings become level, your airplane is crabbed slightly toward the field and into the wind to correct for drift.

   a)   The base leg should be continued at the same distance from the field boundary and at the entry altitude.

   b)   While you are on the base leg, adjust the crab angle as necessary to maintain a uniform distance from the field.

   c)   Since drift correction is being held on the base leg, it is necessary to plan for a turn of less than 90° to align your airplane parallel to the upwind leg boundary.

   d)   This turn should be started with a medium bank angle with a gradual reduction to a shallow bank as the turn progresses.

   i)   This change is necessary due to the crosswind becoming a headwind, causing the groundspeed to decrease throughout the turn.

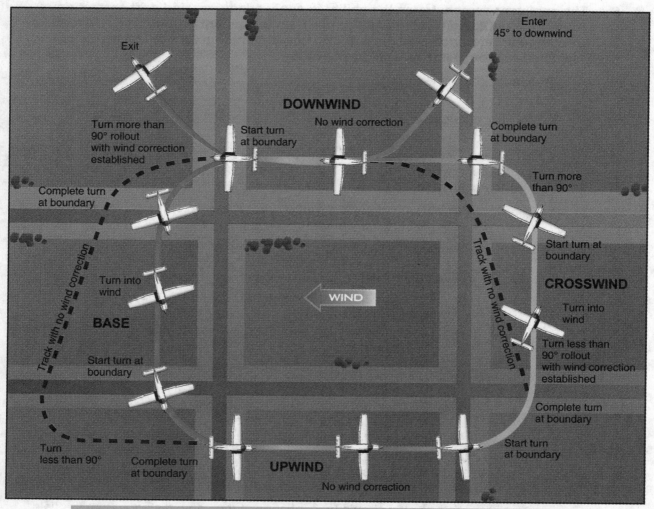

5) The rollout onto this leg (similar to the final approach and upwind leg in a traffic pattern) should be timed to ensure paralleling of the field as the wings become level.

   a) Maintain the same distance from the field boundary and maintain entry altitude.

   b) The next field boundary should be observed as it is being approached, to plan the turn onto the crosswind leg.

   c) Since the wind is a headwind on this leg, it is reducing your airplane's groundspeed and, during the turn onto the crosswind leg, will try to drift your airplane toward the field.

      i) Thus, the roll-in to the turn must be slow and the bank relatively shallow to counteract this effect.

      ii) As the turn progresses, the headwind component decreases, allowing the groundspeed to increase.

        • Consequently, the bank angle and rate of turn must be increased gradually to ensure that, upon completion of the turn, you will continue the crosswind ground track at the same distance from the edge of the field.

      iii) To compensate for drift on the next leg, the amount of turn will be less than 90°.

6) The rollout onto this leg (similar to the crosswind leg of a traffic pattern) is such that, as the wings become level, your airplane is crabbed slightly into the wind (i.e., away from the field) to correct for drift.

   a) Maintain the same distance from the field boundary and maintain entry altitude.

   b) While you are on this leg, adjust the crab angle as necessary to maintain a uniform distance from the field.

   c) As the next field boundary is approached, you should plan the turn onto the downwind leg.

      i) Since the crab angle is being held into the wind and away from the field, this turn will be greater than 90°.

   d) Since the crosswind will become a tailwind, causing the groundspeed to increase during this turn, the bank initially must be medium and then must be progressively increased as the turn proceeds.

   e) To complete the turn, time the rollout so that the wings become level at a point aligned with the crosswind corner of the field just as the longitudinal axis of your airplane becomes parallel to the field boundary.

7) Ideally, drift should not be encountered on the downwind or the upwind leg, but it may be difficult to find a situation where the wind is blowing exactly parallel to the field boundaries.

   a) Since a wind blowing parallel to the boundaries is unlikely, it is usually necessary to crab slightly on all legs.

   b) It is important to anticipate the turns to correct for groundspeed, drift, and turning radius.

   c) You use these same techniques when flying an airport traffic pattern.

b. S-turns:

   1) With your airplane headed downwind, the groundspeed is the greatest, and the rate of departure from the road will be rapid.

      a) The roll into the steep bank (approximately 40°-45°) must be fairly rapid to attain the proper crab angle.

         i) The proper crab angle prevents your airplane from flying too far from your selected reference line and from establishing a ground track of excessive radius.

      b) During the latter portion of the first 90° of turn when your airplane's heading is changing from a downwind heading to a crosswind heading, the groundspeed and the rate of departure from the reference line decrease.

         i) The crab angle will be at the maximum when the airplane is headed directly crosswind (i.e., parallel to the reference line).

   2) After you turn 90°, your airplane's heading becomes more of an upwind heading.

      a) The groundspeed will decrease, and the rate of closure with the reference will become slower.

         i) Thus, it will be necessary to gradually shallow the bank during the remaining 90° of the semicircle so that the crab angle is removed completely and the wings become level as the 180° turn is completed at the moment the reference line is reached.

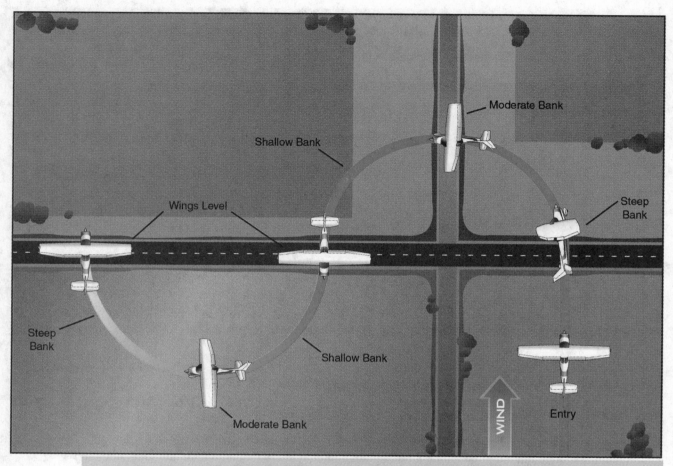

3) Once you are over the reference line, you will start a turn in the opposite direction. Since your airplane is still flying into the headwind, the groundspeed is relatively slow.

   a) The turn will have to be started with a shallow bank so as to avoid an excessive rate of turn, which would establish the maximum crab angle too soon.

   b) The degree of bank should be that which is necessary to attain the proper crab so the ground track describes an arc the same size as the one established on the downwind side.

4) Since your airplane is turning from an upwind to a downwind heading, the groundspeed will increase and, after you turn 90°, the rate of closure with the reference line will increase rapidly.

   a) The angle of bank and rate of turn must be progressively increased so that the airplane will have turned 180° at the time it reaches the reference line.

5) Throughout this maneuver, the bank angle should be changing constantly to track a constant radius turn on each side of the selected reference line.

   a) There should not be any period of straight-and-level flight.

c.   Turns around a point:

1)   With your airplane headed downwind, the groundspeed is the greatest. The steepest bank is used to attain the proper crab angle and to prevent your airplane from flying too far away from your reference point.

a)   During the next 180° of turn (the downwind side), your airplane's heading is changing from a downwind to an upwind heading, and the groundspeed decreases.

b)   During the downwind half of the circle, the nose of your airplane must be progressively crabbed toward the inside of the circle.

i)   The crab angle will be at its maximum when the airplane is headed directly crosswind (i.e., at the 90° point).

ii)   The crab is slowly taken out as your airplane progresses to a direct upwind heading.

c)   Throughout the downwind side of the circle, your airplane goes from its steepest (directly downwind) to its shallowest (directly upwind) bank.

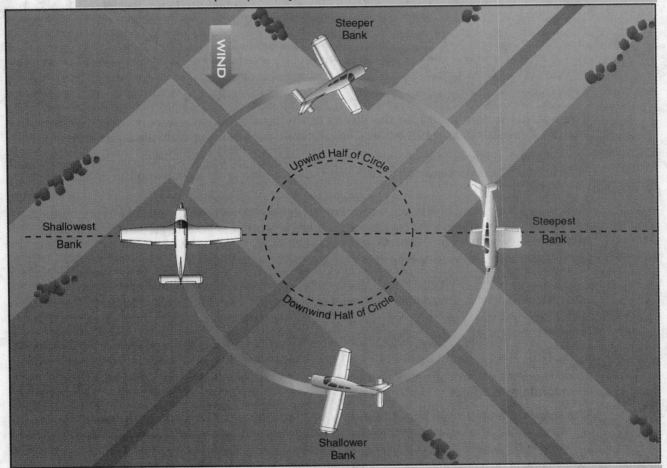

2)   With your airplane headed upwind, the groundspeed is the least. This requires the shallowest bank.

a)   During the next 180° of turn (the upwind side), your airplane's heading is changing from an upwind to a downwind heading, and the groundspeed increases.

b)   During the upwind half of the circle, the nose of your airplane must be progressively crabbed toward the outside of the circle.

   i)   The crab angle will be at its maximum when the airplane is headed directly crosswind.

   ii) The crab is slowly taken out as your airplane progresses to a direct downwind heading.

c)   Throughout the upwind side of the circle, your airplane goes from its shallowest (directly upwind) to its steepest (directly downwind) bank.

6. **The applicant demonstrates the ability to, if performing a pattern such as S-Turns, reverse the turn directly over the selected reference line; if performing turns around a point, complete turns in either direction around the selected reference point.**

   a.   S-turns: You should plan your first 180° turn so you arrive over the reference line at the same moment the turn is completed.

      1)   Then, immediately roll into a 180°turn in the opposite direction.

         a)   Your wings should only be level for an instant as the airplane transitions from a bank in one direction to a bank in the opposite direct (e.g., from left to right).

   b.   Turns around a point: Keep turns in the same direction.

      1)   Be cognizant that as you turn the groundspeed will change. Thus, your bank angle will always slightly be increasing or decreasing.

7. **The applicant demonstrates the ability to divide attention between airplane control, traffic avoidance, and the ground track while maintaining coordinated flight.**

   a.   As with all flight maneuvers by reference to ground objects, you are required to divide your attention between controlling your airplane and maintaining the desired ground track.

      1)   You must divide your attention among watching the ground reference point, maintaining the proper ground track, watching your flight instruments, and watching for other air traffic in your area (collision avoidance).

      2)   You will also need to plan for the next leg of the course or turn.

      3)   Do not become fixated on one item, e.g., watching the ground.

   b.   While dividing your attention, you must keep your airplane in coordinated flight.

      1)   Do not use only the rudder to correct for wind drift, but turn the airplane to establish the proper ground track by coordinated use of aileron and rudder.

      2)   Hold altitude by maintaining level pitch attitude.

   c.   Properly divide your attention and do not fixate on any one item, such as the ground reference point.

8. **The applicant demonstrates the ability to maintain altitude ±100 feet; maintain airspeed ±10 knots or as recommended by aircraft manufacturer to a safe maneuvering altitude.**

   a.   Throughout these maneuvers, a constant altitude should be maintained.

      1)   As the bank increases, you will need to increase back elevator pressure to pitch the airplane's nose up to maintain altitude.

         a)   As the bank decreases, you will need to release some of the back elevator pressure to maintain altitude.

      2)   Maintain pitch awareness by visual references, and use your altimeter to ensure that you are maintaining altitude.

b. Normally these maneuvers are done at cruise airspeed in trainer-type airplanes.

    1) Check your airspeed indicator to ensure that you are maintaining your entry airspeed.

    2) Do not exceed 45° during your steepest banks. This limit should prevent you from increasing the load factor to a point that may require additional power to maintain a constant airspeed and altitude.

        a) There is no reason to add even more tasks (e.g., addition of power) that will cause you to divide your attention.

        b) A 45° angle of bank works well as the steepest bank in S-turns.

c. During these maneuvers, if you maintain your altitude, your airspeed should remain within 10 kt. of your entry airspeed.

    1) Use pitch to make altitude corrections.

    2) Make small power adjustments to make airspeed corrections, if necessary.

END OF SKILLS ELEMENT

34.4 COMMON ERRORS

A. Common Errors during Ground Reference Maneuvers

1. **Faulty entry technique**

   a. S-turns:

      1) You should normally enter this maneuver heading downwind perpendicular to your selected reference line.

      2) As soon as your airplane's lateral axis is over the reference line, you must roll into your steepest bank at a fairly rapid rate.

         a) If the initial bank is too shallow, your airplane will be pushed too far from the reference line, thus establishing a ground track of excessive radius.

   b. Turns around a point:

      1) Though not required, entry should be done on a downwind heading. This will establish your steepest angle of bank at the start of the maneuver.

         a) If you attempt to enter this maneuver at any other point, the radius of the turn must be carefully selected, taking into account the wind velocity and groundspeed so that an excessive angle of bank is not required later on to maintain the proper ground track.

      2) When entering downwind, if the steepest bank is not used, the wind will blow your airplane too far from your reference point to maintain a constant radius.

2. **Poor planning, orientation, or division of attention**

   a. Rectangular course: Poor planning results in your not beginning or ending the turns properly at the corners of the rectangular course. You must plan ahead and anticipate the effects of the wind.

   b. S-turns: Poor planning results in not constantly changing the bank required to effect a true semicircular ground track.

      1) If you do not change to the appropriate degree of bank, your airplane may be in straight-and-level flight before the reference line or still in a bank while crossing the reference line.

   c. Turns around a point: Poor planning results in not changing the bank required to counteract drift to effect a circle of equal radius about a reference point.

   d. Poor orientation normally results in your not being able to identify the wind direction, thus causing problems in your planning.

      1) It may also result in not choosing a prominent reference point or reference line, leading to losing sight of the reference.

   e. Poor division of attention contributes to an inability to maintain a proper ground track, altitude, and/or airspeed.

      1) Also, you may not notice other aircraft that have entered the area near you.

3. **Uncoordinated flight control application**

   a. This error normally occurs when you begin to fixate on your reference and then forget to use the flight controls in a coordinated manner by attempting to only use rudder pressure to correct for drift.

   b. Do not attempt to crab your airplane by using only rudder pressure.

      1) S-turns: Do not use the rudder to yaw the nose of the airplane in an attempt to be directly over and perpendicular to the reference line.

   c. Maintain a coordinated flight condition (i.e., keep the ball centered) throughout these maneuvers.

4. **Improper wind drift correction**

    a. This error occurs either from not fully understanding the effect the wind has on the ground track or from not dividing your attention to recognize the need for wind drift correction.

    b. Once you recognize the need for a correction, take immediate steps to correct for wind drift with coordinated use of the flight controls.

    c. S-turns:

        1) If a constant steep turn is maintained during the downwind side, the airplane will turn too quickly during the last 90° for the slower rate of closure and will be headed perpendicular to the reference line prematurely (i.e., wings level before you arrive over the reference line).

            a) To avoid this error, you must gradually shallow the bank during the last 90° of the semicircle so that the crab angle is removed completely as the wings become level directly over the reference line.

        2) Often there is a tendency to increase the bank too rapidly during the initial part of the turn on the upwind side, which will prevent the completion of the 180° turn before recrossing the road.

            a) To avoid this error, you must visualize the desired half-circle ground track and increase the bank slowly during the early part of this turn.

                i) During the latter part of the turn, when approaching the road, you must judge the closure rate properly and increase the bank accordingly so as to cross the road perpendicular to it just as the rollout is completed.

    d. Turns around a point:

        1) You should use the steepest bank when heading directly downwind.

            a) During the downwind side, the bank will gradually decrease as you approach an upwind heading.

                i) The nose of the airplane will be crabbed toward the inside of the circle.

        2) The bank should be the shallowest when you are heading directly upwind.

            a) During the upwind side, the bank will gradually increase as you approach a downwind heading.

                i) The nose of the airplane will be crabbed toward the outside of the circle.

        3) Do not attempt to keep the wing on the reference point throughout the maneuver.

5. **Turns around a point: An asymmetrical ground track**

    a. Your first semicircle will establish the radii of the semicircles.

        1) You must be able to visualize your ground track and plan for the effect the wind will have on the ground track.

    b. The bank of your airplane must be constantly changing (except in the case of no wind) in order to effect a true semicircular ground track.

6. **Failure to maintain selected altitude or airspeed**

    a. Most student pilots will gain altitude during the initial training in these maneuvers due to poor division of attention and/or a lack of proper pitch awareness.

        1) Learn to divide your attention between the reference point and airplane control (e.g., pitch awareness).

    b. Maintaining a constant altitude and not exceeding a 45° angle of bank will allow you to maintain your airspeed within ±10 kt.

END OF COMMON ERRORS

PART III
SECTION VI:
NAVIGATION

Study Units 35 through 38 of Section VI explain the four FAA ACS tasks (A-D) of Navigation. These tasks include knowledge, risk management, and skill. Your evaluator is required to test you on all four of these tasks.

STUDY UNIT THIRTY-FIVE
PILOTAGE AND DEAD RECKONING

Task	Task A. Pilotage and Dead Reckoning
References	14 CFR part 61; FAA-H-8083-2, FAA-H-8083-25; Navigation Charts
Objective	To determine that the applicant exhibits satisfactory knowledge, risk management, and skills associated with pilotage and dead reckoning.
Knowledge	The applicant demonstrates understanding of:
PA.VI.A.K1	1. Pilotage and dead reckoning.
PA.VI.A.K2	2. Determining heading, speed, and course.
PA.VI.A.K3	3. Estimating time, speed, and distance.
PA.VI.A.K4	4. True airspeed and density altitude.
PA.VI.A.K5	5. Wind correction angle.
PA.VI.A.K6	6. Checkpoint selection.
PA.VI.A.K7	7. Planned versus actual flight plan calculations and required corrections.
PA.VI.A.K8	8. Topography.
PA.VI.A.K9	9. Plotting a course.
PA.VI.A.K10	10. Magnetic compass errors.
PA.VI.A.K11	11. Route selection.
PA.VI.A.K12	12. Altitude selection.
PA.VI.A.K13	13. Power setting selection.
Risk Management	The applicant demonstrates the ability to identify, assess and mitigate risks, encompassing:
PA.VI.A.R1	1. Failure to select an altitude that will maintain the minimally required obstacle clearance.
PA.VI.A.R2	2. Failure to identify the correct landmarks or checkpoints.
PA.VI.A.R3	3. Bracketing strategy.
PA.VI.A.R4	4. Failure to select a suitable alternate.
PA.VI.A.R5	5. Failure to maintain situational awareness.
PA.VI.A.R6	6. Task management.
PA.VI.A.R7	7. Fuel consumption that is different than planned.
PA.VI.A.R8	8. Having to divert to an alternate airport.
PA.VI.A.R9	9. Preflight pilot/operation risk assessment and planning.
PA.VI.A.R10	10. Actual groundspeed and time en route that are different than planned.
Skills	The applicant demonstrates the ability to:
PA.VI.A.S1	1. Prepare a document or electronic equivalent to be used in flight for comparison with planned fuel consumption and times over waypoints while dead reckoning.
PA.VI.A.S2	2. Follow the preplanned course by reference to landmarks.
PA.VI.A.S3	3. Identify landmarks by relating surface features to chart symbols.
PA.VI.A.S4	4. Navigate by means of pre-computed headings, groundspeeds, and elapsed time.
PA.VI.A.S5	5. Demonstrate use of magnetic direction indicator in navigation, to include turns to headings.
PA.VI.A.S6	6. Correct for and record the differences between preflight groundspeed, fuel consumption, and heading calculations and those determined en route.
PA.VI.A.S7	7. Verify the airplane's position within 3 nautical miles of the flight planned route.
PA.VI.A.S8	8. Arrive at the en route checkpoints within 5 minutes of the initial or revised estimated time of arrival and provide a destination estimate.
PA.VI.A.S9	9. Maintain the selected altitude, ±200 feet and headings, ±15°.

A. General Information

1. The objective of this task is for you to demonstrate your knowledge, risk management, and skills related to pilotage and dead reckoning.

2. See *Pilot Handbook* for the following:

   a. Study Unit 9, "Navigation: Charts, Publications, Flight Computers," for a discussion on how to use a manual flight computer.

   b. Study Unit 11, "Cross-Country Flight Planning," for an example of a standard navigation log and an abbreviated navigation log that will be used and filled out during your cross-country flight.

35.1 KNOWLEDGE

A. Task Objectives

1. **The applicant demonstrates understanding of pilotage and dead reckoning.**

   a. **Pilotage** is the action of flying cross-country using only a sectional chart to fly from one visible landmark to another.

      1) Pilotage is accomplished by selecting two landmarks on your desired course and then maneuvering your airplane so that the two landmarks are kept aligned over the nose of your airplane.

         a) Before the first of the two landmarks is reached, another more distant landmark should be selected and a second course steered.

         b) When you notice wind drift away from your course, an adequate crab heading must be applied to maintain the desired ground track.

      2) Pilotage can also be used by flying over, left/right, or between two checkpoints to fly a straight line.

      3) Pilotage becomes difficult in areas lacking prominent landmarks or under conditions of low visibility.

      4) During your flight, you will use pilotage in conjunction with dead reckoning to verify your calculations and keep track of your position.

   b. **Dead reckoning** is the navigation of your airplane solely by means of computations based on true airspeed, course, heading, wind direction and speed, groundspeed, and elapsed time.

      1) Simply, dead reckoning is a system of determining where the airplane should be on the basis of where it has been. Literally, it is deduced reckoning, which is where the term originated, i.e., ded. or "dead" reckoning.

      2) A good knowledge of the principles of dead reckoning will assist you in determining your position after having become disoriented or confused.

         a) By using information from the part of the flight already completed, it is possible to restrict your search for identifiable landmarks to a limited area to verify calculations and to locate yourself.

2.   **The applicant demonstrates understanding of determining heading, speed, and course.**

   a.   **Magnetic Course**

   1)   Because magnetic north and true north are not equal, pilots have to account for the differences between what the compass reads and the true course (TC) of the flight path. Therefore, magnetic course (MC) takes into account the difference between true north and magnetic north.

   2)   To determine the MC from one airport to another, correct the TC only for magnetic variation; i.e., make no allowance for wind correction angle.

   a)   Determine the TC by placing the straight edge of a navigational plotter or protractor along the route, with the hole in the plotter on the intersection of the route and a meridian, or line of longitude (the vertical line with little crosslines).

   i)   The TC is measured by the numbers on the protractor portion of the plotter (semi-circle) at the meridian.

   ii)   Note that up to four numbers (90° apart) are provided on the plotter. You must determine which is the direction of the flight, using a common sense approximation of your direction.

   b)   Alternatively, you can use a line of latitude (horizontal line with little crosslines) if your course is in a north or south direction.

   i)   This is why there are four numbers on the plotter. You may be using either a meridian or line of latitude to measure your course and be going in either direction along the course line.

   c)   Determine the MC by adjusting the TC for magnetic variation (angle between true north and magnetic north).

   i)   On sectional charts, a long dashed line provides the number of degrees of magnetic variation. The variation is either east or west and is signified by "E" or "W," e.g., 3°E or 5°W.

   ii)   If the variation is east, subtract; if west, add (memory aid: east is least and west is best). This is from TC to MC.

   3)   If your course is to or from a VOR, use the compass rose to determine the MC; i.e., no adjustment is needed from TC to MC.

   a)   Compass roses have about a 3-in. diameter on sectional charts.

   b)   Every 30° is labeled, as well as marked with an arrow inside the rose pointing out.

   c)   Use the reciprocal to radials when flying toward the VOR.

   i)   EXAMPLE: If your course is toward an airport on the 180° radial rather than from the airport, your MC is 360°, not 180°.

b. **Magnetic Heading**

1) Magnetic heading (MH) is a step beyond the computation of MC because MH is MC adjusted for wind correction and your aircraft's specific compass deviation due to your avionics.

2) Simply put, to compute MH from MC, you must adjust for the wind and compass error (deviation).

3) There are two methods to compute MH. We suggest that you use the most efficient method, but if you already have your magnetic course or an FAA problem provides magnetic course, then you should use the longer method.

   a) In a nutshell, Gleim's reasoning is as follows: in the left column of the table below, many pilots forget to correct for the magnetic variation of wind because they already corrected for magnetic variation when they found magnetic course. This method makes you correct for magnetic variation twice. Therefore, Gleim believes you should use the most efficient method in the right column of the table below for your actual flight planning and everyday use.

If MC Already Determined	Most Efficient Method
Determine True Course +/- Add/Subtract Magnetic Variation = Magnetic Course	Determine True Course Determine Wind Correction (E6B) +/- Add/Subtract Wind Correction Angle (WCA) +/- Add/Subtract Magnetic Variation (same for course and wind)
+/- Add/Subtract Magnetic Variation to Wind Determine Wind Correction (E6B) +/- Add/Subtract Wind Correction Angle (WCA) +/- Add/Subtract Deviation of Compass Error = Magnetic Heading	+/- Add/Subtract Deviation of Compass Error = Magnetic Heading

4) The following directions will explain each of the components above using the most efficient method:

   a) <u>Determine Wind Correction:</u> To compute wind effect, use the wind side of the computer.

      i) Align the true wind direction on the inner scale under the true index (top of the computer).

      ii) Slide the grid through the computer until the grommet (the hole in the center) is on the 100-kt. wind line. Measure up the vertical line the amount of wind speed in knots and put a pencil mark on the plastic.

      iii) Rotate the inner scale so the TC lies under the true index.

      iv) Slide the grid so that your pencil dot is superimposed over the true airspeed (TAS). The location of the grommet will indicate the groundspeed. This is needed for time en route calculations.

      v) The pencil mark will indicate the wind correction angle (WCA). If to the left, it is a negative wind correction. If to the right, it is a positive wind correction.

   b) <u>WCA:</u> Adjust the TC for the wind correction.

      i) Add the number of degrees the pencil mark is to the right of the centerline or subtract the number of degrees to the left.

   c) <u>Magnetic Variation:</u> Now, further adjust the TC for magnetic variation.

      i) Review item a. for how to determine magnetic variation.

d) <u>Compass Error:</u> Add/subtract deviation for your plane's specific compass error. This is found on the compass deviation card inside your cockpit.

   i) Add or subtract the number of degrees from the calculation to arrive at magnetic heading.

If MC Already Determined

- Wind direction is normally given in true, not magnetic, direction. Thus, you must first adjust the wind direction from true to magnetic.
- Find the magnetic variation on the navigation chart. As with course corrections, add westerly variation and subtract easterly variation.
- See the discussion of magnetic variation under item a.2)c).
- EXAMPLE: Given wind of 330° and a 20°E variation, the magnetic direction of the wind is 310° (330° − 20°).
- When using magnetic wind direction, you should use MC in items b.4)a)iii) and b.4)b). Also, skip item b.4)c) because variation is already applied.

---

5) On your E6B, you will find directions such as

   a) Set Wind Direction opposite True Index.
   b) Mark Wind Dot up from Grommet.
   c) Place TC under True Index.
   d) Slide TAS under Wind Dot.
   e) Read GS under Grommet.
   f) Read WCA under Wind Dot.
   g) Complete the problem by use of the formulas.

6) The formulas given are

   TH = TC ± WCA (wind correction angle)
   MH = TH ± magnetic variation (E−, W+)
   CH = MH ± compass deviation

7) These E6B instructions should also get you to the same answer as our more efficient method.

8) If the FAA provides no information in a question on compass error, assume the aircraft does not have any. It is one less calculation you need to make.

3. **The applicant demonstrates understanding of estimating time, speed, and distance.**

   a. Speed, distance, and time are three interrelated elements. With any two of these elements, you can compute the third (missing) element.

   1) The computations are

      a) *Speed = Distance ÷ Time*
      b) *Distance = Speed × Time*
      c) *Time = Distance ÷ Speed*

   2) You can use your flight computer to make the above computations.

      a) Note that, in any problem, both the speed and distance must be in either SM or NM.

b. **Determining Time Required**

1) If you know the groundspeed and the distance, you can calculate the time. Time equals distance divided by groundspeed.

2) EXAMPLE: How much time will it take to fly 120 NM at a groundspeed of 100 kt.?

    a) Rotate the inner scale so the Index is opposite 100 kt., or "10," on the outer scale, as shown in the figure below.

    b) Locate 120 NM, or "12," on the outer scale.

    c) Under 120 on the outer scale read 72 min. on the inner scale or 1:12 on the hour scale.

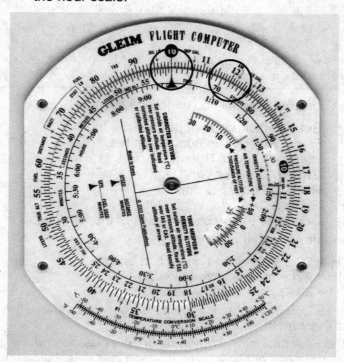

c. **Determining Groundspeed**

1) If you know the time and distance, you can determine the groundspeed. Groundspeed equals distance divided by time.

2) EXAMPLE: What is the groundspeed if the airplane takes 7 min. to go 10.5 NM?

    a) Rotate the inner scale so that 10.5 on the outer scale is opposite 7 on the inner scale, as shown in the figure on the next page.

    b) Locate the Index on the inner scale and read a groundspeed of 90 kt. on the outer scale.

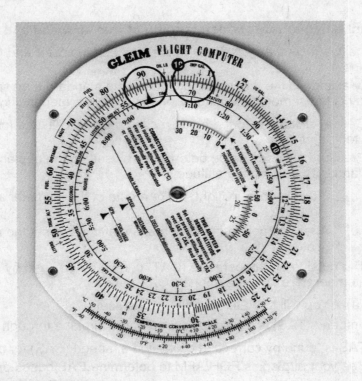

d. **Determining Distance**

1) If you know groundspeed and time, you can determine the distance. Distance equals groundspeed multiplied by time.

2) EXAMPLE: How far will the airplane fly in 8 min. at a groundspeed of 90 kt.?

   a) Rotate the inner scale so the Index is opposite 90, as shown in the figure below.

   b) Locate 8 on the inner scale.

   c) Opposite 8 on the inner scale is 12 NM on the outer scale.

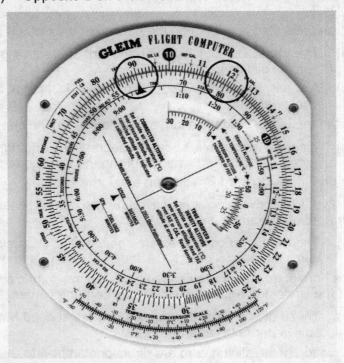

4. **The applicant demonstrates understanding of true airspeed and density altitude.**

    a. Air density affects the indications of the airspeed indicator and the performance of the airplane.

    b. Density altitude is the theoretical altitude in the standard atmosphere where the density is the same as the actual density you are experiencing in flight.

        1) Density altitude is found by correcting pressure altitude for nonstandard temperature.

        2) Pressure altitude can be determined by setting the airplane's altimeter to 29.92 and then reading the altitude.

            a) If this is done in flight, make a note of the altimeter setting before turning it to 29.92.

            b) After you determine the pressure altitude, reset the altimeter to the current setting.

        3) The outside air temperature (OAT) can be determined by reading the current temperature on the airplane's OAT gauge.

            a) You will need to use the Celsius scale.

    c. True airspeed (TAS) is the actual speed of the airplane through the air.

        1) TAS is found by correcting calibrated airspeed (CAS) for density altitude.

        2) See your airplane's POH/AFM to determine CAS based on indicated airspeed.

            a) Generally, there is little error at cruise speeds; i.e., CAS equals indicated airspeed (IAS).

            b) Thus, as a practical matter, you may usually use IAS rather than CAS to determine true airspeed.

5. **The applicant demonstrates understanding of wind correction angle.**

    a. The wind side of the flight computer allows you to determine the effect of wind on the airplane in terms of heading and groundspeed.

    b. The wind side consists of a rotating plotting transparency attached to a frame and a sliding card.

        1) A compass rose is printed on the outside of the plotting transparency.

            a) The transparency allows you to mark on it with a pencil and to see the grid on the sliding card.

            b) A small metal rivet called a grommet is located at the center of the plotting transparency.

        2) At the top of the frame is a large triangle (▽) in the center called the True Index.

            a) A correction scale is shown in degrees left and right of the True Index. This scale can be used when applying the wind correction angle (WCA).

    c. The grid on the sliding card is a section of a large circle.

        1) The vertical converging lines, called wind correction lines, represent degrees left or right of the center line.

            a) The wind correction lines are spaced at 2° intervals between the horizontal arcs labeled "30" to "150," and at 1° intervals above the "150" arc.

        2) The horizontal arcs, called speed arcs, are concentric circles around the center of the circle and represent a distance from the center.

            a) These arcs are used for speed and are spaced two units (usually knots or miles per hour) apart.

        3) At the top of the sliding card are directions on how to use the wind side of the flight computer to determine groundspeed and WCA.

6. **The applicant demonstrates understanding of checkpoint selection.**

   a. There is no set rule for selecting a landmark as a checkpoint. Every locality has its own peculiarities.

   b. As a general rule, do not place complete reliance on any single landmark.

   c. You should have a checkpoint within 5 NM of your departure airport that you can fly over to establish you on your desired course.

      1) If you depart from an airport where ATC provides radar vectors for traffic reasons, be sure to keep track of your position since ATC may inform you to "resume own navigation" at a point that is not on your course line.

   d. Subsequent checkpoints should be easy to see and identify and should be spaced roughly 10 NM apart along your proposed route of flight.

7. **The applicant demonstrates understanding of planned vs. actual flight plan calculations and required corrections.**

   a. Verify you are arriving at each checkpoint within the predetermined time and that you are on course.

      1) If your calculations are not correct as determined by arriving at a checkpoint earlier or later than expected, you can use the methods discussed in the previous section for estimating time and speed to make the necessary corrections.

      2) For example, knowing the actual time elapsed between two points and the distance between them will enable you to determine your actual groundspeed.

         a) Using the known groundspeed, you can recalculate the time it will take to reach subsequent checkpoints.

8. **The applicant demonstrates understanding of topography.**

   a. Ensure that you maintain an altitude appropriate for obstacle and/or terrain clearance as defined in the 14 CFRs.

      1) Within each quadrangle bounded by lines of longitude and latitude on the sectional chart are large, bold numbers that represent the maximum elevation figure (MEF).

         a) The MEF below is given in thousands and hundreds of feet MSL.

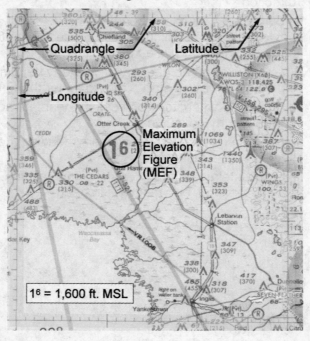

   b) The MEF is based on information available concerning the highest known feature in each quadrangle, including terrain and obstructions (trees, towers, antennas, etc.).

   c) Since the sectional chart is published once every 6 months, you must also check the Aeronautical Chart Bulletin in the Chart Supplement for major changes to the sectional chart (e.g., new obstructions).

9. **The applicant demonstrates understanding of plotting a course.**

   a. Use your plotter to determine the true course (TC), the total distance of your flight, and the distance between each checkpoint.

10. **The applicant demonstrates understanding of magnetic compass errors.**

   a. Errors in the magnetic compass are numerous, making straight flight and turns to headings difficult to accomplish, especially in turbulent air.

   b. Compass errors

   1) **Variation** is the angular difference between true and magnetic north.

      a) This difference varies around the earth and is indicated on charts.

   2) **Deviation** is the magnetic disturbance within your airplane that deflects the compass needles from alignment with magnetic north.

      a) Deviation varies with the electrical components in use, and the magnetism changes with jolts from hard landings and installation of additional radio equipment.

      b) Deviation is compensated for by adjustment of the N-S/E-W magnets, and the errors remaining are recorded on the compass card.

         i) To fly compass headings, you must refer to the compass correction card for corrected headings to steer.

   3) **Magnetic dip** is the tendency of the compass needles to point down as well as to the magnetic pole. The dip causes significant errors when the airplane is turning or accelerating. This error is the greatest at the poles and zero at the magnetic equator.

      a) If you are on a northerly heading and you start a turn to the east or west, the indication of the compass lags, or shows a turn in the opposite direction.

      b) If you are on a southerly heading and you start a turn toward the east or west, the compass indication precedes the turn, showing a greater amount of turn than is actually occurring.

      c) When you are on an easterly or westerly heading, the compass correctly indicates when you start a turn to either the north or the south.

      d) If you are on an easterly or westerly heading, acceleration results in a northerly turn indication.

      e) If you are on an easterly or westerly heading, deceleration results in a southerly turn indication.

      f) If you maintain a northerly or southerly heading, no error results from diving, climbing, or changing airspeed.

11. **The applicant demonstrates understanding of route selection.**

    a. Once you have your course line(s) drawn, survey where your flight will be taking you.

        1) Look for available alternate airports en route.

        2) Look at the type of terrain and obstructions, e.g., mountains, swamps, large bodies of water, that could be a factor if an off-airport landing became necessary.

            a) Mentally prepare for any type of emergency situation and the action to be taken during your flight.

        3) By knowing the highest terrain and obstructions, you will know the minimum safe altitude to meet the requirements of 14 CFR Part 91.

        4) You should check the course and areas on either side of your planned route to determine if any type of airspace along your route should concern you (e.g., restricted, prohibited, etc.) or if any airspace has special operational requirements (e.g., Class B, C, or D airspace).

        5) After you have looked at all of these aspects, you may choose an alternate route that offers fewer hazards and more safety options than your initial choice.

12. **The applicant demonstrates understanding of altitude selection.**

    a. 14 CFR 91.119 requires the following minimum altitudes except during takeoffs and landings:

        1) If an engine fails, an altitude allowing an emergency landing without undue hazards to persons or property on the ground

        2) Over any congested area of a city, town, or settlement, or over any open air assembly of persons, an altitude 1,000 ft. above the highest obstacle within a horizontal radius of 2,000 ft. of the airplane

        3) Over other than congested areas, an altitude of 500 ft. AGL except

            a) No closer than 500 ft. to any person, vessel, vehicle, or structure when over open water or sparsely populated areas

    b. You are requested to maintain a minimum altitude of 2,000 ft. AGL over the following:

        1) National parks, monuments, seashores, lakeshores, recreation areas, and scenic riverways administered by the National Park Service

        2) National wildlife refuges, big game refuges, and wildlife ranges administered by the U.S. Fish and Wildlife Service

        3) Wilderness and primitive areas administered by the U.S. Forest Service

    c. Ensure that you maintain an altitude that allows for the reception of any radio navigation facilities that you will be using.

    d. The most-favorable-winds altitude provides you with the highest groundspeed. This altitude is determined by comparing winds aloft at different altitudes, e.g., 3,000 ft., 6,000 ft., and 9,000 ft.

13. **The applicant demonstrates understanding of power setting selection.**

    a. Use the performance charts in your POH/AFM to determine takeoff distance, cruise performance (i.e., TAS and fuel consumption), and landing distance.

        1) As with all flights, be sure to calculate the weight and balance of your airplane as it will be when loaded for the flight.

            a) Check the weight and balance for takeoff, cruise, and landing to ensure the airplane's CG will remain in the envelope for the entire flight.

END OF KNOWLEDGE ELEMENT

35.2 RISK MANAGEMENT

A.   Task Objectives

1.   **The applicant demonstrates the ability to identify, assess, and mitigate risks encompassing failure to select an altitude that will maintain the minimally required obstacle clearance.**

   a.   For information on terrain/obstacle avoidance, including controlled flight into terrain (CFIT), see Study Unit 7, Subunit 3, beginning on page 62.

2.   **The applicant demonstrates the ability to identify, assess, and mitigate risks encompassing failure to identify the correct landmarks or checkpoints.**

   a.   Nobody plans to get lost, especially in an airplane, but almost all pilots eventually find themselves disoriented. It is critically important that you learn to recognize disorientation quickly and train yourself to methodically implement corrective action to become reoriented.

   b.   **Steps to Avoid Becoming Lost**

      1)   Always use a properly prepared navigation log on cross-country flights.
      2)   Plan ahead, know what your next landmark will be, and look for it.

         a)   Anticipate the indication of your radio navigation systems.
         b)   If you know what you expect to see, you will more quickly recognize an error caused by poor reception or improper tuning.

      3)   If your radio navigation systems or your visual observations of landmarks do not confirm your expectations, become attentive to the situation and take action.

   c.   The greatest hazard to a pilot who fails to arrive at a given checkpoint at a particular time is panic.

      1)   The natural reaction is to fly to where it is assumed the checkpoint is located.

         a)   On arriving at that point and not finding the checkpoint, the pilot usually assumes a second position, and then, panicked, will fly in another direction for some time.
         b)   As a result of this wandering, the pilot may have no idea where the airplane is located.

      2)   Generally, if planning is correct and the pilot uses basic dead reckoning until the ETA, the airplane is going to be within a reasonable distance of the planned checkpoint.

      3)   When you become lost, you should

         a)   Maintain your original heading and watch for landmarks.
         b)   Identify the nearest concentration of prominent landmarks.

            i)   If you see an unmistakable landmark, fly to it, positively identify it on your sectional chart, and proceed from there.

         c)   Use all available radio navigation systems/facilities and/or ask for help from any ATC facility.
         d)   Plan a precautionary landing if weather conditions get worse and/or your airplane is about to run out of fuel.

d.   As soon as you begin to wonder where you are, remember the point at which you last were confident of your location and select the best course of action.

1)   Watch your heading. Know what it is and keep it constant.

   a)   Do not panic. You are not "lost" yet.

2)   Recompute your expected radio navigation indications and visual landmarks.

   a)   Reconfirm your heading (compass and heading indicator should agree).
   b)   Confirm correct radio frequencies and settings.
   c)   Review your sectional chart, noting last confirmed landmark.

3)   Attempt to reconfirm present position.

4)   Use all available means to determine your present location, including asking for assistance.

5)   The best course of action will depend on factors such as ceiling, visibility, hours of daylight remaining, fuel remaining, etc.

   a)   Given the current circumstances, you will have to decide the best course of action.

   b)   Understand and respect your own and your airplane's limitations.

e.   When unsure of your position, you should continue to fly the original heading and watch for recognizable landmarks while rechecking the calculated position.

1)   A climb to a higher altitude may assist you in locating more landmarks.

2)   By plotting the estimated distance and compass direction flown from your last noted checkpoint as though there was no wind, you can determine a point that will be the center of a circle. Your airplane's position should be found within that circle.

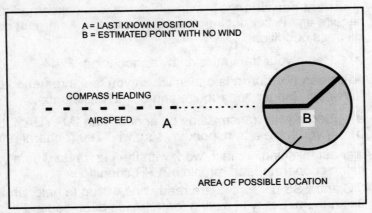

A = LAST KNOWN POSITION
B = ESTIMATED POINT WITH NO WIND

COMPASS HEADING
AIRSPEED   A   B

AREA OF POSSIBLE LOCATION

   a)   If you are certain the wind is no more than 30 kt. and it has been less than 30 min. since the last known checkpoint was crossed, the radius of the circle should be approximately 15 NM.

   b)   Continue straight ahead and check the landmarks within this circle.

      i)   The most likely position will be downwind from your desired course.

f.   If the above procedure fails to identify your position, you should change course toward the nearest prominent landmark or concentration of prominent landmarks shown on your chart.

1)   If you have a prominent landmark in sight, such as a coastline, interstate highway, or a major river, proceed toward it.

2)   When a landmark is recognized or a probable fix obtained, you should at first use the information both cautiously and profitably.

   a)   No abrupt change in course should be made until a second or third landmark is positively identified to corroborate the first.

g.   Use all available navigation systems (VOR, GPS) to locate your position.

1)   Use at least two VOR facilities to find the radial or bearing from the station that you are located on. Plot these lines on your chart. The point where they intersect is your position.

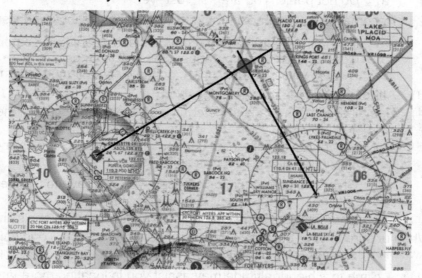

2)   Most GPS units have a function that will display the nearest airport and give its bearing and distance.

h.   You can obtain assistance by contacting an ATC or FSS facility or using the emergency frequency of 121.5 MHz if you encounter a distress or urgent condition.

1)   An **urgent condition** is one in which you are concerned about safety and require timely but not immediate assistance. An urgent condition is a potential distress condition.

a)   Begin your transmission by announcing "PAN-PAN" three times.

2)   A **distress condition** is one in which you feel threatened by serious and/or imminent danger and require immediate assistance.

a)   Begin your transmission by announcing "MAYDAY" three times.
b)   If you have a transponder, squawk 7700 (general emergency).

3)   After establishing contact, work with the person to whom you are talking. Remain calm, cooperate, and remain in VFR conditions.

4)   ATC and FSS personnel are ready and willing to help, and there is no penalty for using them. Delay in asking for help has often caused accidents.

i.   Plan a precautionary landing if deteriorating weather and/or fuel exhaustion is imminent.

1)   If these conditions and others (e.g., darkness approaching) threaten, it is recommended that you make a precautionary landing while adequate visibility, fuel, and daylight are still available.

2)   It is most desirable to land at an airport, but if one cannot be found, a suitable field may be used.

a)   Prior to an off-airport landing, you should first survey the area for obstructions or other hazards.

3. **The applicant demonstrates the ability to identify, assess, and mitigate risks encompassing bracketing strategy.**

   a. Bracketing as it relates to pilotage and dead reckoning is the process of selecting features/checkpoints that make useful boundaries or brackets on each side of the course, such as highways, rivers, railroads, and mountains.

   b. A pilot can keep from drifting too far off course by referring to, and not crossing, the selected brackets.

   c. Never place complete reliance on any single checkpoint.

   d. Choose ample checkpoints. If one is missed, look for the next one while maintaining the heading.

4. **The applicant demonstrates the ability to identify, assess, and mitigate risks encompassing failure to select a suitable alternate.**

   a. Once you have your course line(s) drawn, survey where your flight will be taking you and look for available alternate airports en route.

      1) Look at the type of terrain, e.g., mountains, swamps, large bodies of water, that would have an impact if an off-airport landing became necessary.

      2) Mentally prepare for any type of emergency situation and the action to be taken during your flight.

   b. Additional details on selecting an alternate are presented in Study Unit 37, "Diversion."

5. **The applicant demonstrates the ability to identify, assess, and mitigate risks encompassing failure to maintain situational awareness.**

   a. For information on situational awareness, see Study Unit 7, Subunit 1, beginning on page 57.

6. **The applicant demonstrates the ability to identify, assess, and mitigate risks encompassing task management.**

   a. For information on task management, see Study Unit 6, Subunit 1, beginning on page 49.

7. **The applicant demonstrates the ability to identify, assess, and mitigate risks encompassing fuel consumption that is different than planned.**

   a. While en route, you will maintain your heading and keep track of your time between checkpoints.

      1) During this time, you will be able to compute your actual elapsed time, groundspeed, and fuel consumption.

      2) Correct any variances on your navigation log to ensure your actual vs. planned fuel consumption does not create undue hazards.

8. **The applicant demonstrates the ability to identify, assess, and mitigate risks encompassing having to divert to an alternate airport.**

   a. Among the aeronautical skills that you must develop is the ability to plot courses in flight to alternate destinations when continuation of the flight to the original destination is impracticable.

      1) Reasons include

         a) Low fuel
         b) Bad weather
         c) Pilot or passenger fatigue, illness, etc.
         d) Airplane system or equipment malfunction
         e) Any other reason that causes you to decide to divert to an alternate airport

      2) The diversion may be accomplished by means of pilotage, dead reckoning, and/or navigation systems.

b. Most diversions to alternates are weather related because VFR cross-country flight is so susceptible to weather changes. Learn to recognize adverse weather conditions.

c. Diversion is easiest when you know your present location and are aware of alternate airports.

d. Divert on a TIMELY basis. The longer you wait, the fewer advantages or benefits there are to making the diversion.

e. For more information on diverting to an alternate airport, see Study Unit 37, "Diversion."

9. **The applicant demonstrates the ability to identify, assess, and mitigate risks encompassing preflight pilot/operation risk assessment and planning.**

a. The four risk elements in any flight are the pilot, aircraft, environment, and external pressures of any given aviation situation.

   1) Each of these items, including tools for evaluating these risks, is discussed in Study Unit 5, Subunits 1-2.

b. You must explain to the evaluator what risks are associated with each element in a given scenario and how you evaluated those risks.

   1) EXAMPLE: You explain that, due to pilot-related risk factors, you will not conduct operations in certain inherently risky environmental conditions due to lack of experience personally and with the aircraft in such circumstances. You elect to set personal minimums so that no external pressures (such as a sick relative, business need, etc.) can force you into unsafe situations.

10. **The applicant demonstrates the ability to identify, assess, and mitigate risks encompassing actual groundspeed and time en route that are different than planned.**

a. During your cross-country preflight planning, you would have used all of the available information (e.g., winds aloft forecast, performance charts) to determine a heading, groundspeed, and elapsed time from your departure point to your destination.

b. While en route, you will maintain your heading and keep track of your time between checkpoints.

   1) During this time, you will be able to compute your actual elapsed time, groundspeed, and fuel consumption.

   2) Explain to the evaluator that proper planning and corrections made to your navigation log along with route of flight contributes to situational awareness, thus mitigating risks.

END OF RISK MANAGEMENT ELEMENT

35.3 SKILLS

A. Task Objectives

1. **The applicant demonstrates the ability to prepare a document or electronic equivalent to be used in flight for comparison with planned fuel consumption and times over waypoints while dead reckoning.**

   a. You will not be required to fly an entire cross-country flight. Instead, your evaluator will have you depart on the cross-country flight that you planned during the oral portion and evaluate your ability to navigate by having you fly to the first several checkpoints.

2. **The applicant demonstrates the ability to follow the preplanned course by reference to landmarks.**

   a. Departure

   1) Just before taxiing onto the runway, write down the takeoff time on your navigation log.

   2) Taxi onto the runway, align the airplane with the centerline, and come to a stop. Check the magnetic compass for a correct heading indication and reset the heading indicator to the compass.

   3) After takeoff, there are two methods for establishing yourself on course.

   a) After departing the traffic pattern, you can continue the climb to your planned cruising altitude and return to overfly the airport at least 500 ft. above the traffic pattern altitude.

   i) Once over the airport, turn to your desired heading, look for your first checkpoint (landmark), and head toward it.

   ii) This method is acceptable at an airport without an operating control tower.

   iii) At an airport with an operating control tower, ATC would need to authorize this procedure.

   b) Another method is to select a prominent landmark within 5 NM of the airport.

   i) After takeoff, depart the traffic pattern and fly directly to the selected landmark. Once over the landmark, turn to your desired heading, locate your next checkpoint, and continue on course.

   b. En route

   1) When using your sectional chart, arrange the chart so that your drawn course line runs up the page.

   a) With this arrangement, what you see out the left/right side of the airplane should correspond with the left/right side of the course line.

   2) Once at your cruising altitude, allow your airplane to accelerate, and then set the power and lean the mixture for cruise.

   3) When appropriate, contact the FSS to open your flight plan.

   a) On your practical test, inform your evaluator that you would be opening your VFR flight plan.

   c. Arrival

   1) Plan ahead by listening to the ATIS or an automated weather observation station broadcast, or by obtaining airport advisories, as appropriate.

   2) If you are arriving at an unfamiliar airport, continuing to navigate by the selected landmarks to keep you on course will make it easier to locate the airport.

3.   **The applicant demonstrates the ability to identify landmarks by relating surface features to chart symbols.**

   a.   The topographical information presented on sectional charts portrays surface elevation levels (contours and elevation tinting) and a great number of visual landmarks used for VFR flight.

   1)   These include airports, cities or towns, rivers and lakes, roads, railroads, and other distinctive landmarks.

   2)   Throughout your training, and especially on your cross-country flights, you should have been using your chart to identify landmarks and cross-checking with other landmarks nearby.

4.   **The applicant demonstrates the ability to navigate by means of precomputed headings, groundspeeds, and elapsed time.**

   a.   This objective refers to navigation by dead reckoning.

   b.   During your cross-country preflight planning, you would have used all of the available information (e.g., winds aloft forecast, performance charts) to determine a heading, groundspeed, and elapsed time from your departure point to your destination.

   c.   While en route, you will maintain your heading and keep track of your time between checkpoints.

   1)   During this time, you will be able to compute your actual elapsed time, groundspeed, and fuel consumption.

   2)   From this information, you should recompute your estimated time en route (ETE) to your next checkpoint/destination and deduce when you will be there.

   3)   These calculations are made by using your flight computer.

   d.   Remember to determine where your airplane should be based on where it has been.

5.   **The applicant demonstrates the ability to demonstrate use of magnetic direction indicator in navigation, to include turns to headings.**

   a.   The magnetic compass (the only direction-seeking instrument in the airplane) is used primarily to set the heading indicator prior to flight and to verify its continued accuracy during flight.

   b.   The magnetic compass is important as a standby directional indicator in the event the heading indicator fails.

   1)   With an angle of bank between 15° and 18° (i.e., a standard rate turn – as indicated by the turn coordinator or digital display), the amount of lead or lag to be used when turning to northerly or southerly headings varies with, and is equal to, the latitude of the locality over which the turn is being made.

   a)   When turning to a heading of north, the lead for rollout must include the number of degrees of your latitude, plus your normal lead used in your turn recovery.

   b)   During a turn to a southerly heading, maintain the turn until the compass passes south the number of degrees of your latitude, minus your normal rollout lead.

   c)   When turning to a heading of east or west, use a normal rollout lead.

   d)   For other than cardinal headings, apply proportionally less correction than used for north or south rollouts.

   2)   Timed turns to specified compass headings will assist you in heading changes with the heading indicator inoperative.

   a)   In a timed turn, a clock and the turn coordinator are used to change the heading by a certain number of degrees in a given time.

   i)   Using a standard-rate turn (3° per second), an airplane turns 45° in 15 sec.

          ii)   Using a half-standard-rate turn (1.5° per second), the airplane turns 45° in 30 sec.

          iii) Times for various heading changes (at a standard rate) are as follows:

- 360° = 2 min.
- 180° = 1 min.
- 90° = 30 sec.
- 45° = 15 sec.
- 30° = 10 sec.
- 10° = approximately 3 sec.

          iv) Begin the rollout when the computed number of seconds has elapsed.

     b)   Use the magnetic compass at the completion of the turn to check turn accuracy, taking compass deviation errors into consideration.

6. **The applicant demonstrates the ability to correct for and record differences between preflight groundspeed, fuel consumption, and heading calculations and those determined en route.**

    a.   You must use and complete a navigation log when conducting the cross-country flight during your practical test.

    b.   It is recommended that you use a navigation log for all of your cross-country flights.

7. **The applicant demonstrates the ability to verify your airplane's position within 3 nautical miles of the flight planned route.**

    a.   By constantly dividing your attention among looking for other traffic, performing cockpit procedures, and navigating, you should have no problem in maintaining your route within 2 NM.

       1)   Always be aware of where you have been and where you are going. Use landmarks all around you to help maintain your planned route.

8. **The applicant demonstrates the ability to arrive at the en route checkpoints within 5 minutes of the initial or revised estimated time of arrival and provide a destination estimate.**

    a.   Once en route, you must mark down the time over each checkpoint.

    b.   Since you already know the distance between the checkpoints, you can now use your flight computer to determine your actual groundspeed.

    c.   Using the new groundspeed, you now need to revise your ETA to your next checkpoint and destination. Keep your evaluator informed of these revised times.

9. **The applicant demonstrates the ability to maintain the selected altitude, ±200 feet and headings, ±15°.**

    a.   While conducting your cross-country flight, you are required to maintain your selected cruising altitude, ±100 ft.

       1)   Remember to divide your attention among all of your duties, but your primary duty is to maintain control of your airplane.

       2)   Some pilots become so involved in looking at their charts, navigation log, and flight computer that they forget to look up, and when they do, they discover that the airplane is in an unusual flight attitude.

          a)   Aviate first; then navigate.

    b.   Make the needed adjustments to the heading to maintain your selected route, and maintain that heading. Tell your evaluator when you are adjusting your heading.

END OF SKILLS ELEMENT

35.4 COMMON ERRORS

A.   Common Errors using Pilotage and Dead Reckoning

    1.   **Poorly selected landmarks for planned checkpoints**

        a.   A road diagonally crossing the flight path is a poor choice.

    2.   **Poor division of attention**

        a.   You must divide your attention among flying your airplane, looking for traffic, identifying checkpoints, and working the flight computer.

            1)   Dividing your attention is especially difficult when you are asked to alter your route.

        b.   FLY YOUR AIRPLANE FIRST.

    3.   **Improper use of the magnetic compass to maintain a heading or make turns in flight**

        a.   Reference this task discussion to better understand magnetic compass errors and how to compensate for them in flight.

        b.   Using timed turns is often a more intuitive turning method, and you can use the magnetic compass to validate your new heading once you level out.

END OF COMMON ERRORS

STUDY UNIT THIRTY-SIX
NAVIGATION SYSTEMS AND RADAR SERVICES

Task	Task B. Navigation Systems and Radar Services
References	FAA-H-8083-2, FAA-H-8083-3, FAA-H-8083-6, FAA-H-8083-25; Navigation Equipment Manual; AIM
Objective	To determine that the applicant exhibits satisfactory knowledge, risk management, and skills associated with navigation systems and radar services.
Knowledge	The applicant demonstrates understanding of:
PA.VI.B.K1	1. Ground-based navigation (orientation, course determination, equipment, tests and regulations).
PA.VI.B.K2	2. Satellite-based navigation (e.g., equipment, regulations, authorized use of databases, and Receiver Autonomous Integrity Monitoring (RAIM)).
PA.VI.B.K3	3. Radar assistance to VFR aircraft (e.g., operations, equipment, available services, traffic advisories).
PA.VI.B.K4	4. Transponder (Mode(s) A, C, and S).
Risk Management	The applicant demonstrates the ability to identify, assess and mitigate risks, encompassing:
PA.VI.B.R1	1. Failure to manage automated navigation and autoflight systems.
PA.VI.B.R2	2. Task management.
PA.VI.B.R3	3. Failure to maintain situational awareness.
PA.VI.B.R4	4. Limitations of the navigation system in use.
PA.VI.B.R5	5. Automation distractions.
Skills	The applicant demonstrates the ability to:
PA.VI.B.S1	1. Use an installed electronic navigation system.
PA.VI.B.S2	2. Locate the airplane's position using the navigation system.
PA.VI.B.S3	3. Intercept and track a given course, radial, or bearing, as appropriate.
PA.VI.B.S4	4. Recognize and describe the indication of station passage, if appropriate.
PA.VI.B.S5	5. Recognize signal loss and take appropriate action.
PA.VI.B.S6	6. Use proper communication procedures when utilizing radar services.
PA.VI.B.S7	7. Maintain the appropriate altitude, ±200 feet and headings ±15° or as recommended by aircraft manufacturer to a safe maneuvering altitude.

A. General Information

1. The objective of this task is for you to demonstrate your knowledge, risk management, and skills related to navigation systems and radar services.

2. Radio navigation is a means of navigation by using the properties of radio waves.

    a. This is achieved by a combination of ground (or satellite) and airborne equipment, by means of which the ground facilities (or satellites) transmit signals to airborne equipment.

        1) You then determine and control ground track on the basis of the navigation instrument indications.

3. ATC radar facilities provide a variety of services to participating VFR aircraft on a workload-permitting basis.

    a. To participate, you must be able to communicate with ATC, be within radar coverage, and be radar identified by the controller.

    b. Among the services provided are

        1) VFR radar traffic advisory service (commonly known as flight following)
        2) Terminal radar programs
        3) Radar assistance to lost aircraft

4.   See *Pilot Handbook* for the following:

   a.   Study Unit 3, "Airports, Air Traffic Control, and Airspace," for a discussion on ATC radar, transponder operation, and radar services available to VFR aircraft

   b.   Study Unit 10, "Navigation Systems," for a discussion on various navigation systems, such as VOR and GPS

36.1 KNOWLEDGE

A.   Task Objectives

   1.   **The applicant demonstrates understanding of ground-based navigation (orientation, course determination, equipment, tests and regulations).**

      a.   The VOR is a very high frequency (VHF) radio transmitting ground station. VORs are the most common type of ground-based navigation system.

         1)   The VOR transmits two signals -- an omnidirectional signal and a rotating signal.

            a)   The VOR receiver in your airplane times the interval between reception of the omnidirectional pulse and the rotating signal.

               i)   The receiver converts this time interval into degrees as your magnetic bearing to or from the station.

         2)   In essence then, the VOR can be thought of as projecting 360 signals (or **radials**) out in all directions from the station.

         3)   The VOR ground station is a small, low building topped with a flat white disk upon which are located the antennas and a fiberglass antenna shelter. It has the appearance of an inverted ice cream cone about 30 ft. in height.

            a)   VOR ground stations transmit within a VHF band of 108.00 to 117.95 MHz.

               i)   Since VHF signals are subject to line-of-sight restrictions, the reception range varies proportionally to the altitude of the receiving equipment.

         4)   For the purpose of this discussion, the term VOR will be used to include the following types of ground stations:

            a)   **VOR** provides azimuth (i.e., magnetic course) information.

b) **VORTAC** (VOR/tactical air navigation) provides azimuth in addition to range information from the tactical air navigation (TACAN) component.

   i) If your airplane is equipped with distance-measuring equipment (DME), your distance from the station in nautical miles (NM) will be displayed on the instrument.

   ii) TACAN is used by some military aircraft.

c) **VOR/DME** provides azimuth and range information similar to the VORTAC, but does not have the TACAN component.

b. The VOR equipment in your airplane includes an antenna, a receiver with a tuning device, and a VOR navigation instrument.

   1) The VOR navigation instrument consists of

      a) An **omnibearing selector (OBS)**, sometimes referred to as the course selector

         i) By turning the OBS knob (lower left of the diagram below), the desired course is selected. In the same diagram, the course is shown under the index at the top of the instrument, i.e., 360°.

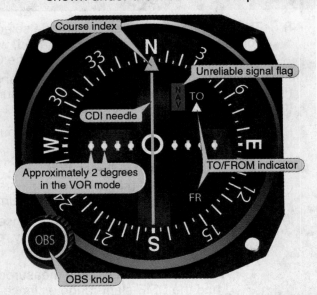

      b) A **course deviation indicator (CDI)**, referred to as the needle

         i) The CDI needle is hinged to move laterally across the face of the instrument.

         ii) It indicates the position of the selected course relative to your airplane.

         iii) The CDI needle centers when your airplane is on the selected radial, as shown in the diagram above.

      c) A **TO/FROM indicator**, also called a sense indicator or ambiguity indicator

         i) The TO/FROM indicator shows whether the selected course will take your airplane TO or FROM the station.

            • It does not indicate the airplane's heading.

            • In the diagram above, the selected course of 360° will take the airplane TO the station.

c.   Distance-Measuring Equipment (DME)

    1)   VORTAC and VOR/DME ground stations provide distance information to those airplanes equipped with DME.

        a)   DME operates on a UHF band of 962 to 1213 MHz, and, like the VOR signal, it is subject to line-of-sight restrictions.

        b)   To use DME, select the VORTAC or VOR/DME frequency band as you do with the VOR. The DME will then be tuned to the correct UHF band. This is called a **paired frequency**.

        c)   The DME in the airplane includes a transceiver and a small shark fin-type antenna. The DME display is on the face of the transceiver and may be part of the VOR receiver or a separate unit, as shown below.

           i)   The DME shown above has a mode selector. In the FREQ mode, distance and frequency are displayed, while distance, groundspeed, and time-to-station are displayed in the GS/T mode.

        d)   In the operation of DME, your airplane first transmits a signal (interrogation) to the ground station. The ground station (transponder) then transmits a signal back to your airplane.

           i)   The DME in your airplane records the round-trip time of this signal exchange. From this it can compute

- Distance (NM) to the station
- Groundspeed (kt.) relative to the station
- Time (min.) to the station at the current groundspeed

           ii)   The mileage readout is the direct distance from the airplane to the DME ground facility. This is commonly referred to as **slant-range** distance.

- The difference between a measured distance on the surface and the DME slant-range distance is known as slant-range error.

  - Slant-range error is smallest at low altitude and long range.
  - This error is greatest when the airplane is at a high altitude close to or over the ground station, at which time the DME receiver will display altitude in NM above the station.
  - Slant-range error is negligible if the airplane is 1 NM or more from the ground facility for each 1,000 ft. of altitude above the elevation of the facility.

d. The **horizontal situation indicator (HSI)** is a more advanced VOR navigation device, but one that offers increased situation awareness to the pilot.

1) The HSI combines the magnetic compass with navigation signals and a glideslope, and it gives the pilot an indication of the location of the aircraft with relationship to the chosen course or radial.

a) In the figure below, the aircraft magnetic heading displayed on the compass card under the lubber line is 183°.

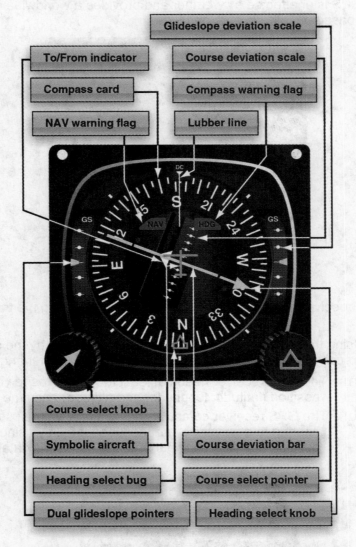

b) The course select pointer shown is set to 295°; the tail of the pointer indicates the reciprocal, 115°. The course deviation bar operates with a VOR/Localizer (VOR/LOC) or GPS navigation receiver to indicate left or right deviations from the course selected with the course select pointer; operating in the same manner, the angular movement of a conventional VOR/LOC needle indicates deviation from course.

2) In some installations, the compass card is controlled and realigned automatically; however, in others, the heading must be checked occasionally against the magnetic compass and reset by the pilot.

2.   **The applicant demonstrates understanding of satellite based navigation [e.g., equipment, regulations, authorized use of databases, and Receiver Autonomous Integrity Monitoring (RAIM)].**

   a.   GPS is a satellite-based radio navigational, positioning, and time transfer system operated by the Department of Defense (DOD).

   1)   GPS provides highly accurate position and velocity information and precise time on a continuous global basis to an unlimited number of users.

   2)   GPS is unaffected by weather and provides a worldwide common grid reference based on latitude and longitude.

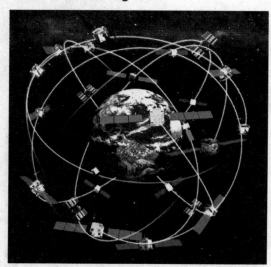

   b.   A GPS receiver measures distance from a satellite using the travel time of a radio signal.

   1)   Using the calculated position information supplied by the satellite, the GPS receiver mathematically determines its position by triangulation.

   a)   The GPS receiver needs at least four satellites to yield a three-dimensional position (latitude, longitude, and altitude) and time solution.

   b)   The GPS receiver computes navigational values, such as distance and bearing to a waypoint, groundspeed, etc., by using the airplane's known position and referencing that to the receiver's database.

   2)   The GPS receiver verifies the usability of the signals received from the satellites through **receiver autonomous integrity monitoring (RAIM)** to determine if a satellite is providing corrupted information.

   a)   At least one satellite, in addition to those required for navigation, must be in view for the receiver to perform the RAIM function.

   i)   Thus, RAIM needs a minimum of five satellites in view, or four satellites and a barometric altimeter setting (baro-aiding), to detect a problem.

        ii)   NOTE: Without RAIM capability, you have no assurance of the accuracy of the GPS position.

    b)   RAIM messages vary somewhat between receivers; however, generally there are two types:

        i)   One type indicates that not enough satellites are available to provide RAIM.

        ii)   The second type indicates that the RAIM has detected a potential error that exceeds the limit for the current phase of flight.

    3)   GPS receivers can be used for VFR navigation, and some properly certified GPS receivers can be used for IFR navigation.

  c.   GPS NOTAMs/Aeronautical Information

    1)   GPS satellite outages are issued as GPS NOTAMs, both domestically and internationally.

    2)   You may obtain GPS RAIM availability information by specifically requesting GPS aeronautical information from an FSS specialist.

        a)   GPS RAIM information can be obtained for a period of 1 hr. before to 1 hr. after your ETA (3 hr.) or during a 24-hr. period at a particular airport.

            i)   FSS specialists will provide the information for the 3-hr. period unless you specifically ask otherwise.

  d.   Conventional vs. GPS Navigation Data

    1)   There may be slight differences between the heading information portrayed on navigation charts and the GPS navigation display when flying along an airway.

    2)   All magnetic courses defined by a VOR radial are determined by the application of magnetic variation at the VOR.

        a)   However, GPS operations may use an algorithm to apply the magnetic variation at the current position, which may produce small differences in the displayed course.

        b)   Both operations should produce the same desired ground track.

  e.   Wide Area Augmentation System (WAAS)

    1)   WAAS is designed to improve the accuracy, integrity, and availability of GPS signals.

        a)   WAAS allows GPS to be used as the aviation navigation system from takeoff through Category I precision approaches.

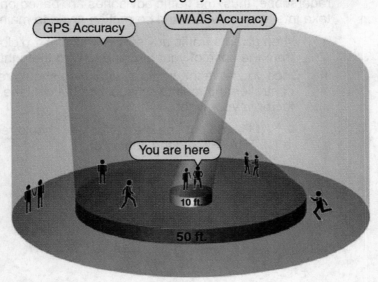

2)   In addition to providing the correction signal, WAAS provides an additional measurement to the aircraft receiver, improving the availability of GPS by providing, in effect, an additional GPS satellite in view.

a)   The integrity of GPS is improved through real-time monitoring, and the accuracy is improved by providing differential corrections to reduce errors.

3.   **The applicant demonstrates understanding of radar assistance to VFR aircraft (e.g., operations, equipment, available services, traffic advisories).**

a.   ATC radar facilities provide a variety of services to participating VFR aircraft on a workload-permitting basis.

1)   To participate, you must be able to communicate with ATC, be within radar coverage, and be radar identified by the controller.

2)   Among the services provided are

a)   VFR radar traffic advisory service (commonly known as flight following)
b)   Terminal radar programs
c)   Radar assistance to lost aircraft

b.   VFR Flight Following

1)   To obtain flight following, you should contact ATC on the appropriate frequency after leaving the traffic area of your departure airport.

a)   Use the departure frequency listed for the airport in the Chart Supplement.
b)   Inform ATC that you are requesting VFR flight following, and announce your departure point and destination.
c)   The controller will assign you a transponder code and ask your aircraft type and cruising altitude.

2)   When you are using flight following, ATC will advise you of any traffic that may be in a position to warrant your attention.

a)   Radar traffic information given to you will include the following:

i)   The traffic's position relative to yours in terms of the 12-hr. clock or distance and direction with respect to a fix
ii)   Distance from you in nautical miles (NM)
iii) Direction in which the target is heading
iv)   Type of aircraft and altitude, if known

b)   The controller can only observe your airplane's track (course) on the radarscope; thus, the traffic advisories are based on this, and you should take into account your wind correction angle to maintain track.

i)   When given a traffic advisory of traffic at 1 o'clock, you should look from the nose of your airplane toward the right for the traffic.
ii)   Once you have the traffic in sight, you should report this to the controller and maintain visual contact until the traffic is no longer a factor in your flight.

● If you do not see the traffic, you should report "NEGATIVE TRAFFIC" to the controller.

3) When receiving this service, you must monitor the assigned frequency at all times to preclude the controller's concern for radio failure or emergency assistance to aircraft under his or her control.

    a) This service does not include vectors (i.e., headings provided by ATC) away from conflicting traffic unless requested by the pilot.

    b) You should inform the controller when changing altitude.

    c) When advisory service is no longer desired, advise the controller before changing frequency, and then change your transponder code to 1200.

    d) When you are outside the controller's airspace, the controller will advise you that radar service is terminated and instruct you to squawk VFR.

c. Terminal Radar Programs

1) Terminal radar programs for VFR aircraft are classified as basic, TRSA, Class C, and Class B service.

    a) Basic radar service provides safety alerts, traffic advisories, and limiting vectoring on a workload-permitting basis.

    b) TRSA service provides sequencing and separation for all participating VFR aircraft operating within a Terminal Radar Service Area (TRSA).

2) Many larger airports have radar facilities that can provide radar advisories, sequencing, and, in some cases, separation from other participating aircraft.

    a) Many of these airports are identified as TRSAs, Class C airspace areas, and Class B airspace areas on the sectional chart.

        i) Other airports that have radar facilities are so indicated in the Chart Supplement.

    b) Pilot participation in this program, although voluntary for VFR traffic, is urged whenever available.

        i) Participation is mandatory when operating in a Class B or Class C airspace area.

3) When arriving, you should contact approach control on the published frequency and state your position, altitude, and destination, and indicate that you have received the ATIS (if available).

    a) The proper frequency may be found on the sectional chart or in the Chart Supplement.

    b) Approach control will specify when to contact the tower.

4) When departing, you should inform ground control or clearance delivery of your destination and/or route of flight and proposed cruising altitude.

    a) ATC will normally advise participating VFR aircraft when leaving the geographical limits of the controller's radar. Radar service is not terminated unless specifically stated by the controller.

5) While operating in Class B airspace, Class C airspace, or a TRSA, you

    a) Must maintain an altitude when ATC assigns it unless the altitude assignment is to maintain at or below a specified altitude

    b) Should coordinate with ATC prior to any altitude change when not assigned an altitude

4. **The applicant demonstrates understanding of transponder (Mode(s) A, C, and S).**

    a. Since most airplanes you will fly will be equipped with a transponder, you should understand the proper operating procedures. The figure below illustrates a typical transponder.

       1) The function switch controls the application of power and selects the operating mode. It has five positions:

         a) OFF -- turns the transponder off.

         b) STY or SBY (standby) -- turns the transponder on for equipment warm-up. The transponder does not reply to interrogations in this position.

         c) ON -- turns the transponder on and allows the transponder to reply to Mode A (no altitude reporting) interrogations.

         d) ALT -- turns the transponder on and allows the transponder to transmit either Mode A or Mode C (altitude reporting) replies as requested by the interrogating signal.

         e) TEST -- checks operation of the transponder.

       2) The reply/monitor light flashes to indicate when the transponder is replying to interrogations. This light will glow steadily during initial warm-up, during transmission of the IDENT signal, and during a self-test operation to show proper operation.

       3) The IDENT (ID) switch, when depressed, selects a special identifier signal that is sent with the transponder reply to an interrogation signal, thus allowing the controller to confirm an aircraft identity or to identify an aircraft.

         a) The IDENT signal should be used only at the request of a controller.

       4) The dimmer (DIM) control allows the pilot to control the intensity level of the reply light.

       5) The self-test (TST) switch causes the transponder to generate a self-interrogating signal to provide a check of the transponder operation.

       6) Code selector knobs (four) allow you to set the proper four-digit transponder code.

       7) Code selector windows (four) display the selected code. In each window, any number between zero and seven can be selected, allowing a total of 4,096 possible codes.

       8) Transponders are required to be inspected and tested every 24 calendar months.

    b. Mode C (Automatic Altitude Reporting)

       1) This system converts your airplane's altitude in 100-ft. increments to coded digital information, which is transmitted in the reply to the interrogating radar facility.

       2) If your airplane is Mode C-equipped, you must set your transponder to reply Mode C (i.e., set function switch to ALT) unless ATC requests otherwise.

3) Mode C is required when flying

 a) At or above 10,000 ft. MSL, except in that airspace below 2,500 ft. AGL
 b) Within 30 NM of a Class B airspace primary airport
 c) Within and above a Class C airspace area
 d) Into, within, or across the U.S. ADIZ (Air Defense Identification Zone)

4) For IFR operations in controlled airspace, the automatic pressure altitude reporting system (Mode C) must be tested and inspected every 24 calendar months.

c. All VFR pilots should set their transponders to code 1200 unless otherwise instructed by ATC.

1) Transponders should be turned to the ON or ALT (if Mode C-equipped) position at all times unless instructed otherwise.

2) Certain special codes have been set aside for emergency use.

 a) 7500 is the code for hijacking.
 b) 7600 is the code for lost radio communications.
 c) 7700 is the code for an emergency.
 d) 7777 is the code used for military interceptor operations.

3) When making code changes, you should avoid the selection of codes 7500, 7600, or 7700. These codes will cause alarms to be activated at the radar facility.

 a) EXAMPLE: When switching from code 2700 to 7200, switch first to 2200 then to 7200, NOT to 7700 and then 7200.

d. Mode S (Selective)

1) Mode S (Selective) transponders are designed to help air traffic control in busy areas and allow automatic collision avoidance.

 a) Mode S transponders allow TCAS (Traffic Alert and Collision Avoidance System) and TIS (Traffic Information System) to function.
 b) Refer to *Pilot Handbook*, Study Unit 3, Subunit 8, item 5., for more information on these systems.

2) Mode S transponders broadcast information about the equipped aircraft to the Secondary Surveillance Radar (SSR) system, TCAS receivers on board aircraft, and to the ADS-B system.

 a) This information includes the call sign of the aircraft and/or the transponder's permanent unit code (i.e., not the four digit user-entered squawk code).
 b) These transponders also receive ground-based radar information through a datalink and can display that information to pilots to aid in collision avoidance.

END OF KNOWLEDGE ELEMENT

36.2 RISK MANAGEMENT

A.   Task Objectives

1.   **The applicant demonstrates the ability to identify, assess, and mitigate risks encompassing failure to manage automated navigation and autoflight systems.**

   a.   For information on automated navigation and autoflight systems, see Study Unit 6, Subunit 3, beginning on page 51.

2.   **The applicant demonstrates the ability to identify, assess, and mitigate risks encompassing task management.**

   a.   For information on task management, see Study Unit 6, Subunit 1, beginning on page 49.

3.   **The applicant demonstrates the ability to identify, assess, and mitigate risks encompassing failure to maintain situational awareness.**

   a.   For information on situational awareness, see Study Unit 7, Subunit 1, beginning on page 57.

4.   **The applicant demonstrates the ability to identify, assess, and mitigate risks encompassing limitations of the navigation system in use.**

   a.   Understand the operating principles of each navigation system, its limitations, and potential errors.

      1)   For ground-based navigation, understand the limitations when flying in the vicinity of VORs in use, usable range of different types of VOR stations, line of sight limitations, DME slant range errors, potential outages, and interference that can occur with satellite (GPS) navigation.

      2)   Understand how to use the equipment installed in your aircraft.

         a)   Not all systems are intuitive.
         b)   Obtain transition training for the specific avionics equipment you will use.

   b.   It is important to remember that electronic flight displays do not replace basic flight knowledge and skills. An electronic flight display us a tool for improving flight safety.

      1)   Risk increases when the pilot believes gadgets compensate for lack of skill and knowledge.

      2)   It is especially important to recognize there are limits to what the electronic systems in any light GA aircraft can do.

      3)   Being pilot in command (PIC) requires sound aeronautical decision making (ADM), which sometimes means saying "no" to a flight.

5.   **The applicant demonstrates the ability to identify, assess, and mitigate risks encompassing automation distractions.**

   a.   Advanced avionics offer multiple levels of automation from strictly manual flight to highly automated flight.

      1)   No one level of automation is appropriate for all flight situations, but in order to avoid potentially dangerous distractions when flying with advanced avionics, the pilot must know how to manage the course deviation indicator (CDI), navigation source, and the autopilot.

      2)   It is important for a pilot to know the peculiarities of the particular automated system being used.

      3)   This ensures the pilot knows what to expect, how to monitor for proper operations, and when to promptly take appropriate action if the system does not perform as expected.

   b.   For more information on automation distractions, see Study Unit 6, Subunit 3, beginning on page 51.

END OF RISK MANAGEMENT ELEMENT

36.3 SKILLS

A. Task Objectives

1. **The applicant demonstrates the ability to use an installed electronic navigation system.**

   a. Determine the frequency of the VOR station.

      1) This determination is normally made during your cross-country planning.

      2) Frequencies can be found in the Chart Supplement or in the appropriate information box on your aeronautical chart.

   b. Tune and identify the station.

      1) Tune the appropriate frequency in on your VOR receiver.

      2) The only positive method of identifying a VOR station is by its three-letter Morse code identification or by the recorded voice identification, which is always indicated by the use of the word "V-O-R" following its name.

         a) During periods of maintenance, the VOR station may transmit the word "T-E-S-T" (– . ... –), or the identifier may be removed.

         b) To monitor the station identifier, select the "ident" feature on the VOR receiver.

      3) Do not use a VOR station for navigation unless you can positively identify it.

   c. Distance Measuring Equipment (DME)

      1) When using both VOR and DME, you must ensure that each is operating properly by listening for the identifiers.

         a) The DME identifier is transmitted one time for each three or four times the VOR identifier is transmitted.

         b) A single coded identification transmitted every 30 sec. indicates that the DME is operative but the VOR is inoperative.

            i) The absence of the single coded identification every 30 sec. indicates the DME is inoperative.

      2) To use the groundspeed and/or time-to-station function of the DME, you must be flying directly to or from the station.

         a) Flying in any other direction will provide you with false groundspeed and time-to-station information.

   d. GPS for VFR Operations

      1) Always check to see if the unit has RAIM capability.

         a) If no RAIM capability exists, be suspicious of a GPS displayed position when any disagreement exists with the position derived from other radio navigation systems, pilotage, or dead reckoning.

         b) While a hand-held GPS receiver can provide excellent navigation capability to VFR pilots, be prepared for intermittent loss of navigation signal, possibly with no RAIM warning to the pilot.

      2) Check the currency of the database, if any.

         a) If expired, update the database using the current revision.

         b) If an update of an expired database is not possible, disregard any moving map display of airspace for critical navigation decisions.

         c) Be aware that named waypoints may no longer exist or may have been relocated since the database expired.

         d) At a minimum, the waypoints planned to be used should be checked against a current official source, such as the Chart Supplement or a Sectional Aeronautical Chart.

2. **The applicant demonstrates the ability to locate the airplane's position using the navigation system.**

    a.   Interpret VOR indications (see the diagram below).

    b.   When you select a course in the OBS, imagine that you have drawn a line through the VOR station in the direction of the course.

        1)   The line should extend outward from the VOR in both the direction of the selected course and the direction of its reciprocal.

        2)   Imagine an arrowhead at the end of the line in the direction of the desired course, as in the diagram.

        3)   Now look at the diagram and imagine the VOR in the center.

            a)   Rotate the diagram until the arrowhead points in the direction of your OBS setting.

            b)   Note that, when you are facing in the direction of the OBS setting, the CDI needle points to the right if you are left of the course and points to the left if you are right of the course.

            c)   If you are directly on the course line, the CDI needle will be centered.

    c.   Imagine also a line drawn through the VOR perpendicular to the selected course, as shown below.

        1)   Again, rotate the diagram until the arrowhead points in the direction of the OBS setting, and imagine that you are facing in that same direction.

            a)   If you are below the 90° line, the TO/FROM indicator will read TO.

            b)   If you are above the 90° line, it will read FROM.

            c)   If you are anywhere on the 90° line, you will see a neutral (i.e., a blank TO/FROM window, NAV, OFF, or red flag) indication.

               i)   You will also see a neutral indication if the VOR signal is too weak for reliable navigation.

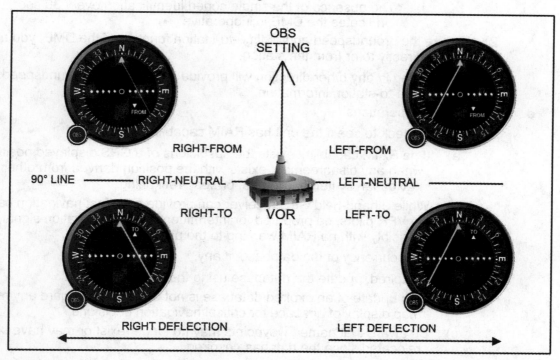

d.   The diagram should be used to understand how to interpret VOR indications in flight. Remember that you must rotate the diagram so the omnibearing direction is pointed in the direction in which your OBS is set (i.e., the selected course).

   1)   When flying, interpret the needle by envisioning your airplane being on a heading indicated by the OBS.

      a)   You can immediately tell which quadrant you are in -- TO or FROM, left or right.

e.   Note that the airplane's heading does not affect the VOR navigation instrument.

   1)   The airplane's position (not heading) relative to the VOR determines the CDI and TO/FROM indications.

   2)   Thus, to obtain a useful indication, your airplane must be heading in the same general direction as your OBS setting.

      a)   A right CDI deflection will indicate that the desired course is to your right, and a left deflection will indicate that it is to your left.

      b)   A TO indication will show that your present course will move you closer to the station, and a FROM indication means that it will take you farther from the station.

   3)   Always be sure that your OBS setting agrees with the direction in which you intend to fly.

3.   **The applicant demonstrates the ability to intercept and track a given course, radial, or bearing, as appropriate.**

a.   Intercepting a desired VOR radial, either inbound or outbound

   1)   Tune and identify the station.

   2)   Turn to a heading that roughly parallels the course you wish to fly (i.e., if you wish to fly TO the station on the 180° radial, turn the airplane to the reciprocal heading of the radial, 360°, as illustrated on the next page).

   3)   Rotate the OBS until the CDI needle centers with a TO indication. Then determine the difference between the radial you are on and the radial you wish to intercept.

      a)   If the CDI centers on 340° TO the station, it indicates you are on the 160° radial FROM the station, 20° to the east of the radial you are planning to intercept.

      b)   Double the difference (i.e., 40°) and use that figure as your intercept angle. Do not use intercept angles of less than 20° or more than 90°.

   4)   Rotate the OBS to the desired course (360° TO the station).

   5)   The CDI will indicate the course is to your left. Your intercept angle suggests a 40° turn to the left, or 320°.

   6)   Hold this magnetic heading constant until the CDI begins to center, indicating that you are on the desired radial or course.

7) Turn to the magnetic heading corresponding to the selected course, and track that radial.

    a) With practice, you will learn to lead the turn to prevent overshooting the course as you intercept it.

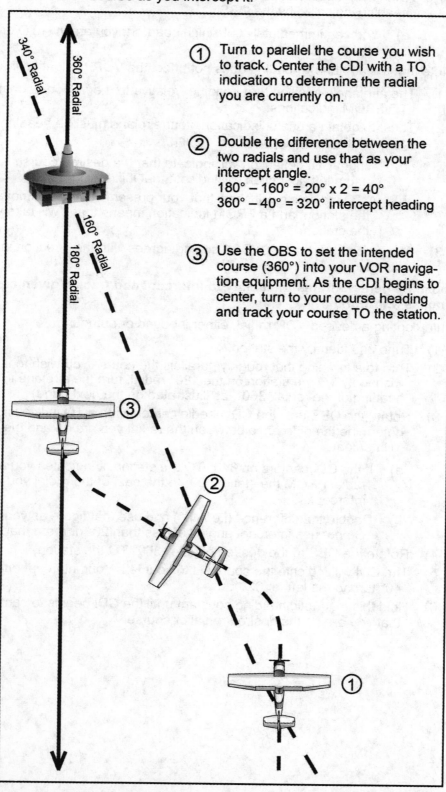

b. Tracking a VOR radial

   1) In the diagram below, you are tracking inbound on the 170° radial on a magnetic course of 350° to the station (Point 1).

   2) If a heading of 350° is maintained with a wind from the right, as shown in the diagram, the airplane will drift to the left of the intended track (Point 2).

      a) As the airplane drifts off course, the CDI needle will gradually move to the right of center and indicate the direction of the desired radial.

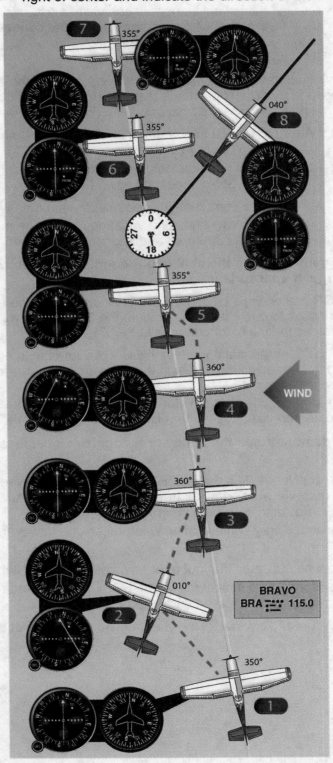

3) To return to the desired radial, the airplane heading must be altered 20° to the right. As the airplane returns to the desired track, the CDI needle will slowly return to center (Point 3).

   a) When the CDI is centered, the airplane will be on the desired radial again, and a left turn must be made toward, but not to, the original heading of 350° in order to establish a wind-drift correction.

      i) The amount of correction depends upon the strength of the wind. If the wind velocity is unknown, a trial-and-error method (i.e., bracketing) can be used to find the correct heading.

      ii) Assume, for this example, that a 10° correction, or a heading of 360°, is maintained.

4) While maintaining a heading of 360°, assume that the CDI needle begins to move to the left. This means that the wind correction of 10° is too great, and the airplane is flying to the right of course (Point 4).

   a) A turn to the left to a heading of 350° should be made to permit the airplane to return to the desired radial.

   b) When the CDI needle centers, a smaller wind-drift correction of 5°, or a heading of 355°, should be flown (Point 5).

      i) If this correction is adequate, the airplane will remain on the radial.

      ii) If not, small heading variations should be made to keep the CDI needle centered and keep the airplane on the radial.

4. **The applicant demonstrates the ability to recognize and describe the indication of station passage, if appropriate.**

   a. As the VOR station is passed, the TO indication will change to FROM (Point 6). If the aircraft passes to one side of the station, the CDI needle will deflect in the direction of the station as the indicator changes to FROM.

      1) As you near the station, the sensitivity of your equipment will appear to increase. Do not be fooled into chasing the CDI with large corrections as station passage nears.

      2) The area directly over the station is known as the "cone of confusion." Expect momentary instances of unreliable to/from indications on your receiver.

5. **The applicant demonstrates the ability to recognize signal loss and take appropriate action.**

   a. The GPS receiver verifies the usability of the signals received from the satellites through **receiver autonomous integrity monitoring (RAIM)** to determine if a satellite is providing corrupted information.

   b. RAIM messages vary somewhat between receivers; however, generally there are two types:

      1) One type indicates that not enough satellites are available to provide RAIM.

      2) The second type indicates that the RAIM has detected a potential error that exceeds the limit for the current phase of flight.

   NOTE: Without RAIM capability, you have no assurance of the accuracy of the GPS position.

6. **The applicant demonstrates the ability to use proper communication procedures when utilizing radar services.**

   a. Use proper radio communication procedures when working with ATC.

   b. When working with a radar controller, you should repeat any altitude and/or heading clearances back to the controller.

      1) This is known as a **read back** of your clearance.

7. **The applicant demonstrates the ability to maintain the appropriate altitude, ±200 feet and headings ±15° or as recommended by aircraft manufacturer to a safe maneuvering altitude.**

   a. You must divide your attention between using and interpreting the radio navigation instruments and/or ATC radar services and flying your airplane.

END OF SKILLS ELEMENT

36.4 COMMON ERRORS

A.   Common Errors Using Radio Navigation

1.   **Improper tuning and identification of station.**

   a.   The only positive way to know you are receiving signals from the proper VOR station is to verify its Morse code identifier.

   b.   GPS systems rely on the proper selection of the fix (airport, VOR, or intersection) identifier.

   1)   Once you have selected and entered the identifier, check to see if the distance and bearing to your destination matches your planned course and distance.

2.   **Poor orientation.**

   a.   This is caused by not following the proper orientation procedures and not understanding the operating principles of the radio navigation instrument.

3.   **Overshooting and undershooting radials/bearings during interception.**

   a.   When you are using a VOR, this error can occur if you have not learned how to lead your turn to the desired heading.

4.   **Failure to recognize station passage.**

   a.   Know where you are at all times and anticipate station passage.

5.   **Failure to recognize signal loss.**

   a.   The VOR TO/FROM indicator will show a neutral or off position. An alarm flag may appear on some VORs.

   1)   All these indicate that your equipment is reading unreliable signals.

   b.   The GPS receiver will normally have some type of alarm indication if the signals are not reliable.

END OF COMMON ERRORS

STUDY UNIT THIRTY-SEVEN
DIVERSION

Task	Task C. Diversion
References	FAA-H-8083-2, FAA-H-8083-25; AIM; Navigation Charts
Objective	To determine that the applicant exhibits satisfactory knowledge, risk management, and skills associated with diversion.
Knowledge	The applicant demonstrates understanding of:
PA.VI.C.K1	1. Selecting an alternate destination.
PA.VI.C.K2	2. Deviating from ATC instructions and/or the flight plan.
Risk Management	The applicant demonstrates the ability to identify, assess and mitigate risks, encompassing:
PA.VI.C.R1	1. Failure to make a timely decision to divert.
PA.VI.C.R2	2. Failure to select an appropriate airport.
PA.VI.C.R3	3. Maintaining airmanship during diversion.
PA.VI.C.R4	4. Collision avoidance, scanning, obstacle and wire strike avoidance.
PA.VI.C.R5	5. Terrain along the diversion flight path.
PA.VI.C.R6	6. Failure to manage tasks associated with diverting to another airport.
PA.VI.C.R7	7. Failure to maintain situational awareness.
PA.VI.C.R8	8. Failure to utilize all available resources while diverting (e.g., automation, ATC, and cockpit planning aids).
Skills	The applicant demonstrates the ability to:
PA.VI.C.S1	1. Select an appropriate diversion airport and route.
PA.VI.C.S2	2. Make an accurate estimate of heading, groundspeed, arrival time, and fuel consumption to the divert airport.
PA.VI.C.S3	3. Maintain the appropriate altitude, ±200 feet and heading, ±15° or as recommended by aircraft manufacturer to a safe maneuvering altitude.

A. General Information

1. The objective of this task is for you to demonstrate your knowledge, risk management, and skills related to diversion.

2. Among the aeronautical skills that you must have is the ability to plot courses in flight to alternate destinations when continuation of the flight to the original destination is impracticable.

   a. Reasons include

      1) Low fuel
      2) Bad weather
      3) Your own or passenger fatigue, illness, etc.
      4) Airplane system or equipment malfunction
      5) Any other reason that you decide to divert to an alternate airport

37.1 KNOWLEDGE

A.   Task Objectives

1.   **The applicant demonstrates understanding of selecting an alternate destination.**

   a.   Selecting an alternate destination starts in preflight planning.

   1)   Study weather reports and forecasts to anticipate possible diversions due to weather.

   2)   Study the route of flight, highlighting possible alternate airports that are varying distances from your route of flight.

   3)   Become familiar with services offered at alternate destinations like fuel and maintenance.

   4)   Become familiar with the airport's runway lengths, lighting, and airspace.

   b.   Although it is impossible to know ahead of time if and why a diversion may be necessary, you can minimize workload during an actual diversion by having a general knowledge of your options before you begin your flight.

   c.   During an actual diversion, you will need to consider why you are diverting in order to pick a suitable alternate destination.

   1)   An emergency like engine failure or fire might require you to divert to an off airport site due to time limitations.

   2)   A diversion due to an unforeseen airport closure from a disabled aircraft on a runway allows for more time to consider an appropriate alternate.

   3)   Diversions due to weather require considering an alternate not affected by the adverse weather yet close enough to reach considering fuel and winds.

2.   **The applicant demonstrates understanding of deviating from ATC instructions and/or the flight plan.**

   a.   14 CFR 91.123 states that once you, as pilot in command (PIC), obtain a clearance from ATC, you may not deviate from that clearance except in an emergency.

   1)   You have the responsibility for the safe operation of your airplane.

   2)   If you cannot accept a clearance from ATC (e.g., flying into clouds), inform ATC of the reason you cannot accept and obtain a new clearance.

   b.   14 CFR 91.3 states that you, the PIC, are directly responsible for, and the final authority as to, the operation of your airplane.

   1)   As a safe and competent pilot, you should obtain clarification on any clearance that you do not understand or that you feel would put you in a bad situation.

END OF KNOWLEDGE ELEMENT

37.2 RISK MANAGEMENT

A.   Task Objectives

1.   **The applicant demonstrates the ability to identify, assess, and mitigate risks encompassing failure to make a timely decision to divert.**

   a.   Divert on a TIMELY basis. The longer you wait, the fewer advantages or benefits there are to making the diversion.

   1)   If your diversion results from an emergency, it is vital to divert to the new course as soon as possible.

      a)   Consider the relative distance to all suitable alternates.

      b)   Select the alternative most appropriate to the emergency at hand.

      c)   Change your heading to establish the approximate course immediately.

      d)   Later, compute wind correction, actual distance, and estimated time and fuel required.

   2)   Courses to alternates can be estimated with reasonable accuracy by using a straightedge and the compass roses shown surrounding VOR stations on the sectional chart or by using your plotter.

      a)   VOR radials and airway courses printed on the chart are already oriented to magnetic direction. These can be used to approximate a new magnetic course during VFR diversions.

      b)   If a VOR is not available for planning purposes, use your plotter as you would for planning a cross-country flight to determine a true course. Apply magnetic variation to determine a new magnetic course.

      c)   Distances can be determined by

         i)   Using the measurement scale on your plotter

         ii) Marking the appropriate place on a piece of paper with a finger or pencil and then using

            • The mileage scale at the bottom of the chart

            • A line of longitude, with 1 min. of latitude (marked north and south on a line of longitude) equal to 1 NM

   3)   If navigation systems are used to divert to an alternate, you should

      a)   Select the appropriate facility.

      b)   Tune and identify the appropriate facility.

      c)   Determine the course or radial to intercept or follow.

      d)   Set heading indicator to agree with the magnetic compass.

   4)   Once established on your new course, use the known (or forecast) wind conditions to determine an estimated groundspeed, ETA, and fuel consumption to your alternate airport.

      a)   Update as you pass over your newly selected checkpoints.

2.   **The applicant demonstrates the ability to identify, assess, and mitigate risks encompassing failure to select an appropriate airport.**

   a.   Determine that your alternate airport will meet the needs of the situation.

   1)   If the diversion is due to weather, ensure that your alternate is in an area of good weather; otherwise, you may be forced into the same situation again.

   2)   Ensure that the alternate airport has a runway long enough for your arrival and future departure.

3) If the diversion was due to low fuel, ensure that the alternate has fuel available. The availability of fuel can be determined by looking at the airport symbol on the sectional chart (tick marks around the airport symbol) or by looking in the Chart Supplement.

b. Determine that your intended route does not penetrate adverse weather or special-use airspace.

3. **The applicant demonstrates the ability to identify, assess, and mitigate risks encompassing maintaining airmanship during diversion.**

a. Skills and procedures are the procedural, psychomotor, and perceptual skills used to control a specific aircraft or its systems.

1) They are "stick and rudder" or airmanship abilities that are gained through conventional training, are perfected, and become almost automatic through experience.

b. Among the aeronautical skills that you must develop is the ability to plot courses in flight to alternate destinations when continuation of the flight to the original destination is impracticable.

1) Reasons include

a) Low fuel
b) Bad weather
c) Pilot or passenger fatigue, illness, etc.
d) Airplane system or equipment malfunction
e) Any other reason that cause you to decide to divert to an alternate airport

2) The diversion may be accomplished by means of pilotage, dead reckoning, and/or navigation systems.

a) For more information about each of these topics, refer to Study Units 35 and 36.

4. **The applicant demonstrates the ability to identify, assess, and mitigate risks encompassing collision avoidance, scanning, and obstacle and wire strike avoidance.**

a. For information on collision avoidance, scanning, and obstacle avoidance, see Study Unit 7, Subunit 4, beginning on page 66.

b. For information on wire strikes, see Study Unit 7, Subunit 6, beginning on page 68.

5. **The applicant demonstrates the ability to identify, assess, and mitigate risks encompassing terrain along the diversion flight path.**

a. When flying between two points, most pilots want to fly a direct route.

b. However, a direct route may not be the best course of action. A pilot must consider

1) Mountainous terrain (will the planned cruising altitude allow for clearance)
2) Large bodies of water (are life vests and rafts on board the aircraft)
3) Special use airspace

c. For more information on terrain avoidance, including controlled flight into terrain (CFIT), see Study Unit 7, Subunit 3, beginning on page 62.

6. **The applicant demonstrates the ability to identify, assess, and mitigate risks encompassing failure to manage tasks associated with diverting to another airport.**

a. For information on task management, see Study Unit 6, Subunit 1, beginning on page 49.

b. Always be prepared to divert by having the proper alternate airport frequencies readily available.

c. If necessary, passengers can help you locate Sectional Charts or airports in the Chart Supplement.

7. **The applicant demonstrates the ability to identify, assess, and mitigate risks encompassing failure to maintain situational awareness.**

   a. For information on situational awareness, see Study Unit 7, Subunit 1.

8. **The applicant demonstrates the ability to identify, assess, and mitigate risks encompassing failure to utilize all available resources while diverting (e.g., automation, ATC, and cockpit planning aids).**

   a. Crew resource management (CRM) is the application of team management concepts in the flight deck environment.

      1) It was initially known as cockpit resource management, but as CRM programs evolved to include cabin crews, maintenance personnel, and others, the phrase "crew resource management" was adopted.

      2) This includes single pilots, as in most general aviation aircraft. Pilots of small aircraft, as well as crews of larger aircraft, must make effective use of all available resources: human, hardware, and information.

   b. A current definition includes all groups routinely working with the flight crew who are involved in decisions required to operate a flight safely.

      1) These groups include, but are not limited to pilots, dispatchers, cabin crewmembers, maintenance personnel, and air traffic controllers.

      2) CRM is one way of addressing the challenge of optimizing the human/machine interface and accompanying interpersonal activities.

END OF RISK MANAGEMENT ELEMENT

37.3 SKILLS

A.   Task Objectives

1.   **The applicant demonstrates the ability to select an appropriate diversion airport and route.**

a.   You should continuously monitor your position on your sectional chart and the proximity of useful alternative airports.

b.   Check the maximum elevation figure (MEF) on your sectional chart in each latitude-longitude quadrant of your route to determine the minimum safe altitude.

1)   MEF is expressed in feet above MSL, which will enable you to make a quick determination by checking your altimeter.

c.   Determine that your alternate airport will meet the needs of the situation.

1)   If the diversion is due to weather, ensure your alternate is in an area of good weather; otherwise, you may be forced into the same situation again.

2)   Ensure that the alternate airport has a runway long enough for your arrival and future departure.

d.   Determine that the intended route does not penetrate adverse weather or special-use airspace.

1)   Divert toward the alternate airport promptly.

a)   Once you have decided on the best alternate airport, you should immediately estimate the magnetic course and turn to that heading.

b)   The longer you wait, the advantages or benefits of making the diversion will decrease.

c)   In the event the diversion results from an emergency, it is vital to divert to the new course as soon as possible.

2.   **The applicant demonstrates the ability to make an accurate estimate of heading, groundspeed, arrival time, and fuel consumption to the divert airport.**

a.   Courses to alternates can be estimated with reasonable accuracy using a straightedge and the compass roses shown at VOR stations on the sectional chart.

1)   The VOR radials and airway courses (already oriented to magnetic direction) printed on the chart can be used satisfactorily for approximation of magnetic bearings during VFR flights.

2)   If a VOR compass rose is not available, use your plotter as you do for planning to determine a true heading; then apply the variation correction to determine a magnetic heading.

3)   Distances can be determined by using the measurements on a plotter or by estimating point to point with a pencil and then measuring the approximate distance on the mileage scale at the bottom of the chart.

b.   If radio aids are used to divert to an alternate, you should

1)   Select the appropriate facility.
2)   Tune to the proper frequency.
3)   Determine the course or radial to intercept or follow.

c.   If your airplane is GPS-equipped, you can make short work of a diversion by plotting an electronic course to the nearest airport or any other airport of your choosing.

1)   Most units offer a "direct-to" feature that will allow you to enter in a nearby airport identifier.

a)   Some units also have a "nearest airport" page where you can see a list of nearby airports, runway length, magnetic direction, and distance.

      2)   Although GPS is an extremely useful tool, you should be skilled in accomplishing this task without it because your evaluator is likely to ask you to divert without using the GPS.

          a)   Be prepared to demonstrate a diversion with and without the GPS for your practical test.

    d.   Once established on your new course, use the known (or forecasted) wind conditions to determine estimated groundspeed, ETA, and fuel consumption to your alternate airport.

      1)   Update as you pass over your newly selected checkpoints.

3.   **The applicant demonstrates the ability to maintain the appropriate altitude, ±200 feet and heading, ±15° or as recommended by aircraft manufacturer to a safe maneuvering altitude.**

    a.   Adjust your cruising altitude to your new magnetic course, if appropriate.

END OF SKILLS ELEMENT

37.4 COMMON ERRORS

A.   Common Errors during a Diversion

1.   **Not recognizing adverse weather conditions**

   a.   Any weather that is below the forecast has the potential to become an adverse weather condition.

   b.   If there are any doubts about the weather, get an update from the nearest FSS.

2.   **Delaying the decision to divert to an alternate**

   a.   As soon as you suspect or become uneasy about a situation in which you may have to divert, you should decide on an alternate airport and proceed there directly.

   b.   A delay will decrease your alternatives.

END OF COMMON ERRORS

STUDY UNIT THIRTY-EIGHT
LOST PROCEDURES

Task	Task D. Lost Procedures
References	FAA-H-8083-2, FAA-H-8083-25; AIM; Navigation Charts
Objective	To determine that the applicant exhibits satisfactory knowledge, risk management, and skills associated with lost procedures and taking appropriate steps to achieve a satisfactory outcome if lost.
Knowledge	The applicant demonstrates understanding of:
PA.VI.D.K1	1. The value of recording time at waypoints.
PA.VI.D.K2	2. The assistance available if lost (radar services, communication procedures).
PA.VI.D.K3	3. The responsibility and authority of the PIC.
PA.VI.D.K4	4. Deviation from ATC instructions.
PA.VI.D.K5	5. Declaring an emergency.
Risk Management	The applicant demonstrates the ability to identify, assess and mitigate risks, encompassing:
PA.VI.D.R1	1. Failure to record times over waypoints.
PA.VI.D.R2	2. Failure to manage tasks with lost procedures.
PA.VI.D.R3	3. Situational awareness.
PA.VI.D.R4	4. Collision avoidance, scanning, obstacle and wire strike avoidance.
PA.VI.D.R5	5. Failure to seek assistance or declare an emergency in a deteriorating situation.
Skills	The applicant demonstrates the ability to:
PA.VI.D.S1	1. Select an appropriate course of action.
PA.VI.D.S2	2. Maintain an appropriate heading and climbs, if necessary.
PA.VI.D.S3	3. Identify prominent landmarks.
PA.VI.D.S4	4. Use navigation systems/facilities and/or contacts an ATC facility for assistance, as appropriate.

A. General Information

1. The objective of this task is for you to demonstrate your knowledge, risk management, and skills related to lost procedures and taking appropriate steps to achieve a satisfactory outcome if lost.

2. Nobody plans to get lost, especially in an airplane, but almost all pilots eventually find themselves disoriented. It is critically important that you learn to recognize disorientation quickly and train yourself to methodically implement corrective action to become reoriented.

3. Steps to avoid becoming lost:

   a. Always use a properly prepared navigation log on cross-country flights.

   b. Plan ahead and know what your next landmark will be and look for it.

      1) Similarly, anticipate the indication of your radio navigation systems.

   c. If your radio navigation systems or your visual observations of landmarks do not confirm your expectations, become concerned and take action.

38.1 KNOWLEDGE

A.   Task Objectives

1.   **The applicant demonstrates understanding of the value of recording time at waypoints.**

   a.   During your flight, you will keep track of your actual compass heading and the time.

   1)   Mark down the time over every checkpoint. This will allow you to compare your estimated groundspeed to your actual groundspeed and revise fuel estimates as necessary.

   2)   From this, you can determine the actual wind conditions, groundspeed, time en route, and fuel consumption.

   3)   Thus, you can deduce your time of arrival at your next checkpoint and the amount of fuel that will be used.

2.   **The applicant demonstrates understanding of the assistance available if lost (radar services, communication procedures).**

   a.   If you become lost, ATC can provide you with radar assistance and vectors to your desired destination.

   1)   You must be within radar coverage to use this service.

   b.   To find the proper frequency for ATC in your area, you may need to contact the nearest control tower or FSS.

   1)   Inform ATC that you are lost, and state your last known position and your destination.

   2)   By assigning you a transponder code and observing you on radar, the controller will be able to tell you your position and suggest a heading to your destination.

   c.   An emergency situation can easily be avoided by asking for help as soon as you are in doubt as to your exact position.

   1)   Taking advantage of flight following when available keeps you operating within the ATC system and allows you always to keep a controller "at your fingertips."

3.   **The applicant demonstrates understanding of the responsibility and authority of PIC.**

   a.   You must clearly understand that radar services in no way relieve you of your primary responsibility of flying the airplane legally and safely.

   a.   It is still your task to

   1)   See and avoid other traffic
   2)   Adjust your operations and flight path as necessary to avoid wake turbulence
   3)   Maintain appropriate terrain and obstruction clearance
   4)   Maintain basic VFR visibility and distance from clouds

   b.   If ATC assigns a route, heading, and/or altitude that will make you compromise your responsibilities in the above areas, you must contact the controller to advise him/her and obtain a revised clearance or instructions.

   c.   14 CFR 91.3 states that you, the pilot in command, are directly responsible for, and the final authority as to, the operation of your airplane.

   1)   As a safe and competent pilot, you should obtain clarification on any clearance that you do not understand or that you feel would put you in a bad situation.

4. **The applicant demonstrates understanding of deviation from ATC instructions.**

   a. 14 CFR 91.123 states that once you, as pilot in command, obtain a clearance from ATC, you may not deviate from that clearance except in an emergency.

      1) You have the responsibility for the safe operation of your airplane.
      2) If you cannot accept a clearance from ATC (e.g., flying into clouds), inform ATC of the reason you cannot accept and obtain a new clearance.

   b. If you deviate from a clearance in an emergency or in response to a TCAS resolution advisory, you must notify ATC as soon as possible.

   c. If you are given priority by ATC in an emergency, you must submit a detailed report of the emergency within 48 hr. to the manager of that ATC facility, if requested.

      1) The report may be requested even if you do not deviate from any rule of Part 91.

5. **The applicant demonstrates understanding of declaring an emergency.**

   a. You can obtain assistance by contacting an ATC or FSS facility or using the emergency frequency of 121.5 MHz if you encounter a distress or urgent condition.

   a. An **urgent condition** is one in which you are concerned about safety and require timely but not immediate assistance. An urgent condition is a potential distress condition.

      1) Begin your transmission by announcing "PAN-PAN" three times.

   b. A **distress condition** is one in which you feel threatened by serious and/or imminent danger and require immediate assistance.

      1) Begin your transmission by announcing "MAYDAY" three times.
      2) If you have a transponder, squawk 7700 (general emergency).

   c. After establishing contact, work with the person to whom you are talking. Remain calm, cooperate, and remain in VFR conditions.

   d. ATC and FSS personnel are ready and willing to help, and there is no penalty for using them. Delay in asking for help has often caused accidents.

END OF KNOWLEDGE ELEMENT

38.2 RISK MANAGEMENT

A.   Task Objectives

1.   **The applicant demonstrates the ability to identify, assess, and mitigate risks encompassing failure to record times over waypoints.**

   a.   Always use a properly prepared navigation log on cross-country flights.

   b.   Plan ahead, know what your next landmark will be, and look for it.

      1)   Anticipate the indication of your radio navigation systems.

      2)   If you know what you expect to see, you will more quickly recognize an error caused by poor reception or improper tuning.

   c.   If your radio navigation systems or your visual observations of landmarks do not confirm your expectations, become attentive to the situation and take action.

2.   **The applicant demonstrates the ability to identify, assess, and mitigate risks encompassing failure to manage tasks with lost procedures.**

   a.   For information on task management, see Study Unit 6, Subunit 1, beginning on page 49.

   b.   Use all the resources available to you, including the help of passengers.

3.   **The applicant demonstrates the ability to identify, assess, and mitigate risks encompassing situational awareness.**

   a.   Maintaining situational awareness requires an understanding of the relative significance of all flight related factors and their future impact on the flight.

      1)   When a pilot understands what is going on and has an overview of the total operation, he or she is not fixated on one perceived significant factor. It is important to know the aircraft's geographical location, and also just as important to understand what is happening.

      2)   Monitoring radio communications for traffic, weather discussion, and ATC communication can enhance situational awareness by helping the pilot develop a mental picture of what is happening.

   b.   In extreme cases, when a pilot gets behind the aircraft, a loss of positional or situational awareness may result.

      1)   The pilot may not know the aircraft's geographical location, or may be unable to recognize deteriorating circumstances.

   c.   For more information on situational awareness, see Study Unit 7, Subunit 1, beginning on page 57.

4.   **The applicant demonstrates the ability to identify, assess, and mitigate risks encompassing collision avoidance, scanning, and obstacle and wire strike avoidance.**

   a.   For information on collision avoidance, scanning, and obstacle avoidance, see Study Unit 7, Subunit 4, beginning on page 66.

   b.   For information on wire strikes, see Study Unit 7, Subunit 6, beginning on page 68.

5. **The applicant demonstrates the ability to identify, assess, and mitigate risks encompassing failure to seek assistance or declare an emergency in a deteriorating situation.**

   a. The greatest hazard to a pilot who fails to arrive at a given checkpoint at a particular time is panic.

      1) The natural reaction is to fly to where it is assumed the checkpoint is located.

      2) On arriving at that point and not finding the checkpoint, the pilot usually assumes a second position, and then, panicked, will fly in another direction for some time.

      3) As a result of this wandering, the pilot may have no idea where the airplane is located.

   b. Generally, if planning is correct and the pilot uses basic dead reckoning until the ETA, the airplane is going to be within a reasonable distance of the planned checkpoint.

   c. When you become lost, you should

      1) Maintain your original heading and watch for landmarks.

      2) Identify the nearest concentration of prominent landmarks.

         a) If you see an unmistakable landmark, fly to it, positively identify it on your sectional chart, and proceed from there.

      3) Use all available radio navigation systems/facilities and/or ask for help from any ATC facility.

      4) Plan a precautionary landing if weather conditions get worse and/or your airplane is about to run out of fuel.

   d. In emergencies, you may deviate from the 14 CFRs to the extent needed to maintain the safety of the airplane and passengers.

   e. If you do deviate from the 14 CFRs in such an emergency, you may be required to file a written report with the FAA.

      1) ATC and FSS personnel are ready and willing to help, and there is no penalty for using them. Delay in asking for help has often caused accidents.

END OF RISK MANAGEMENT ELEMENT

38.3 SKILLS

A.   Task Objectives

1.   **The applicant demonstrates the ability to select an appropriate course of action.**

   a.   As soon as you begin to wonder where you are, remember the point at which you last were confident of your location.

      1)   Watch your heading. Know what it is and keep it constant.
      2)   Do not panic. You are not "lost" yet.
      3)   Recompute your expected navigation system(s) indications and visual landmarks.

         a)   Reconfirm your heading (compass and heading indicator).
         b)   Confirm correct radio frequencies and settings.
         c)   Review your sectional chart, noting last confirmed landmark.

      4)   Attempt to reconfirm present position.

   b.   You should use all available means to determine your present location. This includes asking for assistance.

   c.   You may want to climb to a higher altitude to ensure reception of navigation system signals, radar facilities, and communications.

   d.   If available fuel is becoming a concern, you may want to adjust the power and mixture for maximum endurance until you can confirm your present location.

   e.   The best course of action will depend on such factors as ceiling, visibility, hours of daylight remaining, fuel remaining, etc.

      1)   Given the current circumstances, you will be the only one to decide the best course of action.
      2)   Understand and respect your own and your airplane's limitations.

2.   **The applicant demonstrates the ability to maintain an appropriate heading and climbs, if necessary.**

   a.   When unsure of your position, you should continue to fly the original heading and watch for recognizable landmarks while rechecking the calculated position.

      1)   A climb to a higher altitude may assist you in locating more landmarks.

   b.   By plotting the estimated distance and compass direction flown from your last noted checkpoint as though there was no wind, you will determine a point that will be the center of a circle within which your airplane's position may be located.

      1)   If you are certain the wind is no more than 30 kt., and it has been less than 30 min. since the last known checkpoint was crossed, the radius of the circle should be approximately 15 NM.

   c.   Continue straight ahead and check the landmarks within this circle.

      1)   The most likely position will be downwind from your desired course.

3.   **The applicant demonstrates the ability to identify prominent landmarks.**

   a.   If the above procedure fails to identify your position, change course toward the nearest prominent landmark or concentration of prominent landmarks shown on your chart.

   b.   If you have a prominent landmark, e.g., coastline, interstate highway, etc., proceed toward it.

   c.   When a landmark is recognized, or a probable fix obtained, you should at first use the information both cautiously and profitably.

      1)   No abrupt change in course should be made until a second or third landmark is positively identified to corroborate the first.

4. **The applicant demonstrates the ability to use navigation systems/facilities and/or contacts an ATC facility for assistance, as appropriate.**

    a. Use all available navigation systems (VOR, GPS - as equipped) to locate your position.

        1) Use at least two VOR facilities to find the radial/bearing from the station that you are on. Draw these lines on your chart; where they intersect is your position.

        2) Most GPS units have a function that will display the nearest airport and give its bearing and distance.

            a) GPS units are the most common electronic navigation equipment found in light-sport aircraft. Become familiar with the operation of your unit, including features that can help you find your way should you become lost.

            b) Over-reliance on GPS can make you complacent. Maintain proper pilotage and dead reckoning skills.

                i) Plan all cross-country flights and complete a navigation log.

                ii) Use the GPS to verify your planning while en route.

    b. You can obtain assistance by contacting an ATC or FSS facility, or use the emergency frequency of 121.5 MHz if you encounter a distress or urgent condition.

        1) An **urgent condition** is when you are concerned about safety and require timely but not immediate assistance. This is a potential distress condition.

            a) Begin your transmission by announcing PAN-PAN three times.

        2) A **distress condition** is when you feel threatened by serious and/or imminent danger and require immediate assistance.

            a) Begin your transmission by announcing MAYDAY three times.

            b) If you have a transponder, squawk 7700 (general emergency).

        3) After establishing contact, work with the person you are talking to. Remain calm, cooperate, and remain in VFR conditions.

        4) ATC and FSS personnel are ready and willing to help, and there is no penalty for using them. Delay in asking for help has often caused accidents.

    c. Plan a precautionary landing if deteriorating weather and/or fuel exhaustion is imminent.

        1) If these conditions and others (e.g., darkness approaching) threaten, it is recommended that you make a precautionary landing while adequate visibility, fuel, and daylight are still available.

        2) It is most desirable to land at an airport, but if one cannot be found, a suitable field may be used.

            a) Prior to an off-airport landing, you should first survey the area for obstructions or other hazards.

END OF SKILLS ELEMENT

38.4 COMMON ERRORS

A. Common Errors during Lost Procedures

1. **Attempting to fly to where you assume your checkpoint is located**

    a. Maintain your current heading and use available radio navigation systems and pilotage procedures to determine your position.

    b. Blindly searching tends to compound itself and leads to a panic situation.

2. **Proceeding into marginal VFR weather conditions**

    a. Use a 180° turn to avoid marginal weather conditions.

3. **Failure to ask for help**

    a. At any time you are unsure of your position, ask for help.

    b. Do not let pride get in the way of safety.

    c. Recognizing the need for and seeking assistance is a sign of a mature, competent, and safe pilot.

END OF COMMON ERRORS

PART III
SECTION VII:
SLOW FLIGHT AND STALLS

Study Units 39 through 42 of Section VII explain the four FAA ACS tasks (A-D) of Slow Flight and Stalls. These tasks include knowledge, risk management, and skill. Your evaluator is required to test you on all four of these tasks.

The tasks in this section have several common items, listed and explained here instead of repeated throughout the text.

The following common task item topics are included in this section introduction:

KNOWLEDGE   Page

A. **The applicant demonstrates understanding of the importance of the 1,500-foot AGL minimum altitude.**   503

RISK MANAGEMENT

A. **The applicant demonstrates the ability to identify, assess, and mitigate risks encompassing the interplay of aerodynamic factors (angle of attack (AOA), airspeed, load factor, aircraft configuration, aircraft weight, and aircraft attitude).**   504

B. **The applicant demonstrates the ability to identify, assess, and mitigate risks encompassing the range and limitations of stall warning indicators (e.g., aircraft buffet, stall horn, etc.).**   504

C. **The applicant demonstrates the ability to identify, assess, and mitigate risks encompassing the effect of environmental elements on aircraft performance.**   505

D. **The applicant demonstrates the ability to identify, assess, and mitigate risks encompassing the required actions for aircraft maximum performance and the consequences of failing to do so.**   506

KNOWLEDGE

A. **The applicant demonstrates understanding of the importance of the 1,500-foot AGL minimum altitude.**

     1. This is a requirement you will find with almost all maneuvers.

     2. While all aircraft have different spin characteristics, one thing is certain. A pilot must stall an airplane to spin it. Once an airplane enters a spin, according to some research, a typical training airplane will require 1,100 ft. to recover.

     3. Practicing slow flight puts the pilot closer to the critical angle of attack and thus stalling the aircraft. If that happens, the more altitude means the more time to recover.

     4. Another consideration is obstacle clearance.

     5. Remember, 1,500 ft. AGL is the minimum altitude to perform slow flight.

RISK MANAGEMENT

A.   **The applicant demonstrates the ability to identify, assess, and mitigate risks encompassing the interplay of aerodynamic factors (angle of attack (AOA), airspeed, load factor, aircraft configuration, aircraft weight, and aircraft attitude).**

    1.   Factors to remember include

        a.   An aircraft stalls when it reaches the critical angle of attack regardless of airspeed or attitude

        b.   Indicated stall speed and critical angle attack increase as aircraft weight increases

        c.   Without actually increasing the weight of the plane, a pilot can "make the plane feel heavier" and thus increase stall speed and critical angle of attack by performing maneuvers that increase load factor like constant altitude steep turns.

            1)   Beware of distractions during turns, especially while sightseeing.

        d.   Always use a checklist.

            1)   Checklists will aid in preventing taking off or landing without the proper aircraft configuration, e.g., flaps and gear.

    2.   For a detailed discussion of stall and spin aerodynamics, see Study Unit 1, "Airplanes and Aerodynamics," of *Pilot Handbook*, in Subunit 13, "Stalls and Spins."

B.   **The applicant demonstrates the ability to identify, assess, and mitigate risks encompassing the range and limitations of stall warning indicators (e.g., aircraft buffet, stall horn, etc.).**

    1.   As part of the PAVE checklist (A is for aircraft), a proper preflight inspection should include testing of stall indicators.

    2.   The recognition of a buffet or the sound of a stall horn preceding a stall are dependent on an alert pilot without distractions. (PAVE, P stands for pilot.)

        a.   Listening to satellite broadcast music or other on board music and distractions may not allow the buffet or horn to be heard.

    3.   Several types of stall warning systems have been developed to warn pilots of an approaching stall.

        a.   Some devices have mechanical components that send an electrical signal from a lift detector to a "buzzer" when the component is close to reaching the critical angle of attack (AOA).

        b.   Some devices strictly use a reed horn, such as the stall warning system used on the leading edge of many Cessnas. When the relative wind approaches the critical AOA, it creates suction and the accompanying "horn" is audible in the cabin.

        c.   Other devices are available as after market additions to an aircraft, each with it's own limitations.

        d.   Most mechanical or reed-type stall warning devices sound an audible horn 5-10 kt. before the aircraft stalls.

4. The main reason for practicing stalls is to learn to recognize stalls without the benefit of warning devices. A pilot can always use the following techniques:

    a. Feel is an important sense in recognizing the onset of a stall. The feeling of control pressures is very important. As speed is reduced, the resistance to pressures on the controls becomes progressively less. Pressures exerted on the controls tend to become movements of the control surfaces. The lag between these movements and the response of the airplane becomes greater, until in a complete stall all controls can be moved with almost no resistance, and with little immediate effect on the airplane. Just before the stall occurs, buffeting, uncontrollable pitching, or vibrations may begin.

    b. Hearing is also helpful in sensing a stall condition. In the case of fixed-pitch propeller airplanes in a power-on condition, a change in sound due to loss of revolutions per minute (rpm) is particularly noticeable. The lessening of the noise made by the air flowing along the airplane structure as airspeed decreases is also quite noticeable, and when the stall is almost complete, vibration and incident noises often increase greatly.

    c. Kinesthesia, or the sensing of changes in direction or speed of motion, is probably the most important and the best indicator to the trained and experienced pilot. If this sensitivity is properly developed, it will warn of a decrease in speed or the beginning of a settling or mushing of the airplane.

    d. Vision is useful in detecting a stall condition by noting the attitude of the airplane. This sense can only be relied on when the stall is the result of an unusual attitude of the airplane. Since the airplane can also be stalled from a normal attitude, vision in this instance would be of little help in detecting the approaching stall.

C. **The applicant demonstrates the ability to identify, assess, and mitigate risks encompassing the effect of environmental elements on aircraft performance.**

    1. In the PAVE checklist, V stands for environmental factors to consider when assessing and mitigating risks associated with these maneuvers.

        a. Weather – gusty wind conditions require adjustments to airspeeds to maintain a safe buffer above the critical angle of attack (stall speed)

            1) Cold weather flying requires extra vigilance to make sure stall warning systems are not compromised due to freezing temperatures or contamination like snow or frost.

        b. Airports and airspace – unfamiliar airports and busy airspace can affect a pilot's stress level, which can lead to a decrease in pilot performance and make the pilot more susceptible to distractions, such as improper monitoring of airspeed and attitude.

    2. Environmental element effects on aircraft performance

        a. High density altitude – as air becomes less dense, it reduces

            1) Power, because the engine takes in less air
            2) Thrust, because the propeller is less efficient in thin air
            3) Lift, because the thin air exerts less force on the airfoils

        b. Density altitude is affected by

            1) Temperature (higher temperature higher density altitude
            2) Pressure (lower pressure higher density altitude)
            3) Moisture/humidity (higher humidity higher density altitude)

D.   The applicant demonstrates the ability to identify, assess, and mitigate risks encompassing the required actions for aircraft maximum performance and the consequences of failing to do so.

1.   Above all, proper planning is required for getting maximum performance from an airplane. Proper planning includes review of

a.   Operating area (i.e., runway lengths, obstacles)

b.   Weather conditions

c.   Performance charts

2.   Failure to properly plan can be disastrous.

a.   When proper planning has not taken place, a pilot can become distracted worrying about the unknown instead of flying the airplane.

b.   As pilots, we do not like to be blamed for accidents or incidents, but the statistics show that most accidents or incidents are pilot error. The good news in that conclusion is that we as pilots have a great degree of control in our own safety.

c.   Proper planning and practice of maximum performance maneuvers will go a long way toward lowering accident and incident rates.

3.   Quick reactions, maintaining appropriate airspeeds, etc., are essential to minimizing altitude loss. Recover quickly and avoid secondary stall.

STUDY UNIT THIRTY-NINE
MANEUVERING DURING SLOW FLIGHT

Task	Task A. Maneuvering During Slow Flight
References	FAA-H-8083-2, FAA-H-8083-3; POH/AFM
Objective	To determine that the applicant exhibits satisfactory knowledge, risk management, and skills associated with maneuvering during slow flight.
Knowledge	The applicant demonstrates understanding of:
PA.VII.A.K1	1. This maneuver as it applies to different phases of flight.
PA.VII.A.K2	2. The relationship between angle of attack (AOA), airspeed, load factor, aircraft configuration, aircraft weight, and aircraft attitude.
PA.VII.A.K3	3. The range and limitations of stall warning indicators (e.g., aircraft buffet, stall horn, etc.).
PA.VII.A.K4	4. The difference between AOA and aircraft attitude during all flight conditions and how it relates to aircraft performance.
PA.VII.A.K5	5. How environmental elements affect aircraft performance.
PA.VII.A.K6	6. The importance of the 1,500-foot AGL minimum altitude.
Risk Management	The applicant demonstrates the ability to identify, assess and mitigate risks, encompassing:
PA.VII.A.R1	1. The interplay of aerodynamic factors (angle of attack (AOA), airspeed, load factor, aircraft configuration, aircraft weight, and aircraft attitude).
PA.VII.A.R2	2. Range and limitations of stall warning indicators (e.g., aircraft buffet, stall horn, etc.).
PA.VII.A.R3	3. The effect of environmental elements on aircraft performance.
PA.VII.A.R4	4. Collision avoidance, scanning, obstacle and wire strike avoidance.
PA.VII.A.R5	5. Failure to react appropriately to a stall warning.
PA.VII.A.R6	6. Failure to maintain coordinated flight during the maneuver.
PA.VII.A.R7	7. Failure to manage pitch attitude and power to avoid a stall warning or a stall.
Skills	The applicant demonstrates the ability to:
PA.VII.A.S1	1. Select an entry altitude that will allow the Task to be completed no lower than 1,500 feet AGL.
PA.VII.A.S2	2. Establish and maintain an airspeed, approximately 5-10 knots above the 1G stall speed, at which the airplane is capable of maintaining controlled flight without activating a stall warning.
PA.VII.A.S3	3. Accomplish coordinated straight-and-level flight, turns, climbs, and descents with landing gear and flap configurations specified by the evaluator without activating a stall warning.
PA.VII.A.S4	4. Divide attention between airplane control, traffic avoidance and orientation.
PA.VII.A.S5	5. Maintain the specified altitude, ±100 feet; specified heading, ±10°; airspeed, +10/-0 knots; and specified angle of bank, ±10° or as recommended by aircraft manufacturer to a safe maneuvering altitude.

A. General Information

1. The objective of this task is for you to demonstrate your knowledge, risk management, and skills related to maneuvering during slow flight.

2. This maneuver demonstrates the flight characteristics and degree of controllability of your airplane in slow flight.

   a. It is of great importance that you know the characteristic control responses of your airplane during slow flight.

   b. You must develop this awareness in order to avoid stalls in your (or any) airplane that you may fly at the slower airspeeds that are characteristic of takeoffs, climbs, and landing approaches.

39.1 KNOWLEDGE

A.   Task Objectives

1.   **The applicant demonstrates understanding of this maneuver as it applies to different phases of flight.**

a.   Practicing slow flight maneuvers allows the pilot to fly the airplane at speeds that may be used during takeoffs, climbs, descents, landing approaches, and go-arounds.

2.   **The applicant demonstrates understanding of the relationship between angle of attack (AOA), airspeed, load factor, aircraft configuration, aircraft weight, and aircraft attitude.**

a.   Simply stated, lift is a factor of angle of attack (AOA) times indicated airspeed or velocity ($L = \alpha \times V$).

1)   Note that this is not a precise equation. It merely serves to illustrate the relationship between these three components.

2)   By using this formula we can discuss the relationship between AOA, airspeed, load factor, aircraft configuration, aircraft weight, and aircraft attitude.

b.   For example, during slow level flight, lift must remain the same.

1)   When airspeed decreases (V), AOA (α) must increase to keep the formula balanced.

a)   Aircraft attitude is the angle between the longitudinal axis of the airplane and the actual horizon

b)   AOA is the angle between the relative wind and a reference line on the wing.

c)   In level unaccelerated flight we control AOA by adjusting aircraft attitude (i.e., pitch).

2)   When load factor (or weight) increases, lift must be increased. We must increase AOA. We cannot increase speed because we are trying to fly slow.

3)   Aircraft configuration changes affect flight characteristics.

a)   Retractable landing gear being lowered increases parasite drag

b)   Extending flaps increases lift, allowing the AOA to decrease

c.   It is important to know the relationship among parasite drag, induced drag, and the power needed to maintain a given altitude (or climb angle or glide slope) at a selected airspeed.

d. While straight-and-level flight is maintained at a constant airspeed, thrust is equal in magnitude to drag, and lift is equal in magnitude to weight, but some of these forces are separated into components.

  1) In slow flight, thrust no longer acts parallel to and opposite to the flight path and drag, as shown below. Note that thrust has two components:

    a) One acting perpendicular to the flight path in the direction of lift
    b) One acting along the flight path

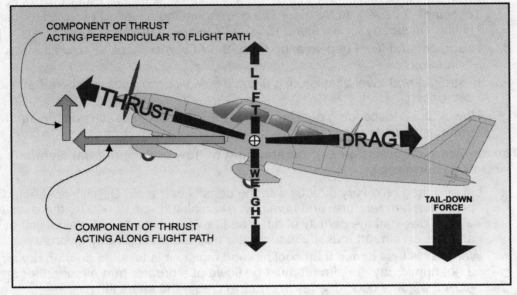

  2) Because the actual thrust is inclined, its magnitude must be greater than drag if its component acting along the flight path is equal to drag.

    a) Note that the forces acting upward (wing lift and the component of thrust) equal the forces acting downward (weight and tail down force).

  3) Wing loading (wing lift) is actually less during slow flight because the vertical component of thrust helps support the airplane.

e. The flight controls in slow flight are less effective than at normal cruise due to the reduced airflow over them.

  1) Anticipate the need of right rudder to counteract the torque effect in a low airspeed, high power setting condition.

  2) Large control movements may be required, but this does not mean rough or jerky movements.

f. See Study Unit 1, "Airplanes and Aerodynamics," Subunit 7, "Dynamics of the Airplane in Flight," in *Pilot Handbook* for a detailed discussion of the relationship of these factors.

3. **The applicant demonstrates understanding of the range and limitations of stall warning indicators (e.g., aircraft buffet, stall horn, etc.).**

a. For information on the range and limitations of stall warning indicators, see Section VII Introduction, Risk Management, item B., beginning on page 504.

4. **The applicant demonstrates understanding of the difference between AOA and aircraft attitude during all flight conditions and how it relates to aircraft performance.**

    a. Aircraft attitude is the angle between the longitudinal axis of the airplane and the actual horizon.

    b. Angle of attack (AOA) is the angle between the relative wind and a reference line on the wing.

    c. From the simplified lift formula (L = α × V), we know that all other factors being constant, for every AOA, there is a corresponding airspeed required to maintain altitude in steady, unaccelerated flight (true only if maintaining "level flight").

    d. In straight-and-level decelerating flight, the AOA increases as aircraft attitude increases.

    e. In straight-and-level accelerating flight, the AOA decreases as aircraft attitude decreases.

    f. However, in descending decelerating flight, the AOA increases as the aircraft attitude remains relatively unchanged.

5. **The applicant demonstrates understanding of how environmental elements affect aircraft performance.**

    a. Lift and drag also vary directly with the density of the air. Density is affected by pressure, temperature, and humidity. At an altitude of 18,000 ft., the density of the air has one-half the density of air at sea level. In order to maintain its lift at a higher altitude, an aircraft must fly at a greater true airspeed for any given AOA.

    b. Warm air is less dense than cool air, and moist air is less dense than dry air. Thus, on a hot humid day, an aircraft must be flown at a greater true airspeed for any given AOA than on a cool, dry day in order to create the same lift.

    c. For more information on atmospheric conditions and how they affect aircraft performance, see Study Unit 9, Subunit 1, beginning on page 77.

6. **The applicant demonstrates understanding of the importance of the 1,500-foot AGL minimum altitude.**

    a. For information on the 1,500-ft. AGL minimum altitude, see Section VII Introduction, Knowledge, item A., on page 503.

END OF KNOWLEDGE ELEMENT

39.2 RISK MANAGEMENT

A. Task Objectives

1. **The applicant demonstrates the ability to identify, assess, and mitigate risks encompassing the interplay of aerodynamic factors [angle of attack (AOA), airspeed, load factor, aircraft configuration, aircraft weight, and aircraft attitude].**

    a. There are several slow flight scenarios to consider.

        1) Pre-departure considerations

            a) Increases in aircraft weight increase AOA for a given airspeed, which increases stall speeds.

        2) Departure climb and turns

            a) Be alert for distractions.

                i) Distractions, including from ATC or passengers, could lead to you allowing aircraft attitude to become excessively high.

            b) As load factor increases in turns, turns should not be performed without sufficient airspeed considering aircraft configuration like flap setting.

        3) Turn from base to final in the traffic pattern

            a) Poor coordination during base to final and distractions can lead to a stall spin scenario.

            b) Stall spin accidents on base to final are almost certainly fatal.

        4) Sightseeing flights

            a) Pilots at all skill levels should be aware of the increased risk of entering into an inadvertent stall or spin while performing tasks that are secondary to controlling the aircraft, such as low and slow flight while sightseeing.

        5) Stalls resulting from improper airspeed management are most likely to occur when the pilot is distracted by one or more other tasks, such as locating a checklist or attempting a restart after an engine failure; flying a traffic pattern on a windy day; reading a chart or making fuel and/or distance calculations; or attempting to retrieve items from the floor, back seat, or glove compartment.

        6) Following slower aircraft in the pattern, so you must slow your plane more than normal.

            a) This increases the risk for inadvertent stalls and spins, especially when turning.

    b. For more information on the interplay of aerodynamic factors, see Section VII Introduction, Risk Management, item A., on page 504.

2. **The applicant demonstrates the ability to identify, assess, and mitigate risks encompassing range and limitations of stall warning indicators (e.g., aircraft buffet, stall horn, etc.).**

    a. For information on the range and limitations of stall warning indicators, see Section VII Introduction, Risk Management, item B., beginning on page 504.

3. **The applicant demonstrates the ability to identify, assess, and mitigate risks encompassing the effect of environmental elements on aircraft performance.**

    a. For information on the effect of environmental elements on aircraft performance, see Section VII Introduction, Risk Management, item C., on page 505.

4. **The applicant demonstrates the ability to identify, assess, and mitigate risks encompassing collision avoidance, scanning, and obstacle and wire strike avoidance.**

    a. For information on collision avoidance, scanning, and obstacle avoidance, see Study Unit 7, Subunit 4, beginning on page 66.

    b. For information on wire strikes, see Study Unit 7, Subunit 6, beginning on page 68.

5. **The applicant demonstrates the ability to identify, assess, and mitigate risks encompassing failure to react appropriately to a stall warning.**

    a. Under normal operating conditions, the stall warning horn should not sound.

        1) Activation of the horn is an indication of an imminent stall and must be responded to immediately by decreasing the angle of attack and/or increasing power to generate adequate lift.

        2) Failure to do so may result in inadvertently encountering a stalled condition and loss of control.

6. **The applicant demonstrates the ability to identify, assess, and mitigate risks encompassing failure to maintain coordinated flight during the maneuver.**

    a. During slow flight, you will already be flying on the cusp of an imminent stall.

        1) Failure to maintain coordinated flight could result in a spin if a stall is also encountered.

7. **The applicant demonstrates the ability to identify, assess, and mitigate risks encompassing failure to manage pitch attitude and power to avoid a stall warning or a stall.**

    a. Ensure that you divide your attention inside and outside in order to "stay ahead of the plane."

        1) Anticipate the effects of pitch and power changes to avoid a stall warning horn or stall.

END OF RISK MANAGEMENT ELEMENT

39.3 SKILLS

A.   Task Objectives

1.   **The applicant demonstrates the ability to select an entry altitude that will allow the Task to be completed no lower than 1,500 feet AGL.**

   a.   Select an altitude that is easy to read from your altimeter.

      1)   The FAA requires the maneuver to be completed no lower than 1,500 ft. AGL. If the terrain elevation is 300 ft. above sea level, start by adding 1,500 ft. (1,800 ft. MSL). Add a 1,000 ft. margin of safety (2,800 ft. MSL). Then round to the next highest 500-ft. increment (3,000 ft. MSL). This will make it easier to identify on your altimeter.

      2)   During your training, you will learn how much altitude you need to perform this maneuver.

   b.   Perform clearing turns to ensure the area is clear of other traffic.

2.   **The applicant demonstrates the ability to establish and maintain an airspeed, approximately 5-10 knots above the 1G stall speed, at which the airplane is capable of maintaining controlled flight without activating a stall warning.**

   a.   Begin slowing the airplane by gradually reducing power from the cruise power setting.

      1)   While the airspeed decreases, the position of the nose in relation to the horizon should be noted and raised as necessary to maintain altitude.

   b.   When the airspeed reaches the maximum allowable for landing gear operation (V_{LO}), the landing gear (if retractable) should be extended as directed by your evaluator.

      1)   Perform all gear-down checks, e.g., three in green.

   c.   As the airspeed reaches the maximum allowable speed for flap operation (V_{FE}), full flaps should be incrementally lowered to a setting specified by your evaluator.

      1)   This will allow you to maintain pitch control of your airplane as flaps are extended.

   In your airplane, V_{FE} _____.

   d.   Additional power will be required to maintain altitude as airspeed decreases below L/D_{MAX}.

      1)   Here, induced drag increases faster than parasite drag decreases.

      2)   This phenomenon is known as "the backside of the power curve" or the "region of reverse command."

         a)   The region of reverse command means that you need more power (not less) to fly at a slower airspeed at a constant altitude.

   In your airplane, the appropriate indicated airspeed for slow flight is _____.

   e.   As the flight conditions change, it is important to retrim your airplane as often as necessary to compensate for changes in control pressures.

   f.   When the desired airspeed and pitch attitude have been established, it is important to continually cross-check the attitude indicator, altimeter, and airspeed indicator, as well as outside references, to ensure that accurate control is being maintained.

3. **The applicant demonstrates the ability to accomplish coordinated straight-and-level flight, turns, climbs, and descents with landing gear and flap configurations specified by the evaluator without activating a stall warning.**

    a. Once you have stabilized at the desired airspeed, you should maintain coordinated straight-and-level flight and perform level turns at a constant altitude.

    b. During the turns, the pitch attitude and power may need to be increased to maintain airspeed and altitude.

        1) Your evaluator will specify the angle of bank to use, not to exceed 30°.

    c. To climb, you will need to add power and adjust the pitch attitude to maintain airspeed.

    d. To descend, you will need to lower the nose and reduce power to maintain airspeed.

    e. Your evaluator will specify the configuration to use (i.e., full flaps, no flaps, partial flaps, gear up, gear down).

4. **The applicant demonstrates the ability to divide attention between airplane control, traffic avoidance, and orientation.**

    a. When you are performing this maneuver, it is important to continually cross-check your attitude, altitude, airspeed, and coordination (shown via the inclinometer or "ball"), as well as outside references, to ensure that accurate control is being maintained.

        1) Do not become focused on one item, e.g., the altitude.

    b. You must also divide your attention to watch for other aircraft in your area; i.e., practice collision avoidance.

5. **The applicant demonstrates the ability to maintain the specified altitude, ±100 feet; specified heading, ±10°; airspeed, +10/-0 knots; and specified angle of bank, ±10° or as recommended by aircraft manufacturer to a safe maneuvering altitude.**

    a. At slow airspeeds, the flight controls are less effective than in cruise. Make authoritative control inputs, but do not overcontrol the airplane.

END OF SKILLS ELEMENT

39.4 COMMON ERRORS

A.   Common Errors while Maneuvering during Slow Flight

1.   **Failure to establish specified configuration**

   a.   This maneuver can be performed in various configurations of landing gear (if retractable) and flaps.

   b.   You should form a habit of repeating instructions given to you for all maneuvers. This ensures that you understand your evaluator's instructions.

2.   **Improper entry technique**

   a.   To begin this maneuver, reduce power and gradually raise the nose. Use carburetor heat if applicable.

   b.   When the desired airspeed is attained, increase power and adjust both power and pitch to maintain airspeed and altitude.

      1)   Anticipate the need of right rudder to counteract the effect of torque as power is applied.

   c.   Retrim the airplane as often as necessary.

3.   **Failure to establish and maintain the specified airspeed**

   a.   This is caused by the improper use of power and pitch adjustments.

4.   **Excessive variations of altitude, heading, and bank when a constant altitude, heading, and bank are specified**

   a.   It is important to continually cross-check the attitude indicator, altimeter, and airspeed indicator, as well as outside references, to ensure that accurate control is being maintained.

5.   **Rough or uncoordinated control technique**

   a.   A stall may occur as a result of abrupt or rough control movements.

   b.   Uncoordinated control technique could risk the possibility of a crossed-control stall.

6.   **Faulty trim technique**

   a.   Trim should be used to relieve control pressures.

   b.   Faulty trim technique may be evidenced by poor altitude control and by the pilot's tiring quickly.

7.   **Unintentional stall**

   a.   A stall may be caused by uneven or sudden control inputs.

   b.   You must maintain your smooth control technique.

   c.   Check airspeed frequently.

8.   **Inappropriate removal of hand from throttle**

   a.   You should keep your hand on the throttle control at all times unless making an adjustment, such as trim.

END OF COMMON ERRORS

STUDY UNIT FORTY
POWER-OFF STALLS

Task	Task B. Power-Off Stalls
References	FAA-H-8083-2, FAA-H-8083-3; AC 61-67; POH/AFM
Objective	To determine that the applicant exhibits satisfactory knowledge, risk management, and skills associated with power-off stalls.
Knowledge	The applicant demonstrates understanding of:
PA.VII.B.K1	1. The importance of the 1,500-foot AGL minimum altitude.
PA.VII.B.K2	2. How the maneuver relates to a normal flight.
PA.VII.B.K3	3. The components of a stabilized descent.
PA.VII.B.K4	4. Approach to stall indications.
PA.VII.B.K5	5. Full stall indications.
PA.VII.B.K6	6. Which aircraft inputs are required to meet heading or bank angle requirements.
PA.VII.B.K7	7. The stall recovery procedure.
PA.VII.B.K8	8. The importance of establishing the correct aircraft configuration during the recovery process and the consequences of failing to do so.
PA.VII.B.K9	9. Aerodynamics associated with stalls and spins in various aircraft configurations and attitudes.
PA.VII.B.K10	10. The circumstances that can lead to an inadvertent stall or spin.
Risk Management	The applicant demonstrates the ability to identify, assess and mitigate risks, encompassing:
PA.VII.B.R1	1. The interplay of aerodynamic factors (angle of attack (AOA), airspeed, load factor, aircraft configuration, aircraft weight, and aircraft attitude).
PA.VII.B.R2	2. The range and limitations of stall warning indicators (e.g., aircraft buffet, stall horn, etc.).
PA.VII.B.R3	3. The effect of environmental elements on aircraft performance.
PA.VII.B.R4	4. Required actions for aircraft maximum performance and the consequences of failing to do so.
PA.VII.B.R5	5. Collision avoidance, scanning, obstacle and wire strike avoidance.
PA.VII.B.R6	6. Failure to follow the stall recovery procedure.
PA.VII.B.R7	7. Failure to maintain coordinated flight during the maneuver.
PA.VII.B.R8	8. Secondary stalls.
PA.VII.B.R9	9. Inadvertent stall or spin.
Skills	The applicant demonstrates the ability to:
PA.VII.B.S1	1. Select an entry altitude that will allow the Task to be completed no lower than 1,500 feet AGL.
PA.VII.B.S2	2. Establish a stabilized descent in the approach or landing configuration, as specified by the evaluator.
PA.VII.B.S3	3. Transition smoothly from the approach or landing attitude to a pitch attitude that will induce a stall.
PA.VII.B.S4	4. Maintain a specified heading, ±10°, if in straight flight, and maintain a specified angle of bank not to exceed 20°, ±10° if in turning flight, while inducing the stall or as recommended by the aircraft manufacturer to a safe maneuvering altitude.
PA.VII.B.S5	5. Recognize and recover promptly after a full stall has occurred.
PA.VII.B.S6	6. Retract the flaps to the recommended setting; retract the landing gear, if retractable, after a positive rate of climb is established.
PA.VII.B.S7	7. Execute a stall recovery in accordance with procedures set forth in the AFM/POH.
PA.VII.B.S8	8. Accelerates to V_X or V_Y speed before the final flap retraction and return to the altitude, heading and airspeed specified by the examiner.

A. General Information

1. The objective of this task is for you to demonstrate your knowledge, risk management, and skills related to a power-off stalls.

2. When a stall occurs, you must promptly recover so your airplane does not remain in a stalled condition.

40.1 KNOWLEDGE

A.   Task Objectives

1.   **The applicant demonstrates understanding of the importance of the 1,500-foot AGL minimum altitude.**

    a.   For information on the 1,500-ft. AGL minimum altitude, see Section VII Introduction, Knowledge, item A., on page 503.

2.   **The applicant demonstrates understanding of how the maneuver relates to a normal flight.**

    a.   Power-off stalls are practiced to simulate approach and landing conditions and are usually performed in the landing configuration, i.e., with gear and flaps fully extended.

    b.   Many stall/spin accidents have occurred in these power-off situations, including

        1)   Crossed-control turns (aileron pressure in one direction, rudder pressure in the opposite direction) from base leg to final approach, which results in a skidding or slipping (uncoordinated) turn

        2)   Attempting to recover from a high sink rate on final approach by only increasing pitch attitude

        3)   Improper airspeed control on final approach or in other segments of the traffic pattern

        4)   Attempting to "stretch" a glide in a power-off approach

3.   **The applicant demonstrates understanding of the components of a stabilized descent.**

    a.   A stabilized descent has been achieved when the approach attitude and airspeed have stabilized, which will also result in a constant rate of descent.

4.   **The applicant demonstrates understanding of approach to stall indications.**

    a.   Indications that an airplane is in an approach to stall situation includes

        1)   Decay of control effectiveness.

            a)   Feel is an important sense in recognizing the onset of a stall. As speed is reduced, the resistance to pressures on the controls becomes progressively less.

        2)   Kinesthesia, the sensing of changes in direction or speed of motion, is probably the most important and the best indicator to the trained and experienced pilot.

        3)   Warning light or horn goes off usually 5-10 kt. before stall.

        4)   Buffeting or shaking.

5.   **The applicant demonstrates understanding of full stall indications.**

    a.   The stall will be recognized by clues such as

        1)   Full up-elevator
        2)   High descent rate
        3)   Uncontrollable nosedown pitching
        4)   Possible airframe buffeting or shaking
        5)   Warning light or horn

6.   **The applicant demonstrates understanding of determining which aircraft inputs are required to meet heading or bank angle requirements.**

    a.   Factors to consider to maintain heading and bank angle:

        1)   When the airplane is in a nose-high turning attitude, the angle of bank has a tendency to increase; therefore, aileron pressure must be constantly adjusted.

2) Because of the decreasing airspeed and lift on both wings, the pitch attitude tends to lower; therefore, back-elevator pressure must be continually increased to maintain the pitch attitude.

3) Because the airspeed is decreasing while the power setting remains constant, the effect of torque becomes more prominent, which causes the airplane to yaw; therefore, right rudder pressure must be increased to keep the airplane coordinated, the ball centered, and to prevent adverse yaw from changing the turn rate.

7. **The applicant demonstrates understanding of determining the stall recovery procedure.**

   a. Recovering from the stall should be accomplished by

   1) Releasing the back elevator
   2) Advancing the throttle to maximum available power
   3) Applying right rudder pressure as necessary to overcome the engine torque effects as power is advanced and the nose is being lowered.
   4) Leveling wings if in a banked attitude
   5) After establishing a positive rate of climb, retracting the flaps and landing gear to the recommended setting, as necessary
   6) Returning the throttle to cruise power setting

   b. After recovery is complete, a climb or go-around procedure should be initiated, as the situation dictates, to ensure a minimal loss of altitude.

8. **The applicant demonstrates understanding of the importance of establishing the correct aircraft configuration during the recovery process and the consequences of failing to do so.**

   a. Prompt and proper recovery techniques are important for the following reasons:

   1) Failure to recover from a stalled condition can result in loss of control or impact with terrain.
   2) Abrupt control movements during recovery could result in a secondary stall.
   3) Failure to retract flaps and gear during climbout decreases climb performance.
   4) Failure to reach sufficient climb speeds before flap retraction could result in a secondary stall.
   5) An uncoordinated stall could result in a spin.

9. **The applicant demonstrates understanding of aerodynamics associated with stalls and spins in various aircraft configurations and attitudes.**

   a. For a detailed discussion of stall and spin aerodynamics, see Study Unit 1, "Airplanes and Aerodynamics," Subunit 13, "Stalls and Spins," in *Pilot Handbook*.

10. **The applicant demonstrates understanding of the circumstances that can lead to an inadvertent stall or spin.**

    a. Circumstances that can lead to an inadvertent stall or spin include

    1) Distractions during landing
    2) Improper control inputs during base to final turn including cross control situations
    3) Improper stall recovery
    4) Improper aircraft configuration for the phase of flight (e.g., flaps not extended)
    5) Improper airspeed control
    6) Attempting to stretch a glide

END OF KNOWLEDGE ELEMENT

40.2 RISK MANAGEMENT

A.   Task Objectives

1.   **The applicant demonstrates the ability to identify, assess, and mitigate risks encompassing the interplay of aerodynamic factors [angle of attack (AOA), airspeed, load factor, aircraft configuration, aircraft weight, and aircraft attitude].**

   a.   For information on the interplay of aerodynamic factors, see Section VII Introduction, Risk Management, item A., on page 504.

2.   **The applicant demonstrates the ability to identify, assess, and mitigate risks encompassing the range and limitations of stall warning indicators (e.g., aircraft buffet, stall horn, etc.).**

   a.   For information on the range and limitations of stall warning indicators, see Section VII Introduction, Risk Management, item B., beginning on page 504.

3.   **The applicant demonstrates the ability to identify, assess, and mitigate risks encompassing the effect of environmental elements on aircraft performance.**

   a.   For information on the effect of environmental elements on aircraft performance, see Section VII Introduction, Risk Management, item C., on page 505.

4.   **The applicant demonstrates the ability to identify, assess, and mitigate risks encompassing the required actions for aircraft maximum performance and the consequences of failing to do so.**

   a.   For information on the required actions for aircraft maximum performance, see Section VII Introduction, Risk Management, item D., on page 506.

5.   **The applicant demonstrates the ability to identify, assess, and mitigate risks encompassing collision avoidance, scanning, and obstacle and wire strike avoidance.**

   a.   For information on collision avoidance, scanning, and obstacle avoidance, see Study Unit 7, Subunit 4, beginning on page 66.

   b.   For information on wire strikes, see Study Unit 7, Subunit 6, beginning on page 68.

6.   **The applicant demonstrates the ability to identify, assess, and mitigate risks encompassing failure to follow the stall recovery procedure.**

   a.   Failure to follow the stall recovery procedure can result in loss of control and/or excessive loss of altitude.

      1)   Because one goal of stall recovery is to minimize the loss of altitude, failure to do so could result in uncontrolled flight into terrain.

7.   **The applicant demonstrates the ability to identify, assess, and mitigate risks encompassing failure to maintain coordinated flight during the maneuver.**

   a.   The hazard of stalling during uncoordinated flight is that you may enter a spin.

      1)   The correct amount of rudder pressure must be applied to keep the airplane coordinated.

      2)   If you maintain directional control (coordinated flight), the wing will not drop further before the stall is broken and thus prevent a spin.

8.   **The applicant demonstrates the ability to identify, assess, and mitigate risks encompassing secondary stalls.**

   a.   Attempting to recover from a stall too quickly could result in entering a secondary stall, followed by loss of altitude.

      1)   Your stall recovery technique should be deliberate yet smooth.

9. **The applicant demonstrates the ability to identify, assess, and mitigate risks encompassing inadvertent stall or spin.**

    a.   Divide your attention inside and outside the plane while anticipating the effects of attitude and power setting changes.

        1)   Do not allow the aircraft to operate under conditions such that a stall could be inadvertently encountered.

END OF RISK MANAGEMENT ELEMENT

40.3 SKILLS

A.   Task Objectives

1.   **The applicant demonstrates the ability to select an entry altitude that will allow the Task to be completed no lower than 1,500 feet AGL.**

   a.   Select an altitude that is easy to read from your altimeter.

   1)   The FAA requires the maneuver to be completed no lower than 1,500 ft. AGL. If the terrain elevation is 300 ft. above sea level, start by adding 1,500 ft. (1,800 ft. MSL). Add a 1,000 ft. margin of safety (2,800 ft. MSL). Then round to the next highest 500-ft. increment (3,000 ft. MSL). This will make it easier to identify on your altimeter.

   2)   During your training, you will learn how much altitude you need to perform this maneuver.

   3)   You will likely perform power-off stalls after setting the airplane up for slow flight. You should already be at a safe altitude.

   a)   If you do not feel that you can recover before 1,500 ft. AGL (or a higher manufacturer's recommended altitude), explain this to your evaluator and proceed to climb to a higher altitude.

   b.   **Perform clearing turns** to ensure the area is clear of other traffic.

2.   **The applicant demonstrates the ability to establish a stabilized descent in the approach or landing configuration, as specified by the evaluator.**

   a.   Your evaluator will specify the airplane configuration to use for this task. You should repeat these instructions back to your evaluator to ensure that you heard the instructions correctly.

   1)   At this time, you should also confirm with your evaluator the altitude, heading, and airspeed that you should return to after recovering from the stall.

   2)   This should be a climb at V_X or V_Y (as appropriate) on the entry heading to a safe altitude. In other words, simulate a go-around procedure.

   b.   Use the same procedure that you use to go into slow flight in the landing configuration.

   c.   Maintain a constant altitude and heading while you are slowing your airplane to the normal approach speed.

In your airplane, normal approach speed _____.

   d.   As your airplane approaches the normal approach speed, adjust pitch and power to establish a stabilized approach (i.e., descent).

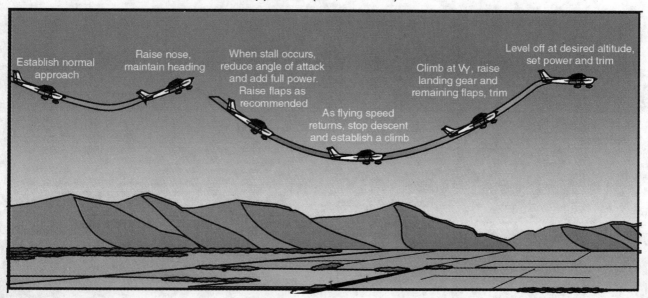

3. **The applicant demonstrates the ability to transition smoothly from the approach or landing attitude to a pitch attitude that will induce a stall.**

    a. Once established in a stabilized approach in the approach or landing configuration, you should smoothly raise the airplane's nose to an attitude which will induce a stall.

        1) In straight flight, maintain directional control with the rudder, the wings held level with the ailerons, and a constant pitch attitude with the elevator.

        2) In turning flight, maintain coordinated flight with the rudder, bank angle with the ailerons, and a constant pitch attitude with the elevator.

            a) No attempt should be made to stall your airplane on a predetermined heading.

        3) In most training airplanes, the elevator should be smoothly brought fully back.

4. **The applicant demonstrates the ability to maintain a specified heading, ±10°, if in straight flight, and maintain a specified angle of bank not to exceed 20°, ±10° if in turning flight, while inducing the stall or as recommended by the aircraft manufacturer to a safe maneuvering altitude.**

    a. As you enter the maneuver, do not neglect your responsibility to maintain heading or bank angle as appropriate.

5. **The applicant demonstrates the ability to recognize and recover promptly after a full stall has occurred.**

    a. Recognize and recover promptly after the stall occurs by simultaneously reducing the angle of attack, increasing power to maximum allowable, and leveling the wings to return to a straight-and-level flight attitude with a minimum loss of altitude appropriate for your airplane.

    b. Though the recovery actions must be taken in a coordinated manner, they are broken down into three steps here for explanation purposes.

        1) First, the key factor in recovering from a stall is regaining positive control of your airplane by reducing the angle of attack.

            a) Because the basic cause of a stall is always an excessive angle of attack, the cause must be eliminated by releasing the back elevator pressure that was necessary to attain that angle of attack or by moving the elevator control forward.

                i)   Each airplane may require a different amount of forward pressure.

                ii) Too much forward pressure can hinder the recovery by imposing a negative load on the wing.

            b) The objective is to reduce the angle of attack but only enough to allow the wing to regain lift. Remember that you want to minimize your altitude loss.

        2) Second, promptly and smoothly apply maximum allowable power to increase airspeed and to minimize the loss of altitude. In most airplanes, the maximum allowable power will be full power, but do not exceed the RPM red line speed.

            a) If carburetor heat is on, you need to turn it off.

            b) Right rudder pressure will be necessary to overcome the torque effect as power is advanced and the nose is being lowered.

       3)   Third, straight-and-level flight should be established with coordinated use of the controls.

          a)   At this time, the wings should be leveled if they were previously banked.

          b)   Do not attempt to deflect the ailerons until the angle of attack has been reduced.

              i)   The adverse yaw caused by the downward aileron may place the airplane in uncoordinated flight, and if the airplane is still in a stalled condition, a spin could be induced.

          c)   After the initial reduction in the angle of attack, the pitch should be adjusted to that required for a climb at V_Y.

          d)   Maintain coordinated flight throughout the recovery.

6. **The applicant demonstrates the ability to retract the flaps to the recommended setting; retract the landing gear, if retractable, after a positive rate of climb is established.**

   a.   Flaps should be partially retracted to reduce drag during recovery from the stall.

      1)   Follow the procedures in your POH/AFM.

   b.   Landing gear (if retractable) should be retracted after a positive rate of climb has been established on the vertical speed indicator.

7. **The applicant demonstrates the ability to execute stall recovery in accordance with procedures set forth in the POH/AFM.**

   a.   Refer to your aircraft's POH/AFM.

8. **The applicant demonstrates the ability to accelerate to V_X or V_Y speed before the final flap retraction and returns to the altitude, heading, and airspeed specified by the examiner.**

   a.   Allow your airplane to accelerate to V_Y before you make the final flap retraction.
   b.   Return to the altitude, heading, and airspeed, as specified by your evaluator.

END OF SKILLS ELEMENT

40.4 COMMON ERRORS

A. Common Errors during Power-Off Stalls

1. **Failure to establish the specified flap and gear (if retractable) configuration prior to entry**

    a. While maintaining altitude, reduce airspeed to slow flight with wing flaps and landing gear (if retractable) extended to the landing configuration.

    1) Use the normal landing configuration unless otherwise specified by your evaluator.

    b. Remember to **perform the required clearing turns**.

2. **Improper pitch, heading, and bank control during straight ahead stalls**

    a. Use your visual and instrument references as in straight descents but with an increasing pitch attitude to induce a stall.

    b. Maintain directional control with the rudder and wings level with the ailerons.

3. **Improper pitch and bank controls during turning stalls**

    a. Use your visual and instrument references as in turning descents but with an increasing pitch attitude to induce a stall.

    b. Use whatever control pressure is necessary to maintain the specified angle of bank and coordinated flight.

4. **Rough or uncoordinated control technique**

    a. As your airplane approaches the stall, the controls become increasingly sluggish, and you may assume that the controls need to be moved in a rough or jerky manner.

    1) Maintain smooth control applications at all times.

    b. Keep your airplane in coordinated flight, even if the controls feel crossed.

    1) If a power-off stall is not properly coordinated, one wing will often drop before the other, and the nose will yaw in the direction of the low wing during the stall.

5. **Failure to achieve a stall**

    a. You must maintain sufficient elevator back pressure to induce a stall.

6. **Improper torque correction**

    a. During recovery, right rudder pressure is necessary to overcome the torque effects as power is advanced and the nose is being lowered.

    b. You must cross-check outside references with the turn coordinator to ensure that the ball remains centered.

7. **Poor stall recognition and delayed recovery**

    a. Some pilots may attempt to hold a stall attitude because they are waiting for a particular event to occur, e.g., an abrupt pitch-down attitude.

    1) While waiting for this to occur, the airplane is losing altitude from the high sink rate of a stalled condition.

    b. Delayed recovery aggravates the stall situation, and if you do not remain in coordinated flight, the airplane is likely to enter a spin.

    c. Recognition and recovery must be immediate and prompt.

8. **Excessive altitude loss or excessive airspeed during recovery**

    a. Do not maintain a pitch-down attitude during recovery.

    1) Move the control yoke forward to reduce the angle of attack; then smoothly adjust the pitch to the desired attitude.

9. **Secondary stall during recovery**

   a. This happens when you hasten to complete your stall recovery (to straight-and-level flight or climb) before the airplane has realigned itself with the flight path (relative wind).

END OF COMMON ERRORS

STUDY UNIT FORTY-ONE
POWER-ON STALLS

Task	Task C. Power-On Stalls
References	FAA-H-8083-2, FAA-H-8083-3; AC 61-67; POH/AFM
Objective	To determine that the applicant exhibits satisfactory knowledge, risk management, and skills associated with power-on stalls. **Note:** *(See Appendix 6 – Safety of Flight)*
Knowledge	The applicant demonstrates understanding of:
PA.VII.C.K1	1. The importance of the 1,500-foot AGL minimum altitude.
PA.VII.C.K2	2. How the maneuver relates to a normal flight.
PA.VII.C.K3	3. Rationale for power setting variances.
PA.VII.C.K4	4. Approach to stall indications.
PA.VII.C.K5	5. Full stall indications.
PA.VII.C.K6	6. Which aircraft inputs are required to meet heading or bank angle requirements.
PA.VII.C.K7	7. Determining the most efficient stall recovery procedure.
PA.VII.C.K8	8. The importance of establishing the correct aircraft configuration during the recovery process and the consequences of failing to do so.
PA.VII.C.K9	9. The aerodynamics associated with stalls and spins in various aircraft configurations and attitudes.
PA.VII.C.K10	10. The circumstances that can lead to an inadvertent stall or spin.
PA.VII.C.K11	11. The circumstances that can lead to an accelerated stall.
Risk Management	The applicant demonstrates the ability to identify, assess and mitigate risks, encompassing:
PA.VII.C.R1	1. Aerodynamic factors (angle of attack (AOA), airspeed, load factor, aircraft configuration, aircraft weight, and aircraft attitude).
PA.VII.C.R2	2. The range and limitations of stall warning indicators (e.g., aircraft buffet, stall horn, etc.).
PA.VII.C.R3	3. The effect of environmental elements on aircraft performance.
PA.VII.C.R4	4. Required actions for aircraft maximum performance and the consequences of failing to do so.
PA.VII.C.R5	5. Accelerated stalls.
PA.VII.C.R6	6. Collision avoidance, scanning, obstacle and wire strike avoidance.
PA.VII.C.R7	7. Failure to follow the stall recovery procedure.
PA.VII.C.R8	8. Failure to maintain coordinated flight during the maneuver.
PA.VII.C.R9	9. Secondary stalls.
PA.VII.C.R10	10. Inadvertent stall or spin.
Skills	The applicant demonstrates the ability to:
PA.VII.C.S1	1. Select an entry altitude that will allow the Task to be completed no lower than 1,500 feet AGL.
PA.VII.C.S2	2. Establish the takeoff, departure, or cruise configuration as specified by the evaluator.
PA.VII.C.S3	3. Set power (as assigned by the evaluator) to no less than 65 percent available power.
PA.VII.C.S4	4. Transition smoothly from the takeoff or departure attitude to the pitch attitude that will induce a stall.
PA.VII.C.S5	5. Maintain a specified heading, ±10°, if in straight flight, and maintain a specified angle of bank not to exceed 20°, ±10°, if in turning flight, while inducing the stall or as recommended by the aircraft manufacturer to a safe maneuvering altitude.
PA.VII.C.S6	6. Recognize and recover promptly after a fully developed stall occurs.
PA.VII.C.S7	7. Retract the flaps to the recommended setting; retract the landing gear if retractable, after a positive rate of climb is established.
PA.VII.C.S8	8. Execute a stall recovery in accordance with procedures set forth in the AFM/POH.
PA.VII.C.S9	9. Accelerate to V_X or V_Y speed before the final flap retraction; return to the altitude, heading, and airspeed specified by the evaluator.

A.   General Information

   1.   The objective of this task is for you to demonstrate your knowledge, risk management, and skills related to power-on stalls.

   2.   You can read the FAA's "Appendix 6 – Safety of Flight" in the Gleim *Private Pilot ACS and Oral Exam Guide* book.

   3.   When a stall occurs, you must promptly recover so your airplane does not remain in a stalled condition.

41.1   KNOWLEDGE

A.   Task Objectives

   1.   **The applicant demonstrates understanding of the importance of the 1,500-foot AGL minimum altitude.**

      a.   For information on the 1,500-ft. AGL minimum altitude, see Section VII Introduction, Knowledge, item A., on page 503.

   2.   **The applicant demonstrates understanding of how the maneuver relates to a normal flight.**

      a.   Power-on stalls are practiced to simulate takeoff and climbout conditions and configurations.

      b.   Many stall/spin accidents have occurred during these phases of flight, particularly during go-arounds. A causal factor in go-arounds has been pilot failure to maintain positive control due to a nose-high trim setting or premature flap retraction.

      c.   Failure to maintain positive control during short-field and soft-field takeoffs has also been an accident factor.

   3.   **The applicant demonstrates understanding of the rationale for power setting variances.**

      a.   Certain high-performance aircraft have so much power that they would require an excessive pitch attitude greater than 30° nose up in order to slow the airplane to a stall speed.

      b.   This excessive pitch may not allow for proper cooling of such a high-performance engine and could cause engine temperatures to exceed limitations.

      c.   Therefore, in these aircraft, you may simulate a power-on stall without using maximum power.

   4.   **The applicant demonstrates understanding of approach to stall indications.**

      a.   Indications that an airplane is in an approach to stall situation includes

         1)   Decay of control effectiveness

            a)   Feel is an important sense in recognizing the onset of a stall. As speed is reduced, the resistance to pressure on the controls becomes progressively less.

         2)   Kinesthesia, the sensing of changes in direction or speed of motion, is probably the most important and the best indicator to the trained and experienced pilot.

         3)   Warning light or horn goes off usually 5-10 knots before stall

         4)   Buffeting or shaking

5. **The applicant demonstrates understanding of full stall indications.**

    a.   The stall will be recognized by clues such as

        1) Full up elevator
        2) High descent rate
        3) Uncontrollable nose-down pitching
        4) Possible airframe buffeting or shaking
        5) Warning light or horn

6. **The applicant demonstrates understanding of which aircraft inputs are required to meet heading or bank angle requirements.**

    a.   Factors to consider to maintain heading and bank angle:

        1) When the airplane is in a nose-high turning attitude, the angle of bank has a tendency to increase; therefore, aileron pressure must be constantly adjusted.
        2) Because of the decreasing airspeed and lift on both wings, the pitch attitude tends to lower; therefore, back-elevator pressure must be continually increased to maintain the pitch attitude.
        3) Because the airspeed is decreasing while the power setting remains constant, the effect of torque becomes more prominent, which causes the airplane to yaw; therefore, right rudder pressure must be increased to keep the airplane coordinated, the ball centered, and to prevent adverse yaw from changing the turn rate.

7. **The applicant demonstrates understanding of determining the most efficient stall recovery procedure.**

    a.   Recovering from the stall should be accomplished by

        1) Releasing the back elevator
        2) Advancing the throttle to maximum available power or verifying it already is at sufficient setting
        3) Applying right rudder pressure as necessary to overcome the engine torque effects as power is advanced and the nose is being lowered
        4) Leveling wings if in a banked attitude
        5) After establishing a positive rate of climb, retracting the flaps and landing gear to the recommended setting, as necessary
        6) Returning the throttle to cruise power setting

    b.   After recovery is complete, a climb or go-around procedure should be initiated, as the situation dictates, to assure a minimum loss of altitude.

8. **The applicant demonstrates understanding of the importance of establishing the correct aircraft configuration during the recovery process and the consequences of failing to do so.**

    a.   Prompt and proper recovery techniques are important for the following reasons:

        1) Failure to recover from a stalled condition can result in a spin.
        2) Abrupt control movements during recovery could result in a secondary stall.
        3) Failure to retract flaps and gear during climbout decreases climb performance.
        4) Failure to reach sufficient climb speed before flap retraction could result in a secondary stall.

9. **The applicant demonstrates understanding of the aerodynamics associated with stalls and spins in various aircraft configurations and attitudes.**

   a. For a detailed discussion of stall and spin aerodynamics, see Study Unit 1, "Airplanes and Aerodynamics," Subunit 13, "Stalls and Spins," in *Pilot Handbook*.

10. **The applicant demonstrates understanding of the circumstances that can lead to an inadvertent stall or spin.**

   a. Circumstances that can lead to an inadvertent stall or spin include

      1) Distractions during takeoff
      2) Improper go around procedures
      3) Improper stall recovery
      4) Improper aircraft configuration for the phase of flight (e.g., flaps not extended)
      5) Improper airspeed control
      6) Attempting to stretch a glide

11. **The applicant demonstrates understanding of the circumstances that can lead to an accelerated stall.**

   a. Accelerated stalls are given this name because they are not associated with any particular airspeed. They are demonstrated to show that stalls occur when an airplane reaches the critical angle of attack, not necessarily at a particular airspeed.

   b. Accelerated stalls occur during steep turns, pull ups, or other abrupt maneuvers.

END OF KNOWLEDGE ELEMENT

41.2 RISK MANAGEMENT

A.   Task Objectives

1.   **The applicant demonstrates the ability to identify, assess, and mitigate risks encompassing aerodynamic factors [angle of attack (AOA), airspeed, load factor, aircraft configuration, aircraft weight, and aircraft attitude].**

   a.   For information on the interplay of aerodynamic factors, see Section VII Introduction, Risk Management, item A., on page 504.

2.   **The applicant demonstrates the ability to identify, assess, and mitigate risks encompassing the range and limitations of stall warning indicators (e.g., aircraft buffet, stall horn, etc.).**

   a.   For information on the range and limitations of stall warning indicators, see Section VII Introduction, Risk Management, item B., beginning on page 504.

3.   **The applicant demonstrates the ability to identify, assess, and mitigate risks encompassing the effect of environmental elements on aircraft performance.**

   a.   For information on the effects of environmental elements on aircraft performance, see Section VII Introduction, Risk Management, item C., on page 505.

4.   **The applicant demonstrates the ability to identify, assess, and mitigate risks encompassing the required actions for aircraft maximum performance and the consequences of failing to do so.**

   a.   For information on the required actions for aircraft maximum performance, see Section VII Introduction, Risk Management, item D., on page 506.

5.   **The applicant demonstrates the ability to identify, assess, and mitigate risks encompassing avoiding accelerated stalls.**

   a.   Avoiding accelerated stalls is best accomplished by

      1)   Avoiding distractions
      2)   Avoiding extreme maneuvers
      3)   Proper planning

   b.   An accelerated stall occurs in a turn, which means the aircraft will stall at higher speeds.

      1)   This may not be expected, which could result in improper recovery technique and loss of control.

6.   **The applicant demonstrates the ability to identify, assess, and mitigate risks encompassing collision avoidance, scanning, and obstacle and wire strike avoidance.**

   a.   For information on collision avoidance, scanning, and obstacle avoidance, see Study Unit 7, Subunit 4, beginning on page 66.

   b.   For information on wire strikes, see Study Unit 7, Subunit 6, beginning on page 68.

7.   **The applicant demonstrates the ability to identify, assess, and mitigate risks encompassing failure to follow the stall recovery procedure.**

   a.   Failure to follow the stall recovery procedure can result in loss of control and/or excessive loss of altitude.

      1)   Since one goal of stall recovery is to minimize the loss of altitude, failure to do so could result in uncontrolled flight into terrain.

8. **The applicant demonstrates the ability to identify, assess, and mitigate risks encompassing failure to maintain coordinated flight during the maneuver.**

    a. The likelihood of stalling in uncoordinated flight is increased during a power-on stall due to the greater torque from high pitch attitude, high power setting, and low airspeed.

        1) A power-on stall will often result in one wing dropping.
        2) Maintaining directional control with the rudder is vital to avoiding a spin.

9. **The applicant demonstrates the ability to identify, assess, and mitigate risks encompassing secondary stalls.**

    a. Attempting to recover from a stall too quickly could result in entering a secondary stall, followed by loss of altitude.

        1) Your stall recovery technique should be deliberate, yet smooth.

10. **The applicant demonstrates the ability to identify, assess, and mitigate risks encompassing inadvertent stall or spin.**

    a. Divide your attention inside and outside the plane while anticipating the effects of attitude and power setting changes.

        1) Do not allow the aircraft to operate under conditions such that a stall could be inadvertently encountered.

END OF RISK MANAGEMENT ELEMENT

41.3 SKILLS

A.   Task Objectives

1.   **The applicant demonstrates the ability to select an entry altitude that will allow the Task to be completed no lower than 1,500 feet AGL.**

   a.   Select an altitude that is easy to read from your altimeter.

      1)   The FAA requires the maneuver to be completed no lower than 1,500 ft. AGL. If the terrain elevation is 300 ft. above sea level, start by adding 1,500 ft. (1,800 ft. MSL). Add a 1,000 ft. margin of safety (2,800 ft. MSL). Then round to the next highest 500-ft. increment (3,000 ft. MSL). This will make it easier to identify on your altimeter.

   b.   During your training, you will learn how much altitude you need to perform this maneuver.

      1)   If you do not feel that you can recover before 1,500 ft. AGL (or a higher manufacturer's recommended altitude), explain this to your evaluator and proceed to climb to a higher altitude.

   c.   **Perform clearing turns** to ensure the area is clear of other traffic.

2.   **The applicant demonstrates the ability to establish the takeoff, departure, or cruise configuration as specified by the evaluator.**

   a.   Power-on stalls should be performed in a takeoff configuration (e.g., for a short-field takeoff) or in a normal climb configuration (flaps and/or gear retracted).

      1)   Use the recommended takeoff or normal climb configuration in your POH/AFM, unless specified otherwise by your evaluator.

   b.   Ensure that you understand which configuration your evaluator wants you to use. If you have any doubt of what (s)he wants, ask for clarification.

      1)   At this time, you should also confirm with your evaluator the altitude, heading, and airspeed that you should return to after recovering from the stall.

   c.   Reduce power to achieve the airspeed specified by your evaluator while establishing the desired configuration.

      1)   You will likely use your normal rotation or climbout speed.
      2)   Maintain a constant altitude while you are slowing your airplane.

3. **The applicant demonstrates the ability to set power (as assigned by evaluator) to no less than 65 percent available power.**

   a. When the desired speed is attained, you should set the power to the takeoff or climb power setting specified by your evaluator while establishing a climb attitude.

      1) For high performance airplanes, a lower power setting may be required to prevent excessive nose-up attitudes, but you should expect to perform this maneuver with at least 65% power.

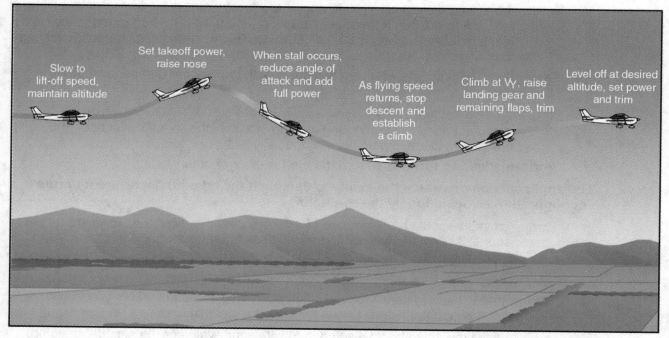

Slow to lift-off speed, maintain altitude

Set takeoff power, raise nose

When stall occurs, reduce angle of attack and add full power

As flying speed returns, stop descent and establish a climb

Climb at V$_y$, raise landing gear and remaining flaps, trim

Level off at desired altitude, set power and trim

4. **The applicant demonstrates the ability to transition smoothly from the takeoff or departure attitude to the pitch attitude that will induce a stall.**

   a. After the climb has been established, the nose is then brought smoothly upward to an attitude obviously impossible for the airplane to maintain (i.e., greater than V$_x$ pitch attitude) and is held at that attitude until the stall occurs.

      1) Increased back-elevator pressure will be necessary to maintain this attitude as the airspeed decreases.

      2) Do not use an extreme pitch attitude, which could result in loss of control.

   b. In straight flight, maintain directional control with the rudder, the wings held level with the ailerons, and a constant pitch attitude with the elevator.

   c. In turning flight, maintain coordinated flight while using a bank angle specified by your evaluator, but no greater than 20°.

   d. Increased right rudder pressure will be required during this maneuver as the airspeed decreases to counteract torque.

5. **The applicant demonstrates the ability to maintain a specified heading, ±10°, if in straight flight, and maintain a specified angle of bank not to exceed 20°, ±10°, if in turning flight, while inducing the stall or as recommended by the aircraft manufacturer to a safe maneuvering altitude.**

   a. As you enter the maneuver, do not neglect your responsibility to maintain heading or bank angle as appropriate.

6. **The applicant demonstrates the ability to recognize and recover promptly after a fully developed stall occurs.**

    a. Though the recovery actions must be taken in a coordinated manner, they are broken down into three steps here for explanation purposes.

    b. First, the key factor in recovering from a stall is regaining positive control of your airplane by reducing the angle of attack.

        1) Because the basic cause of a stall is always an excessive angle of attack, the cause must be eliminated by releasing the back elevator pressure that was necessary to attain that angle of attack or by moving the elevator control forward.

            a) Each airplane may require a different amount of forward pressure.

            b) Too much forward pressure can hinder the recovery by imposing a negative load on the wing.

        2) The objective is to reduce the angle of attack but only enough to allow the wing to regain lift. Remember that you want to minimize your altitude loss.

    c. Second, promptly and smoothly apply maximum allowable power (if not already there) to increase airspeed and to minimize the loss of altitude. In most airplanes, this will be full power, but do not exceed the RPM red line speed.

        1) Because the throttle will most likely be at the takeoff or climb power setting, the addition of power should be relatively slight, if any.

            a) Use this step to confirm that you have maximum allowable power.

    d. Third, straight-and-level flight should be established with coordinated use of the controls.

        1) At this time, the wings should be leveled if they were previously banked.

        2) Do not attempt to deflect the ailerons until the angle of attack has been reduced.

            a) The adverse yaw caused by the downward aileron may place the airplane in uncoordinated flight, and if the airplane is still in a stalled condition, a spin could be induced.

        3) After the initial reduction in the angle of attack, the pitch should be adjusted to that required for a climb at V_Y.

        4) Maintain coordinated flight throughout the recovery.

7. **The applicant demonstrates the ability to retract the flaps to the recommended setting; retract the landing gear if retractable, after a positive rate of climb is established.**

    a. The wing flaps normally will be set to simulate a stall during a short-field takeoff or retracted to simulate a stall during a normal takeoff and/or climb.

        1) If flaps are extended, retract them to the setting recommended by your POH/AFM.

            a) Do not extend the flaps if they are retracted.

        2) Make the final flap retraction only after your airplane has accelerated to V_Y.

    b. A power-on stall is normally performed with the landing gear retracted (if retractable).

        1) If you have the gear down, it should be retracted only after you have established a positive rate of climb on the vertical speed indicator.

8. **The applicant demonstrates the ability to execute stall recovery in accordance with procedures set forth in the POH/AFM.**

   a.   Refer to your aircraft's POH/AFM.

9. **The applicant demonstrates the ability to accelerate to V_X or V_Y speed before the final flap retraction and return to the altitude, heading, and airspeed specified by the evaluator.**

   a.   Return to the altitude, heading, and airspeed (e.g., V_Y or cruise) as instructed by your evaluator.

END OF SKILLS ELEMENT

41.4 COMMON ERRORS

A. Common Errors during Power-On Stalls

1. **Failure to establish the specified landing gear (if retractable) and flap configuration prior to entry**

    a. Repeat the instructions that your evaluator gave to you regarding the airplane configuration for the stall.

        1) Your airplane will be configured for a takeoff or a normal departure climb.

    b. Remember to **perform the required clearing turns**.

2. **Improper pitch, heading, and bank control during straight-ahead stalls**

    a. Use your visual and instrument references as in straight climbs but with a pitch attitude that will induce a stall.

    b. Maintain heading and wings level during the straight-ahead stall.

    c. Use rudder pressure to counteract the torque effects.

3. **Improper pitch and bank control during turning stalls**

    a. Use your visual and instrument references as in a turning climb but with a pitch attitude that will induce a stall.

    b. Use whatever control pressure is necessary to maintain a specified bank angle of not more than 20° in coordinated flight.

4. **Rough or uncoordinated control technique**

    a. As your airplane approaches the stall, the controls will become increasingly sluggish, and you may assume that the controls need to be moved in a rough or jerky manner.

        1) Maintain smooth control applications at all times.
        2) Do not try to muscle your way through this maneuver.

    b. Keep your airplane in coordinated flight (i.e., the ball centered), even if the controls feel crossed.

        1) If a power-on stall is not properly coordinated, one wing will often drop before the other wing, and the nose will yaw in the direction of the low wing during the stall.

5. **Failure to achieve a stall**

    a. You must maintain sufficient back-elevator pressure to induce a stall.

6. **Improper torque correction**

    a. Since the airspeed is decreasing with a high power setting and a high angle of attack, the effect of torque becomes more prominent. Right rudder pressure must be used to counteract torque.

7. **Poor stall recognition and delayed recovery**

    a. Some pilots may attempt to hold a stall attitude because they are waiting for a particular event to occur, e.g., an abrupt pitch-down attitude.

        1) While waiting for this to occur, the airplane is losing altitude from the high sink rate of a stalled condition.

    b. Delayed recovery aggravates the stall situation, and if you do not remain in coordinated flight, the airplane is likely to enter a spin.

    c. Recognition and recovery must be immediate and prompt.

8. **Excessive altitude loss or excessive airspeed during recovery**

    a. Do not maintain a pitch-down attitude during recovery.

        1) Move the control yoke forward to reduce the angle of attack, then smoothly adjust the pitch to the desired climb attitude.

9. **Secondary stall during recovery**

    a. This happens when you rush your stall recovery to straight-and-level flight or climb before the airplane has realigned itself with the flight path (relative wind).

10. **Elevator trim stall**

    a. Using excessive up-elevator trim during entry could make recovery difficult (e.g., it will be more difficult to lower the nose).

END OF COMMON ERRORS

STUDY UNIT FORTY-TWO
SPIN AWARENESS

Task	**Task D. Spin Awareness**
References	FAA-H-8083-2, FAA-H-8083-3; AC 61-67; POH/AFM
Objective	To determine that the applicant exhibits satisfactory knowledge, risk management, and skills associated with spins, flight situations where unintentional spins may occur and procedures for recovery from unintentional spins.
Knowledge	The applicant demonstrates understanding of:
PA.VII.D.K1	1. Aerodynamics associated with stalls and spins in various aircraft configurations and attitudes.
PA.VII.D.K2	2. The circumstances that can lead to an inadvertent stall or spin.
PA.VII.D.K3	3. Spin recovery procedures.
Risk Management	The applicant demonstrates the ability to identify, assess and mitigate risks, encompassing:
PA.VII.D.R1	1. The interplay of aerodynamic factors (angle of attack (AOA), airspeed, load factor, aircraft configuration, aircraft weight, and aircraft attitude).
PA.VII.D.R2	2. The range and limitations of stall warning indicators (e.g., aircraft buffet, stall horn, etc.).
PA.VII.D.R3	3. The environmental element effects on aircraft performance.
PA.VII.D.R4	4. The required actions for aircraft maximum performance and the consequences of failing to do so.
PA.VII.D.R5	5. Uncoordinated flight.
PA.VII.D.R6	6. Hazards associated with the improper application of flight control inputs during the spin recovery.
PA.VII.D.R7	7. Collision avoidance, scanning, obstacle and wire strike avoidance.
Skills	The applicant demonstrates the ability to:
PA.VII.D.S1	1. Assess and avoid situations where unintentional spins may occur.
PA.VII.D.S2	2. Explain procedures for recovery from unintentional spins.

A. General Information

1. The objective of this task is for you to demonstrate your knowledge, risk management, and skills related to spins, flight situations where unintentional spins may occur, and procedures for recovery from unintentional spins.

2. This is an oral task during your practical exam.

a. You are not required to perform spins either during your training or on your practical test.

42.1 KNOWLEDGE

A. Task Objectives

    1.   **The applicant demonstrates understanding of aerodynamics associated with stalls and spins in various aircraft configurations and attitudes.**

        a.   A spin is an aggravated stall that results in autorotation, in which the airplane follows a corkscrew path in a downward direction.

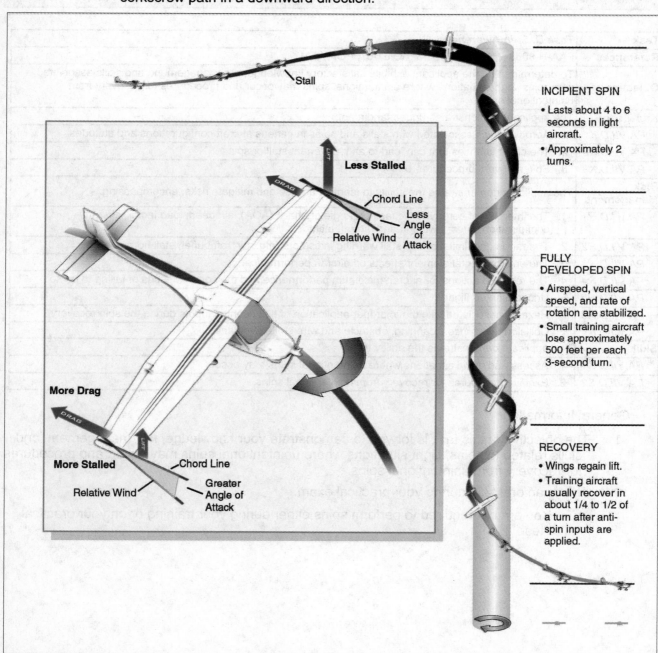

    b.   A spin may be broken down into four phases.

        1)   The **entry phase** is when the pilot provides the necessary elements for the spin, either accidentally or intentionally.

            a)   Similar to a power-off stall, power should be reduced to idle, then pitch increased to induce a stall.

            b)   As the airplane approaches a stall, smoothly apply full rudder in the direction of the desired spin rotation while applying full back (up) elevator.

            c)   Ailerons should be maintained in the neutral position unless specified otherwise in the POH/AFM.

        2)   The **incipient phase** is the transient period between a stall and a fully developed spin, when a final balancing of aerodynamic and inertial forces has not yet occurred.

        3)   The **developed phase** is that portion of the spin in which it is stabilized with a nearly vertical flight path and the aerodynamic forces are in balance.

        4)   The **recovery phase** begins when controls are applied to stop the spin and ends when level flight is attained.

    c.   For a detailed discussion of stall and spin aerodynamics, see Study Unit 1, "Airplanes and Aerodynamics," of *Pilot Handbook*, see Subunit 13, "Stalls and Spins."

2.   **The applicant demonstrates understanding of circumstances that can lead to an inadvertent stall or spin.**

    a.   The primary cause of an inadvertent spin is stalling the airplane while executing a turn with excessive or insufficient rudder.

    b.   The critical phases of flight for stall/spin accidents are

        1)   Takeoff and departure
        2)   Approach and landing and go-around
        3)   Engine failure

    c.   Spins can occur when practicing stalls with

        1)   Uncoordinated flight control input
        2)   Aileron deflection at critical angles of attack

3.   **The applicant demonstrates understanding of spin recovery procedures.**

    a.   For a detailed discussion of spin recovery procedures, see Subunit 42.3, item A.2.

END OF KNOWLEDGE ELEMENT

42.2 RISK MANAGEMENT

A.   Task Objectives

1.   **The applicant demonstrates the ability to identify, assess, and mitigate risks encompassing the interplay of aerodynamic factors [angle of attack (AOA), airspeed, load factor, aircraft configuration, aircraft weight, and aircraft attitude.]**

   a.   For information on the interplay of aerodynamic factors, see Section VII Introduction, Risk Management, item A., on page 504.

2.   **The applicant demonstrates the ability to identify, assess, and mitigate risks encompassing the range and limitations of stall warning indicators (e.g., aircraft buffet, stall horn, etc.).**

   a.   For information on the range and limitations of stall warning indicators, see Section VII Introduction, Risk Management, item B., beginning on page 504.

3.   **The applicant demonstrates the ability to identify, assess, and mitigate risks encompassing the environmental element effects on aircraft performance.**

   a.   For information on the effect of environmental elements on aircraft performance, see Section VII Introduction, Risk Management, item C., on page 505.

4.   **The applicant demonstrates the ability to identify, assess, and mitigate risks encompassing the required actions for aircraft maximum performance and the consequences of failing to do so.**

   a.   For information on the required action for aircraft maximum performance, see Section VII Introduction, Risk Management, item D., on page 506.

5.   **The applicant demonstrates the ability to identify, assess, and mitigate risks encompassing uncoordinated flight.**

   a.   A spin is caused when the airplane's wing exceeds its critical angle of attack (stall) with a sideslip or yaw acting on the airplane (uncoordinated flight) at, or beyond, the actual stall.

   b.   Simply put, don't stall in uncoordinated flight and you won't spin the plane.

   c.   Pay special attention to those critical parts of flying where angles of attack are high and uncoordinated flight is possible, such as climbout and turns.

6.   **The applicant demonstrates the ability to identify, assess, and mitigate risks encompassing hazards associated with the improper application of flight control inputs during the spin recovery.**

   a.   Power aggravates the spin for use only in the absence of the manufacturer's characteristics.

   b.   Aileron control in the direction of the spin may speed up the rate of rotation and delay the recovery. Aileron control opposite the direction of the spin may cause the down aileron spin to move the wing deeper into the stall and aggravate the situation.

   c.   If the rudder is not neutralized at the proper time, the ensuing increased airspeed acting upon the fully deflected rudder will cause an excessive and unfavorable yawing effect. This places great strain on the airplane and may cause a secondary spin in the opposite direction.

   d.   Improper use of elevator pressure and/or application of rudder and ailerons during the recovery can result in a secondary stall and possibly another spin.

   e.   Slow and overly cautious control movements during spin recovery must be avoided.

7. **The applicant demonstrates the ability to identify, assess, and mitigate risks encompassing collision avoidance, scanning, and obstacle and wire strike avoidance.**

   a. For information on collision avoidance, scanning, and obstacle avoidance, see Study Unit 7, Subunit 4, beginning on page 66.

   b. For information on wire strikes, see Study Unit 7, Subunit 6, beginning on page 68.

END OF RISK MANAGEMENT ELEMENT

42.3 SKILLS

A. Task Objectives

1. **The applicant demonstrates the ability to assess and avoid situations where unintentional spins may occur.**

    a. A classic situation where a pilot could play an important role in a stall/spin accident is during a go-around or short field takeoff where the airplane is at a high pitch attitude, high power setting, and low airspeed.

    b. The pilot may not be aware that a critical angle of attack is approaching until the stall warning device activates. If a stall recovery is not promptly initiated, the airplane is more likely to enter an inadvertent spin.

    c. For example, stall/spin accidents have occurred during a turn from base to final because the pilot attempted to rudder the airplane around (skid) so as not to overshoot the runway or use excessive bank angle in the traffic pattern.

2. **The applicant demonstrates the ability to explain procedures for recovery from unintentional spins.**

    a. Continued practice in stalls will help you to develop a more instinctive and prompt reaction in recognizing an approaching spin.

        1) It is essential to learn to apply immediate corrective action anytime it is apparent that your airplane is near a spin condition.

        2) If an unintentional spin can be prevented, it should be.

            a) Avoiding a spin shows sound pilot judgment and is a positive indication of alertness.

        3) If it is impossible to avoid a spin, you should execute an immediate recovery.

    b. In the absence of specific recovery techniques in your airplane's POH/AFM, the following technique is suggested for spin recovery.

        1) The first corrective action taken during any power-on spin is to close the throttle completely to eliminate power and minimize loss of altitude.

            a) Power aggravates the spin characteristics and causes an abnormal loss of altitude in the recovery.

        2) To recover from the spin, you should neutralize the ailerons, determine the direction of the turn, and apply full opposite rudder.

            a) Opposite rudder should be maintained until the rotation stops. Then the rudder should be neutralized. Continue to use the rudder for directional control.

            b) If the rudder is not neutralized at the proper time, the ensuing increased airspeed acting upon the fully deflected rudder will cause an excessive and unfavorable yawing effect. This places great strain on the airplane and may cause a secondary spin in the opposite direction.

        3) When the rotation slows, apply brisk, positive straight-forward movement of the elevator control (forward of the neutral position). The control should be held firmly in this position.

            a) The forceful movement of the elevator will decrease the excessive angle of attack and will break the stall.

        4) Once the stall is broken, the spinning will stop. When the rudder is neutralized, gradually apply enough back elevator pressure to return to level flight.

            a) Too much or abrupt back elevator pressure and/or application of rudder and ailerons during the recovery can result in a secondary stall and possibly another spin.

END OF SKILLS ELEMENT

PART III
SECTION VIII:
BASIC INSTRUMENT MANEUVERS

Study Units 43 through 48 of Section VIII explain the six FAA ACS tasks (A-F) of Basic Instrument Maneuvers. These tasks include knowledge, risk management, and skill. Your evaluator is required to test you on all six of these tasks.

Accident investigations reveal that weather continues to be cited as a factor in general aviation accidents more frequently than any other cause. The data also show that weather-involved accidents are more likely to result in fatalities than are other accidents. Low ceilings, rain, and fog continue to head the list in the fatal, weather-involved, general aviation accidents. This type of accident is usually the result of inadequate preflight preparation and/or planning, continued VFR flight into adverse weather conditions, and attempted operation beyond the pilot's experience/ability level.

A pilot cannot cope with flight when external visual references are obscured unless visual reference is transferred to the flight instruments. The motion sensing by the inner ear in particular tends to confuse the pilot. False sensations often are generated, leading the pilot to believe the attitude of his or her airplane has changed when, in fact, it has not. These sensations result in spatial disorientation.

This training in the use of flight instruments does not prepare you for unrestricted operations in instrument weather conditions. It is intended as an emergency measure only (although it is also excellent training in the smooth control of an airplane). Intentional flight in such conditions should be attempted only by those who have been thoroughly trained, hold their instrument rating, and are approved by ATC to fly into IFR conditions.

The objective of learning basic instrument maneuvers as part of your private pilot (VFR) training is to allow you to return to VFR conditions should you inadvertently/accidentally find yourself in instrument conditions. Having some experience flying by instruments and entering instrument conditions briefly will prepare you for this eventuality as a private pilot.

The tasks in this section have several common items, listed and explained here instead of repeated throughout the text.

The following common task item topics are included in this section introduction:

KNOWLEDGE — Page

A. The applicant demonstrates understanding of flight instrument function and operation. — 547

B. The applicant demonstrates understanding of flight instrument sensitivity, limitations, and potential errors in unusual attitudes. — 554

C. The applicant demonstrates understanding of flight instrument correlation (pitch instruments/bank instruments). — 560

D. The applicant demonstrates understanding of vestibular illusions (leans) and spatial disorientation. — 560

E. The applicant demonstrates understanding of appropriate pitch, bank, and power setting for the airplane being flown. — 561

RISK MANAGEMENT

A. The applicant demonstrates the ability to identify, assess, and mitigate risks encompassing lack of proficiency in flight by reference to instruments. — 562

B. The applicant demonstrates the ability to identify, assess, and mitigate risks encompassing poor cockpit management. — 562

C. The applicant demonstrates the ability to identify, assess, and mitigate risks encompassing lack of awareness of the direction for nearest VMC. — 563

D. The applicant demonstrates the ability to identify, assess, and mitigate risks encompassing loss of situational awareness during low visibility or instrument conditions. — 564

KNOWLEDGE

A. **The applicant demonstrates understanding of flight instrument function and operation.**

1. **Pitot-Static System**

   a. The pitot-static system provides the source of atmospheric air pressure for operation of the altimeter, vertical speed indicator, and airspeed indicator.

   b. The two major parts of the pitot-static system are

      1) The pitot tube lines
      2) The static port(s) and lines

   c. Ram air pressure is taken from a pitot tube, which is normally mounted on or beneath the leading edge of the left wing (so it can be seen easily by the pilot, especially in icing conditions) and aligned with the relative wind.

      1) The pitot line is connected only to the airspeed indicator.
      2) Some pitot tubes are equipped with an electric heating element to prevent ice from blocking the pitot tube.
      3) Pitot tubes also have a drain opening to remove water.

   d. The static pressure (pressure of the still air) is usually taken from the static line attached to a vent or vents mounted flush with the side of the fuselage.

      1) In some airplanes, the static source is found on the back of the pitot tube.
      2) The static pressure lines provide static air pressure to the altimeter, vertical speed indicator, and airspeed indicator.

   e. During the visual inspection of your airplane, it is important for you to check that none of the openings on the pitot tube and static vents are blocked.

      1) If they are blocked, they should be cleared by a certified maintenance technician.

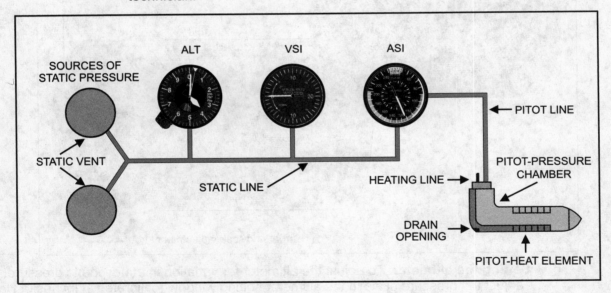

2.   **Altimeter (ALT)**

    a.   The altimeter measures the height of the airplane above a given level.

    b.   **Principle of operation.** The pressure altimeter is simply an aneroid (mechanical) barometer that measures the pressure of the atmosphere at the altimeter's location to display an altitude indication in feet.

        1)   The altimeter uses static pressure as its source of operation. Thus, altitude is determined in terms of air pressure.

        2)   The basic component of the altimeter is the aneroid wafer.

           a)   A stack of these wafers expands or contracts as atmospheric pressure changes and, through a shaft and gearing linkage, rotates the pointers on the dial of the altimeter.

        3)   The presentation of altitude varies considerably among different types of altimeters. Some have only one pointer (or hand), but most have three pointers.

           a)   The altimeter below indicates an altitude of 14,500 ft.

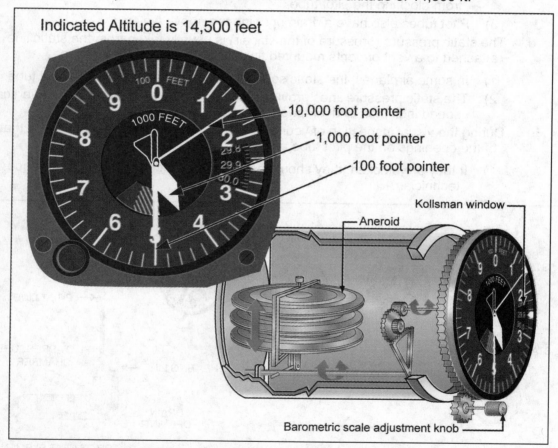

Indicated Altitude is 14,500 feet

10,000 foot pointer

1,000 foot pointer

100 foot pointer

Kollsman window

Aneroid

Barometric scale adjustment knob

    c.   **Setting the altimeter.** To adjust the altimeter for variation in atmospheric pressure, adjust the pressure scale in the altimeter setting window (calibrated in inches of Hg) to correspond with the given altimeter setting.

3.   **Vertical Speed Indicator (VSI)**

    a.   The VSI indicates whether the airplane is climbing, descending, or flying level. The rate of climb or descent is indicated in feet per minute (fpm). If properly calibrated, the indicator will register zero in level flight.

4.   **Airspeed Indicator (ASI)**

    a.   The ASI indicates the speed at which the airplane is moving through the air.

        1)   Airspeed must not be confused with groundspeed, which is the speed at which the airplane is moving across the ground.

    b.   **Principle of operation.** The ASI is a differential air pressure instrument that measures the difference between the **total pressure** (measured from the pitot line) and static pressure. This difference is called **dynamic pressure**.

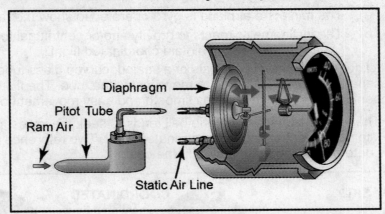

    a.   To measure the dynamic pressure, the ASI is constructed as a sealed case in which a diaphragm is mounted.

        1)   The pitot line (total pressure) is connected to one side of the diaphragm.
        2)   The static line is connected to the other side of the diaphragm.

    b.   As the airplane moves, ram pressure becomes greater than static pressure, causing the diaphragm to expand.

        1)   Expansion or contraction of the diaphragm moves the indicator needle by means of gears and levers.

    c.   The airspeed dial may be calibrated to convert dynamic pressure into units of knots (kt.), miles per hour (mph), or both.

    d.   The ASI is calibrated to display an airspeed representative of a given dynamic pressure only at ISA sea-level values; thus, it does not reflect changes in density altitude.

5.   **Gyroscopic Flight Instruments**

    a.   Several flight instruments contain gyroscopes that are used for their operation. These instruments are the turn indicator, the heading indicator, and the attitude indicator.

        1)   Gyroscopic instruments are operated by either a vacuum or an electrical system. In most light airplanes, the vacuum system powers the heading and attitude indicators, and the electrical system powers the turn indicator.

    b.   **Vacuum system.** The vacuum or suction system spins the gyro by drawing a stream of air against the rotor vanes to spin the rotor at high speeds in essentially the same way as a water wheel or turbine operates. Normally, a vacuum pump is used to provide the vacuum required to spin the rotors. Some airplanes are equipped with a pressure pump that works in basically the same way except the air is pushed through the gyros rather than pulled through.

    c.   For more information about gyroscopic principles, see Study Unit 2 in *Pilot Handbook*.

6. **Turn Coordinator (TC)**

    a.   The TC is a type of turn indicator commonly used in airplanes to indicate rate and quality of turn and to serve as an emergency source of bank information if the attitude indicator fails.

        1)   The TC is illustrated below.

        2)   The TC is actually a combination of two instruments: a miniature airplane and an inclinometer (or ball).

           a)   The miniature airplane is gyro-operated to show the rate of turn.

           b)   The inclinometer reacts to gravity and/or centrifugal force to indicate the need for rudder to maintain coordinated flight.

    b.   The inclinometer of the TC consists of a sealed, curved glass tube containing kerosene and a ball that is free to move inside the tube. The fluid provides a dampening action, which ensures smooth and easy movement of the ball.

        1)   The tube is curved so that the ball tends to seek the lowest point, which is the center of the tube during coordinated flight. Two reference markers aid in determining when the ball is in the center.

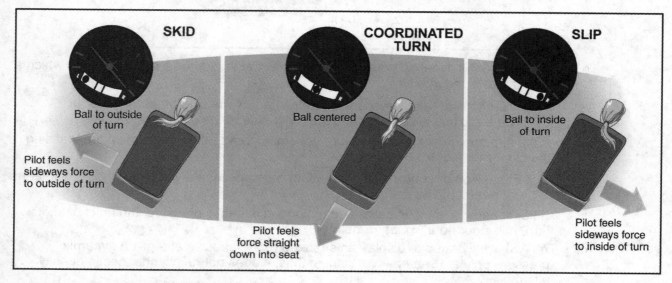

7. **Turn-and-Slip Indicator (T&SI)**

    a.   The T&SI is another type of turn indicator used in some older airplanes. The T&SI has a needle instead of a miniature airplane and indicates movement only around the vertical (yaw) axis, not the longitudinal (roll) axis.

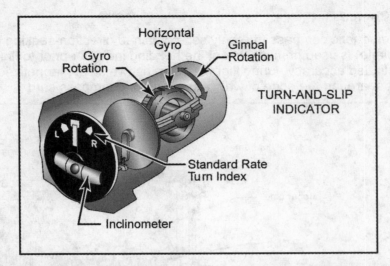

b. The inclinometer in the T&SI works in the same manner as in the TC.

8. **Attitude Indicator (AI)**

   a. The AI, with its miniature aircraft and horizon bar, depicts the attitude of the airplane.

   1) The relationship of the miniature airplane to the horizon bar is the same as the relationship of the real airplane to the actual horizon.

   2) The instrument gives an instantaneous indication of even the smallest changes in attitude.

   3) In most light airplanes, the AI is powered by the vacuum system.

   b. The gyro in the attitude indicator is mounted on a horizontal plane and depends upon rigidity in space for its operation. The horizon bar is fixed to the gyro. It remains in a horizontal plane as the airplane is pitched or banked about its lateral or longitudinal axis. The dial (banking scale) indicates the bank angle.

   c. An adjustment knob is provided with which you may move the miniature airplane up or down to align it with the horizon bar to suit your line of vision. Normally, it is adjusted so that the wings overlap the horizon bar during straight-and-level cruising flight.

9. **Heading Indicator (HI)**

   a. The HI is a gyroscopic instrument commonly used in light airplanes as the primary source of heading information.

   1) In most light airplanes, the HI is powered by the vacuum system.

10. **Magnetic Compass**

   a. The magnetic compass (the only self-contained direction-seeking instrument in the airplane) is used primarily to set the heading indicator prior to flight and to verify its continued accuracy during flight. It contains two steel magnetized needles fastened to a float around the edge of which is mounted a compass card.

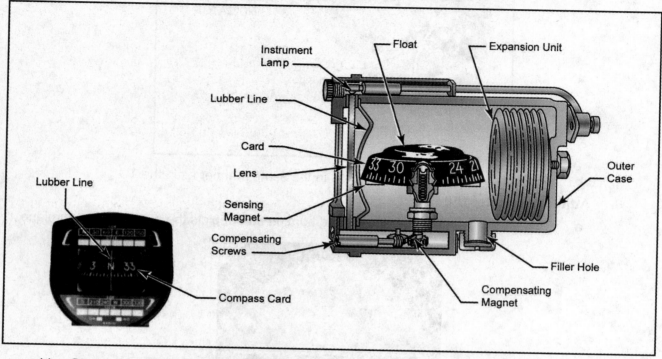

11. **Glass Cockpit Instrumentation**

   a. It is now very common in general aviation airplanes to find glass cockpit instrumentation and automation of basic flight indications.

      1) All major aircraft manufacturers now have a full glass cockpit as standard or optional equipment.

      2) A **glass cockpit** is a system of electronic flight displays (EFDs) and associated components that display information, such as

         a) Aircraft flight attitude and direction
         b) Location via a moving map
         c) Pertinent engine information

      3) **Integrated avionics systems** take glass cockpits one step further by pairing them with communication and navigation radios, transponders, autopilots, weather and traffic display systems, and even cabin controls.

   b. Although all glass cockpit, or EFD, systems are slightly different, they almost always contain two central components.

      1) **Primary Flight Display (PFD)**

         a) The PFD usually consists of the six basic flight instruments (displayed electronically).

         b) Navigational instruction can also be displayed.

         c) Various insets of traffic, terrain, and moving map information can be selected.

         d) The image on the next page describes how the basic flight instruments are represented on a PFD.

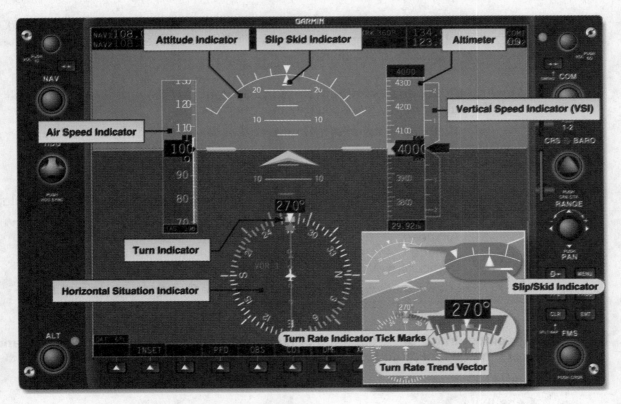

2) **Multi-Function Display (MFD)**

    a)   The MFD usually includes a large moving map (several map pages may be available) and engine instrumentation. With some installations, it is used as a backup for the PFD.

    b)   The MFD can usually interface with (display) weather radar, traffic avoidance systems, terrain warning systems, and various forms of navigational charts and/or instrument approach plates.

    c)   A typical MFD presentation is shown below.

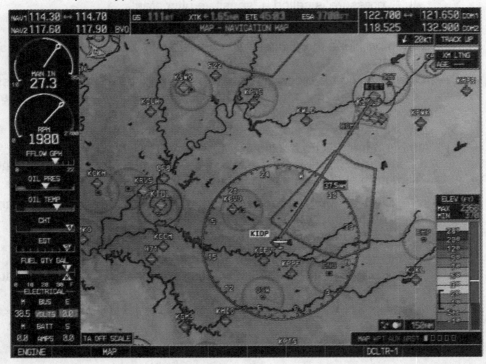

c. Glass cockpit systems get their display information from electronic sources instead of traditional pitot-static and vacuum systems. This increases the internal, error-monitoring capability of the units while making them more reliable and reducing maintenance.

1) An **Attitude and Heading Reference System (AHRS)** provides information typically given by gyroscopic instruments, such as

a) Attitude (pitch/bank) information
b) Heading
c) Rate of turn
d) Turn coordination

2) An **Air Data Computer (ADC)** provides information typically given by pitot-static instruments, such as

a) Airspeed
b) Altitude
c) Vertical speed

3) These devices are typically referred to as **Line Replaceable Units (LRUs)** because of their stand-alone nature and the ease with which they can be replaced.

B. **The applicant demonstrates understanding of flight instrument sensitivity, limitations, and potential errors in unusual attitudes.**

1. **Altimeter (ALT)**

a. **Sensitivity**

1) The altimeter provides an instantaneous measurement of static pressure of the atmosphere at the altimeter's location.

2) Static pressure, or ambient pressure, is always present whether the airplane is moving or at rest.

3) Because actual atmospheric pressure continually changes, a means is provided to adjust the altimeter to compensate for nonstandard pressure.

a) An altimeter with the means of adjusting to the changes in barometric pressure is called a "sensitive altimeter."

b. **Limitations**

1) During preflight, the pilot should check to make sure that the static source (port) is clear.

2) If the static port is blocked, static pressure will be trapped in the system and the altimeter will show a fixed altitude, regardless of whether the aircraft climbs or descends.

3) The altimeter is only correct if set to local altimeter setting.

4) Although there is no maximum error for VFR flight, you should check the amount of error in calibration before takeoff. This can be done by setting the current altimeter setting and making note of the error.

a) For IFR flight, the error should not exceed 75 feet. This tolerance is also recommended for VFR flight.

c. **Potential Errors in Unusual Attitudes**

1) The altimeter is a secondary instrument to the airspeed indicator when determining a nose-low unusual attitude or nose-high unusual attitude.

2.   **Vertical Speed Indicator (VSI)**

    a.   **Sensitivity**

        1)   When the airplane is on the ground or in level flight, the pressures inside the diaphragm and the instrument case remain the same, and the pointer indicates zero.

        2)   When the airplane climbs or descends, the VSI indicates immediate movement of the instrument needle.

            a)   Due to instrument design, it may take several seconds to read accurately.

    b.   **Limitations**

        1)   Use of the alternate static source will have the VSI initially indicate a climb while in level flight, then return to a level indication.

        2)   A blockage of the static port would cause the VSI to indicate zero.

        3)   The time period from the initial change in the rate of climb until the VSI displays an accurate indication of the new rate is called the lag.

            a)   Rough control technique and turbulence can extend the lag period and cause erratic and unstable rate indications.

    c.   **Potential Errors in Unusual Attitudes**

        1)   Although the VSI will give you an immediate indication of whether the airplane is climbing, descending, or flying level, the pilot must be sure to cross-check instrumentation to evaluate the situation before making control inputs.

        2)   The VSI is a secondary instrument in the determination if in a nose-high unusual attitude or a nose-low unusual attitude.

3.   **Airspeed Indicator (ASI)**

    a.   **Sensitivity**

        1)   The ASI provides the immediate indication of differential air pressure, or dynamic pressure. As the airplane moves and ram air pressure (pitot pressure) changes in reference to static pressure, the internal diaphragm immediately senses the changes and correspondingly expands or contracts resulting in immediate indication on the airspeed dial.

    b.   **Limitations**

        1)   Indicated airspeed (IAS) errors exist within the airspeed range.

            a)   Installation (position) error is caused by the static port(s) sensing erroneous static pressure. The slipstream flow causes disturbances at the static port(s), preventing true static pressure measurement.

            b)   Also, at varying angles of attack, the pitot tube does not always point directly into the relative wind, which causes erroneous total (or impact) pressure measurement.

            c)   At certain airspeeds and with certain flap settings, the installation and instrument error may be several knots. This error is generally greatest at low airspeeds.

            d)   In the cruising and higher airspeed ranges, IAS and calibrated airspeed (CAS) are approximately the same.

        2)   The ASI does not correct for density altitude.

            a)   True airspeed (TAS) is CAS corrected for density altitude. TAS is the true speed of an airplane through the air.

c.   **Potential Errors in Unusual Attitudes**

1)   When recovering from unusual attitudes by reference to instruments, it is necessary to cross-check instrumentation to evaluate the situation before making control inputs. Initiating a recovery based on a single instrument may exacerbate the situation if the failure of that instrument was a link in the chain of events that led to the unusual attitude in the first place.

2)   Caution must be taken to keep the airspeed in a safe operating range, and not overstress the aircraft during the recovery process from an unusual attitude.

4.   **Turn Coordinator (TC)**

a.   **Sensitivity**

1)   The TC design tilts the gimbal axis of the electrically operated gyro up about 30° so that the gyro precesses in reaction to movement about both the vertical (yaw) and the longitudinal (roll) axes.

2)   The principle of precession allows the TC to provide an immediate indication of direction of roll, and when stabilized, a rate of turn.

3)   The inclinometer of the TC consists of a sealed, curved glass tube containing kerosene and a ball that is free to move inside the tube. The fluid provides a dampening action, which ensures smooth and easy movement of the ball.

b.   **Limitations**

1)   The TC indicates direction of roll or yaw and rate of turn.

a)   The TC does not give a direct indication of the banked attitude of the airplane.

b)   The miniature airplane will show a turn in a wings-level yaw or during a turn while taxiing.

2)   The gyro of the TC is normally electrically driven; therefore, an electrical failure will render the miniature airplane unusable.

3)   The bearings of the gyro can wear and eventually fail. A grinding sound from the TC will indicate the need for inspection and possible replacement.

c.   **Potential Errors in Unusual Attitudes**

1)   When recovering from unusual attitudes by reference to instruments, it is necessary to cross-check instrumentation to evaluate the situation before making control inputs. Initiating a recovery based on a single instrument may exacerbate the situation if the failure of that instrument was a link in the chain of events that led to the unusual attitude in the first place.

2)   The TC is a primary instrument for bank indication in the recovery from an unusual attitude.

5.   **Turn-and-Slip Indicator (T&SI)**

a.   **Sensitivity**

1)   The dampened action of the ball in the inclinometer measures the relative strength of the force of gravity and the force of inertia cased by a turn.

2)   When the aircraft yaws, or rotates about its vertical axis, it produces a force in the horizontal plane that, due to precession, causes the gyro and its gimbal to rotate about the gimbal's (lateral) axis. Restrained by a calibration spring, just enough rolling over motion is created to cause the pointer to deflect until it aligns with one of the dog-house shaped markers.

b. **Limitations**

1) The major limitation of the older T&SI is that it senses rotation only about the vertical (yaw) axis; it tells nothing of the rotation around the longitudinal (roll) axis, which, in normal flight, occurs before the aircraft begins to turn.

   a) The turn needle indicates only the rate at which the airplane is rotating about its vertical axis.

   b) The needle will deflect in a wings-level yaw or during a turn while taxiing.

2) The inclinometer does not indicate the amount bank, nor does it indicate slip; it only indicates the relationship between the angle of bank and the rate of yaw.

6. **Attitude Indicator (AI)**

a. **Sensitivity**

1) The instrument gives an instantaneous indication of even the smallest changes in attitude (pitch and roll) due to aircraft movement about the vertically upright and two-gimbaled gyro.

2) The AI is highly reliable and the most realistic flight instrument on the instrument panel. Its indications are very close approximations of the actual attitude of the airplane.

b. **Limitations**

1) The AI will give an erroneous reading if there is a low vacuum or loss of vacuum situation.

   a) Some airplanes are equipped with a low-vacuum warning light to warn you of a possible low-vacuum condition. When the light is on, you should check the suction gauge and be prepared for erroneous readings on the vacuum-driven gyro instruments because the air flow is not spinning the gyros fast enough.

   b) Some airplanes are also equipped with a standby vacuum system that is driven by the manifold induction system on the airplane engine.

2) The gyro in the AI takes time (within about 5 min.) to stabilize. After it is stabilized, the indication should be a level attitude and not indicate a bank.

   a) If the horizon bar fails to remain in the horizontal position during straight taxiing or indicates a bank in excess of 5° during taxi turns, the instrument is to be considered unreliable.

3) The failure of the AI while in instrument meteorological conditions (IMC) is a major reason for the instrument cross-check.

   a) Usually when an AI fails and the horizon falls over, you follow it because it appears you are banking in the opposite direction.

   b) Remember, when the AI does NOT respond to a significant control movement (pitch or bank), it has probably failed.

4) The AI indicates a bank, but a bank is not necessarily a turn. What appears to be a turn could be the result of crossed controls where a slight bank is offset by opposite rudder to obtain straight but uncoordinated flight.

   a) Always perform instrument cross-check to confirm the attitude of the aircraft.

c. **Potential Errors in Unusual Attitudes**

1) In moderate unusual attitudes, the pilot can normally reorient by establishing a level flight indication on the AI.

   a) However, the pilot should not depend on this instrument if the AI is the spillable type because it's upset limits may have been exceeded or it may have become inoperative due to mechanical malfunction.

2) If it is the nonspillable-type instrument and is operating properly, errors up to 5° of pitch-and-bank may result and its indications are very difficult to interpret in extreme attitudes.

3) As soon as the unusual attitude is detected, the recommended recovery procedures stated in the POH/AFM should be initiated.

   a) If there are no recommended procedures stated in the POH/AFM, the recovery should be initiated by reference to the ASI, altimeter, VSI, and turn coordinator.

4) It is important to remember that when recovering from unusual altitudes by reference to instruments, it is necessary to cross-check instrumentation to evaluate the situation before making control inputs. Initiating a recovery based on a single instrument may exacerbate the situation if the failure of that instrument was a link in the chain of events that led to the unusual attitude in the first place.

5) AIs are free from most errors, but depending upon the speed with which the erection system functions, there may be a slight nose-up indication during a rapid acceleration and a nose-down indication during a rapid deceleration. There is also a possibility of a small bank angle and pitch error after a 180° turn. These inherent errors are small and correct themselves within a minute or so after returning to straight-and-level flight.

7. **Heading Indicator (HI)**

   a. **Sensitivity**

      1) The gyro in the HI is mounted in a double gimbal, spinning horizontally to allow the sensing of rotation about the vertical axis.

      2) As both the instrument case and the airplane revolve around the vertical axis, the card provides clear and accurate heading information.

   b. **Limitations**

      1) Because of precession, caused chiefly by bearing friction or improper vacuum pressure, the HI may creep or drift from a heading to which it is set.

         a) Among other factors, the amount of drift depends largely upon the condition of the instrument. If the bearings are worn, dirty, or improperly lubricated, drift may be excessive.

         b) The HI should be compared to the magnetic compass every 15 min. for accuracy.

            i) This comparison can be done accurately only when the airplane is in straight, level, and unaccelerated flight.

      2) The bank and pitch limits of the HI vary with the particular design and make of instrument.

         a) Some HIs found in light airplanes have limits of approximately 55° of pitch and 55° of bank.

            i) When either of these attitude limits is exceeded, the precessional force causes the instrument to tumble or spill, which causes the heading card to spin rapidly, and the instrument no longer gives the correct indication until reset.

            ii) After spilling, the HI may be reset with the adjustment knob at the edge of the instrument.

         b) Other HIs are designed not to tumble.

      3) A failed vacuum pump will result in the loss of the AI and the HI.

c. **Potential Errors in Unusual Attitudes**

    1) Due to precession error, the HI is not used in recovery of an unusual attitude. The TC or turn-and-slip indicator is used to determine if the aircraft is in a turn.

8. **Magnetic Compass**

  a. **Sensitivity**

    1) A magnetic compass has two small magnets attached to a metal float sealed inside a bowl of clear fluid similar to kerosene.

      a) The magnets align with the Earth's magnetic field and the pilot reads the direction on the scale opposite the lubber line.

      b) The float has the freedom to rotate and tilt up to approximately an 18° angle of bank.

      c) At steeper bank angles, the compass indications are erratic and unpredictable.

      d) The fluid dampens the oscillation of the float.

  b. **Limitations**

    1) Errors in the magnetic compass are numerous, making straight flight and precision turns to headings difficult, particularly in turbulent air.

    2) The magnetic compass does not respond quickly and is subject to various errors as a result of properties of magnetism.

    3) Compass errors include

      a) **Magnetic variation,** which is the angular difference between true north and magnetic north (technically not a compass error).

      b) **Compass deviation,** which is the difference between the heading indicated by a magnetic compass in an airplane and the airplane's actual magnetic heading.

      c) **Magnetic dip,** which is the tendency of the compass needles to point down as well as to the magnetic pole. The resultant error is known as dip error, greatest at the poles and zero at the magnetic equator.

      d) **Compass card oscillation,** which results from erratic movement of the compass card. This may be caused by turbulence or rough control technique.

  c. **Potential Errors in Unusual Attitudes**

    1) Due to the inherent errors of the magnetic compass, it is not used in the recovery from unusual attitudes.

9. **Glass Cockpit Instrumentation**

  a. **Sensitivity**

    1) An Attitude and Heading Reference System (AHRS) provides information typically given by gyroscopic instruments, such as attitude (pitch/bank) information, heading, rate of turn, and turn coordination.

    2) An Air Data Computer (ADC) provides information typically given by pitot-static instruments, such as airspeed, altitude, and vertical distance.

  b. **Limitations**

    1) Glass cockpit systems increase safety through internal, automatic error-monitoring and alerting systems.

      a) A typical glass cockpit system will alert a pilot if any operational tolerance is exceeded in any system component.

      b) In the case of a PFD or MFD failure, information from both displays can be shown on a single screen, called reversionary mode.

        2) In the event of an electrical failure, the pilot still has emergency instrumentation as a backup. These instruments either do not require electrical power or, in many cases, are battery operated. These back-up instrumentations are often not in the direct view of the pilot and are off to the side of the PFD.

        3) An effective scan that correctly interprets all the available information provided by the EFD will provide the least amount of limitations during flight.

    c. **Potential Errors in Unusual Attitudes**

        1) How a pilot gathers the necessary information to control the aircraft varies by individual pilot. No specific method of cross-checking (scanning) is recommended; the pilot must learn to determine which instruments give the most pertinent information for unusual attitude recovery. With practice, the pilot is able to observe the primary instruments quickly and cross-check with the supporting instruments for appropriate recovery. At no time during instrument flying should the pilot stop cross-checking the instrumentation.

C. **The applicant demonstrates understanding of flight instrument correlation (pitch instruments/bank instruments).**

    1. As a general rule, any time an instrument rate of movement or indication other than those associated with the basic instrument flight maneuvers is noted, assume an unusual attitude and increase the speed of cross-check to confirm the attitude, instrument error, or instrument malfunction.

    2. To recover from an unusual attitude, a pilot should correct pitch and bank attitude and adjust power as necessary.

        a. All components are changed almost simultaneously, with little lead of one over the other. A pilot must be able to perform this task with and without the attitude indicator.

        b. If the aircraft is in a climbing or descending turn, adjust bank, pitch, and power.

            1) The bank attitude should be corrected by referring to the turn-and-slip indicator and attitude indicator.

            2) Pitch attitude should be corrected by reference to the altimeter, airspeed indicator, vertical speed indicator, and attitude indicator.

            3) Adjust power by referring to the airspeed indicator and tachometer or manifold pressure.

D. **The applicant demonstrates understanding of vestibular illusions (leans) and spatial disorientation.**

    1. **Vestibular illusions** involve the semicircular canals of the vestibular system. They occur primarily under conditions of unreliable of unavailable external visual references and result in false sensations of rotation.

        a. The **leans** is the most common vestibular illusion during flight. After inadvertently entering a bank attitude too slowly for the motion-sensing system of the inner ear to detect it, an abrupt correction can create the illusion of a bank in the opposite direction. The disoriented pilot may roll the aircraft back into the original, dangerous bank if (s)he relies on his or her own senses, rather than the airplane's instrumentation, to orient the aircraft.

    2. **Spatial disorientation** is state of temporary confusion resulting from misleading information being sent to the brain by various sensory organs.

        a. If you lose outside visual references and become disoriented, you are experiencing spatial disorientation. This occurs when you rely on the sensations of muscles, joints, tissues, and the inner ear to tell you what the airplane's attitude is.

            1) This might occur during a night flight, in clouds, or in dust.

    3. The best way to overcome the leans or any type of spatial disorientation is to rely on the airplane flight instruments and disregard your sensory perceptions.

E. **The applicant demonstrates understanding of appropriate pitch, bank, and power setting for the airplane being flown.**

1. Each aircraft has a specific pitch attitude, power, and airspeed that corresponds to normal straight-and-level flight for a specified weight. The POH/AFM contains the power settings.

2. Each aircraft has a specific pitch attitude and airspeed that corresponds to the most efficient climb rate for a specified weight.

   a. The POH/AFM contains the speeds that produce the desired climb. These numbers are based on maximum gross weight.

      1) Pilots must be familiar with how the speeds vary with weight so they can compensate during flight.

3. Consult the POH/AFM for specific climb power settings if anything other than a full power climb is desired.

   a. Pitch attitudes vary depending on the type of aircraft being flown.

   b. As airspeed decreases, control forces need to be increased in order to compensate for the additional elevator deflection required to maintain attitude.

   c. Utilize trim to eliminate any control pressures.

4. Control technique varies according to the lift and drag characteristics of each airplane.

   a. Accordingly, knowledge of the power settings and trim changes associated with different combinations of airspeed, gear, and flap configurations reduces instrument cross-check and interpretation problems.

5. Pilots must learn and utilize proper power settings.

   a. Any time a pilot is not familiar with an aircraft's specific pitch and power settings or does not utilize them, a change in flightpath takes longer.

   b. Learn pitch and power settings in order to expedite changing the flightpath.

6. Turns should be made at standard rate.

   a. Standard rate is defined as a turning rate of 3° per second, which yields a complete 360° turn in 2 min.

   b. In order to initiate a standard rate turn, approximate the bank angle and then establish that bank angle on the attitude indicator.

      1) The higher the true airspeed, the greater the bank will be required to achieve standard rate.

      2) Correspondingly, the slower the true airspeed the aircraft is traveling, the lower the bank angle will be to achieve standard rate.

      3) The pilot should be familiar with the appropriate bank angle required to achieve a standard rate for the aircraft they are flying, and at varying speeds.

RISK MANAGEMENT

A. **The applicant demonstrates the ability to identify, assess, and mitigate risks encompassing lack of proficiency in flight by reference to instruments.**

1. The purpose of learning basic instrument maneuvers as part of your private pilot (VFR) training is to allow you to return to VFR conditions should you inadvertently/accidentally find yourself in instrument conditions.

    a. An inadvertent encounter into IFR conditions is an emergency situation that will require proficiency in basic instrument maneuvers for successful exiting.

2. Accident statistics show that pilots who have not been trained in attitude instrument flying or whose basic instrument skills have eroded will lose control of the airplane in about 10 min. when forced to fly solely by reference to instruments.

    a. Pilots should remember that the skill of flying by reference to instruments requires practice on a continuing and regular basis; otherwise, skill erosion begins immediately.

    b. Continued practice of basic instrument maneuvers with a certified flight instructor or with a safely pilot is a good way to maintain proficiency.

B. **The applicant demonstrates the ability to identify, assess, and mitigate risks encompassing poor cockpit management.**

1. Cockpit management is more than just maintaining an organized and neat cockpit. Cockpit management is a process that combines you, your airplane, and the environment for safer and more efficient operations.

2. Some of the elements of cockpit management include

    a. Communication -- the exchange of information with ATC, FSS personnel, maintenance personnel, and other pilots.

        1) To be effective, you must develop good speaking and listening skills.

    b. Decision making and problem solving -- the manner in which you respond to problems that you encounter from preflight preparation to your postflight procedures.

    c. Situational Awareness -- your knowledge of how you, your airplane, and the environment are interacting. This is a continuous process throughout your flight.

        1) As you increase your situational awareness, you will become a safer pilot by being able to identify clues that signify a problem prior to an impending accident or incident.

    d. Standardization -- your use of standardized checklists and procedures.

        1) Checklist discipline will help you because you will develop a habit of reading a checklist item and then performing the task.

        2) Procedural learning is learning a standardized procedure pattern while using the checklist as a backup, as you may do in the first few steps of an emergency.

    e. Leader/follower. Below are the desirable characteristics of both:

        1) A leader will manage those resources that contribute to a safe flight, e.g., ensuring the proper quantity and grade of fuel.

        2) A good follower will ask for help at the first indication of trouble.

    f.   Psychological factors -- your attitude, personality, and motivation in the decision-making process.

        1)   Hazardous attitudes include antiauthority, impulsive, invulnerable, macho, and resigned.

        2)   Personality is the way you cope with problems.

        3)   Your motivation to achieve a goal can be internal (you are attracted to the goal) or external (an outside force is driving you to perform).

    g.   Planning ahead -- anticipation of and preparation for future situations.

        1)   Always think and stay ahead of what needs to be done at any specific time.

        2)   Always picture your location and your heading with respect to nearby navigational aids (NAVAIDs), airports, and other geographical fixes.

        3)   Confirm your present position and anticipate future positions with as many NAVAIDs as possible; i.e., use them all.

    h.   Stress management -- the manner in which you manage the stress in your life, which will follow you into the cockpit. Stress is your reaction to a perceived (real or imaginary) threat to your body's equilibrium.

        1)   Learn to reduce the stress in your life or to cope with it better.

3.   The cockpit and/or cabin should be checked for loose articles or cargo that may be tossed about if turbulence is encountered and must be secured.

4.   On every flight, you should be in the habit of organizing and neatly arranging your materials and equipment in an efficient manner that makes them readily available.

    a.   Be in the habit of "good housekeeping."

        1)   A disorganized cockpit will complicate even the simplest of flights.

    b.   Organization will contribute to safe and efficient flying.

5.   For more information, see Study Unit 19, "Cockpit Management."

C.   The applicant demonstrates the ability to identify, assess, and mitigate risks encompassing lack of awareness of the direction for nearest VMC.

1.   A thorough and careful preflight weather briefing with an FSS weather briefer will give you a good idea of where VMC and IMC conditions exists for your route of flight. Take special note of where the VFR weather is and where it is forecast to be.

2.   Of course, weather is always changing and often does not develop as forecast. En route, the pilot can maintain situational awareness of VMC conditions by

    a.   Contacting FSS on 122.2 MHz for current conditions of where VMC conditions exists.

    b.   Listen to ATIS/ASOS/AWOS reports ahead of your route of flight and confirm this information with FSS on 122.2 MHz.

    c.   Know how to access and interpret the weather information available to you in an advanced automated cockpit with weather capability, and, if needed, confirm this information with FSS on 122.2 MHz.

    d.   Listen to ATC/traffic communications regarding weather and how it is affecting traffic.

3.   Maintaining situational awareness with regard to VMC conditions will prevent an inadvertent encounter with IFR conditions and provide you an "out" if it does occur. It will also provide you with added confidence and thus a more enjoyable flight experience knowing that you are in control and actively managing your flight.

D. **The applicant demonstrates the ability to identify, assess, and mitigate risks encompassing loss of situational awareness during low visibility or instrument conditions.**

    1. Situational awareness is not simply a mental picture of aircraft location; rather, it is an overall assessment of each element of the environment and how it affects a flight.

        a. With good situational awareness, the pilot is able to make decisions well ahead of time and evaluate several different options.

            1) Good situational awareness allows the pilot to be proactive in decision making.

        b. With poor situational awareness, a pilot lacks a vision of future events and is forced to make decisions quickly, often with limited options.

            1) Poor situational awareness puts the pilot in a reactive state of decision making.

        c. Factors that reduce situational awareness include

            1) Distractions
            2) Unusual or unexpected events
            3) Complacency
            4) High workload
            5) Unfamiliar situations
            6) Inoperative equipment

        d. Pilots should be alert to a loss of situational awareness anytime they are in a reactive mindset.

        e. To regain situational awareness, reassess the situation and seek additional information from other sources, such as the navigation instruments or ATC.

STUDY UNIT FORTY-THREE
STRAIGHT-AND-LEVEL FLIGHT

Task	Task A. Straight-and-Level Flight
References	FAA-H-8083-2, FAA-H-8083-3, FAA-H-8083-15
Objective	To determine that the applicant exhibits satisfactory knowledge, risk management, and skills associated with attitude instrument flying during straight-and-level flight.
Knowledge	The applicant demonstrates understanding of:
PA.VIII.A.K1	1. Flight instrument function and operation.
PA.VIII.A.K2	2. Flight instrument sensitivity, limitations, and potential errors in unusual attitudes.
PA.VIII.A.K3	3. Flight instrument correlation (pitch instruments/bank instruments).
PA.VIII.A.K4	4. Aerodynamic factors related to maintaining straight-and-level flight.
PA.VIII.A.K5	5. Vestibular illusions (leans) and spatial disorientation.
PA.VIII.A.K6	6. Appropriate pitch, bank, and power settings for the airplane being flown.
Risk Management	The applicant demonstrates the ability to identify, assess and mitigate risks, encompassing:
PA.VIII.A.R1	1. Lack of proficiency in flight by reference to instruments.
PA.VIII.A.R2	2. Poor cockpit management.
PA.VIII.A.R3	3. Lack of awareness of the direction for the nearest VMC.
PA.VIII.A.R4	4. Continued flight into IMC or conditions outside of personal minimums.
PA.VIII.A.R5	5. Loss of situational awareness during low visibility and/or instrument conditions.
PA.VIII.A.R6	6. The hazards of abrupt control movements when flying by sole reference to instruments.
Skills	The applicant demonstrates the ability to:
PA.VIII.A.S1	1. Control the aircraft solely by reference to instruments in straight-and-level flight.
PA.VIII.A.S2	2. Perform an instrument scan and instrument cross-check.
PA.VIII.A.S3	3. Perform coordinated, smooth control application to correct for altitude, heading, airspeed, and bank deviations during straight-and-level flight.
PA.VIII.A.S4	4. Maintain altitude ±200 feet, heading ±20° and airspeed ±10 knots.

A. General Information

1. The objective of this task is for you to demonstrate your knowledge, risk management, and skills related to attitude instrument flying during straight-and-level flight.

2. The content of Subunits 43.1 and 43.2 is abbreviated based on the assumption that you have thoroughly read and understood pages 545 through 564, and the additional common task topics found in Part II. The task objectives and specific references are provided here for your convenience.

43.1 KNOWLEDGE

A. Task Objectives

1. **The applicant demonstrates understanding of flight instrument function and operation.**

    a. For information on flight instrument function and operation, see Section VIII Introduction, Knowledge, item A., beginning on page 547.

2. **The applicant demonstrates understanding of flight instrument sensitivity, limitations, and potential errors in unusual attitudes.**

    a. For information on flight instrument sensitivity, limitations, and potential errors in unusual attitudes, see Section VIII Introduction, Knowledge, item B., beginning on page 554.

3. **The applicant demonstrates understanding of flight instrument correlation (pitch instruments/bank instruments).**

    a. For information on flight instrument correlation, see Section VIII Introduction, Knowledge, item C., on page 560.

4. **The applicant demonstrates understanding of aerodynamic factors related to maintaining straight-and-level flight.**

    a. For information on aerodynamic factors, see Study Unit 4, Subunit 2, beginning on page 25.

5. **The applicant demonstrates understanding of vestibular illusions (leans) and spatial disorientation.**

    a. For information on vestibular illusions (leans) and spatial disorientation, see Section VIII Introduction, Knowledge, item D., on page 560.

6. **The applicant demonstrates understanding of appropriate pitch, bank, and power settings for the airplane being flown.**

    a. For information on pitch, bank, and power settings for the airplane being flown, see Section VIII Introduction, Knowledge, item E., on page 561.

END OF KNOWLEDGE ELEMENT

43.2 RISK MANAGEMENT

A. Task Objectives

1. **The applicant demonstrates the ability to identify, assess, and mitigate risks encompassing lack of proficiency in flight by reference to instruments.**

   a. For information on proficiency in flight by reference to instruments, see Section VIII Introduction, Risk Management, item A., on page 562.

2. **The applicant demonstrates the ability to identify, assess, and mitigate risks encompassing poor cockpit management.**

   a. For information on cockpit management, see Section VIII Introduction, Risk Management, item B., beginning on page 562.

3. **The applicant demonstrates the ability to identify, assess, and mitigate risks encompassing lack of awareness of the direction for the nearest VMC.**

   a. For information on awareness of the direction for the nearest VMC, see Section VIII Introduction, Risk Management, item C., on page 563.

4. **The applicant demonstrates the ability to identify, assess, and mitigate risks encompassing continued flight into IMC or conditions outside of personal minimums.**

   a. For information on continued flight into IMC or conditions outside of personal minimums, see Study Unit 5, Subunit 4, beginning on page 47.

5. **The applicant demonstrates the ability to identify, assess, and mitigate risks encompassing loss of situational awareness during low visibility or instrument conditions.**

   a. For information on situational awareness during low visibility or instrument conditions, see Study Unit 7, Subunit 1, beginning on page 57.

6. **The applicant demonstrates the ability to identify, assess, and mitigate risks encompassing the hazards of abrupt control movements when flying by sole reference to instruments.**

   a. When flying by reference to instruments, avoid making abrupt control movements, as this can lead to spacial disorientation.

   b. Explain how some flight instruments may not immediately indicate the full effect of control inputs.

      1) This can lead to over correcting, loss of orientation, and loss of control.

END OF RISK MANAGEMENT ELEMENT

43.3 SKILLS

A.   Task Objectives

1.   **The applicant demonstrates the ability to control the aircraft solely by reference to instruments in straight-and-level flight.**

   a.   Attitude instrument flying may be defined in general terms as the control of an airplane's spatial position by use of instruments rather than by outside visual reference. Thus, proper interpretation of the flight instruments provides the same information as visual references outside the airplane.

      1)   Flying straight means to maintain a constant heading on the leading indicator (HI), which is done by keeping the wings level on the attitude indicator (AI) and the ball centered on the turn coordinator (TC).

      2)   Flying level means to maintain a constant altitude on the ALT, which is done by holding a level pitch attitude on the AI.

      3)   Steady airspeed is maintained by holding a constant power [RPM or manifold pressure (MP)] setting.

2.   **The applicant demonstrates the ability to perform an instrument scan and instrument cross-check.**

   a.   Attitude control is stressed in this book (and by the FAA) in terms of pitch control, bank control, power control, and trim control. Instruments are divided into the following three categories:

      1)   Pitch instruments

         a)   Attitude indicator (AI)
         b)   Altimeter (ALT)
         c)   Airspeed Indicator (ASI)
         d)   Vertical speed indicator (VSI)

      2) Bank instruments

          a)   Attitude indicator (AI)
          b)   Heading indicator (HI)
          c)   Turn coordinator (TC) or turn-and-slip indicator (T&SI)
          d)   Magnetic compass

      3) Power instruments

          a)   Manifold pressure gauge (MP), if equipped
          b)   Tachometer (RPM)
          c)   Airspeed indicator (ASI)

b.   For a particular maneuver or condition of flight, the pitch, bank, and power control requirements are most clearly indicated by certain key instruments.

      1) Those instruments that provide the most pertinent and essential information are referred to as primary instruments.

      2) Supporting instruments back up and supplement the information shown on the primary instruments.

      3) For each maneuver, there will be one primary instrument from each of the categories above. There may be several supporting instruments from each category.

c.   This concept of primary and supporting instruments in no way lessens the value of any particular instrument.

      1) The AI is the basic attitude reference, just as the real horizon is used in visual conditions. It is the only instrument that portrays instantly and directly the actual flight attitude.

          a)   It should always be used, when available, in establishing and maintaining pitch and bank attitudes.

d.   Remember, the primary instruments (for a given maneuver) are the ones that will show the greatest amount of change over time if the maneuver is being improperly controlled (pitch, bank, power).

e.   During your attitude instrument training, you should develop three fundamental skills involved in all instrument flight maneuvers: instrument cross-check, instrument interpretation, and airplane control.

      1) **Cross-checking** (also called scanning) is the continuous and logical observation of instruments for attitude and performance information.

          a)   You will maintain your airplane's attitude by reference to instruments that will produce the desired result in performance. To maintain situational awareness, you should always know

             i)   Your airplane's pitch and bank (AI)
             ii)   Your present heading (HI)

                 • And your desired heading

             iii) Your present altitude

                 • And your desired altitude (ALT)

b)   Because your AI is your reference instrument for airplane control and provides you with a quick reference as to your pitch and bank attitude, it should be your start (or home base) for your instrument scan. You should begin with the AI and scan one instrument (e.g., the HI) and then return to the AI before moving to a different instrument, as shown below.

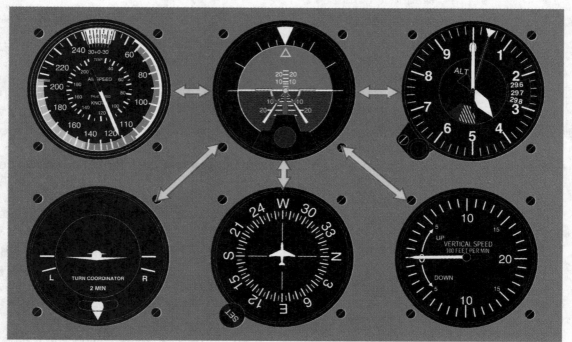

   i)   Thus, you continuously visualize your present attitude, heading, and altitude in conjunction with your intended heading and altitude.

   ii)   Last and certainly not least, interrupt your flight instrument scan every few minutes to review all your other instruments, including

   •   Compass to HI for precession (resetting HI as necessary)
   •   Engine RPM and/or MP, as appropriate
   •   Engine temperatures (oil, cylinder head, and EGT)
   •   Oil pressure
   •   Fuel level
   •   Vacuum pressure
   •   Ammeter

   iii) Your CFI will have his or her suggested approach to the instrument scan.

   iv)   You should write down (using pencil and paper) your scan -- what you do and why.

   •   This will force you to think "what and why" and avoid haphazard scanning of your instruments.

c)   Frequent cross-check faults are

   i)   Fixation, or staring at a single instrument

   ii)   Omission of an instrument from cross-check

   iii) Emphasis on a single instrument, instead of a combination of instruments necessary for attitude information

3. **The applicant demonstrates the ability to perform coordinated, smooth control application to correct for altitude, heading, airspeed, and bank deviations during straight-and-level flight.**

   a. The figure below illustrates the instrument indications for straight-and-level flight.

   b. Maintain straight flight by holding the wings level on the AI and maintaining your heading on the HI.

      1) Because you want to maintain a specific heading, the HI is primary for bank.

         a) The supporting instruments for bank are the AI and the TC.

      2) If you deviate from your heading, use the AI to level your wings and ensure the ball of the TC is centered.

         a) Determine the direction you must turn to return to your desired heading, and use the AI to establish a bank in the proper direction.

            i) Use an angle of bank no greater than the number of degrees to be turned, but limit the bank angle to that required for a standard-rate turn.

         b) Use coordinated aileron and rudder.

      3) The ball of the TC should be centered. If not, you may be holding rudder pressure, or your airplane is improperly trimmed (if rudder trim is available).

   c. Maintain level flight by adjusting your pitch as necessary on the AI to maintain your altitude.

      1) Because you want to maintain a specific altitude, the ALT is primary for pitch.

         a) The supporting instruments for pitch are the AI and VSI.

            i) As a trend instrument, the VSI will show immediately, even before your ALT, the initial vertical movement of your airplane.

2) If you deviate from your altitude, use the AI to return to level flight and determine if you need to climb or descend to return to your desired altitude.

    a) Use the AI to make a small pitch adjustment in the proper direction, and use the VSI to ensure that you are moving in the proper direction.

    b) Small altitude deviations (i.e., 100 ft. or less) should be corrected with pitch only, using a rate of approximately 200 fpm on the VSI.

    c) Large altitude deviations (i.e., greater than 100 ft.) may be more easily corrected by adjusting both pitch and power, using a greater rate of return to altitude (approximately double your error in altitude).

3) The VSI becomes the primary pitch instrument while returning to altitude after a deviation is noticed during level flight.

d. During straight-and-level flight, you should maintain a constant airspeed; thus, the ASI is the primary power instrument. Maintain airspeed with power.

e. You will need to learn to overcome a natural tendency to make a large control movement for a pitch change and learn to apply small control pressures smoothly, cross-checking rapidly for the results of the change and continuing with the pressures as your instruments show the desired results at a rate that you can interpret.

1) Small attitude changes can be easily controlled, stopped, and corrected.
2) Large changes are more difficult to control.

f. Coordination of controls requires that the ball of the TC be kept centered and that the available trim control devices be used whenever a change in flight conditions disturbs the existing trim.

1) Trim is used to relieve all possible control pressures held after a desired attitude has been attained.

2) The pressure you feel on the control yoke must be that which you apply while controlling a planned change in airplane attitude, not pressure held because you are letting the airplane control you.

4. **The applicant demonstrates the ability to maintain altitude ±200 feet, heading ±20°, and airspeed ±10 knots.**

a. Divide your attention between scanning outside the aircraft and scanning the flight instruments.

b. With experience, you will become proficient at maintaining the specified altitude, heading, and airspeed.

END OF SKILLS ELEMENT

43.4 COMMON ERRORS

A.   Common Errors during Straight-and-Level Flight

   1.   **Fixation, omission, and emphasis errors during instrument cross-check**

      a.   Fixation, or staring at a single instrument, usually occurs for a good reason, but with poor results.

         1)   You may stare at (or fixate on) the ALT, which reads 200 ft. below assigned altitude, wondering how the needle got there. During that time, perhaps with increasing tension on the controls, a heading change occurs unnoticed, and more errors accumulate.

         2)   It may not be entirely a cross-checking error. It may be related to difficulties with one or both of the other fundamental skills (i.e., interpretation and control).

      b.   Omission of an instrument from the cross-check may be caused by failure to anticipate significant instrument indications following attitude changes.

         1)   All instruments should be included in the scan.

      c.   Emphasis on a single instrument, instead of on the combination of instruments necessary for attitude information, is normal during the initial stages of instrument training.

         1)   You may tend to rely on the instrument that you understand the best, e.g., the ALT.

         2)   The VSI can give more immediate pitch information than the ALT.

   2.   **Improper instrument interpretation**

      a.   This error may indicate that you do not fully understand each instrument's operating principle and relationship to the performance of your airplane.

      b.   You must be able to interpret small changes in your instrument indications from your cross-checking.

   3.   **Improper control applications**

      a.   This error normally occurs when you incorrectly interpret the instruments and then apply the improper controls to obtain a desired performance, e.g., using rudder pressure to correct for a heading error.

      b.   It may also occur when you apply control inputs (pitch and bank) without referring to the AI.

   4.   **Failure to establish proper pitch, bank, or power adjustments during altitude, heading, or airspeed corrections**

      a.   You must understand which instruments provide information for pitch, bank, and power.

         1)   The AI is the only instrument for pitch and bank control inputs.

      b.   This error may indicate that you do not fully understand instrument cross-check, interpretation, and/or control.

   5.   **Faulty trim technique**

      a.   Trim should be used, not to substitute for control with the control yoke and rudder, but to relieve pressures already held to stabilize attitude.

      b.   Use trim frequently and in small amounts.

      c.   Improper adjustment of seat or rudder pedals for comfortable positioning of legs and feet may contribute to trim errors.

         1)   Tension in the ankles makes it difficult to relax rudder pressures.

END OF COMMON ERRORS

STUDY UNIT FORTY-FOUR
CONSTANT AIRSPEED CLIMBS

Task	Task B. Constant Airspeed Climbs
References	FAA-H-8083-2, FAA-H-8083-3, FAA-H-8083-15
Objective	To determine that the applicant exhibits satisfactory knowledge, risk management, and skills associated with attitude instrument flying during constant airspeed climbs.
Knowledge	The applicant demonstrates understanding of:
PA.VIII.B.K1	1. Flight instrument function and operation.
PA.VIII.B.K2	2. Flight instrument sensitivity, limitations, and potential errors in unusual attitudes.
PA.VIII.B.K3	3. Flight instrument correlation (pitch instruments/bank instruments).
PA.VIII.B.K4	4. Vestibular illusions (leans) and spatial disorientation.
PA.VIII.B.K5	5. Aerodynamic factors related to establishing and maintaining a constant airspeed climb, making turns while climbing, and then returning to level flight.
PA.VIII.B.K6	6. Appropriate pitch, bank, and power settings for the airplane being flown.
Risk Management	The applicant demonstrates the ability to identify, assess and mitigate risks, encompassing:
PA.VIII.B.R1	1. Lack of proficiency in flight by reference to instruments.
PA.VIII.B.R2	2. Poor cockpit management.
PA.VIII.B.R3	3. Lack of awareness of the direction for the nearest VMC.
PA.VIII.B.R4	4. Failure to descend straight ahead or make level turns under emergency instrument conditions.
PA.VIII.B.R5	5. Continued flight into IMC or conditions outside of personal minimums.
PA.VIII.B.R6	6. Loss of situational awareness during low visibility or instrument conditions.
Skills	The applicant demonstrates the ability to:
PA.VIII.B.S1	1. Control the aircraft solely by reference to instruments.
PA.VIII.B.S2	2. Perform an instrument scan and instrument cross-check.
PA.VIII.B.S3	3. Transition to the climb pitch attitude and power setting on an assigned heading using proper instrument cross-check and interpretation, and coordinated flight control application.
PA.VIII.B.S4	4. Demonstrate climbs solely by reference to instruments at a constant airspeed to specific altitudes in straight flight and turns.
PA.VIII.B.S5	5. Perform coordinated, smooth control application to correct for airspeed, heading and bank deviations during climb and then for level off.
PA.VIII.B.S6	6. Perform appropriate trimming to relieve control pressures.
PA.VIII.B.S7	7. Level off at the assigned altitude and maintain altitude ±200 feet, heading ±20° and airspeed ±10 knots.

A. General Information

1. The objective of this task is for you to demonstrate your knowledge, risk management, and skills related to attitude instrument flying during constant airspeed climbs.

2. When adverse weather is encountered, a climb by reference to instruments may be required to assure clearance of obstructions or terrain or to climb above a layer of fog, haze, or low clouds.

3. Much of the content of Subunits 44.1 and 44.2 is abbreviated based on the assumption that you have thoroughly read and understood pages 545 through 564 and the additional common task topics found in Part II. The task objectives and specific references are provided here for your convenience.

44.1 KNOWLEDGE

A.   Task Objectives

1.   **The applicant demonstrates understanding of flight instrument function and operation.**

a.   For information on flight instrument function and operation, see Section VIII Introduction, Knowledge, item A. beginning on page 547.

2.   **The applicant demonstrates understanding of flight instrument sensitivity, limitations, and potential errors in unusual attitudes.**

a.   For information on flight instrument sensitivity, limitations, and potential errors in unusual attitudes, see Section VIII Introduction, Knowledge, item B., beginning on page 554.

3.   **The applicant demonstrates understanding of flight instrument correlation (pitch instruments/bank instruments).**

a.   For information on flight instrument correlation, see Section VIII Introduction, Knowledge, item C., on page 560.

4.   **The applicant demonstrates understanding of vestibular illusions (leans) and spatial disorientation.**

a.   For information on vestibular illusions (leans) and spatial disorientation, see Section VIII Introduction, Knowledge, item D., on page 560.

5.   **The applicant demonstrates understanding of aerodynamic factors related to establishing and maintaining a constant airspeed climb, making turns while climbing, and then returning to level flight.**

a.   For all practical purposes, the wing's lift in a steady state normal climb is the same as it is in a steady level flight at the same airspeed.

1)   Although the aircraft's flightpath changes when climb is established, the angle of attack (AOA) of the wing with respect to the inclined flight path reverts to practically the same values, as does the lift.

2)   When elevator pressure is first applied, there is an initial momentary increase in lift (an increase in AOA of the wing), during the transition from straight-and-level flight to a climb.

a)   Lift at this moment is now greater than weight and starts the aircraft climbing.

b)   After the flightpath is stabilized on the upward incline, the AOA and lift again revert to about the level flight values.

3)   When the flightpath is inclined upward, a component of the aircraft's weight acts in the same direction as, and parallel to, the total drag of the aircraft, thereby increasing total drag.

a)   Additional power is required to maintain the same airspeed as in level flight.

b)   The amount of power depends on the angle of climb.

c)   Aircraft are able to sustain a climb due to excess thrust; when excess thrust is gone, the aircraft is no longer able to climb.

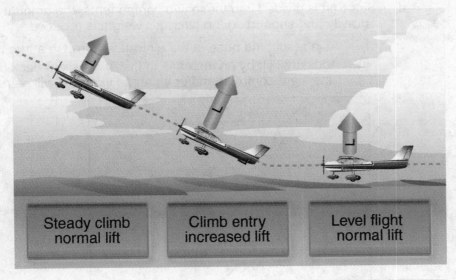

Steady climb
normal lift

Climb entry
increased lift

Level flight
normal lift

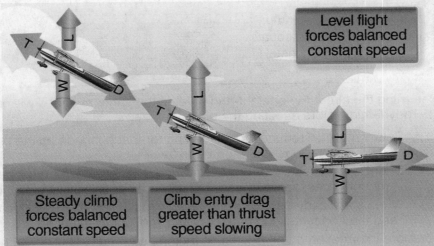

Level flight
forces balanced
constant speed

Steady climb
forces balanced
constant speed

Climb entry drag
greater than thrust
speed slowing

b.   When an aircraft banks, lift acts inward toward the center of the turn, as well as
     upward.

   1)   The force of lift during a turn is separated into two components.

        a)   The "vertical component of lift" acts vertically and opposite to the weight
             (gravity).

        b)   The "horizontal component of lift," or centripetal force, acts horizontally
             toward the center of the turn.

             i)   The horizontal component of lift is the force that pulls the aircraft from
                  a straight flightpath to make it turn.

        c)   Centrifugal force is the "equal and opposite reaction" to the horizontal
             component of lift.

d) Since lift is divided into these two components, the amount of lift opposing gravity and supporting the aircraft's weight is reduced.

i) As a result, the nose of the aircraft will drop in a turn.

ii) Additional lift by an increase in the AOA (slight back pressure using the flight controls) and/or increase in power will be required.

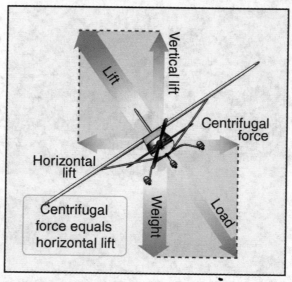

c. Returning the aircraft to straight-and-level at the same airspeed will change the aerodynamic factors affecting the aircraft.

1) Power must be reduced to the setting for that airspeed as the pitch attitude is lowered and wings are returned to level.

2) During the transition, as AOA is reduced, excess power must be reduced to the amount necessary for the weight and drag at steady level flight.

3) When stabilized at straight-and-level, opposing aerodynamic forces will be equal and the horizontal component of lift is no longer a factor.

d. For more information on aerodynamic factors, see Study Unit 4, Subunit 2, beginning on page 25.

6. **The applicant demonstrates understanding of appropriate pitch, bank, and power settings for the airplane being flown.**

a. For information on appropriate pitch, bank, and power settings for the airplane being flown, see Section VIII Introduction, Knowledge, item E., on page 561.

END OF KNOWLEDGE ELEMENT

44.2 RISK MANAGEMENT

A.   Task Objectives

1.   **The applicant demonstrates the ability to identify, assess, and mitigate risks encompassing lack of proficiency in flight by reference to instruments.**

a.   For information on proficiency in flight by reference to instruments, see Section VIII Introduction, Risk Management, item A., on page 562.

2.   **The applicant demonstrates the ability to identify, assess, and mitigate risks encompassing poor cockpit management.**

a.   For information on cockpit management, see Section VIII Introduction, Risk Management, item B., beginning on page 562.

3.   **The applicant demonstrates the ability to identify, assess, and mitigate risks encompassing lack of awareness of the direction for the nearest VMC.**

a.   For information on awareness of the direction for the nearest VMC, see Section VIII Introduction, Risk Management, item C., on page 563.

4.   **The applicant demonstrates the ability to identify, assess, and mitigate risks encompassing failure to descend straight ahead or make level turns under emergency instrument conditions.**

a.   The pilot must remember that flight in instrument conditions for a VFR pilot is an emergency situation.

1)   In any emergency situation, the pilot must first fly the aircraft above any other task.

2)   An emergency is a high workload situation; therefore, an increase in concentration is necessary to maintain an instrument scan.

b.   Descending straight

1)   The pilot must be cautious not to overcontrol pitch on the beginning of the descent.

a)   Aircraft familiarization with a pitch attitude associated with a specific airspeed is the key to achieving precise attitude instrument flying.

b)   Changes in pitch for a descent do not produce instantaneous and stabilized results; patience must be maintained until stabilization occurs.

c)   Avoid making a change and then rushing into making another change until the first one is validated.

2)   The pilot must increase the rate of instrument cross-check any time a pitch or power change is made.

a)   A slow cross-check can lead to deviations in other flight attitudes.

3)   Once a pitch change is made to correct for a deviation, that pitch attitude must be maintained until the change is validated.

a)   Utilize trim to assist in maintaining the new pitch attitude.

b)   If the pitch is allowed to change, it is impossible to validate whether the initial pitch change was sufficient to correct the deviation.

4)   The pilot must utilize effective trim techniques.

a)   If constant control pressures are used by the pilot, validation of the initial correction is impossible if the pitch is allowed to vary.

b)   Use trim to relieve control pressures.

5) The pilot must learn and utilize proper pitch and power settings for the descent in order to safely expedite this changing flightpath.

6) The pilot must cross-check both airspeed and vertical speed prior to making adjustments to pitch and/or power.

7) The pilot must simultaneously use pitch and power during level off from the descent.

8) The pilot must always use the attitude indicator as the control instrument to change the pitch for the descent.

c. Turning

1) The pilot must maintain a standard rate turn by holding the appropriate bank angle.

    a) The primary bank instrument during the turn is the turn rate indicator.

    b) Use an aggressive cross-check to minimize errors arising from over- or underbanking.

2) The pilot must use an efficient and adequate cross-check technique.

    a) Establishing an aggressive cross-check will help in detecting and eliminating all deviations from altitude, airspeed, and bank angle during turning in IMC conditions.

3) Pilots should be aware not to fixate on the turn rate indicator and abandon their cross-check during turning flight in IMC.

    a) Use a modified radial scan to effectively scan all instruments during turning flight.

5. **The applicant demonstrates the ability to identify, assess, and mitigate risks encompassing continued flight into IMC or conditions outside of personal minimums.**

a. For information on continued flight into IMC or conditions outside of personal minimums, see Study Unit 5, Subunit 4, beginning on page 47.

6. **The applicant demonstrates the ability to identify, assess, and mitigate risks encompassing loss of situational awareness during low visibility or instrument conditions.**

a. For information on situational awareness during low visibility or instrument conditions, see Study Unit 7, Subunit 1, beginning on page 57.

END OF RISK MANAGEMENT ELEMENT

44.3 SKILLS

A.   Task Objectives

1.   **The applicant demonstrates the ability to control the aircraft solely by reference to instruments.**

   a.   The figure below illustrates the instrument indications for straight, constant airspeed climbs.

2.   **The applicant demonstrates the ability to perform an instrument scan and instrument cross-check.**

   a.   For general information on instrument scans and instrument cross-check, see Study Unit 43, Subunit 3, item A.2., beginning on page 568.

   b.   As you establish the climb, you must increase your rate of instrument cross-check and interpretation.

3.   **The applicant demonstrates the ability to transition to the climb pitch attitude and power setting on an assigned heading using proper instrument cross-check and interpretation, and coordinated control application.**

   a.   To enter a constant airspeed climb, use the AI to raise the nose to the approximate pitch attitude for the desired climb speed. Thus, during entry, the AI is primary for pitch.

   1)   As the airspeed approaches the desired climb speed, advance the power to the climb power setting (e.g., full power).

   b.   In a straight climb, the primary instrument for bank is the HI.

   1)   In a turning climb, the primary bank instrument is the TC.

   c.   As you establish the climb, you must increase your rate of instrument cross-check and interpretation.

   d.   Coordination of controls requires that the ball of the TC be kept centered and that the available trim control devices be used whenever a change in flight conditions disturbs the existing trim.

       1)   Trim is used to relieve all possible control pressures held after a desired attitude has been attained.

       2)   The pressure you feel on the controls must be that which you apply while controlling a planned change in airplane attitude, not pressure held because you are letting the airplane control you.

4.   The applicant demonstrates the ability to climb solely by reference to instruments at a constant airspeed to specific altitudes in straight flight and turns.

   a.   In a constant airspeed climb, the AI is your primary for pitch.

       1)   In a straight flight, the primary instrument for bank is the HI.
       2)   In turning flight, the primary bank instrument is the TC.

   b.   Initiate level off at a specific altitude by using the attitude indicator.

   c.   During a constant airspeed climb, the ASI becomes the primary pitch instrument.

       1)   If the airspeed is higher than desired, the pitch must be increased. Use the AI to make a small increase in pitch, and then check the ASI to determine if additional corrections are necessary.

       2)   If the airspeed is lower than desired, the pitch must be decreased. Use the AI to make a small decrease in pitch, and check the ASI.

   d.   Maintain straight flight as discussed in Study Unit 43, "Straight-and-Level Flight," beginning on page 565.

       1)   Maintain turning flight as discussed in Study Unit 46, "Turns to Headings," beginning on page 597.

   e.   The RPM remains the primary power instrument, which is used to ensure that the proper climb power is maintained.

5.   The applicant demonstrates the ability to perform coordinated, smooth control application to correct for airspeed, heading, and bank deviations during climb and then for level off.

   a.   You will need to learn to overcome a natural tendency to make a large control movement for a pitch change and learn to apply small control pressures smoothly, cross-checking rapidly for the results of the change, and continuing with the pressures as your instruments show the desired results at a rate that you can interpret.

       1)   Small attitude changes can be easily controlled, stopped, and corrected.
       2)   Large changes are more difficult to control.

6.   The applicant demonstrates the ability to perform appropriate trimming to relieve control pressures.

   a.   Trim should be used, not to substitute for control with the control yoke and rudder but to relieve pressures already held to stabilize attitude.

   b.   Use trim frequently and in small amounts.

   c.   Improper adjustment of seat or rudder pedals for comfortable positioning of legs and feet may contribute to trim errors.

       1)   Tension in the ankles makes it difficult to relax rudder pressures.

       2)   Trim is used to relieve all possible control pressures held after a desired attitude has been attained.

       3)   The pressure you feel on the controls must be that which you apply while controlling a planned change in airplane attitude, not pressure held because you are letting the airplane control you.

    d.   An aircraft is trimmed for a specific airspeed, not pitch attitude or altitude.

    e.   When trimming the aircraft,

        1)   Apply pressure to the control surface that needs trimming and roll the trim wheel in the direction pressure is being held

        2)   Relax the pressure that is being applied to the control surface and monitor the primary instrument for that attitude

        3)   If the desired performance is achieved, fly hands off

        4)   If additional trimming is required, redo the trimming steps

7.   **The applicant demonstrates the ability to level off at the assigned altitude and maintain altitude ±200 feet, heading ±20°, and airspeed ±10 knots.**

    a.   To level off from a climb, it is necessary to start the level-off before reaching the desired altitude. An effective practice is to lead the altitude by 10% of the vertical speed (e.g., at 500 fpm, the lead would be 50 ft.).

    b.   Apply smooth, steady forward elevator pressure toward level flight attitude for the speed desired. As the AI shows the pitch change, the VSI will move toward zero, the ALT will move more slowly, and the ASI will increase.

    c.   Once the ALT, AI, and VSI show level flight, constant changes in pitch and application of nose-down trim will be required as the airspeed increases.

    d.   Maintain straight flight by holding the wings level on the AI and maintaining your heading on the HI.

    e.   Once again, increase the rate of your cross-check and interpretation during level-off until straight-and-level flight is resumed at cruise airspeed and power.

END OF SKILLS ELEMENT

44.4 COMMON ERRORS

A.   Common Errors during Constant Airspeed Climbs

1.   **Fixation, omission, and emphasis errors during instrument cross-check**

   a.   Fixation, or staring at a single instrument, usually occurs for a good reason, but with poor results.

      1)   You may stare at the ASI, which reads 20 kt. below assigned airspeed, wondering how the needle got there. During that time, perhaps with increasing tension on the controls, a heading change occurs unnoticed, and more errors accumulate.

      2)   It may not be entirely a cross-checking error. It may be related to difficulties with one or both of the other fundamental skills (i.e., interpretation and control).

   b.   Omission of an instrument from the cross-check may be caused by failure to anticipate significant instrument indications following attitude changes.

      1)   All instruments should be included in the scan.

   c.   Emphasis on a single instrument, instead of on the combination of instruments necessary for attitude information, is normal during the initial stages of instrument training.

      1)   You may tend to rely on the instrument that you understand the best, e.g., the AI.

      2)   The ALT will be changing; however, the ASI is primary for pitch during this maneuver.

2.   **Improper instrument interpretation**

   a.   This error may indicate that you do not fully understand each instrument's operating principle and relationship to the performance of the airplane.

   b.   You must be able to interpret even the slightest changes in your instrument indications from your cross-checking.

3.   **Improper control applications**

   a.   This error occurs when you incorrectly interpret the instruments and/or apply the improper controls to obtain a desired performance, e.g., using power instead of pitch to correct a minor airspeed error.

4.   **Failure to establish proper pitch, bank, or power adjustments during heading and airspeed corrections**

   a.   You must understand which instruments provide information for pitch, bank, and power.

      1)   The AI is the only instrument for pitch and bank control inputs.

   b.   This error may indicate that you do not fully understand instrument cross-check, interpretation, and/or control.

5. **Improper entry or level-off technique**

   a. Until you learn and use the proper pitch attitudes in climbs, you may tend to make larger-than-necessary pitch adjustments.

      1) You must restrain the impulse to change a flight attitude until you know what the result will be.

         a) Do not chase the needles.

         b) The rate of cross-check must be varied during speed, power, or attitude changes.

         c) During leveling off, you must note the rate of climb to determine the proper lead.

            i) Failure to do this will result in overshooting or undershooting the desired altitude.

      2) You must maintain an accelerated cross-check until straight-and-level flight is positively established.

6. **Faulty trim technique**

   a. Trim should be used, not to substitute for control with the control yoke and rudder, but to relieve pressures already held to stabilize attitude.

   b. Use trim frequently and in small amounts.

      1) Trim should be expected during any pitch, power, or airspeed change.

   c. Improper adjustment of seat or rudder pedals for comfortable positioning of legs and feet may contribute to trim errors.

      1) Tension in the ankles makes it difficult to relax rudder pressures.

END OF COMMON ERRORS

STUDY UNIT FORTY-FIVE
CONSTANT AIRSPEED DESCENTS

Task	Task C. Constant Airspeed Descents
References	FAA-H-8083-2, FAA-H-8083-3, FAA-H-8083-15
Objective	To determine that the applicant exhibits satisfactory knowledge, risk management, and skills associated with attitude instrument flying during constant airspeed descents.
Knowledge	The applicant demonstrates understanding of:
PA.VIII.C.K1	1. Flight instrument function and operation.
PA.VIII.C.K2	2. Flight instrument sensitivity, limitations, and potential errors in unusual attitudes.
PA.VIII.C.K3	3. Flight instrument correlation (pitch instruments/bank instruments).
PA.VIII.C.K4	4. Vestibular illusions (leans) and spatial disorientation.
PA.VIII.C.K5	5. Aerodynamic factors related to establishing and maintaining a constant airspeed descent, making turns while descending, and then returning to level flight.
PA.VIII.C.K6	6. Appropriate pitch, power and bank settings for the airplane being flown.
Risk Management	The applicant demonstrates the ability to identify, assess and mitigate risks, encompassing:
PA.VIII.C.R1	1. Lack of proficiency in flight by reference to instruments.
PA.VIII.C.R2	2. Poor cockpit management.
PA.VIII.C.R3	3. Lack of awareness of the direction for the nearest VMC.
PA.VIII.C.R4	4. Failure to descend straight ahead or make level turns under emergency instrument conditions.
PA.VIII.C.R5	5. Continued flight into IMC or conditions outside of personal minimums.
PA.VIII.C.R6	6. Loss of situational awareness during low visibility or instrument conditions.
Skills	The applicant demonstrates the ability to:
PA.VIII.C.S1	1. Control the aircraft solely by reference to instruments.
PA.VIII.C.S2	2. Perform an instrument scan and instrument cross-check.
PA.VIII.C.S3	3. Establish the descent configuration specified by the evaluator.
PA.VIII.C.S4	4. Transition to the descent pitch attitude and power setting on an assigned heading using proper instrument cross-check and interpretation, and coordinated flight control application.
PA.VIII.C.S5	5. Demonstrate descents solely by reference to instruments at a constant airspeed to specific altitudes in straight flight and turns.
PA.VIII.C.S6	6. Perform appropriate trimming to relieve control pressures.
PA.VIII.C.S7	7. Level off at the assigned altitude and maintain altitude ±200 feet, heading ±20° and airspeed ±10 knots.

A. General Information

1. The objective of this task is for you to demonstrate your knowledge, risk management, and skills related to attitude instrument flying during constant airspeed descents.

2. When unexpected adverse weather is encountered, the most likely situation is that of being trapped in or above a broken or solid layer of clouds or haze, requiring that a descent be made to an altitude where you can reestablish visual reference to the ground.

3. Much of the content of Subunits 45.1 and 45.2 is abbreviated based on the assumption that you have thoroughly read and understood pages 545 through 564 and the additional common task topics found in Part II. The task objectives and specific references are provided here for your convenience.

45.1 KNOWLEDGE

A.   Task Objectives

1.   **The applicant demonstrates understanding of flight instrument function and operation.**

     a.   For information on flight instrument function and operation, see Section VIII Introduction, Knowledge, item A., beginning on page 547.

2.   **The applicant demonstrates understanding of flight instrument sensitivity, limitations, and potential errors in unusual attitudes.**

     a.   For information on flight instrument sensitivity, limitations, and potential errors in unusual attitudes, see Section VIII Introduction, Knowledge, item B. beginning on page 554.

3.   **The applicant demonstrates understanding of flight instrument correlation (pitch instruments/bank instruments).**

     a.   For information on flight instrument correlation, see Section VIII Introduction, Knowledge, item C., on page 560.

4.   **The applicant demonstrates understanding of vestibular illusions (leans) and spatial disorientation.**

     a.   For information on vestibular illusions (leans) and spatial disorientation, see Section VIII Introduction, Knowledge, item D., on page 560.

5.   **The applicant demonstrates understanding of aerodynamic factors related to establishing and maintaining a constant airspeed descent, making turns while descending, and then returning to level flight.**

     a.   For all practical purposes, the wing's lift in a steady state normal descent is the same as it is in a steady level flight at the same airspeed.

          1)   Although the aircraft's flightpath changed when the descent was established, the angle of attack (AOA) of the wing with respect to the inclined flight path eventually reverts to practically the same values, as does the lift.

          2)   As forward pressure is applied to initiate the descent, the AOA is decreased (causing total lift to decrease) momentarily.

               a)   Initially, the momentum of the aircraft causes the aircraft to briefly continue along the same flight path

               b)   Weight is now greater than lift, and the aircraft begins to descend.

               c)   At the same time, aircraft thrust and elevator control are manipulated by the pilot to create a descending flightpath.

          3)   To descend at the same airspeed, power must be reduced as the descent is entered.

               a)   The component of weight acting forward along the flightpath increases as the angle of rate of descent increases

    b.   When an aircraft banks, lift acts inward toward the center of the turn, as well as upward.

        1)   The force of lift during a turn is separated into two components

            a)   The "vertical component of lift" acts vertically and opposite to the weight (gravity)

            b)   The "horizontal component of lift," or centripetal force, acts horizontally toward the center of the turn

                i)   The horizontal component of lift is the force that pulls the aircraft from a straight flightpath to make it turn.

        2)   Centrifugal force is the "equal and opposite reaction" to the horizontal component of lift

        3)   Because lift is divided into vertical and horizontal components, the amount of lift opposing gravity and supporting the aircraft's weight is reduced, and additional lift (power) is required.

    c.   Returning the aircraft to straight-and-level at the same airspeed, power must be increased to the setting for that airspeed as the pitch attitude is raised and wings are returned to level.

        1)   During the transition, as AOA is increased, and additional power must be added to the amount necessary for the weight and drag at steady level flight

        2)   When stabilized at straight-and-level, opposing aerodynamic forces will then return to being equal

    d.   For more information on aerodynamic factors, see Study Unit 4, Subunit 2, beginning on page 25.

6. **The applicant demonstrates understanding of appropriate pitch, power and bank settings for the airplane being flown.**

    a.   For information on pitch, bank, and power settings for the airplane being flown, see Section VIII Introduction, Knowledge, item E., on page 561.

END OF KNOWLEDGE ELEMENT

45.2 RISK MANAGEMENT

A.   Task Objectives

1.   **The applicant demonstrates the ability to identify, assess, and mitigate risks encompassing lack of proficiency in flight by reference to instruments.**

a.   For information on proficiency in flight by reference to instruments, see Section VIII Introduction, Risk Management, item A., on page 562.

2.   **The applicant demonstrates the ability to identify, assess, and mitigate risks encompassing poor cockpit management.**

a.   For information on cockpit management, see Section VIII Introduction, Risk Management, item B., beginning on page 562.

3.   **The applicant demonstrates the ability to identify, assess, and mitigate risks encompassing lack of awareness of the direction for the nearest VMC.**

a.   For information on awareness of the direction for the nearest VMC, see Section VIII Introduction, Risk Management, item C., on page 563.

4.   **The applicant demonstrates the ability to identify, assess, and mitigate risks encompassing failure to descend straight ahead or make level turns under emergency instrument conditions.**

a.   For information on descending straight ahead and making level turns under emergency instrument conditions, see Study Unit 44, Subunit 2, item A.4.

5.   **The applicant demonstrates the ability to identify, assess, and mitigate risks encompassing continued flight into IMC or conditions outside of personal minimums.**

a.   For information on continued flight into IMC or conditions outside of personal minimums, see Study Unit 5, Subunit 4, beginning on page 47.

6.   **The applicant demonstrates the ability to identify, assess, and mitigate risks encompassing loss of situational awareness during low visibility or instrument conditions.**

a.   For information on situational awareness during low visibility or instrument conditions, see Study Unit 7, Subunit 1, beginning on page 57.

END OF RISK MANAGEMENT ELEMENT

45.3 SKILLS

A. Task Objectives

1. **The applicant demonstrates the ability to control the aircraft solely by reference to instruments.**

    a. In instrument flight, aircraft attitude is controlled by reference to the flight instruments.

    b. Proper interpretation of the flight instruments provides essentially the same information that outside references do in visual flight.

    c. Once the role of each instrument in establishing and maintaining a desired aircraft attitude is learned, a pilot is better equipped to control the aircraft in instrument flight conditions.

    d. When flying by reference to flight instruments alone, it is imperative that all of the flight instruments be cross-checked to better visualize the aircraft attitude at all times.

    e. Good aircraft control solely by reference to instruments takes practice and patience.

    f. The figure below illustrates the instrument indications for straight, constant airspeed descent, which is similar to that of a climb except the ALT and VSI indicate a descent.

PRIMARY PITCH

SUPPORTING PITCH AND BANK

SUPPORTING BANK

PRIMARY BANK

SUPPORTING PITCH

    g. Maintain straight flight as discussed in Study Unit 43, "Straight-and-Level Flight," beginning on page 565.

    h. Maintain turning flight as discussed in Study Unit 46, "Turns to Headings," beginning on page 597.

2. **The applicant demonstrates the ability to perform an instrument scan and instrument cross-check.**

    a. For general information on instrument scans and instrument cross-check, see Study Unit 43, Subunit 3, item A.2., beginning on page 568.

    b. In a straight descent, the HI is the primary bank instrument.

        1) In a turning descent, the primary bank instrument is the TC.

    c. As you establish the descent, you must increase your rate of instrument cross-check and interpretation.

3. **The applicant demonstrates the ability to establish the descent configuration specified by the evaluator.**

   a.   Establish the descent configuration, landing gear (if retractable), and flaps, as specified by your evaluator.

      1)   The landing gear, if retractable, and flaps should be positioned as specified by your evaluator.

         a)   Ensure that your airspeed is below V_{FE} and V_{LO} before extending flaps or landing gear, respectively.

      2)   Establishing the desired configuration before starting the descent will permit a more stabilized descent and require less division of your attention once the descent is started.

   b.   You should form a habit of repeating instructions given to you for all maneuvers. This ensures that you understand your evaluator's instructions.

4. **The applicant demonstrates the ability to transition to the descent pitch attitude and power setting on an assigned heading using proper instrument cross-check and interpretation, and coordinated flight control application.**

   a.   To enter a constant airspeed descent at an airspeed lower than cruise, use the following method:

      1)   Reduce power to a predetermined setting for the descent; thus, RPM is the primary power instrument.

      2)   Maintain straight-and-level flight as the airspeed decreases.

      3)   As the airspeed approaches the desired speed for the descent, lower the nose on the AI to maintain constant airspeed, and trim off control pressures. The ASI is now the primary pitch instrument.

   b.   In straight flight, the HI is the primary bank instrument and in turning flight, the primary bank instrument is the TC.

   c.   As you establish the descent, you must increase your rate of instrument cross-check and interpretation.

   d.   You will need to learn to overcome a natural tendency to make a large control movement for a pitch change, and learn to apply small control pressures smoothly, cross-checking rapidly for the results of the change and continuing with the pressures as your instruments show the desired results at a rate that you can interpret.

      1)   Small pitch changes can be easily controlled, stopped, and corrected.
      2)   Large changes are more difficult to control.

   e.   Coordination of controls requires that the ball of the TC be kept centered and that the available trim control devices be used whenever a change in flight conditions disturbs the existing trim.

      1)   Trim is used to relieve all possible control pressures held after a desired attitude has been attained.

      2)   The pressure you feel on the control yoke must be that which you apply while controlling a planned change in airplane attitude, not pressure held because you are letting the airplane control you.

5. **The applicant demonstrates the ability to demonstrate descents solely by reference to instruments at a constant airspeed to specific altitudes in straight flight and turns.**

   a. The figure on page 591 illustrates the instrument indications for straight, constant airspeed descent, which is similar to that of a climb except the ALT and VSI will indicate a descent.

   b. During a constant airspeed descent, the ASI becomes the primary pitch instrument. Make small pitch changes to maintain the desired airspeed.

      1) If the airspeed is higher than desired, the pitch must be increased. Use the AI to raise the nose, and then check the ASI to determine if additional corrections are necessary.

      2) If the airspeed is lower than desired, the pitch must be decreased. Use the AI to lower the nose, and then check the ASI.

   c. The RPM remains the primary power instrument, which is used to ensure that the proper descent power is maintained.

6. **The applicant demonstrates the ability to perform appropriate trimming to relieve control pressures.**

   a. For information on appropriate trimming to relieve control pressures, see Study Unit 44, Subunit 3, item A.6., beginning on page 582.

7. **The applicant demonstrates the ability to level off at the assigned altitude and maintain altitude ±200 feet, heading ±20°, and airspeed ±10 knots.**

   a. The level-off from a descent must be started before you reach the desired altitude. Assuming a 500-fpm rate of descent, lead the altitude by 100 to 150 ft. for a level-off at an airspeed higher than descending airspeed (i.e., to level off at cruise airspeed).

      1) At the lead point, add power to the appropriate level flight cruise setting. Since the nose will tend to rise as the airspeed increases, hold forward elevator pressure to maintain the descent until approximately 50 ft. above the altitude; then smoothly adjust pitch to the level flight attitude.

      2) Application of trim will be required as you resume normal cruise airspeed.

   b. Increase your rate of instrument cross-check and interpretation throughout the level-off.

      1) Maintain a constant heading by using the HI.

END OF SKILLS ELEMENT

45.4 COMMON ERRORS

A.   Common Errors during Constant Airspeed Descents

1.   **Fixation, omission, and emphasis errors during instrument cross-check**

   a.   Fixation, or staring at a single instrument, usually occurs for a good reason, but with poor results.

   1)   You may stare at the ASI, which reads 20 kt. below assigned airspeed, wondering how the needle got there. During that time, perhaps with increasing tension on the controls, a heading change occurs unnoticed, and more errors accumulate.

   2)   It may not be entirely a cross-checking error. It may be related to difficulties with one or both of the other fundamental skills (i.e., interpretation and control).

   b.   Omission of an instrument from the cross-check may be caused by failure to anticipate significant instrument indications following attitude changes.

   1)   All instruments should be included in the scan.

   c.   Emphasis on a single instrument, instead of on the combination of instruments necessary for attitude information, is normal during the initial stages of instrument training.

   1)   You may tend to rely on the instrument that you understand the best, e.g., the AI.

   2)   The ALT will be changing; however, the ASI is primary for pitch during this maneuver.

2.   **Improper instrument interpretation**

   a.   This error may indicate that you do not fully understand each instrument's operating principle and relationship to the performance of the airplane.

   b.   You must be able to interpret even the slightest changes in your instrument indications from your cross-checking.

3.   **Improper control applications**

   a.   This error occurs when you incorrectly interpret the instruments and/or apply the improper controls to obtain a desired performance, e.g., using power instead of pitch to correct a minor airspeed error.

4.   **Failure to establish proper pitch, bank, or power adjustments during heading and airspeed corrections**

   a.   You must understand which instruments provide information for pitch, bank, and power.

   1)   The AI is the only instrument for pitch and bank control inputs.

   b.   This error may indicate that you do not fully understand instrument cross-check, interpretation, and/or control.

5.   **Improper entry or level-off technique**

   a.   Until you learn to use the proper power setting and pitch attitudes in descents, you may tend to make larger-than-necessary pitch adjustments.

   1)   You must restrain the impulse to change a flight attitude until you know what the result will be.

   a)   Do not chase the needles.

   b)   The rate of cross-check must be varied during speed, power, or attitude changes on descents.

   c)   During leveling off, you must note the rate of descent to determine the proper lead.

   i)   Failure to do this will result in overshooting or undershooting the desired altitude.

   2)   "Ballooning" (allowing the nose to pitch up) on level-off results when descent attitude with forward elevator pressure is not maintained as power is increased.

   3)   You must maintain an accelerated cross-check until straight-and-level flight is positively established.

6.   **Faulty trim technique**

   a.   Trim should be used, not to substitute for control with the control yoke and rudder, but to relieve pressures already held to stabilize attitude.

   b.   Use trim frequently and in small amounts.

   1)   Trim should be expected during any pitch, power, or airspeed change.

   c.   Improper adjustment of seat or rudder pedals for comfortable positioning of legs and feet may contribute to trim errors.

   1)   Tension in the ankles makes it difficult to relax rudder pressures.

END OF COMMON ERRORS

STUDY UNIT FORTY-SIX
TURNS TO HEADINGS

Task	Task D. Turns to Headings
References	FAA-H-8083-2, FAA-H-8083-3, FAA-H-8083-15
Objective	To determine that the applicant exhibits satisfactory knowledge, risk management, and skills associated with attitude instrument flying during turns to headings.
Knowledge	The applicant demonstrates understanding of:
PA.VIII.D.K1	1. Flight instrument function and operation.
PA.VIII.D.K2	2. Flight instrument sensitivity, limitations, and potential errors in unusual attitudes.
PA.VIII.D.K3	3. Flight instrument correlation (pitch instruments/bank instruments).
PA.VIII.D.K4	4. Vestibular illusions (leans) and spatial disorientation.
PA.VIII.D.K5	5. Aerodynamic factors related to establishing turns while maintaining level flight.
PA.VIII.D.K6	6. Appropriate pitch, power and bank settings for the airplane being flown.
Risk Management	The applicant demonstrates the ability to identify, assess and mitigate risks, encompassing:
PA.VIII.D.R1	1. Lack of proficiency in flight by reference to instruments.
PA.VIII.D.R2	2. Poor cockpit management.
PA.VIII.D.R3	3. Lack of awareness of the direction for the nearest VMC.
PA.VIII.D.R4	4. Failure to descend straight ahead or make level turns under emergency instrument conditions.
PA.VIII.D.R5	5. Continued flight into IMC or conditions outside of personal minimums.
PA.VIII.D.R6	6. Loss of situational awareness during low visibility or instrument conditions.
Skills	The applicant demonstrates the ability to:
PA.VIII.D.S1	1. Control the aircraft solely by reference to instruments.
PA.VIII.D.S2	2. Perform an instrument scan and instrument cross-check.
PA.VIII.D.S3	3. Perform coordinated, smooth flight control application to establish a standard rate turn, to correct for altitude and bank deviations, and to rollout on a specified heading.
PA.VIII.D.S4	4. Perform appropriate trimming to relieve control pressures.
PA.VIII.D.S5	5. Demonstrate turns to headings solely by reference to instruments, maintain altitude ±200 feet and maintain a standard rate turn and rolls out on the assigned heading ±10°; maintain airspeed ±10 knots.

A. General Information

1. The objective of this task is for you to demonstrate your knowledge, risk management, and skills related to with attitude instrument flying during turns to headings.

2. Most of the content of Subunits 46.1 and 46.2 is abbreviated based on the assumption that you have thoroughly read and understood pages 545 through 564 and the additional common task topics found in Part II. The task objectives and specific references are provided here for your convenience.

46.1 KNOWLEDGE

A.   Task Objectives

1.   **The applicant demonstrates understanding of flight instrument function and operation.**

   a.   For information on flight instrument function and operation, see Section VIII Introduction, Knowledge, item A., beginning on page 547.

2.   **The applicant demonstrates understanding of flight instrument sensitivity, limitations, and potential errors in unusual attitudes.**

   a.   For information on flight instrument sensitivity, limitations, and potential errors in unusual attitudes, see Section VIII Introduction, Knowledge, item B., beginning on page 554.

3.   **The applicant demonstrates understanding of flight instrument correlation (pitch instruments/bank instruments).**

   a.   For information on flight instrument correlation, see Section VIII Introduction, Knowledge, item C., on page 560.

4.   **The applicant demonstrates understanding of vestibular illusions (leans) and spatial disorientation.**

   a.   For information on vestibular illusions (leans) and spatial disorientation, see Section VIII Introduction, Knowledge, item D., on page 560.

5.   **The applicant demonstrates understanding of aerodynamic factors related to establishing turns while maintaining level flight.**

   a.   When an aircraft banks, lift acts inward toward the center of the turn as well as upward.

      1)   The force of lift during a turn is separated into two components.

         a)   The "vertical component of lift" acts vertically and opposite to the weight (gravity).

         b)   The "horizontal component of lift," or centripetal force, acts horizontally toward the center of the turn.

            i)   The horizontal component of lift is the force that pulls the aircraft from a straight flightpath to make it turn.

      2)   Centrifugal force is the "equal and opposite reaction" to the horizontal component of lift.

    3)   Since lift is divided into these two components, the amount of lift opposing gravity and supporting the aircraft's weight is reduced.

        a)   The nose of the aircraft will drop in a turn.

        b)   Additional lift by an increase in the angle of attack (slight back pressure using the flight controls) and/or increase in power will be required.

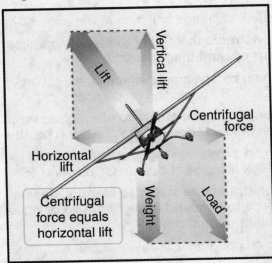

    b.   For more information on aerodynamic factors, see Study Unit 4, Subunit 2, beginning on page 25.

6. **The applicant demonstrates understanding of appropriate pitch, power and bank settings for the airplane being flown.**

    a.   For information on pitch, bank, and power settings for the airplane being flown, see Section VIII Introduction, Knowledge, item E., on page 561.

END OF KNOWLEDGE ELEMENT

46.2 RISK MANAGEMENT

A.   Task Objectives

1.   **The applicant demonstrates the ability to identify, assess, and mitigate risks encompassing lack of proficiency in flight by reference to instruments.**

   a.   For information on proficiency in flight by reference to instruments, see Section VIII Introduction, Risk Management, item A., on page 562.

2.   **The applicant demonstrates the ability to identify, assess, and mitigate risks encompassing poor cockpit management.**

   a.   For information on cockpit management, see Section VIII Introduction, Risk Management, item B., beginning on page 562.

3.   **The applicant demonstrates the ability to identify, assess, and mitigate risks encompassing lack of awareness of the direction for the nearest VMC.**

   a.   For information on awareness of the direction for the nearest VMC, see Section VIII Introduction, Risk Management, item C., on page 563.

4.   **The applicant demonstrates the ability to identify, assess, and mitigate risks encompassing failure to descend straight ahead or make level turns under emergency instrument conditions.**

   a.   For information on descending straight ahead and making level turns under emergency instrument conditions, see Study Unit 44, Subunit 2, item A.4., beginning on page 579.

5.   **The applicant demonstrates the ability to identify, assess, and mitigate risks encompassing continued flight into IMC or conditions outside of personal minimums.**

   a.   For information on continued flight into IMC or conditions outside of personal minimums, see Study Unit 5, Subunit 4, beginning on page 47.

6.   **The applicant demonstrates the ability to identify, assess, and mitigate risks encompassing loss of situational awareness during low visibility or instrument conditions.**

   a.   For information on situational awareness during low visibility or instrument conditions, see Study Unit 7, Subunit 1, beginning on page 57.

END OF RISK MANAGEMENT ELEMENT

46.3 SKILLS

A.　Task Objectives

1.　**The applicant demonstrates the ability to control the aircraft solely by reference to instruments.**

    a.　Training in the use of flight instruments does not prepare you for unrestricted operations in instrument weather conditions. It is intended as an emergency measure only (although it is also excellent training in the smooth control of an airplane).

    b.　The objective of learning basic instrument maneuvers, such as straight descents and level turns by reference to instruments as part of your private pilot (VFR) training is to allow you to return to VFR conditions should you inadvertently/accidentally find yourself in instrument conditions.

        1)　Having some experience flying by instruments and entering instrument conditions briefly will prepare you for this eventuality as a private pilot.

    c.　Sometimes upon encountering adverse weather conditions, it is advisable for you to use radio navigation aids or to obtain directional guidance from ATC facilities.

        1)　Such guidance usually requires that you make turns and/or maintain specific headings.

2.　**The applicant demonstrates the ability to perform an instrument scan and instrument cross-check.**

    a.　For general information on instrument scans and instrument cross-check, see Study Unit 43, Subunit 3, item A.2., beginning on page 568.

    b.　Transition to the level-turn attitude using proper instrument cross-check and interpretation and coordinated control application.

        1)　Before starting the turn to a new heading, you should hold the airplane straight and level and determine in which direction the turn is to be made. Then decide the rate or angle of bank required to reach the new heading.

        2)　To enter a turn, use coordinated aileron and rudder pressure to establish the desired bank angle on the AI. If using a standard-rate turn, check the miniature airplane of the TC for the standard rate indication.

            a)　Control pitch attitude and altitude throughout the turn as described in Study Unit 43, Subunit 3.

3. **The applicant demonstrates the ability to perform coordinated, smooth control application to establish a standard rate turn, to correct for altitude and bank deviations, and to rollout on a specified heading.**

   a.   When making turns in adverse weather conditions, you gain nothing by maneuvering your airplane faster than your ability to keep up with the changes that occur in the flight instrument indications.

      1) You should limit all turns to a standard rate, which is a heading change of 3° per second.

         a) This rate is shown on a TC when the wingtip of the representative airplane is opposite the standard rate marker.

         b) On a turn and slip indicator, this rate is shown when the needle is deflected to the doghouse marker.

         c) Most training airplanes require no more than 15° to 20° of bank for a standard-rate turn.

      2) For small heading changes (less than 15° to 20°), use a bank angle no greater than the number of degrees of turn desired.

         a) The rate at which a turn should be made is dictated generally by the amount of turn desired.

   b.   To roll out on a desired heading, apply coordinated aileron and rudder pressure to level the wings on the AI and stop the turn.

      1) Begin the rollout about 10° before the desired heading (less for small heading changes).

      2) Adjust elevator pressure referencing the AI to maintain altitude on the ALT.

   c.   The figure below illustrates the instrument indications while in a turn.

PRIMARY POWER   PRIMARY BANK INITIALLY SUPPORTING PITCH   PRIMARY PITCH

PRIMARY BANK AS TURN IS ESTABLISHED   SUPPORTING PITCH

4. **The applicant demonstrates the ability to perform appropriate trimming to relieve control pressures.**

    a. For information on appropriate trimming to relieve control pressures, see Study Unit 44, Subunit 3, item A.6., beginning on page 582.

    b. Coordination of controls requires that the ball of the TC be kept centered and that the available trim control devices be used whenever a change in flight conditions disturbs the existing trim.

        1) Trim is used to relieve all possible control pressures held after a desired attitude has been attained.

        2) The pressure you feel on the control yoke must be that which you apply while controlling a planned change in airplane attitude, not pressure held because you are letting the airplane control you.

    c. The trim should not be used as a substitute for control with the control yoke and rudder pedals, but to relieve pressures already held to stabilize attitude.

    d. Use trim frequently and in small amounts.

    e. You cannot feel control pressures with a tight grip on the control yoke.

        1) Relax and learn to control with the eyes and the brain instead of only the muscles.

5. **The applicant demonstrates the ability to demonstrate turns to headings solely by reference to instruments, maintain altitude ±200 feet and maintain a standard rate turn and rolls out on the assigned heading ±10°; maintain airspeed ±10 knots.**

    a. With experience, you will become proficient in the use of flight instruments without reference to the horizon.

    b. Avoid making abrupt control maneuvers, allowing time to scan, interpret, and react to flight instrument changes.

END OF SKILLS ELEMENT

46.4 COMMON ERRORS

A.   Common Errors during Turns to Headings

1.   **Fixation, omission, and emphasis errors during instrument cross-check**

   a.   Fixation, or staring at a single instrument, usually occurs for a good reason, but with poor results.

      1)   You may stare at the TC to maintain a standard-rate turn. During this time, an altitude change occurs unnoticed, and more errors accumulate.

   b.   Omission of an instrument from your cross-check may be caused by a failure to anticipate significant instrument indications following attitude changes.

      1)   All instruments should be included in your scan.

   c.   Emphasis on a single instrument, instead of on the combination of instruments necessary for attitude information, is normal in your initial stages of flight solely by reference to instruments.

      1)   You will tend to rely on the instrument you understand the best, e.g., the AI.

2.   **Improper instrument interpretation**

   a.   You can avoid this error by understanding each instrument's operating principle and relationship to the performance of your airplane.

3.   **Improper control applications**

   a.   Before you start your turn, look at the HI to determine your present heading and the desired heading.

   b.   Decide in which direction to turn and how much bank to use; then apply control pressure to turn the airplane in that direction.

   c.   Do not rush yourself.

4.   **Failure to establish proper pitch, bank, and power adjustments during altitude, bank, and airspeed corrections**

   a.   You must understand which instruments provide information for pitch, bank, and power.

      1)   The AI is the only instrument for pitch and bank control inputs.

   b.   As control pressures change with bank changes, your instrument cross-check must be increased and pressure readjusted.

5.   **Improper entry or rollout technique**

   a.   This error is caused by overcontrolling, resulting in overbanking on turn entry, and overshooting and undershooting headings on rollout.

      1)   Enter and roll out at the rate of your ability to cross-check and interpret the instruments.

   b.   Maintain coordinated flight by keeping the ball centered.

   c.   Remember the heading you are turning to.

6.   **Faulty trim technique**

   a.   The trim should not be used as a substitute for control with the control yoke and rudder pedals, but to relieve pressures already held to stabilize attitude.

   b.   Use trim frequently and in small amounts.

   c.   You cannot feel control pressures with a tight grip on the control yoke.

      1)   Relax and learn to control with the eyes and the brain instead of only the muscles.

END OF COMMON ERRORS

STUDY UNIT FORTY-SEVEN
RECOVERY FROM UNUSUAL FLIGHT ATTITUDES

Task	Task E. Recovery from Unusual Flight Attitudes
References	FAA-H-8083-2, FAA-H-8083-3, FAA-H-8083-15
Objective	To determine that the applicant exhibits satisfactory knowledge, risk management, and skills associated with attitude instrument flying while recovering from unusual attitudes.
Knowledge	The applicant demonstrates understanding of:
PA.VIII.E.K1	1. Flight instrument function and operation.
PA.VIII.E.K2	2. Flight instrument sensitivity, limitations, and potential errors in unusual attitudes.
PA.VIII.E.K3	3. Flight instrument correlation (pitch instruments/bank instruments).
PA.VIII.E.K4	4. Vestibular illusions (leans) and spatial disorientation.
PA.VIII.E.K5	5. Aerodynamic factors related to unusual pitch and bank attitudes and returning to level flight.
PA.VIII.E.K6	6. The appropriate pitch, power and bank settings for airplane being flown.
PA.VIII.E.K7	7. The hazards of inappropriate control response.
Risk Management	The applicant demonstrates the ability to identify, assess and mitigate risks, encompassing:
PA.VIII.E.R1	1. Lack of proficiency in flight by reference to instruments.
PA.VIII.E.R2	2. Poor cockpit management.
PA.VIII.E.R3	3. Lack of awareness of the direction for the nearest VMC.
PA.VIII.E.R4	4. Failure to descend straight ahead or make level turns under emergency instrument conditions.
PA.VIII.E.R5	5. Operating outside of the normal operating envelope during the recovery.
Skills	The applicant demonstrates the ability to:
PA.VIII.E.S1	1. Perform timely recognition of the nature of the unusual attitude.
PA.VIII.E.S2	2. Recognize unusual flight attitudes solely by reference to instruments and perform the correct, coordinated, and smooth flight control application to resolve unusual pitch and bank attitudes while staying within the airplane's limitations and flight parameters.
PA.VIII.E.S3	3. Perform appropriate trimming to relieve control pressures.
PA.VIII.E.S4	4. When level, maintain altitude ±200 feet, heading ±20° and airspeed ±10 knots.

A. General Information

1. The objective of this task is for you to demonstrate your knowledge, risk management, and skills related to attitude instrument flying while recovering from unusual attitudes.

2. When visual references are inadequate or lost, you may unintentionally let your airplane enter a critical (unusual) attitude. Because such attitudes are unintentional and unexpected, the inexperienced pilot may react incorrectly and stall or overstress the airplane.

3. Much of the content of Subunits 47.1 and 47.2 is abbreviated based on the assumption that you have thoroughly read and understood pages 545 through 564 and the additional common task topics found in Part II. The task objectives and specific references are provided here for your convenience.

47.1 KNOWLEDGE

A. Task Objectives

1. **The applicant demonstrates understanding of flight instrument function and operation.**

    a. For information on flight instrument function and operation, see Section VIII Introduction, Knowledge, item A., beginning on page 547.

2. **The applicant demonstrates understanding of flight instrument sensitivity, limitations, and potential errors in unusual attitudes.**

    a. For information on flight instrument sensitivity, limitations, and potential errors in unusual attitudes, see Section VIII Introduction, Knowledge, item B., beginning on page 554.

3. **The applicant demonstrates understanding of flight instrument correlation (pitch instruments/bank instruments).**

    a. For information on flight instrument correlation, see Section VIII Introduction, Knowledge, item C., on page 560.

4. **The applicant demonstrates understanding of vestibular illusions (leans) and spatial disorientation.**

    a. For information on vestibular illusions (leans) and spatial disorientation, see Section VIII Introduction, Knowledge, item D., on page 560.

5. **The applicant demonstrates understanding of aerodynamic factors related to unusual pitch and bank attitudes and returning to level flight.**

    a. During unusual pitch and bank attitudes and returning to level flight, care must be taken as to not exceed the aircraft limitations.

        1) Load factor with respect to aircraft design, effect on stall speed, and turning flight should be understood.
        2) (V_A) design maneuvering speed and (V_{NE}) should be reviewed and understood.
        3) For information on load and load factor, see *Pilot Handbook*, Study Unit 1, Subunit 12.

    b. Recovery from a nose-low unusual attitude must take place in the following sequence, but almost simultaneously, so as not to overstress the airplane or create structural failure.

        1) Reduce power to stop the airspeed from increasing.
        2) Level the wings to prevent overloading the wings during recovery.
        3) Smoothly raise the nose (increase elevator pressures) until the aircraft is level.

    c. Recovery from a nose-high unusual attitude must take place in the following sequence, but almost simultaneously, so as not to create a stall/spin situation or overstress the airplane.

        1) Increase power to prevent a stall.
        2) Level the wings and simultaneously push the nose over to establish level flight.
        3) Allow airspeed to increase before reducing power to establish a normal cruise.

    d. Control movements may be large if necessary but must be smooth, positive, prompt, and coordinated.

    e. For more information on aerodynamic factors, see Study Unit 4, Subunit 2, beginning on page 25.

6. **The applicant demonstrates understanding of the appropriate pitch, power, and bank settings for airplane being flown.**

    a. For information on pitch, power, and bank settings for the airplane being flown, see Section VIII Introduction, Knowledge, item E., on page 561.

7. **The applicant demonstrates understanding of the hazards of inappropriate control response.**

    a. Unusual attitudes are some of the most hazardous situations for a pilot to be in.

        1) Without proper recovery training on instrument interpretation and aircraft control, a pilot can quickly aggravate an abnormal flight attitude into a potentially fatal accident.

    b. Due to the unexpected nature of unusual attitudes, the reaction of an inexperienced or inadequately trained pilot to an unexpected abnormal flight attitude is usually instinctive rather than intelligent and deliberate.

        1) This individual reacts with abrupt muscular effort, which is purposeless and even hazardous in turbulent conditions, at excessive speeds, or at low altitudes.

    c. After initial control has been applied in an unusual attitude recovery, continue with a fast cross-check for possible overcontrolling because the necessary initial control pressures may be large.

    d. Aircraft load limit factors and airspeed limitations should not be exceeded to prevent structural damage or structural failure.

    e. Inappropriate control response may exacerbate an already hazardous situation and also may use up available altitude for a successful recovery.

        1) In the recovery from a nose-high attitude, deflecting ailerons to level the wings before the angle of attack is reduced could result in a spin.

    f. Recovery from a nose-low attitude

        1) With the higher-than-normal airspeed, it is vital to raise the nose very smoothly to avoid overstressing the airplane.

        2) Increasing elevator back pressure before the wings are leveled will tend to increase the bank and make the situation worse.

        3) Excessive G-loads may be imposed, resulting in structural failure.

END OF KNOWLEDGE ELEMENT

47.2 RISK MANAGEMENT

A.   Task Objectives

   1.   **The applicant demonstrates the ability to identify, assess, and mitigate risks encompassing lack of proficiency in flight by reference to instruments.**

       a.   For information on proficiency in flight by reference to instruments, see Section VIII Introduction, Risk Management, item A., on page 562.

   2.   **The applicant demonstrates the ability to identify, assess, and mitigate risks encompassing poor cockpit management.**

       a.   For information on cockpit management, see Section VIII Introduction, Risk Management, item B., beginning on page 562.

   3.   **The applicant demonstrates the ability to identify, assess, and mitigate risks encompassing lack of awareness of the direction for the nearest VMC.**

       a.   For information on awareness of the direction for nearest VMC, see Section VIII Introduction, Knowledge, item C., on page 563.

   4.   **The applicant demonstrates the ability to identify, assess, and mitigate risks encompassing failure to descend straight ahead or make level turns under emergency instrument conditions.**

       a.   For information on descending straight ahead and making level turns under emergency instrument conditions, see Study Unit 44, Subunit 2, item A.4., beginning on page 579.

   5.   **The applicant demonstrates the ability to identify, assess, and mitigate risks encompassing operating outside of the normal operating envelope during the recovery.**

       a.   Recovery techniques and load factor

           1)   A positive load occurs when back pressure is applied to the elevator control, causing centrifugal force to act in the same direction as weight.

           2)   A negative load occurs when forward pressure is applied to the elevator control, causing centrifugal force to act in a direction opposite to that of weight.

           3)   The load factor increases at a rapid rate after the angle of bank reaches 50°; the approximate maximum bank angle for conventional light airplanes in a level coordinated turn is 60°, which produces a load factor of 2.0.

               a)   Stall speed increases with the increase of load factor.

4)   When operating below V_A, a damaging positive flight load cannot (theoretically) be produced. The airplane should stall before the load becomes excessive.

   a)   Operating at or below design maneuvering speed does not provide structural protection against multiple full control inputs in one axis or full control inputs in more than one axis at the same time.

   b)   Pilots should avoid full application of pitch, roll, or yaw controls to speeds below maneuvering speed and should avoid rapid and large alternating control inputs, as they may result in structural failures at any speed, including below V_A.

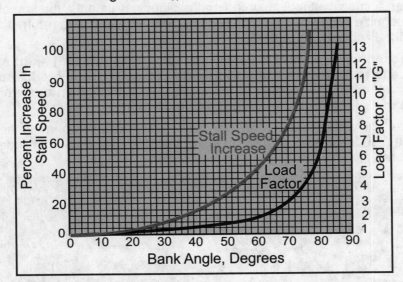

5)   The airplane must be operated within the flight envelope to prevent the airplane's primary structure from being deformed or damaged in the recovery from unusual attitudes. Thus, the airplane in flight is limited to a regime of airspeeds and load factors that do not exceed either of the following:

   a)   The positive or negative limit load factors
   b) V_{NE}

END OF RISK MANAGEMENT ELEMENT

47.3 SKILLS

A. Task Objectives

1. **The applicant demonstrates the ability to perform timely recognition of the nature of the unusual attitude.**

    a. As a general rule, any time there is an instrument rate of movement or indication other than those associated with basic instrument flight maneuvers, assume an unusual attitude and increase the speed of cross-check to confirm the attitude, instrument error, or instrument malfunction.

    b. When a critical attitude is noted on the flight instruments, the immediate priority is to recognize what your airplane is doing and decide how to return it to straight-and-level flight as quickly as possible.

2. **The applicant demonstrates the ability to recognize unusual flight attitudes solely by reference to instruments and perform the correct, coordinated, and smooth flight control application to resolve unusual pitch and bank attitudes while staying within the airplane's limitations and flight parameters.**

    a. Nose-high attitudes are shown by the rate and direction of movement of the ALT, VSI, and ASI needles, in addition to the obvious pitch and bank attitude on the AI (see the figure below).

Unusual Attitude -- Nose High

1. ASI is decreasing from 165 kt. down to 85 kt.
2. ALT is increasing from 4,500 ft. toward 5,000 ft.
3. TC indicates a right turn.
4. HI indicates a right turn from 270° toward 330°.
5. VSI indicates a positive rate of climb.

b.   Nose-low attitudes are shown by the same instruments, but in the opposite direction, as shown in the figure below.

Unusual Attitude -- Nose Low

1.   ASI is increasing from 170 kt. to 225 kt.
2.   ALT is decreasing from 6,500 ft. to 6,000 ft.
3.   TC indicates a right turn.
4.   HI indicates a right turn from 270° toward 330°.
5.   VSI indicates a negative vertical speed (i.e., a descent).

---

c.   To avoid aggravating the critical attitude with a control application in the wrong direction, the initial interpretation of the instruments must be accurate.

d.   Recovery from a Nose-High Attitude

1)   Nose-high unusual attitude is indicated by

a)   Nose high and wings banked on AI
b)   Decreasing airspeed
c)   Increasing altitude
d)   A turn on the TC

2) Take action in the following sequence:

    a) Add power. If the airspeed is decreasing or below the desired airspeed, increase power (as necessary in proportion to the observed deceleration).

    b) Reduce pitch. Apply forward elevator pressure to lower the nose on the AI and prevent a stall.

        i) Deflecting ailerons to level the wings before the angle of attack is reduced could result in a spin.

    c) Level the wings. Correct the bank (if any) by applying coordinated aileron and rudder pressure to level the miniature airplane of the AI and center the ball of the TC.

3) The corrective control applications should be made almost simultaneously but in the sequence above.

4) After initial control has been applied, continue with a fast cross-check for possible overcontrolling because the necessary initial control pressures may be large.

    a) As the rate of movement of the ALT and VSI needles decreases, the attitude is approaching level flight. When the needles stop and reverse direction, your airplane is passing through level flight.

5) When airspeed increases to normal speed, set cruise power.

e. Recovery from a Nose-Low Attitude

1) Nose-low unusual attitude is indicated by

    a) Nose low and wings banked on AI
    b) Increasing airspeed
    c) Decreasing altitude
    d) A turn on the TC

2) Take action in the following sequence:

    a) Reduce power. If the airspeed is increasing or is above the desired speed, reduce power to prevent excessive airspeed and loss of altitude.

    b) Level the wings. Correct the bank attitude with coordinated aileron and rudder pressure to straight flight by referring to the AI and TC.

        i) Increasing elevator back pressure before the wings are leveled will tend to increase the bank and make the situation worse.

        ii) Excessive G-loads may be imposed, resulting in structural failure.

    c) Raise the nose. Smoothly apply back elevator pressure to raise the nose on the AI to level flight.

        i) With the higher-than-normal airspeed, it is vital to raise the nose very smoothly to avoid overstressing the airplane.

3) The corrective control applications should be made almost simultaneously but in the sequence above.

4) After initial control has been applied, continue with a fast cross-check for possible overcontrolling because the necessary initial control pressures may be large.

    a) As the rate of movement of the ALT and VSI needles decreases, the attitude is approaching level flight. When the needles stop and reverse direction, your airplane is passing through level flight.

5) When airspeed decreases to normal speed, set cruise power.

  f.   As the indications of the ALT, TC, and ASI stabilize, the AI and TC should be checked to determine coordinated straight flight; i.e., the wings are level and the ball is centered.

      1)   Slipping or skidding sensations can easily aggravate disorientation and retard recovery.
      2)   You should return to your last assigned altitude after stabilizing in straight-and-level flight.

  g.   Unlike the control applications in normal maneuvers, larger control movements in recoveries from unusual attitudes may be necessary to bring the airplane under control.

      1)   Nevertheless, such control applications must be smooth, positive, prompt, and coordinated.
      2)   Once the airplane is returned to approximately straight-and-level flight, control movements should be limited to small adjustments.

3. **The applicant demonstrates the ability to perform appropriate trimming to relieve control pressures.**

  a.   For information on appropriate trimming to relieve control pressures, see Study Unit 44, Subunit 3, item A.6., beginning on page 582.

4. **The applicant demonstrates the ability to, when level, maintain altitude ±200 feet, heading ±20°, and airspeed ±10 knots.**

  a.   When recovering from unusual attitudes, maintain the altitude heading and airspeed specified by the evaluator.

END OF SKILLS ELEMENT

47.4 COMMON ERRORS

A.   Common Errors during Recovery from Unusual Flight Attitudes

1.   **Failure to recognize an unusual flight attitude**

   a.   This error is due to poor instrument cross-check and interpretation.

   b.   Once you are in an unusual attitude, determine how to return to straight-and-level flight, NOT how your airplane got there.

   c.   Unusually loud or soft engine and wind noise may provide an indication.

2.   **Attempting to recover from an unusual flight attitude by "feel" rather than by instrument indications**

   a.   The most hazardous illusions that lead to spatial disorientation are created by the information received by your motion-sensing system located in each inner ear.

   b.   The motion-sensing system is not capable of detecting a constant velocity or small changes in velocity, nor can it distinguish between centrifugal force and gravity.

   c.   The motion-sensing system, functioning normally in flight, can produce false sensations.

   d.   During unusual flight attitudes, you must believe and interpret the flight instruments because spatial disorientation is normal in unusual flight attitudes.

3.   **Inappropriate control applications during recovery**

   a.   Accurately interpret the initial instrument indications before recovery is started.

   b.   Follow the recovery steps in sequence.

   c.   Control movements may be larger, but must be smooth, positive, prompt, and coordinated.

4.   **Failure to recognize from instrument indications when the airplane is passing through level flight**

   a.   With an operative attitude indicator, level flight attitude exists when the miniature airplane is level with the horizon.

   b.   Without an attitude indicator, level flight is indicated by the reversal and stabilization of the airspeed indicator and altimeter needles.

END OF COMMON ERRORS

STUDY UNIT FORTY-EIGHT
RADIO COMMUNICATIONS, NAVIGATION SYSTEMS/FACILITIES, AND RADAR SERVICES

Task	Task F. Radio Communications, Navigation Systems/Facilities, and Radar Services
References	FAA-H-8083-2, FAA-H-8083-3, FAA-H-8083-15, FAA-H-8083-25
Objective	To determine that the applicant exhibits satisfactory knowledge, risk management, and skills associated with radio communications, navigation systems/facilities, and radar services available for use during flight solely by reference to instruments.
Knowledge	The applicant demonstrates understanding of:
PA.VIII.F.K1	1. Flight instrument function and operation.
PA.VIII.F.K2	2. Flight instrument sensitivity, limitations and potential errors in unusual attitudes.
PA.VIII.F.K3	3. Flight instrument correlation (pitch instruments/bank instruments).
PA.VIII.F.K4	4. How to determine the minimum safe altitude for the location.
PA.VIII.F.K5	5. Radio communications equipment and procedures.
PA.VIII.F.K6	6. Air traffic control facilities and services.
PA.VIII.F.K7	7. Installed navigation equipment function and displays.
PA.VIII.F.K8	8. Pilot interface including: pilot monitoring duties and interaction with charts and avionics equipment.
Risk Management	The applicant demonstrates the ability to identify, assess and mitigate risks, encompassing:
PA.VIII.F.R1	1. Lack of proficiency in flight by reference to instruments.
PA.VIII.F.R2	2. Poor cockpit management.
PA.VIII.F.R3	3. Lack of awareness of the direction for the nearest VMC.
PA.VIII.F.R4	4. Failure to descend straight ahead or make level turns under emergency instrument conditions.
Skills	The applicant demonstrates the ability to:
PA.VIII.F.S1	1. Maintain controlled flight while selecting proper communications frequencies, identifying the appropriate facility, and setting up navigation equipment to select the desired course.
PA.VIII.F.S2	2. Maintain aircraft control while complying with ATC instructions.
PA.VIII.F.S3	3. Maintain aircraft control while navigating using radio aids.
PA.VIII.F.S4	4. Maintain altitude ±200 feet, heading ±20° and airspeed ±10 knots.

A. General Information

1. The objective of this task is for you to demonstrate your knowledge, risk management, and skills related to radio communications, navigation systems/facilities, and radar services available for use during flight solely by reference to instruments.

2. See *Pilot Handbook* for the following:

   a. Study Unit 3, "Airports, Air Traffic Control, and Airspace," for a discussion on ATC radar, transponder operation, and radar services available to VFR aircraft

   b. Study Unit 10, "Navigation Systems," for a discussion on the method of operation and use of various navigation systems, such as VOR and GPS

3. Much of the content of Subunits 48.1 and 48.2 is abbreviated based on the assumption that you have thoroughly read and understood pages 545 through 564 and the additional common task topics found in Part II. The task objectives and specific references are provided here for your convenience.

48.1 KNOWLEDGE

A. Task Objectives

1. **The applicant demonstrates understanding of flight instrument function and operation.**

    a. For information on flight instrument function and operation, see Section VIII Introduction, Knowledge, item A., beginning on page 547.

2. **The applicant demonstrates understanding of flight instrument sensitivity, limitations, and potential errors in unusual attitudes.**

    a. For information on flight instrument sensitivity, limitations, and potential errors in unusual attitudes, see Section VIII Introduction, Knowledge, item B., beginning on page 554.

3. **The applicant demonstrates understanding of flight instrument correlation (pitch instruments/bank instruments).**

    a. For information on flight instrument correlation, see Section VIII Introduction, Knowledge, item C., on page 560.

4. **The applicant demonstrates understanding of how to determine the minimum safe altitude for a location.**

    a. You can use the maximum elevation figures (MEF) on your sectional chart to determine the minimum safe altitude (MSA).

        1) If you knew your location prior to losing outside references, you can locate the MEF in the latitude-longitude quadrant where you are located.

        2) Add 1,000 ft. (2,000 ft. in a mountainous area) to the MEF to determine the MSA.

    b. Using direction finding or radar services, the controller can inform you of the MSA for your location.

5. **The applicant demonstrates understanding of radio communications equipment and procedures.**

    a. For information on radio communications equipment and procedures, see Study Unit 23, beginning on page 265.

6. **The applicant demonstrates understanding of air traffic control facilities and services.**

    a. See *Pilot Handbook,* Study Unit 3, "Airports, Air Traffic Control, and Airspace," for a discussion on ATC radar, transponder operation, and radar services available to VFR aircraft.

    b. Services are available to you for which all you need is a VHF radio communication system.

        1) VHF Direction Finding (DF) is a ground-based station (located at a FSS) capable of indicating the bearing from its antenna to the transmitting airplane.

            a) It is used to locate lost aircraft and to guide aircraft to areas of good (VFR) weather or to airports.

            b) The DF operator on the ground can note your airplane's bearing from the facility by looking at a scope, similar to a radarscope. Each of your transmissions shows up on the scope as a line radiating out from the center.

        2) Radar-equipped ATC facilities can provide radar assistance and navigation services (vectors), provided you can talk to the controller (VHF radio), are within radar coverage, and can be identified by the ATC radar controller.

7. **The applicant demonstrates understanding of installed navigation equipment function and displays.**

    a.   The use of the airplane's navigation systems is the same whether you are flying by outside references or solely by instrument reference.

    b.   To use a radio navigation aid, you must select the proper station, tune it on the receiver, and positively identify the station by its Morse code identifier, as appropriate.

        1)   If you do not positively identify a station, you cannot be sure you are navigating to the station that you selected or that the components of the station are functioning normally.

    c.   See Study Unit 36, "Navigation Systems and Radar Services," for a discussion on the method of operation and use of various navigation systems, such as VOR and GPS.

    d.   When a VFR flight progresses from good to deteriorating weather and you continue in the hope that conditions will improve, the need for navigational help may arise. In most cases, some type of radio navigation aid will be available to help you return to a good weather area.

8. **The applicant demonstrates understanding of the pilot interface including pilot monitoring duties and interaction with charts and avionics equipment.**

    a.   The most valuable resource a pilot has is the ability to manage workload.

        1)   Resources must not only be identified, but a pilot must also develop the skills to evaluate whether there is time to use a particular resource and the impact its use will have upon the safety of flight.

        2)   Effective workload management ensures essential operations are accomplished by planning, prioritizing, and sequencing tasks to avoid work overload.

        3)   Reviewing the appropriate chart and setting radio frequencies well in advance of when they are needed helps reduce workload as the flight nears the airport. In addition, a pilot should listen to ATIS, Automated Surface Observing System (ASOS), or Automated Weather Observing System (AWOS), if available, and then monitor the tower frequency or Common Traffic Advisory Frequency (CTAF) to get a good idea of what traffic conditions to expect.

        4)   Checklists should be performed well in advance so there is time to focus on traffic and ATC instructions. These procedures are especially important prior to entering a high-density traffic area, such as Class B airspace.

        5)   Cockpit materials should be neatly arranged and organized in a manner that makes them readily available. All pilots should form the habit of good housekeeping.

        6)   The pilot must be familiar with advanced avionics cockpits and how to access the necessary information in a timely manner.

    b.   The pilot must be able to divide his or her attention between flying the aircraft, monitoring instruments, scanning for traffic, radio communications, and utilizing the appropriate navigation systems/facilities and radar services.

        1)   This ability depends upon experience, discipline, and training.

    c.   When a work overload situation exists, a pilot needs to stop, think, slow down, and prioritize tasks.

        1)   The most important task is to fly the airplane.

END OF KNOWLEDGE ELEMENT

48.2 RISK MANAGEMENT

A.   Task Objectives

1.   **The applicant demonstrates the ability to identify, assess, and mitigate risks encompassing lack of proficiency in flight by reference to instruments.**

   a.   For information on proficiency in flight by reference to instruments, see Section VIII Introduction, Risk Management, item A., on page 562.

2.   **The applicant demonstrates the ability to identify, assess, and mitigate risks encompassing poor cockpit management.**

   a.   For information on cockpit management, see Section VIII Introduction, Risk Management, item B., beginning on page 562.

3.   **The applicant demonstrates the ability to identify, assess, and mitigate risks encompassing lack of awareness of the direction for the nearest VMC.**

   a.   For information on awareness of the direction for the nearest VMC, see Section VIII Introduction, Risk Management, item C., on page 563.

4.   **The applicant demonstrates the ability to identify, assess, and mitigate risks encompassing failure to descend straight ahead or make level turns under emergency instrument conditions.**

   a.   For information on descending straight ahead and making level turns under emergency instrument conditions, see Study Unit 44, Subunit 2, item A.4., beginning on page 579.

END OF RISK MANAGEMENT ELEMENT

48.3 SKILLS

A. Task Objectives

   1. **The applicant demonstrates the ability to maintain controlled flight while selecting proper communications frequencies, identifying the appropriate facility, and setting up navigation equipment to select the desired course.**

      a. Your first priority is to maintain control of your airplane.

      b. Do not increase your workload -- seek help.

      c. As soon as you encounter an urgent situation, immediately seek assistance.

        1) An urgent situation occurs the moment you enter weather conditions below VFR weather minimums and/or you become doubtful about position, fuel endurance, deteriorating weather, or any other condition that may affect flight safety.

      d. To seek assistance from ATC, FSS, or any other facility, use the appropriate frequency.

        1) If you cannot locate a frequency, use the emergency frequency of 121.5 MHz.

        2) Remember, if you are flying by reference to instruments and you are not instrument rated, you are in (at least) an urgent situation.

      e. To use a radio navigation aid, you must select the proper station, tune it on the receiver, and positively identify the station by its Morse code identifier, as appropriate.

        1) If you do not positively identify a station, you cannot be sure you are navigating to the station that you selected, or that all components of the station are functioning normally.

   2. **The applicant demonstrates the ability to maintain aircraft control while complying with ATC instructions.**

      a. If you feel you are in an urgent or distress situation and cannot contact help on your current frequency, select the emergency frequency of 121.5 MHz on your communication radio.

        1) If you are already in contact with ATC, do not change frequency unless instructed to do so.

      b. Follow verbal instructions and/or navigation facilities for guidance.

        1) When using either DF or radar services, you need to follow the verbal instructions you receive.

          a) If you do not understand the instructions, tell the controller and ask for clarification.

          b) Inform the controller if you regain visual reference to the ground and can remain in VFR weather conditions.

      c. Remember that your primary task is to maintain positive control of the aircraft, then communicate with ATC and follow their instructions.

   3. **The applicant demonstrates the ability to maintain aircraft control while navigating using radio aids.**

      a. The pilot must be able to maintain positive control of the aircraft while selecting, tuning, and identifying the appropriate navigation facility/system.

      b. You must learn to divide your attention among flying, collision avoidance, performing checklists, and radio communications. Experience and discipline will help develop this skill.

   4. **The applicant demonstrates the ability to maintain altitude ±200 feet, heading ±20°, and airspeed ±10 knots.**

      a. Maintain the altitude, heading, and airspeed specified by the evaluator at all times.

END OF SKILLS ELEMENT

48.4 COMMON ERRORS

A.   Common Errors while Using Radio Communications, Navigation Systems/Facilities, and Radar Services

    1.   **Delaying the use of a radio aid or obtaining radar services**

        a.   As soon as you encounter an urgent situation, you should immediately seek assistance.

            1)   An urgent situation occurs the moment you enter weather conditions below VFR weather minimums and/or you become doubtful about position, fuel endurance, deteriorating weather, or any other condition that may affect flight safety.

    2.   **Failure to control the airplane properly**

        a.   Your first priority is to maintain control of your airplane.

        b.   Do not increase your workload -- seek help.

    3.   **Failure to select, tune, or identify a radio station properly**

        a.   To use a radio navigation aid, you must select the proper station, tune it on the receiver, and positively identify the station by its Morse code identifier, as appropriate.

            1)   If you do not positively identify a station, you cannot be sure you are navigating to the station that you selected.

        b.   To seek assistance from ATC, FSS, or any other facility, use the appropriate frequency.

            1)   If you cannot locate a frequency, use the emergency frequency of 121.5 MHz.

            2)   Remember, if you are flying by reference to instruments and you are not instrument rated, you are in (at least) an urgent situation.

    4.   **Failure to maintain minimum safe altitude**

        a.   Maintain at least 1,000 ft. (2,000 ft. in mountainous areas) MSL above the MEF on your sectional chart.

        b.   Do not attempt to go below this altitude to regain visual references.

END OF COMMON ERRORS

PART III
SECTION IX:
EMERGENCY OPERATIONS

Study Units 49 through 52 of Section IX explain the four FAA ACS tasks (A-D) of Emergency Operations. These tasks include knowledge, risk management, and skill. Your evaluator is required to test you on all four of these tasks.

There are several factors that may interfere with your ability to act promptly and properly when faced with an emergency.

1. **Reluctance to accept the emergency situation:** Allowing your mind to become paralyzed by the emergency may lead to failure to maintain flying speed, delay in choosing a suitable landing area, and indecision in general.

2. **Desire to save the airplane:** If you have been conditioned to expect to find a suitable landing area whenever your instructor simulated a failed engine, you may be apt to ignore good procedures in order to avoid rough terrain where the airplane may be damaged. There may be times that the airplane will have to be sacrificed so that you and your passengers can walk away.

3. **Undue concern about getting hurt:** Fear is a vital part of self-preservation, but it must not lead to panic. You must maintain your composure and apply the proper concepts and procedures.

Emergency operations require that you maintain situational awareness of what is happening. You must develop an organized process for decision making that can be used in all situations. One method is to use **DECIDE**:

D etect a change -- Recognize immediately when indications, whether visual, aural, or intuitive, are different from those expected.

E stimate need to react -- Determine whether these different indications constitute an adverse situation and, if so, what sort of action, if any, will be required to deal with it.

C hoose desired outcome -- Decide how, specifically, you would like the current situation altered.

I dentify actions to control change -- Formulate a definitive plan of action to remedy the situation.

D o something positive -- Even if no ideal plan of action presents itself, something can always be done to improve things at least.

E valuate the effects -- Have you solved the predicament, or is further action required?

The following are ideas about good judgment and sound operating practice as you prepare to meet emergencies.

1. All pilots hope to be able to act properly and efficiently when the unexpected occurs. As a safe pilot, you should cultivate coolness in an emergency.

2. You must know your airplane well enough to interpret the indications correctly before you take the corrective action. This requires regular study of your airplane's POH/AFM.

3. While difficult, you must make a special effort to remain proficient in procedures you will seldom, if ever, have to use.

4. Do not be reluctant to accept the fact that you have an emergency. Take appropriate action immediately without overreacting. Explain your problem to ATC so they can help you plan alternatives and be in a position to grant you priority.

5. You should assume that an emergency will occur every time you take off; i.e., expect the unexpected. If it does not happen, you have a pleasant surprise. If it does, you will be in the correct mindset to recognize the problem and handle it in a safe and efficient manner.

6. Avoid putting yourself into a situation where you have no alternatives. Be continuously alert for suitable emergency landing spots.

The tasks in this section have several common items, listed and explained here instead of repeated throughout the text.

The following common task item topics are included in this section introduction:

KNOWLEDGE

RISK MANAGEMENT

KNOWLEDGE

A. **The applicant demonstrates understanding of glide speed and distance.**

1. **Best glide airspeed (V_{GLIDE})** is the airspeed that provides the best lift/drag (i.e., L/D_{MAX}) ratio angle of attack in a power-off glide. It will allow the airplane to glide the farthest.

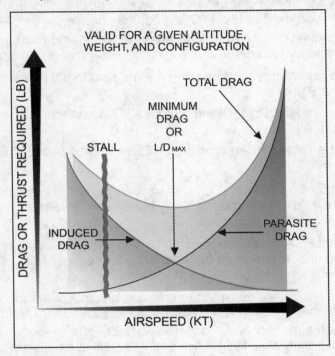

2. The airspeed at which minimum drag occurs is the same airspeed at which the maximum lift/drag ratio (L/D_{MAX}) takes place.

   a. At this point, the least amount of thrust is required for level flight.

   b. Many important items of airplane performance are obtained in flight at L/D_{MAX}. These include

      1) Maximum range.
      2) Maximum power-off glide range. Thus, the airspeed for L/D_{MAX} is the airplane's best glide airspeed.

   c. Flight below L/D_{MAX} produces more drag and requires more thrust to maintain level flight.

B. **The applicant demonstrates understanding of communications.**

1. Contact 121.5 MHz in an emergency.

2. You should immediately state your

   a. Airplane call sign
   b. Location and altitude
   c. Problem
   d. Extent of the distress, e.g., requiring no delay, priority, or emergency handling

3. If equipped with a radar beacon transponder and if unable to establish voice communications with an air traffic control facility, set the transponder to Code 7700.

C. **The applicant demonstrates understanding of ATC clearance deviations.**

1. Once you have been given ATC instructions or a clearance, you may not deviate from it unless you obtain amended instructions or clearance, an emergency exists, or the deviation is in response to a traffic alert and collision avoidance system (TCAS) resolution advisory.

    a. If you deviate from a clearance in an emergency or in response to a TCAS resolution advisory, you must notify ATC as soon as possible.

    b. If you are given priority by ATC in an emergency, you must submit a detailed report of the emergency within 48 hr. to the manager of that ATC facility, if requested.

        1) The report may be requested even if you do not deviate from any rule of 14 CFR Part 91.

2. If you are uncertain about the meaning of an ATC clearance, you should immediately ask for clarification from ATC.

D. **The applicant demonstrates understanding of ELTs and/or other emergency locating devices.**

1. Emergency locator transmitters (ELTs) of various types are independently powered and of incalculable value in an emergency. They have been developed as a means of locating downed aircraft and their occupants.

    a. The newest ELTs available transmit on 406 MHz, providing better reliability and reception and, therefore, a better chance to receive assistance, especially in a remote location due to satellite monitoring.

        1) Older ELTs are designed to emit a distinctive audio tone for homing purposes on the emergency frequencies 121.5 MHz and 243.0 MHz only.

        2) Satellite monitoring for non-406 MHz ELTs is no longer available. Older ELTs will still transmit on 121.5 MHz and 243.0 MHz as appropriate to the unit's design.

    b. The power source is designed to be capable of providing power for continuous operation for at least 48 hr. or more at a very wide range of temperatures. The ELT can expedite search and rescue operations as well as facilitate accident investigation.

    c. The ELT is required for most general aviation and small private aircraft. The pilot and other occupants could survive a crash impact only to die of exposure before they are located.

2. The ELT is equipped with a gravity switch that, when armed, automatically activates the ELT upon an impact of sufficient force.

    a. Once the transmitter is activated and the signal detected, search aircraft with homing equipment can locate the scene. Search aircraft use special search patterns to locate the transmitter site.

3. ELTs generally have three switch positions: "ON," "OFF," and "ARMED."

    a. "On" provides continuous signal broadcast.

    b. "Off" means no broadcast is possible and the gravity switch cannot be activated.

    c. "Armed" means the gravity switch will be activated in a crash situation, which turns on the broadcast.

    d. Normally, the ELT is in a rear area of the airplane and is always set on "armed." It is affixed as far aft as possible to avoid possible damage from crash impact.

4. Do not inadvertently activate the ELT in the air or on the ground.

    a. Accidental or unauthorized activation will generate an emergency signal that will lead to expensive and wasteful searches.

    b. A false ELT signal could also interfere with genuine emergency transmissions and hinder or prevent the timely location of crash sites.

5. ELTs should be tested in accordance with the manufacturer's instructions, preferably in a shielded or screened room to prevent the broadcast of signals that could trigger a false alert.

    a. When this cannot be done, airplane operational testing is authorized on 121.5 MHz and 243.0 MHz as follows:

        1) Tests should be conducted only during the first 5 min. after any hour.

    b. ELT batteries must be replaced after 1 cumulative hr. of use or after 50% of their useful life (or charge, if rechargeable) expires.

    c. The expiration date for batteries used in an ELT must be legibly marked on the outside of the transmitter.

    d. The ELT must be inspected every 12 calendar months for

        1) Proper installation
        2) Battery corrosion
        3) Operation of the controls and crash sensor
        4) Sufficient signal radiated from its antenna

RISK MANAGEMENT

A. **The applicant demonstrates the ability to identify, assess, and mitigate risks encompassing wind.**

   1. For emergency descents, approaches, and landings, pilot should try to fly into the wind. However, wind should not be your only consideration.

      a. When the pilot has time to maneuver, the planning of the approach should be governed by three factors.

         1) Wind direction and velocity
         2) Dimensions and slope of the chosen field
         3) Obstacles in the final approach path

      b. These three factors are seldom compatible. When compromises have to be made, the pilot should aim for a wind/obstacle/terrain combination that permits a final approach with some margin for error in judgment or technique.

      c. A pilot who overestimates the gliding range may be tempted to stretch the glide across obstacles in the approach path. For this reason, it is sometimes better to plan the approach over an unobstructed area, regardless of wind direction.

      d. Experience shows that a collision with obstacles at the end of a ground roll, or slide, is much less hazardous than striking an obstacle at flying speed before the touchdown point is reached.

B. **The applicant demonstrates the ability to identify, assess, and mitigate risks encompassing selecting a suitable landing area.**

   1. You should always be aware of suitable forced-landing fields. The perfect field would be an established airport or a hard-packed, long, smooth field with no high obstacles on the approach end. You need to select the best field available.

      a. Pick a landing area and continue to evaluate the area and define your landing spot as you fly your pattern and go through the appropriate procedures.

      b. If a poor field has been selected–one that would obviously result in disaster if a landing were to be made–and there is a more advantageous field within gliding distance, a change to the better field should be made.

      c. The hazards in these last-minute decisions should be thoroughly understood.

   2. Many pilots select from locations in front or to the left of them when there may be a perfect site just behind or to the right. You may want to perform a 180° turn to the right to look for a suitable field if altitude permits and you do not have a suitable field in sight.

   3. Attempt to land into the wind, although other factors may dictate a crosswind or downwind landing.

      a. Insufficient altitude may make it inadvisable or impossible to attempt to maneuver into the wind.

      b. Ground obstacles may make landing into the wind impractical or inadvisable because they shorten the effective length of the available field.

      c. The distance from a suitable field upwind from the present position may make it impossible to reach the field from the altitude at which the engine failure occurs.

      d. The best available field may be on a hill and at such an angle to the wind that a downwind landing uphill would be preferable and safer.

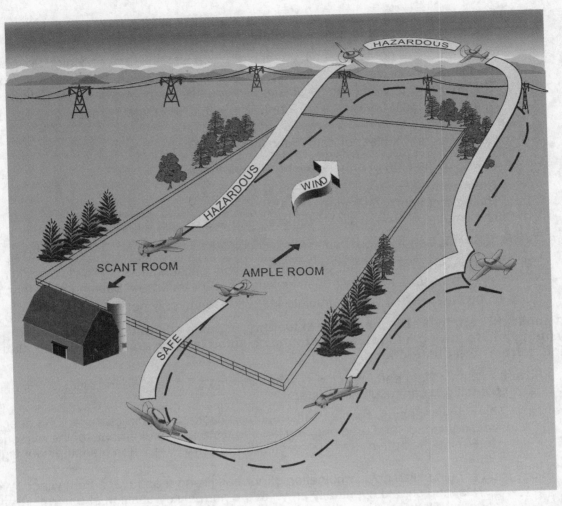

4.   Choose a smooth, grassy field if possible. If you land in a cultivated field, land parallel to the furrows.

5. Roads should be used only as a last resort. They almost always have power lines crossing them that cannot be seen until you are committed to the road.

    a. Wires often are not seen at all, and the airplane just goes out of control, to the surprise of the pilot.
    b. The presence of wires can be assumed if you see telephone or power poles.
    c. Also, roads must be wide (e.g., four lanes) because of fences, adjacent trees, and road signs.
    d. Use roads only if clear of both traffic and electric/telephone wires.

6. Your altitude at the time of engine failure will determine

    a. The number of alternative landing sites available
    b. The type of approach pattern
    c. The amount of time available to determine and correct the engine problem

7. Check for traffic and ask your evaluator to check for traffic.

    a. Inform your evaluator that you would ask your passengers, especially one sitting in the right front seat, to assist you in looking for other traffic and pointing it out to you.
    b. (S)he may instruct you to simulate that you are the only person in the airplane.

C. **The applicant demonstrates the ability to identify, assess, and mitigate risks encompassing planning and following a flight pattern to the selected landing area considering altitude, wind, terrain, and obstructions.**

1. Failure to plan a flight pattern to the selected landing area considering altitude, wind, terrain, and obstructions can result in disaster.

    a. The many variables, such as altitude, obstructions, wind direction, landing direction, landing surface and gradient, and landing distance requirements of the airplane will determine the pattern and approach procedures to use when planning your flight pattern.
    b. You should utilize any combination of normal gliding maneuvers, from wings level to spirals, and should eventually arrive at the normal key position at a normal traffic pattern altitude for the selected landing area.

        1) From this point on, the approach will be as nearly as possible as a normal power-off approach.
    c. Slipping the airplane, using flaps, varying the position of the base leg, and varying the turn onto final approach should be stressed as ways of correcting for misjudgment of altitude and glide angle.
    d. It is important to maintain a constant glide speed because variations of gliding speed nullify all attempts at accuracy in judgment of gliding distance and the landing spot.
    e. Practicing simulated emergency approach and landings with a qualified instructor is the best way to develop the skills to plan an appropriate flight pattern.

STUDY UNIT FORTY-NINE
EMERGENCY DESCENT

Task	Task A. Emergency Descent
References	FAA-H-8083-2, FAA-H-8083-3; POH/AFM
Objective	To determine that the applicant exhibits satisfactory knowledge, risk management, and skills associated with an emergency descent.
Knowledge	The applicant demonstrates understanding of:
PA.IX.A.K1	1. Glide speed, distance.
PA.IX.A.K2	2. Stabilized approach.
PA.IX.A.K3	3. Energy management.
PA.IX.A.K4	4. Wind conditions and effects.
PA.IX.A.K5	5. Situations, such as depressurization, cockpit smoke and/or engine fire that require an emergency descent.
PA.IX.A.K6	6. Emergency procedures.
PA.IX.A.K7	7. Communications.
PA.IX.A.K8	8. ATC clearance deviations.
PA.IX.A.K9	9. ELTs and/or other emergency locating devices.
PA.IX.A.K10	10. Radar assistance to VFR aircraft.
PA.IX.A.K11	11. Transponder.
Risk Management	The applicant demonstrates the ability to identify, assess and mitigate risks, encompassing:
PA.IX.A.R1	1. Wind.
PA.IX.A.R2	2. Failure to select a suitable landing area.
PA.IX.A.R3	3. Failure to plan and follow a flight pattern to the selected landing area considering altitude, wind, terrain, and obstructions.
PA.IX.A.R4	4. Improper aircraft and propeller configurations.
PA.IX.A.R5	5. Improper management of tasks associated with an emergency descent.
PA.IX.A.R6	6. Low altitude maneuvering.
PA.IX.A.R7	7. Collision avoidance, scanning, obstacle and wire strike avoidance.
PA.IX.A.R8	8. Having the right-of-way in an emergency.
PA.IX.A.R9	9. Failure to maintain situational awareness during an emergency descent.
PA.IX.A.R10	10. Low altitude stalls/spins.
PA.IX.A.R11	11. Difference between using V_{NE} and V_{FE}, and when each one is appropriate.
Skills	The applicant demonstrates the ability to:
PA.IX.A.S1	1. Analyze the situation and select an appropriate course of action.
PA.IX.A.S2	2. Establish and maintain the appropriate airspeed and configuration for the emergency descent.
PA.IX.A.S3	3. Establish appropriate propeller pitch (if constant speed), flap deployment, and gear position (if retractable) relative to the distance and altitude to the selected landing area.
PA.IX.A.S4	4. Exhibit orientation, division of attention and proper planning.
PA.IX.A.S5	5. Maintain positive load factors during the descent.
PA.IX.A.S6	6. Complete the appropriate checklist.

A.   General Information

   1.   The objective of this task is for you to demonstrate your knowledge, risk management, and skills related to an emergency descent.

   2.   Much of the content of Subunits 49.1 and 49.2 is abbreviated based on the assumption that you have thoroughly read and understood pages 287 through 304, pages 621 through 628, and the additional common task topics found in Part II. The task objectives and specific references are provided here for your convenience.

49.1 KNOWLEDGE

A.   Task Objectives

   1.   **The applicant demonstrates understanding of glide speed and distance.**

      a.   For information on glide speed and distance, see Section IX Introduction, Knowledge, item A., beginning on page 623.

   2.   **The applicant demonstrates understanding of stabilized approach.**

      a.   For information on stabilized approach, see Section IV Introduction, Knowledge, item D., beginning on page 292.

   3.   **The applicant demonstrates understanding of energy management.**

      a.   For information on energy management, see Study Unit 8, Subunit 1, beginning on page 71.

   4.   **The applicant demonstrates understanding of wind conditions and effects.**

      a.   For information on wind conditions and effects, see Study Unit 9, Subunit 3, beginning on page 80.

   5.   **The applicant demonstrates understanding of situations, such as depressurization, cockpit smoke, and/or engine fire that require an emergency descent.**

      a.   This maneuver is a procedure for establishing the fastest practical rate of descent during emergency conditions that may arise as the result of an uncontrollable fire, a sudden loss of cabin pressurization, smoke in the cockpit, or any other situation demanding an immediate and rapid descent.

         1)   The objective, then, is to descend your airplane as soon and as rapidly as possible, within the limitations of your airplane, to an altitude from which a safe landing can be made or at which pressurization or supplemental oxygen is not needed.

            a)   The descent is accomplished by decreasing the airplane's thrust and increasing drag.

      b.   A fire in flight demands immediate and decisive action.

         1)   An in-flight engine compartment fire is usually caused by a failure that allows a flammable substance such as fuel, oil, or hydraulic fluid to come in contact with a hot surface.

            a)   This may be caused by a mechanical failure of the engine itself, an engine-driven accessory, a defective induction or exhaust system, or a broken line.

            b)   Engine compartment fires can be indicated by smoke and/or flames coming from the engine cowling area. They can also be indicated by discoloration, bubbling, and/or melting of the engine cowling skin in cases where flames and/or smoke is not visible to the pilot.

2) The initial indication of an electrical fire is usually the distinct odor of burning insulation.

    a) Once an electrical fire is detected, the pilot should attempt to identify the faulty circuit by checking circuit breakers, instruments, avionics, and lights.

    b) Even if you can isolate the circuit breaker and discontinue the use of the circuit, any materials that have been ignited may continue to burn.

    c) The most prudent course of action is to land as soon as possible.

3) Cabin fires generally result from one of three sources: (1) careless smoking on the part of the pilot and/or passengers, (2) electrical system malfunctions, or (3) heating system malfunctions.

    a) A fire in the cabin presents the pilot with two immediate demands: attacking the fire and getting the airplane safely on the ground as quickly as possible.

    b) A fire or smoke in the cabin should be controlled by identifying and shutting down the faulty system. In many cases, smoke may be removed from the cabin by opening the cabin air vents. This should be done only after the fire extinguisher (if available) is used.

6. **The applicant demonstrates understanding of emergency procedures.**

    a. For information on emergency procedures, see Study Unit 8, Subunit 2, beginning on page 73.

7. **The applicant demonstrates understanding of communications.**

    a. For information on communications, see Section IX Introduction, Knowledge, item B., on page 623.

8. **The applicant demonstrates understanding of ATC clearance deviations.**

    a. For information on ATC clearance deviations, see Section IX Introduction, Knowledge, item C., on page 624.

9. **The applicant demonstrates understanding of ELTs and/or other emergency locating devices.**

    a. For information on ELTs and/or other emergency locating devices, see Section IX Introduction, Knowledge, item D., beginning on page 624.

10. **The applicant demonstrates understanding of radar assistance to VFR aircraft.**

    a. For information on radar assistance to VFR aircraft, see Study Unit 23, Subunit 1, item A.5., and Study Unit 38, Subunit 1, item A.2,

11. **The applicant demonstrates understanding of transponder.**

    a. In an emergency descent, you, a crew member, or one of your passengers should enter the emergency transponder code (7700). Then press IDENT.

        1) The IDENT (ID) switch, when depressed, selects a special identifier signal that is sent with the transponder reply to an interrogation signal, thus allowing ATC to rapidly identify and track an aircraft in an emergency situation and track the aircraft as it descends.

        2) "Squawking 7700" or operating a transponder with the designated emergency code lets ATC know there is an emergency and can work to get aircraft out of your way.

    b. For more information about transponders, see *Pilot Handbook*, Study Unit 3, Subunit 22.

END OF KNOWLEDGE ELEMENT

49.2 RISK MANAGEMENT

A. Task Objectives

1. **The applicant demonstrates the ability to identify, assess, and mitigate risks encompassing wind.**

    a. For information on wind, see Section IX Introduction, Risk Management, item A., on page 626.

2. **The applicant demonstrates the ability to identify, assess, and mitigate risks encompassing failure to select a suitable landing area.**

    a. For information on selecting a suitable landing area, see Section IX Introduction, Risk Management, item B., beginning on page 626.

3. **The applicant demonstrates the ability to identify, assess, and mitigate risks encompassing failure to plan and follow a flight pattern to the selected landing area considering altitude, wind, terrain, and obstructions.**

    a. For information on planning and following a flight pattern to the selected landing area, see Section IX Introduction, Risk Management, item C., on page 628.

4. **The applicant demonstrates the ability to identify, assess, and mitigate risks encompassing improper aircraft and propeller configurations.**

    a. It is imperative that you follow the recommended guidance in your POH/AFM.

        1) Disregarding your POH/AFM's checklist and not operating within the limitations of your aircraft could cause catastrophic damage.

    b. However, the weakening of the airplane structure is a major concern and descent at low airspeed would place less stress on the airplane.

        1) If the descent is conducted in turbulent conditions, the pilot must also comply with the design maneuvering speed (V_A) limitations.

    c. By disregarding your POH/AFM or structure speeds, one emergency may become exacerbated into multiple emergencies or system failures.

5. **The applicant demonstrates the ability to identify, assess, and mitigate risks encompassing improper management of tasks associated with an emergency descent.**

    a. Improper management of tasks associated with an emergency descent could make an already challenging situation even more difficult or impossible to handle.

        1) Improper task management (or improper workload management) means that proper planning and then the placing of essential operations does not take place, resulting in task saturation (or work overload). During an emergency, this could lead to catastrophic results.

        2) When task saturation occurs during an emergency,

            a) Additional information gets unattended or it displaces other tasks and information being processed.

            b) Additional stress and complication are added to an already challenging situation.

        3) An important part of managing work overload is recognizing that an overload situation exists.

            a) The effects of task saturation include

                i)   Pilots work faster.
                ii) Fixation occurs.
                iii) Decisions are made on incomplete information, and the possibility of error increases.

        b)   When a work overload situation exists, a pilot needs to

            i)   Stop,
            ii)   Think,
            iii) Slow down, and then
            iv) Prioritize.

b.   During an emergency, to execute effective task management, a pilot should place the situation in proper perspective, remain calm, and think rationally.

   1)   The ability to do this is dependent upon experience, discipline, and training

   2)   Executing effective task management during an emergency requires planning and practice. Consider doing the following to help develop successful task management skills for such an event:

      a)   Simulate the event with a qualified instructor.
      b)   Memorize the lead items of each emergency checklist.
      c)   Visualize the process and say out loud what you will do.
      d)   Maintain good CRM skills.

c.   The essential thing is to not panic; continue to fly the plane.

d.   For more information on task management, see Study Unit 6, Subunit 1, beginning on page 49.

6.   **The applicant demonstrates the ability to identify, assess, and mitigate risks encompassing low altitude maneuvering.**

a.   For information on low altitude maneuvering, see Section IV Introduction, Risk Management, item C., on page 299.

7.   **The applicant demonstrates the ability to identify, assess, and mitigate risks encompassing collision avoidance, scanning, and obstacle and wire strike avoidance.**

a.   For information on collision avoidance, scanning, and obstacle avoidance, see Study Unit 7, Subunit 4, beginning on page 66.

b.   For information on wire strikes, see Study Unit 7, Subunit 6, beginning on page 68.

8.   **The applicant demonstrates the ability to identify, assess, and mitigate risks encompassing having the right-of-way in an emergency.**

a.   Aircraft in distress have the right-of-way over another aircraft.

   1)   Keep in mind that other aircraft may be unaware that you are in distress.

b.   For more information on right-of-way rules, see Section IV Introduction, Risk Management, item F., on page 300.

9.   **The applicant demonstrates the ability to identify, assess, and mitigate risks encompassing failure to maintain situational awareness during an emergency descent.**

a.   You must maintain situational awareness during an emergency so as to avoid making the situation worse.

   1)   Do no fixate on any one thing, but continue to fly the airplane, navigate, and communicate as necessary.

   2)   Stress is increased during an emergency and you must be determined to exercise good judgment and effectively handle the situation.

   3)   You do not want to execute a successful emergency descent and then lose sight of your intended landing place or forget to put the gear down before landing.

b.   For more information on situational awareness, see Study Unit 7, Subunit 1, beginning on page 57.

10. **The applicant demonstrates the ability to identify, assess, and mitigate risks encompassing low altitude stalls/spins.**

    a. For more information on low altitude stall/spin, see Section IV Introduction, Risk Management, item H., beginning on page 301.

11. **The applicant demonstrates the ability to identify, assess, and mitigate risks encompassing difference between using V_{NE} and V_{FE}, and when each one is appropriate.**

    a. In an emergency descent, you should descend the airplane as rapidly as possible to a lower altitude or to the ground and do so within the limitations set by the manufacturer in the POH/AFM.

        1) V_{NE}, or never-exceed speed, is an absolute limit and operations beyond this limit should never occur for any reason, even an emergency; operations beyond this limit will likely result in structural failure.

        2) V_{FE} is maximum flap extended speed where, if exceeded, you may cause structural damage to the flaps.

            a) Flaps increase drag, allow for a steeper angle of descent at slower airspeeds, and decrease glide distance.

            b) The use of flaps during final approach is recommended and requires caution in the timing and extent of their application.

        3) An emergency descent should be made at the maximum allowable airspeed consistent with the type of emergency descent situation at hand. This will provide increased drag and, therefore, the loss of altitude as quickly as possible.

            a) For example, in the case of an engine fire, a high airspeed descent at V_{NE} may blow out the fire; then a slowing to V_{FE} for flap extension in preparation for landing would likely follow.

END OF RISK MANAGEMENT ELEMENT

49.3 SKILLS

A.   Task Objectives

1.   **The applicant demonstrates the ability to analyze the situation and select an appropriate course of action.**

   a.   One of the first steps in analyzing the situation is detecting the problem.

   1)   Be sure you have correctly identified the issue and have not misdiagnosed the problem.

   b.   Determine the best course of action and stick to the plan.

   1)   Consult the emergency procedures checklist and follow every step.

   2)   Some of the most urgent, time sensitive situations should be committed to memory, e.g., engine fire.

   c.   As with any emergency, you must understand and recognize the urgency of the situation.

   d.   Remember that an emergency situation exists (e.g., loss of pressurization, cockpit smoke, and/or fire), and you have decided that the best course of action is an emergency descent.

   1)   EXAMPLE: If you are in a pressurized airplane at 18,000 ft. MSL and you lose pressurization, you must descend to a lower altitude at the fastest rate practicable before the effects of hypoxia overcome you and your passengers.

   e.   Once you decide that you must make an emergency descent, establish the descent as quickly as possible and maintain it until you have achieved the desired outcome.

2.   **The applicant demonstrates the ability to establish and maintain the appropriate airspeed and configuration for the emergency descent.**

   a.   You must use the configuration specified for your airplane in Section 3, Emergency Procedures, of your airplane's POH/AFM.

   1)   Use the power setting as specified in your POH/AFM.

   2)   Some manufacturers may have an entry power setting (idle) and then may specify that a minimum power setting be maintained after a descent is established.

   b.   If your airplane's POH/AFM does not have an emergency descent procedure, it is generally recommended that you

   1)   Reduce the power to idle.

   2)   Move the propeller control to the high RPM position (if equipped with a constant speed propeller).

   a)   This will allow the propeller to act as an aerodynamic brake to help prevent excessive airspeed during the descent.

   3)   As quickly as practicable, extend the landing gear and full flaps to provide maximum drag so that a descent can be made as rapidly as possible without excessive airspeed.

   c.   To maintain positive load factors and for the purpose of clearing the area below, a 30° to 45° bank should be established for at least a 90° heading change while initiating the descent.

   d.   Do not exceed V_{NE}, V_{LE}, or V_{FE}, depending on your airplane's configuration.

3. **The applicant demonstrates the ability to establish appropriate propeller pitch (if constant speed), flap deployment, and gear position (if retractable) relative to the distance and altitude to the selected landing area.**

    a.   Except when prohibited by the manufacturer, the power should be reduced to idle and the propeller control (if the airplane is so equipped) should be placed in the low pitch (or high RPM) position.

        1)   This will allow the propeller to act as an aerodynamic brake to increase drag and help prevent a buildup of excessive airspeed during the descent.

    b.   The landing gear (if retractable) and flaps should be extended as recommended by the manufacturer.

        1)   This configuration will provide maximum drag so that the descent can be made as rapidly as possible and without a buildup of excessive airspeed.

        2)   The pilot should not allow the airplane's airspeed to exceed the never-exceed speed (V_{NE}), the maximum landing gear extended speed (V_{LE}), or the maximum flap extended speed (V_{FE}), as applicable.

    c.   Establishing the appropriate propeller pitch, flap deployment, and gear position should be accomplished at the appropriate distance and altitude relative to the selected landing area.

4. **The applicant demonstrates the ability to exhibit orientation, division of attention, and proper planning.**

    a.   You must be able to divide your attention between flying the airplane and coping with the emergency while maintaining your emergency descent.

    b.   Plan ahead for your desired outcome.

        1)   EXAMPLE: If you are making an emergency descent due to an uncontrollable fire, you must select an appropriate landing area and plan your transition from the emergency descent to the landing.

5. **The applicant demonstrates the ability to maintain positive load factors during the descent.**

    a.   Remember, your airplane is designed to withstand more positive load factors than negative.

        1)   EXAMPLE: An airplane certificated in the utility category has limit load factors of +4.4 and -1.76 while an airplane in the normal category has limit load factors of +3.8 and -1.52.

    b.   If you abruptly push the control forward, you will feel a negative load factor (or a negative G).

        1)   At cruise airspeed, an abrupt nose-down pitch attitude could easily exceed the negative load limits and cause structural failure.

    c.   Always maintain positive load factors (G forces) during the emergency descent.

        1)   Initiating an emergency descent with a bank of approximately 30-45° avoids imposing excessive negative loads on the airframe.

6. **The applicant demonstrates the ability to complete the appropriate checklist.**

    a.   You must use the appropriate checklists in your POH/AFM, if available.

END OF SKILLS ELEMENT

49.4 COMMON ERRORS

A. Common Errors during an Emergency Descent

1. **Failure to recognize the urgency of an emergency descent**

   a. Once you decide that you must make an emergency descent, establish the descent as quickly as possible and maintain it until you have achieved the desired outcome.

2. **Failure to establish the recommended configuration and airspeed**

   a. The configuration and airspeed will be specified in the emergency checklist in your airplane's POH/AFM.

3. **Poor orientation, division of attention, or planning**

   a. Poor orientation normally results in not knowing where you are, thus causing problems in your planning.

   b. Poor division of attention normally results in poor airspeed control and poor control of the airplane during the emergency.

   c. Poor planning results in not achieving your desired outcome.

      1) Remember, during a transition from an emergency descent to level flight, do not attempt to level off quickly as this may cause a stall.

END OF COMMON ERRORS

STUDY UNIT FIFTY
EMERGENCY APPROACH AND LANDING (SIMULATED)

Task	Task B. Emergency Approach and Landing (Simulated)
References	FAA-H-8083-2, FAA-H-8083-3; POH/AFM
Objective	To determine that the applicant exhibits satisfactory knowledge, risk management, and skills associated with emergency approach and landing procedures.
Knowledge	The applicant demonstrates understanding of:
PA.IX.B.K1	1. Glide speed and distance.
PA.IX.B.K2	2. Landing distance.
PA.IX.B.K3	3. Hazards of other than hard surfaced runway.
PA.IX.B.K4	4. Stabilized approach.
PA.IX.B.K5	5. Energy management.
PA.IX.B.K6	6. Wind conditions and effects.
PA.IX.B.K7	7. Density altitude.
PA.IX.B.K8	8. Emergency procedures.
PA.IX.B.K9	9. Communications.
PA.IX.B.K10	10. ATC clearance deviations.
PA.IX.B.K11	11. Minimum fuel.
PA.IX.B.K12	12. Selecting a landing location.
PA.IX.B.K13	13. ELTs and/or other emergency locating devices.
PA.IX.B.K14	14. Radar assistance to VFR aircraft.
Risk Management	The applicant demonstrates the ability to identify, assess and mitigate risks, encompassing:
PA.IX.B.R1	1. Wind.
PA.IX.B.R2	2. Failure to select a suitable landing area.
PA.IX.B.R3	3. Failure to plan and follow a flight pattern to the selected landing area considering altitude, wind, terrain, and obstructions.
PA.IX.B.R4	4. Improper management of tasks associated with an emergency approach and landing.
PA.IX.B.R5	5. Low altitude maneuvering.
PA.IX.B.R6	6. Startle response.
PA.IX.B.R7	7. Collision avoidance, scanning, obstacle and wire strike avoidance.
PA.IX.B.R8	8. Having the right-of-way in an emergency.
PA.IX.B.R9	9. Obstacles on approach and landing paths.
PA.IX.B.R10	10. Low altitude stall/spin.
PA.IX.B.R11	11. Failure to maintain the appropriate airspeed (e.g., best glide speed, minimum sink speed) or configuration during the descent.
Skills	The applicant demonstrates the ability to:
PA.IX.B.S1	1. Analyze the situation, select an appropriate course of action, and select a suitable landing area.
PA.IX.B.S2	2. Establish and maintain the recommended best-glide airspeed, ±10 knots.
PA.IX.B.S3	3. Plan and follow a flight pattern to the selected landing area considering altitude, wind, terrain, and obstructions that would allow a safe landing.
PA.IX.B.S4	4. Prepare for landing, or go-around, as specified by the evaluator.
PA.IX.B.S5	5. Complete the appropriate checklist.
PA.IX.B.S6	6. Make appropriate radio calls, when conditions allow.

A.   General Information

1.   The objective of this task is for you to demonstrate your knowledge, risk management, and skills related to emergency approach and landing procedures.

2.   You will need to know and understand the procedures discussed in Section 3, Emergency Procedures, of your POH/AFM.

3.   Much of the content of Subunits 50.1 and 50.2 is abbreviated based on the assumption that you have thoroughly read and understood pages 287 through 304, pages 621 through 628, and the additional common task topics found in Part II. The task objectives and specific references are provided here for your convenience.

50.1 KNOWLEDGE

A.   Task Objectives

1.   **The applicant demonstrates understanding of glide speed and distance.**

a.   For information on glide speed and distance, see Section IX Introduction, Knowledge, item A., on page 623.

2.   **The applicant demonstrates understanding of landing distance.**

a.   For information on landing distance, see Section IV Introduction, Knowledge, item B., beginning on page 289.

3.   **The applicant demonstrates understanding of the hazards of other than hard surfaced runway.**

a.   For information on the hazards of other than hard surfaced runway, see Section IV Introduction, Knowledge, item G., on page 298.

4.   **The applicant demonstrates understanding of stabilized approach.**

a.   For information on stabilized approach, see Section IV Introduction, Knowledge, item D., beginning on page 292.

5.   **The applicant demonstrates understanding of energy management.**

a.   For information on energy management, see Study Unit 8, Subunit 1.

6.   **The applicant demonstrates understanding of wind conditions and effects.**

a.   For information on wind conditions and effects, see Study Unit 9, Subunit 3.

7.   **The applicant demonstrates understanding of density altitude.**

a.   For information on density altitude, see Study Unit 9, Subunit 1.

8.   **The applicant demonstrates understanding of emergency procedures.**

a.   For information on emergency procedures, see Study Unit 8, Subunit 2.

9.   **The applicant demonstrates understanding of communications.**

a.   For information on communications, see Section IX Introduction, Knowledge, item B., on page 623.

10. **The applicant demonstrates understanding of ATC clearance deviations.**

a.   For information on ATC clearance deviations, see Section IX Introduction, Knowledge, item C., on page 624.

11. **The applicant demonstrates understanding of minimum fuel.**

    a. Minimum fuel requirements

        1) You may not fly VFR during the day unless there is enough fuel to fly to the destination and at least 30 min. beyond that point at normal cruise speed.

        2) You may not fly VFR at night unless there is enough fuel to fly to the destination and at least 45 min. beyond that point at normal cruise speed.

    b. Flight with less than the required minimum fuel is never reasonable.

        1) Ignoring minimum fuel reserve requirements while either VFR or IFR is generally the result of overconfidence, lack of flight planning, or ignoring the regulations.

        2) Remember that most aircraft are manufactured to a standard that requires the fuel indicator be accurate when the fuel quantity is full.

    c. Questions to always keep in mind:

        1) Does this aircraft have sufficient fuel capacity, with reserves, for the trip legs planned?

        2) Is the fuel quantity correct? Did I check?

    d. Flying without minimum fuel requirements is typically the result of external pressures.

        1) EXAMPLE: For a ferry flight to deliver an airplane from the factory, a pilot calculated groundspeed, determining he would arrive at his destination with only 10 min. of fuel remaining. A check of the weather revealed he would be flying into marginal weather conditions. By asking himself whether it was more critical to maintain the schedule or to arrive with an intact aircraft, the pilot decided to schedule a refuel stop even though it would mean he would not be able to keep to the schedule. He chose not to "stretch" the fuel supply in marginal weather conditions, which could have resulted in an emergency landing.

    e. A minimum fuel condition is an example of an "urgent" situation and may call for a **precautionary emergency approach and landing**.

        1) A precautionary landing is a **premeditated landing, on or off an airport, when further flight is possible but inadvisable**.

12. **The applicant demonstrates understanding of selecting a landing location.**

    a. For information on selecting a suitable landing area, see Section IX Introduction, Risk Management, item B., beginning on page 626.

13. **The applicant demonstrates understanding of ELTs and/or other emergency locating devices.**

    a. For information on ELTs and/or other emergency locating devices, see Section IX Introduction, Knowledge, item D., beginning on page 624.

14. **The applicant demonstrates understanding of radar assistance to VFR aircraft.**

    a. For information on radar assistance to VFR aircraft, see Study Unit 23, Subunit 1, item A.5., and Study Unit 38, Subunit 1, item A.2,

END OF KNOWLEDGE ELEMENT

50.2 RISK MANAGEMENT

A.   Task Objectives

1.   **The applicant demonstrates the ability to identify, assess, and mitigate risks encompassing wind.**

   a.   For information on wind, see Section IX Introduction, Risk Management, item A., on page 626.

2.   **The applicant demonstrates the ability to identify, assess, and mitigate risks encompassing failure to select a suitable landing area.**

   a.   For information on selecting a suitable landing area, see Section IX Introduction, Risk Management, item B., beginning on page 626.

3.   **The applicant demonstrates the ability to identify, assess, and mitigate risks encompassing failure to plan and follow a flight pattern to the selected landing area considering altitude, wind, terrain, and obstructions.**

   a.   For information on planning and following a flight pattern to the selected landing area, see Section IX Introduction, Risk Management, item C., on page 628.

4.   **The applicant demonstrates the ability to identify, assess, and mitigate risks encompassing improper management of tasks associated with an emergency approach and landing.**

   a.   Improper management of tasks associated with an emergency approach and landing can further complicate an already challenging situation, and possibly lead to catastrophic results.

   1)   You must be able to fly the airplane from the point of the emergency requiring the emergency approach and landing to where a reasonably safe landing can be made, and also perform the necessary cockpit procedures.

   2)   Cockpit procedures should be developed to such an extent that, when an emergency occurs, you will check the critical items that would be necessary to handle the emergency while selecting a field and planning an approach.

   3)   Learning to accomplish emergency procedures while planning and flying the approach is difficult in early training.

   4)   Definite steps and procedures are to be followed, and the use of a checklist is strongly recommended.

   a)   Most airplane manufacturers provide a checklist of the appropriate items.

   b)   Many actual emergency landings have been made and later found to be the result of the incorrect turn of a switch or the executing of procedures in the incorrect order.

   c)   Many actual emergency landings could have been prevented if, during training, the pilots had developed the habit of checking the critical items and using the appropriate checklist during training to the extent that it carried over into later flying.

   b.   For more information on task management, see Study Unit 6, Subunit 1, beginning on page 49.

5.   **The applicant demonstrates the ability to identify, assess, and mitigate risks encompassing low altitude maneuvering.**

   a.   For information on low altitude maneuvering, see Section IV Introduction, Risk Management, item C., on page 299.

6.   **The applicant demonstrates the ability to identify, assess, and mitigate risks encompassing startle responses.**

   a.   The ability to make effective decisions during flight can be impaired by stress.

    b.   There are several factors that may interfere with a pilot's ability to act promptly and properly when faced with an emergency.

        1)   Reluctance to accept the emergency situation

            a)   A pilot who allows the mind to become paralyzed at the thought that the airplane will be on the ground in a very short time, regardless of the pilot's actions or hopes, is severely handicapped in the handling of the emergency.

            b)   An unconscious desire to delay the dreaded moment may lead to such errors as failure to lower the nose to maintain flying speed, delay in the selection of the most suitable landing area within reach, and indecision in general.

        2)   Desire to save the airplane

            a)   The pilot who has been conditioned during training to expect to find a relatively safe landing area, whenever the flight instructor closed the throttle for a simulated forced landing, may ignore all basic rules of airmanship to avoid a touchdown in terrain where airplane damage is unavoidable.

            b)   The desire to save the airplane, regardless of the risks involved, may be influenced by two other factors: the pilot's financial stake in the airplane and the certainty that an undamaged airplane implies no bodily harm. There are times, however, when a pilot should be more interested in sacrificing the airplane so that the occupants can safely walk away from it.

        3)   Undue concern about getting hurt

            a)   Fear is a vital part of the self-preservation mechanism. However, when fear leads to panic, we invite that which we want most to avoid.

            b)   The survival records favor pilots who maintain their composure and know how to apply the general concepts and procedures that have been developed through the years. The success of an emergency landing is as much a matter of the mind as of skills.

7.   **The applicant demonstrates the ability to identify, assess, and mitigate risks encompassing collision avoidance, scanning, and obstacle and wire strike avoidance.**

    a.   For information on collision avoidance, scanning, and obstacle avoidance, see Study Unit 7, Subunit 4, beginning on page 66.

    b.   For information on wire strikes, see Study Unit 7, Subunit 6, beginning on page 68.

8.   **The applicant demonstrates the ability to identify, assess, and mitigate risks encompassing having the right-of-way in an emergency.**

    a.   Aircraft in distress have the right-of-way over other aircraft.

        1)   Keep in mind that other aircraft may be unaware that you are in distress.

    b.   For more information on right-of-way rules, see Section IV Introduction, Risk Management, item F., on page 300.

9.   **The applicant demonstrates the ability to identify, assess, and mitigate risks encompassing obstacles on approach and landing paths.**

    a.   For information on obstacles on approach and landing paths, see Section IV Introduction, Risk Management, item D., on page 300.

10.   **The applicant demonstrates the ability to identify, assess, and mitigate risks encompassing low altitude stall/spin.**

    a.   For more information on low altitude stalls and spins, see Section IV Introduction, Risk Management, item H., beginning on page 301.

11. **The applicant demonstrates the ability to identify, assess, and mitigate risks encompassing the difference between best glide speed and minimum sink speed and when each one is appropriate.**

   a.   The decision to fly at best glide speed or minimum sink rate depends on what you are trying to do: go the farthest distance or stay in the air the longest.

   b.   Best glide speed is the speed at which the airplane will travel the greatest forward distance for a given loss of altitude in still air. This speed corresponds to an angle of attack resulting in the least drag on the airplane and giving the best lift-to-drag ratio (L/D_{MAX}).

      1)   Any speed other than the best glide speed results in more drag and will result in a proportionate change in glide ratio.

   c.   To glide and stay in the air as long as possible (to either fix a problem or to communicate intentions and prepare for a forced landing), the minimum sink speed (the airspeed at which the airplane loses altitude at the lowest rate) is what you need to maintain.

      1)   Minimum sink speed is rarely found in a POH/AFM, but it will be a little slower than maximum glide range speed.

      2)   To identify minimum sink speed (with an instructor), start at V_Y (or the manufacturer's recommended best glide speed) with power off and note speed vs. sink rate as you adjust pitch to reduce airspeed.

         a)   The highest speed forward that gives you the lowest rate of descent is the minimum sink speed (at that particular weight).

END OF RISK MANAGEMENT ELEMENT

50.3 SKILLS

A. Task Objectives

1. **The applicant demonstrates the ability to analyze the situation, select an appropriate course of action, and select a suitable landing area.**

   a. The first step in any emergency is deciding an appropriate course of action.

      1) The action will depend on how critical a situation is.

      2) An engine failure on takeoff is a very critical situation that will not allow time for emergency checklists or a restart in most cases. However, an engine failure at altitude will allow some time to attempt a restart and go through the appropriate emergency checklists.

   b. After you decide the appropriate course of action, immediately implement your decision.

2. **The applicant demonstrates the ability to establish and maintain the recommended best-glide airspeed, ±10 knots.**

   a. Your evaluator can and will normally simulate a complete power loss with the airplane in any configuration and/or at any altitude. This is accomplished by the reduction of power to idle and the statement by your evaluator that you have just experienced an engine failure.

   b. Your first reaction should be to establish the best-glide attitude immediately and ensure that the landing gear and flaps are retracted (if so equipped).

      1) The best-glide airspeed is indicated in your POH/AFM.

         In your airplane, best-glide airspeed _____.

      2) If the airspeed is above the proper glide speed, altitude should be maintained, and the airspeed allowed to dissipate to the best glide speed.

         a) When the proper glide speed is attained, the nose of your airplane should be lowered to maintain that speed and the airplane trimmed for the glide.

   c. A constant gliding speed and pitch attitude should be maintained because variations of gliding speed will disrupt your attempts at accuracy in judgment of gliding distance and the landing spot.

3. **The applicant demonstrates the ability to plan and follow a flight pattern to the selected landing area considering altitude, wind, terrain, and obstructions that would allow a safe landing.**

   a. During your selection of a suitable landing area, you should have taken into account your altitude, the wind speed and direction, the terrain, obstructions, and other factors.

      1) Now you must finalize your plan and follow your flight pattern to the landing area.
      2) You are now executing what you planned.

   b. Utilize any combination of normal gliding maneuvers, from wings level to spirals.

      1) You should eventually arrive at the normal "key" position at a normal traffic pattern altitude for your selected field, i.e., abeam the touchdown point on the downwind leg.

         a) If you arrive at the key position significantly higher than pattern altitude, it is recommended that you circle your intended landing point until near pattern altitude.

            i) Avoid extending your downwind leg too far from your landing site.

2)   From this point on, your approach should be similar to a soft-field power-off approach.

    a)   Plan your turn onto final approach, as shown below.

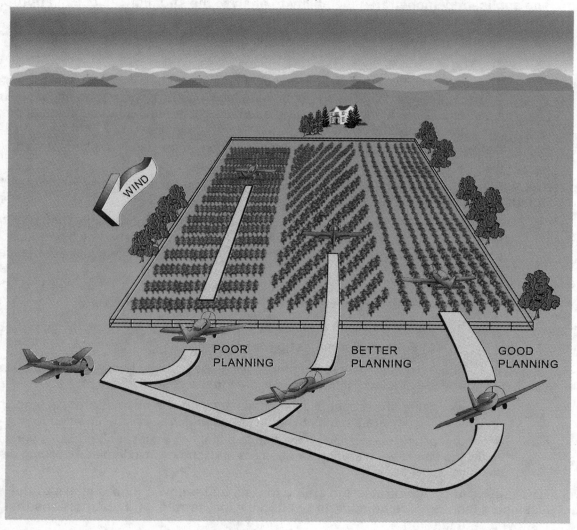

c.   Make a decision as to whether to land with the gear up or down (if retractable).

    1)   When the field is smooth, firm, and long enough to bring your airplane to a stop, a gear-down landing is appropriate.

        a)   If the field has stumps, rocks, or other large obstacles, the gear down will better protect you and your passengers.

        b)   If you suspect the field to be excessively soft, wet, short, or snow-covered, a gear-up landing will normally be safer, to eliminate the possibility of your airplane nosing over as a result of the wheels digging in.

    2)   Allow time for the gear to extend or for you to lower the gear manually.

    3)   Lower the gear and any flaps only after a landing at your selected field is assured.

    d.   The altitude is, in many ways, the controlling factor in the successful accomplishment of an emergency approach and landing.

        1)   If you realize you have selected a poor landing area (one that would obviously result in a disaster) AND there is a more advantageous field within gliding distance, a change should be made and explained to your evaluator.

            a)   You must understand that this is an exceptional situation, and the hazards involved in last-minute decisions (i.e., excessive maneuvering at very low altitudes) must be thoroughly understood.

        2)   Slipping the airplane, using flaps, varying the position of the base leg, and varying the turn onto final approach are ways of correcting for misjudgment of altitude and glide angle.

4.   **The applicant demonstrates the ability to prepare for landing, or go-around, as specified by the evaluator.**

    a.   The setting where the emergency approach and landing are simulated will dictate how this task will terminate.

        1)   If your evaluator simulates the emergency approach over anything but a runway, the maneuver will result in a go-around.

            a)   Remember that you will probably have full flaps and a large amount of nose-up trim when you initiate the go-around. Increasing power to the go-around setting will result in a strong tendency to pitch nose-up; this is a classic setup for a stall or spin accident.

                i)   Apply full power to go-around and be prepared for the large amount of forward pressure required to keep the airplane from going into an extreme nose-up attitude.

                ii)   Retract the flaps incrementally while simultaneously reducing the nose-up trim. If you are flying a retractable gear airplane, retract the gear as specified in the POH/AFM.

            b)   A go-around should be initiated no lower than 500 ft. AGL.

        2)   Many evaluators simulate an emergency approach and landing over a runway.

            a)   In this case, plan to make a normal landing. This should not be a critical or difficult situation, as most training airplanes are landed without power during normal operations.

            b)   It is common for students to overshoot the runway during this maneuver.

                i)   Avoid this by knowing the glide characteristics of your airplane. In many cases, a power-off glide results in an approach similar to that of normal operations.

5.   **The applicant demonstrates the ability to complete the appropriate checklist.**

    a.   Use the appropriate checklist in your POH/AFM.

    b.   You should be in the habit of performing from memory the first few critical steps that would be necessary to get the engine operating again.

        1)   If you are at sufficient altitude, you should use your printed checklist.

            a)   Select the correct checklist and read each item out loud. Comment on your action as you perform the task.

    c.   Simulate reporting to ATC, "Mayday, mayday, mayday."

        1)   Once contact is established, identify yourself and your position, problem, and intentions.

        2)   Switch your communication radio to 121.5 MHz if unable to contact ATC or FSS on the normal frequencies.

        3)   Squawk "7700" on your transponder.

    d.   Once you are committed to the forced landing, you should reduce the chance of fire by completing the appropriate checklist in your POH/AFM. This would normally include

        1)   Turning the fuel valve, the fuel pump (if electric), and the ignition switch to "OFF," and moving the mixture (if equipped) to the idle cut-off position.

            a)   Turn off the master switch after electrically driven flaps are extended.

        2)   Depending on configuration, wedge or fully open the door to prevent it from being jammed shut upon impact.

            a)   Protect passengers from head injury with pillows, coats, or other padded items.

    e.   For training or demonstrating emergencies, only simulate these procedures.

6.   **The applicant demonstrates the ability to make appropriate radio calls, when conditions allow.**

    a.   Follow the mantra: "aviate, navigate, communicate."

    b.   When able, simulate communications to ATC (if you are established with ATC) or on 121.5 MHz. Inform them of the following:

        1)   Your situation
        2)   Position
        3)   Number of passengers
        4)   Fuel remaining
        5)   Type and color of aircraft

END OF SKILLS ELEMENT

50.4 COMMON ERRORS

A.   Common Errors during an Emergency Approach and Landing

   1.   **Improper airspeed control**

      a.   Eagerness to get down to the ground is one of the most common errors.

         1)   In your rush to get down, you will forget about maintaining your airspeed and arrive at the edge of the landing area with too much speed to permit a safe landing.

      b.   Once you establish the best-glide airspeed, you should trim off the control pressures.

         1)   This will assist you in airspeed control as you perform the various tasks of the checklist(s) and planning your approach.

      c.   Monitor your airspeed and pitch attitude.

   2.   **Poor judgment in the selection of an emergency landing area**

      a.   Always be aware of suitable fields.

      b.   Make timely decisions and stay with your decision. Even at higher altitudes, this should be done in a timely manner.

   3.   **Failure to estimate the approximate wind speed and direction**

      a.   Use all available means to determine wind speed and direction.

         1)   Smoke, trees, windsocks, and/or wind lines on water are good indicators of surface winds.

         2)   Be aware of the crab angle you are maintaining for wind-drift correction.

      b.   Failure to know the wind speed and direction will lead to problems during the approach to your selected field.

   4.   **Failure to fly the most suitable pattern for the existing situation**

      a.   Constantly evaluate your airplane's position relative to the intended spot for landing.

      b.   Attempt to fly as much of a normal traffic pattern as possible since that is known to you, and the key points will prompt you to make decisions.

      c.   Do not rush to the landing spot, and do not attempt to extend a glide to get to that spot.

   5.   **Failure to accomplish the emergency checklist**

      a.   The checklist is important from the standpoint that it takes you through all the needed procedures to regain power.

      b.   If power is not restored, the checklist will prepare you and your airplane for the landing.

   6.   **Undershooting or overshooting the selected emergency landing area**

      a.   This error is due to poor planning and not constantly evaluating and making the needed corrections during the approach.

      b.   Familiarity with your airplane's glide characteristics and the effects of forward slips, flaps, and gear (if retractable) is essential.

END OF COMMON ERRORS

STUDY UNIT FIFTY-ONE
SYSTEMS AND EQUIPMENT MALFUNCTION

Task	Task C. Systems and Equipment Malfunction
References	FAA-H-8083-2, FAA-H-8083-3; POH/AFM
Objective	To determine that the applicant exhibits satisfactory knowledge, risk management, and skills associated with system and equipment malfunctions appropriate to the airplane provided for the practical test and analyzing the situation and take appropriate action for simulated emergencies.
Knowledge	The applicant demonstrates understanding of:
PA.IX.C.K1	1. The elements related to system and equipment malfunctions appropriate to the airplane, including:
PA.IX.C.K1a	a. Partial or complete power loss
PA.IX.C.K1b	b. Engine roughness or overheat
PA.IX.C.K1c	c. Carburetor or induction icing
PA.IX.C.K1d	d. Loss of oil pressure
PA.IX.C.K1e	e. Fuel starvation
PA.IX.C.K1f	f. Electrical malfunction
PA.IX.C.K1g	g. Vacuum/pressure, and associated flight instruments malfunction
PA.IX.C.K1h	h. Pitot/static system malfunction
PA.IX.C.K1i	i. Landing gear or flap malfunction
PA.IX.C.K1j	j. Inoperative trim
PA.IX.C.K1k	k. Inadvertent door or window opening
PA.IX.C.K1l	l. Structural icing
PA.IX.C.K1m	m. Smoke/fire/engine compartment fire
PA.IX.C.K1n	n. Any other emergency appropriate to the airplane
PA.IX.C.K1o	o. Glass cockpit operations
PA.IX.C.K2	2. Supplemental oxygen.
PA.IX.C.K3	3. Load factors.
PA.IX.C.K4	4. High drag versus low drag.
Risk Management	The applicant demonstrates the ability to identify, assess and mitigate risks, encompassing:
PA.IX.C.R1	1. Hazardous attitudes.
PA.IX.C.R2	2. Failure to complete a preflight inspection.
PA.IX.C.R3	3. Improper maintenance.
PA.IX.C.R4	4. Failure to use the proper checklist during a system or equipment malfunction.
PA.IX.C.R5	5. Failure to recognize situations, such as:
PA.IX.C.R5a	a. Depressurization
PA.IX.C.R5b	b. Cockpit smoke
PA.IX.C.R5c	c. Fire
PA.IX.C.R6	6. Loss of orientation, failure to divide attention, and improper planning.
PA.IX.C.R7	7. Failure to properly manage the airplane's energy during a system or equipment malfunction.
Skills	The applicant demonstrates the ability to:
PA.IX.C.S1	1. Analyze the situation and take appropriate action for simulated emergencies, with reference to at least three of the systems listed in the Knowledge section above.
PA.IX.C.S2	2. Complete the appropriate checklist or procedure.

A. General Information

　　1. The objective of this task is for you to demonstrate your knowledge, risk management, and skills related to system and equipment malfunctions appropriate to the airplane provided for the practical test and analyzing the situation and taking appropriate action for simulated emergencies.

51.1 KNOWLEDGE

A. Task Objectives

1. **The applicant demonstrates understanding of the elements related to system and equipment malfunctions appropriate to the airplane.**

    a. To best prepare for this element, you must have a good working knowledge of all the systems and equipment in your airplane.

    b. Since this task will be airplane specific, you will need to know Section 3, Emergency Procedures, of your POH/AFM.

        1) This section will include both the checklists and the amplified procedures.

        2) Have these checklists within easy access to you in the cockpit at all times.

    c. The following items are airplane and model specific. You will need to research each item in your POH/AFM and, if you are uncertain about any, ask for information from your CFI. You will be tested on a minimum of three of the failures listed below.

        1) Partial or complete power loss

        2) Engine roughness or overheat

        3) Carburetor or induction icing

        4) Loss of oil pressure

        5) Fuel starvation

        6) Electrical system malfunction

        7) Vacuum/pressure, and associate flight instruments malfunction

        8) Pitot/static system malfunction

        9) Landing gear or flap malfunction

        10) Inoperative trim

        11) Inadvertent door or window opening

        12) Structural icing

        13) Smoke, fire, or engine compartment fire

        14) Any other emergency appropriate to the airplane you are using for your practical test

        15) Glass cockpit operations

2. **The applicant demonstrates understanding of supplemental oxygen.**

    a. Supplemental oxygen helps mitigate hypoxia.

        1) Hypoxia is a state of oxygen deficiency in the body sufficient to impair functions of the brain and other organs.

        2) Hypoxia is prevented by understanding the factors that reduce your tolerance to altitude and by using supplemental oxygen above 10,000 ft. during the day and above 5,000 ft. at night.

            a) Corrective action if hypoxia is suspected or recognized includes

                i)   Use of supplemental oxygen
                ii) An emergency descent to a lower altitude

    b. Supplemental oxygen helps mitigate carbon monoxide poisoning.

        1) If you smell exhaust odors or begin to experience any of the symptoms, you should immediately assume carbon monoxide is present and take the following precautions:

            a) Immediately shut off the cabin air heater and close any other openings that might allow air from the engine compartment into the cockpit.

            b) Open outside air vents immediately.

c) Avoid smoking.

d) Use supplemental oxygen set to deliver 100% oxygen, if available.

e) If you are flying, land at the first opportunity, and ensure that any effects from carbon monoxide are gone before further flight.

    i) If symptoms are severe or continue after landing, medical treatment should be sought.

f) Determine that carbon monoxide is not being allowed to enter the cabin because of a defective exhaust, an unsealed opening between engine compartment and cabin, or any other factor.

c. Supplemental oxygen can help motion sickness.

   1) Motion sickness is caused by continued stimulation of the tiny portion of the inner ear that controls your sense of balance. The symptoms are progressive. If suffering from airsickness, you should

    a) Open the air vents.

    b) Loosen clothing.

    c) **Use supplemental oxygen, if available.**

    d) Keep the eyes on a point outside the airplane.

    e) Avoid unnecessary head movements.

    f) Cancel the flight and land as soon as possible.

d. The 14 CFRs for supplemental oxygen

   1) At cabin pressure altitudes above 12,500 ft. MSL up to and including 14,000 ft. MSL, the required minimum crew must use oxygen after 30 min. at those altitudes.

   2) At cabin pressure altitudes above 14,000 ft. MSL, the required minimum flight crew must continuously use oxygen.

   3) At cabin pressure altitudes above 15,000 ft. MSL, each passenger must be provided supplemental oxygen.

3. **The applicant demonstrates understanding of load factors.**

a. Any force applied to deflect an airplane from a straight line produces a stress on its structure. The amount of this force is called load factor.

   1) **Load factor** is the ratio of the total load supported by the airplane's wings (i.e., lift) to the actual weight of the airplane and its contents.

b. **Load factors and airplane design.** To be certified by the FAA, the structural strength (maximum allowable load factor) of airplanes must conform with prescribed standards set forth by the Federal Aviation Regulations. Airplanes are classified as to strength and operational use by means of the category system. Most general aviation trainer-type airplanes are classified in one or more of the following categories:

   1) The normal category has a maximum limit load factor of 3.8 positive Gs and 1.52 negative Gs.

    a) Permissible maneuvers include

      i) Any maneuver incidental to normal flying

      ii) Stalls

      iii) Lazy eights, chandelles, and steep turns (maximum bank of 60°) **without** angle of bank exceeding 60°

    2)   The utility category has a maximum limit load factor of 4.4 positive Gs and 1.76 negative Gs.

        a)   Permissible maneuvers include

            i)   All operations in the normal category

            ii)   Spins (if approved for that airplane)

            iii) Lazy eights, chandelles, and steep turns (maximum bank of 60°) **with** angle of bank exceeding 60°

    3)   The acrobatic category has a maximum limit load factor of 6.0 positive Gs and 3.0 negative Gs.

        a)   There are no restrictions except those shown to be necessary as a result of required flight tests.

  c.   **Effect of turns on load factor.**

    1)   In any airplane, if a constant altitude is maintained during the turn, the load factor for a given degree of bank is the same.

    2)   The load factor increases at a rapid rate after the angle of bank reaches 50°. The wing must produce lift equal to this load factor if altitude is to be maintained.

  d.   **Effect of load factor on stalling speed.** Any airplane, within the limits of its structure and the strength of the pilot, can be stalled at any airspeed. At a given airspeed, the load factor increases as angle of attack increases, and the wing stalls because the angle of attack has been increased beyond the critical angle. Therefore, there is a direct relationship between the load factor imposed upon the wing and its stalling characteristics.

4.   **The applicant demonstrates understanding of high drag versus low drag.**

  a.   Drag is the rearward-acting force resulting from the forward movement of the airplane through the air. Drag acts parallel to, and in the same direction as, the relative wind, as shown in the diagram below. Every part of the airplane exposed to the air while the airplane is in motion produces some resistance and contributes to the total drag. Total drag may be classified into two main types: induced drag and parasite drag.

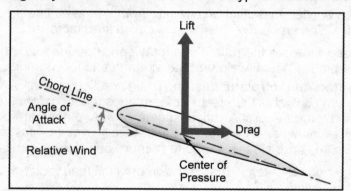

  b.   **Induced drag** is the undesirable but unavoidable by-product of lift.

    1)   Whenever the wing is producing lift, the pressure on the lower surface of the wing is greater than that on the upper surface. As a result, the air tends to flow from the high-pressure area below the wingtip upward to the low-pressure area above the wing. As a result of this pressure differential, at the end of each wingtip, a pair of rotational vortices is created that trail behind the airfoil. These vortices induce a downwash flow behind the wing's trailing edge that is the source of induced drag.

    c.   **Parasite drag** is the resistance of the air as the airplane passes through it.

        1)   Several factors affect parasite drag:

            a)   The more streamlined an object, the less the parasite drag.

            b)   The larger the size of the object in the airstream, the greater the parasite drag.

            c)   As speed increases, the amount of parasite drag increases as the square of the velocity. If speed is doubled, four times as much drag is produced.

    d.   Pilots can create situations of high drag.

        1)   The use of spoilers: high-drag devices that can be raised into the air flowing over an airfoil, reducing lift and increasing drag

        2)   High angle of attacks on initial climbs or other situations create induced and parasite drag

        3)   Lowering the landing gear, if retractable

END OF KNOWLEDGE ELEMENT

51.2 RISK MANAGEMENT

A.   Task Objectives

1.   **The applicant demonstrates the ability to identify, assess, and mitigate risks encompassing hazardous attitudes.**

   a.   For information on hazardous attitudes, see Study Unit 5, Subunit 3, beginning on page 46.

2.   **The applicant demonstrates the ability to identify, assess, and mitigate risks encompassing failure to complete a preflight inspection.**

   a.   Do not treat preflight inspections as "walking through the motions."

      1)   Systems and equipment rarely break in the air without notice.

      2)   Your aircraft is going to "speak" to you on the ground and you should always "listen" to it.

   b.   Never assume your aircraft is safe to fly without completing a thorough preflight inspection and using a checklist to confirm you checked the aircraft correctly and thoroughly.

3.   **The applicant demonstrates the ability to identify, assess, and mitigate risks encompassing improper maintenance.**

   a.   Always check the aircraft's maintenance records.

      1)   Check to ensure all inspections are current (i.e., 100-hr., annual, transponder).

   b.   Never assume rental aircraft are current without confirming for yourself. You are the pilot-in-command, not the FBO or flight school.

4.   **The applicant demonstrates the ability to identify, assess, and mitigate risks encompassing failure to use the proper checklist during a system or equipment malfunction.**

   a.   Always use a checklist. Do not assume you know what to check.

   b.   It is okay to preflight an aircraft from memory, but always confirm you completed every inspection by using a checklist.

   c.   To be prepared for emergency situations, memorize the immediate action items and, after completion, refer to the appropriate checklist.

5.   **The applicant demonstrates the ability to identify, assess, and mitigate risks encompassing failure to recognize situations, such as**

   a.   **Depressurization**

      1)   Depressurization is a serious risk to the safety of flight. It does not necessarily happen rapidly.

      2)   Be cognizant of the signs of hypoxia, which include headache, drowsiness, dizziness, and either a sense of well-being (euphoria) or belligerence.

      3)   The corrective action is to initiate an emergency descent.

   b.   **Cockpit smoke**

      1)   Smoke in the cockpit indicates the presence of a cabin fire.

      2)   Carbon monoxide poisoning is a major concern. If supplemental oxygen is available, use the oxygen. Be aware that oxygen can increase the risk of a fire.

c. **Fire**

1) Cabin fires generally result form one of three sources: (1) careless smoking on the part of the pilot and/or passengers, (2) electrical system malfunctions, and (3) heating system malfunctions.

a) A fire to the cabin presents the pilot with two immediate demands: attacking the fire, and getting the airplane safely on the ground as quickly as possible.

b) A fire or smoke in the cabin should be controlled by identifying and shutting down the faulty system. In many cases, smoke may be removed from the cabin by opening the cabin air vents. This should be done only after the fire extinguisher (if available) is used.

6. **The applicant demonstrates the ability to identify, assess, and mitigate risks encompassing loss of orientation, failure to divide attention, and improper planning.**

a. You must be able to divide your attention between flying the airplane and coping with the emergency, while continuing your emergency approach and landing.

b. Plan ahead for your desired outcome.

1) EXAMPLE: If you are making an emergency approach and landing due to an uncontrollable fire, you must select an appropriate landing area and plan your transition from the emergency descent to the landing.

7. **The applicant demonstrates the ability to identify, assess, and mitigate risks encompassing failure to properly manage the airplane's energy during a system or equipment malfunction.**

a. For information on energy management, see Study Unit 8, Subunit 1, beginning on page 71.

END OF RISK MANAGEMENT ELEMENT

51.3 SKILLS

A.   Task Objectives

1.   **The applicant demonstrates the ability to analyze the situation and take appropriate action for simulated emergencies, with reference to at least three of the systems listed in the Knowledge section.**

a.   Any emergency will require you to gather information and identify the problem, analyze the information, and make timely decisions.

1)   You are expected to analyze an emergency in light of experience level, personal minimums, and current physical and mental readiness level, and make your own timely decision.

b.   Deciding on the appropriate course of action will depend on how critical a situation is.

1)   After you decide the appropriate course of action, immediately implement your decision.

2.   **The applicant demonstrates the ability to complete the appropriate checklist or procedure.**

a.   Use the appropriate checklist for system and equipment malfunctions, which are in the "Emergency Procedures" section of your POH/AFM.

b.   Your emergency checklists must be readily available to you while you are in your airplane.

c.   While you may know the first few steps of the emergency checklist for some of the system and equipment malfunctions, you must use the appropriate checklist to ensure that you have followed the manufacturer's recommended procedures to correct the situation.

END OF SKILLS ELEMENT

51.4 COMMON ERRORS

A.   Common Errors during Systems and Equipment Malfunctions

1.   **Failure to understand the systems and equipment in your airplane**

a.   You must know how the various systems and equipment operate in your airplane.

1)   Then you will be able to analyze the malfunction correctly and take the appropriate steps to correct the situation.

2)   You will also understand the effect(s) it will have on the operation of your airplane.

2.   **Failure to accomplish the emergency checklist**

a.   Have your checklists readily available to you in the cockpit.

b.   Follow the checklist in order to take the appropriate steps to correct the malfunction and/or emergency.

END OF COMMON ERRORS

STUDY UNIT FIFTY-TWO
EMERGENCY EQUIPMENT AND SURVIVAL GEAR

Task	Task D. Emergency Equipment and Survival Gear
References	FAA-H-8083-2, FAA-H-8083-3; POH/AFM
Objective	To determine that the applicant exhibits satisfactory knowledge, risk management, and skills associated with emergency equipment, and survival gear appropriate to the airplane and environment encountered during flight and identifying appropriate equipment that should be onboard the airplane.
Knowledge	The applicant demonstrates understanding of:
PA.IX.D.K1	1. Emergency equipment.
PA.IX.D.K2	2. Climate extremes (hot/cold).
PA.IX.D.K3	3. The hazards of mountainous terrain.
PA.IX.D.K4	4. The hazards of overwater operations.
PA.IX.D.K5	5. Gear to meet basic physical needs until rescue.
PA.IX.D.K6	6. ELT operation, limitations and testing requirements.
Risk Management	The applicant demonstrates the ability to identify, assess and mitigate risks, encompassing:
PA.IX.D.R1	1. Being unprepared to meet basic needs (water, clothing, shelter) for 48 to 72 hours in the event of an unplanned off airport landing.
PA.IX.D.R2	2. Not knowing survival techniques, to include being located by search and rescue, in the event of an unplanned off airport landing.
Skills	The applicant demonstrates the ability to:
PA.IX.D.S1	1. Identify appropriate equipment that should be onboard the airplane.
PA.IX.D.S2	2. Identify appropriate personal gear to meet physical needs until rescue.
PA.IX.D.S3	3. Brief the proper use of the fire extinguisher and other survival equipment.

A. General Information

1. The objective of this task is for you to demonstrate your knowledge, risk management, and skills related to emergency equipment, and survival gear appropriate to the airplane and environment encountered during flight and identifying appropriate equipment that should be onboard the airplane.

52.1 KNOWLEDGE

A.   Task Objectives

1.   **The applicant demonstrates understanding of emergency equipment.**

   a.   Equipment and survival gear appropriate for operation in various climates and topographical environments

   1)   Survival kits should have appropriate equipment and gear for the climate and terrain over which your flight will be conducted.

   2)   Different items are needed for cold vs. hot weather and mountainous vs. flat terrain.

   a)   Survival manuals that are published commercially and by the government suggest items to be included.

   3)   In addition to your emergency equipment and survival gear, pack and carry a PSK (Personal Survival Kit) appropriate to your flight.

   a)   Choose a pack that fits your equipment proportionately and is easy and convenient to carry, (e.g., a fanny pack because it is always with you and will keep your hands free for other tasks).

   b)   At a minimum, you should have a minimal first aid kit, shelter from elements, water purifying items and purifier, and some sort of signaling device.

   c)   In selecting items, you should identify your flying environment, pack according to your priorities, and pack items that meet specific needs (e.g., medication, extra sunglasses, and dual purpose items like garbage bags to collect garbage and provide shelter from the sun).

   4)   While no 14 CFR requires any type of survival gear for over water operations under Part 91 (other than large and turbine-powered multiengine airplanes), it is a good operating practice to provide a life preserver and a life raft(s) to accommodate everyone on the airplane.

   5)   It is best to be prepared for an emergency; you should always prepare for the worst possible scenario.

2.   **The applicant demonstrates understanding of climate extremes (hot/cold).**

   a.   If your flight track takes you through areas of the world with extreme temperatures (i.e., Alaska, Death Valley, etc.), you should take the necessary survival gear.

   b.   Extreme heat or "hot land" survival will require you to control your internal water (hydration) and to find or create (solar still) water. A good rule of thumb to adhere to is to "ration your sweat, not your water." Techniques to do this include

   1)   Staying out of the direct sunlight
   2)   Staying off the desert floor (12" above or below may be 40° cooler)
   3)   No activity during the daylight (all work done at night)
   4)   Proper clothing (light colors, baggy and layered)
   5)   No smoking (this hastens dehydration)
   6)   No alcohol (this promotes dehydration)

   c.   Extreme cold or "cold land" environments can exist over any region you fly.

   1)   Hypothermia is the greatest threat (a little sweat and wind, coupled with inadequate clothing can add up to trouble). Consider the following regarding the prevention of hypothermia:

   a)   The first line of defense against hypothermia is shelter (clothing is considered "shelter"). Wear the appropriate clothing for the flight.
   b)   Stay dry and protected from the elements (e.g., wind).
   c)   Consider using the aircraft structure or equipment for shelter.

     d.   Desert conditions create both cold and hot extremes.

          1)   Water to stay hydrated during the day

          2)   Survival blankets to keep warm at night

3.   **The applicant demonstrates understanding of the hazards of mountainous terrain.**

     a.   Flying in mountainous terrain creates unique hazards not typically encountered by pilots who do not usually fly in these areas.

     b.   There are usually stronger winds aloft. Strong winds in mountainous terrain can cause severe turbulence and downdrafts that are hazardous for aircraft even when there is no other significant weather.

     c.   Although the wind flows smoothly up the windward side of the mountain and the upward currents help to carry an aircraft over the peak of the mountain, the wind on the leeward side does not act in a similar manner.

          1)   As the air flows down the leeward side of the mountain, it follows the contour of the terrain and is increasingly turbulent.

          2)   This tends to push an aircraft into the side of a mountain. The stronger the wind, the greater the downward pressure and turbulence become.

          3)   Due to the effect terrain has on the wind in valleys or canyons, downdrafts can be severe.

     d.   Thunderstorms are more prevalent in and around mountainous terrain due to the upslope motion of air in the mountainous regions. This provides the additional lifting action necessary to generate thunderstorms.

     e.   For a pilot whose experience consists mostly of local flights in good VMC, launching a long cross-country flight over mountainous terrain in hazy conditions could lead to pilot disorientation and increase the risk of an accident.

          1)   In mountainous terrain, consider having higher minimums for ceiling and visibility, particularly if the terrain is unfamiliar.

     f.   Before conducting a flight in or near mountainous terrain, it is helpful for a pilot unfamiliar with mountainous areas to get a checkout with a mountain-qualified flight instructor.

4.   **The applicant demonstrates understanding of the hazards of overwater operations.**

     a.   A well-executed water landing normally involves less deceleration violence than a tree landing or touchdown on extremely rough terrain.

          1)   Also, an airplane that is ditched at minimum speed and in a normal landing attitude will not immediately sink upon touchdown.

          2)   Intact wings and fuel tanks provide flotation for at least several minutes.

          3)   When landing on a wide expanse off smooth water, a loss of depth perception may occur resulting in the risk of flying into the water or stalling in from excessive altitude.

              a)   To avoid this hazard, the airplane should be "dragged in" when possible.

          4)   Use no more than intermediate flaps on low-wing airplanes, as the water resistance of fully extended flaps may result in asymmetrical flap failure and slowing of the airplane.

          5)   Keep a retractable gear up unless the POH/AFM advises otherwise.

          6)   If a swell exists, land parallel if you can; but most importantly, AVOID THE FACE OF A SWELL.

     b.   Life vests for every passenger are absolutely necessary.

     c.   Also consider a raft with cover to help keep you from sun exposure during the day.

     d.   Finally, consider carrying a portable ELT that would send out a signal to help rescuers locate yourself and your passenger on the water.

5. **The applicant demonstrates understanding of gear to meet basic physical needs until rescue.**

   a.   Your basic physical needs in a survival situation are the same as those at home: shelter, food, water, and first-aid.

   b.   Some of the gear to consider for meeting basic needs are water (two pints of water per passenger), food (1,000 calories per day for each passenger for 3 days), toilet paper, light clothing, survival blankets, extra socks, coats, boots, hats, gloves, flares, whistle, compass, flashlight, and spare batteries.

6. **The applicant demonstrates understanding of ELT operation, limitations, and testing requirements.**

   a.   For information on ELT operation, limitations, and testing requirements, see Section IX Introduction, Knowledge, item D., beginning on page 624.

END OF KNOWLEDGE ELEMENT

52.2 RISK MANAGEMENT

A.   Task Objectives

1.   **The applicant demonstrates the ability to identify, assess, and mitigate risks encompassing being unprepared to meet basic needs (water, clothing, shelter) for 48 to 72 hours in the event of an unplanned off airport landing.**

   a.   Once ATC, the FAA, or local authorities are made aware of an airplane gone missing or down, they will initiate search and rescue.

      1)   Ensure you can meet basic needs until found, such as staying warm and dry.

   b.   You may need to build a shelter and/or keep a fire going near the downed aircraft until you are rescued.

   c.   Prepare a survival kit to sustain you for 3 days, which greatly increases your odds of surviving until rescue.

   d.   Consider taking a basic survival course. Having the knowledge of the intended use of gear, or the ability to improvise using gear, increases confidence and ultimately your chances of survival.

2.   **The applicant demonstrates the ability to identify, assess, and mitigate risks encompassing not knowing survival techniques, to include being located by search and rescue, in the event of an unplanned off airport landing.**

   a.   After landing, evacuate the aircraft until you are sure there is no chance of a fire.

   b.   Always stay warm and dry. Try to build a shelter and/or light a fire.

   c.   Stay near the airplane.

      1)   Time and time again, searchers have found people who have survived the crash only to die trying to walk to safety.

   d.   Try to help search and rescue find your location.

      1)   Ensure the ELT is ON.
      2)   Make radio calls on 121.5 MHz.
      3)   Light three fires equidistant from each other.
      4)   Burn a flare.
      5)   Raise and lower slowly and repeatedly both arms outstretched to each side.
      6)   Fire a gun or other explosive signal at intervals of about a minute.

   e.   If there are significant extenuating circumstances (e.g., you have not been found within 3 days), you may increase your chances of being located by following streams downstream, which should eventually get you to a populated area.

      1)   If you reach a large body of water, follow the shore until you reach a populated area.

   f.   Consider taking a survival training course to better prepare you mentally and physically to increase your chances for a successful outcome.

END OF RISK MANAGEMENT ELEMENT

52.3 SKILLS

A.   Task Objectives

1.   **The applicant demonstrates the ability to identify appropriate equipment that should be onboard the airplane.**

    a.   Emergency Locator Transmitter (ELT)

        1)   Most general aviation airplanes are equipped with an ELT.

            a)   Normally, the ELT is located in the aft fuselage section.

        2)   Ensure that the ELT is stored and appropriately secured in the airplane.

    b.   Fire Extinguisher

        1)   A fire extinguisher will normally have a gauge by the handle to indicate if it is properly charged and a card attached to tell when the next inspection is required.

            a)   This should be checked during your visual inspection.

            b)   Most fire extinguishers should be checked and serviced by an authorized person.

            c)   The fire extinguisher should be located near the pilot's seat to provide easy access.

    c.   Ballistic Recovery System

        1)   Reference the "Emergency Procedures" section of your POH/AFM to understand proper use of a ballistic recovery system.

        2)   A ballistic parachute should only be deployed in emergency situations.

            a)   Significant structural damage to the airplane is likely.

            b)   The system should be used in the event of loss of control, failure of the aircraft structure, or other in-flight emergencies where you determine there is no other viable, safe alternative.

            c)   Be sure you slow the airplane to the design deployment speed as specified in your POH/AFM before deploying the parachute.

            d)   The parachutes are typically installed in the aft section of the fuselage.

    d.   Survival Gear

        1)   While in the airplane, your survival gear should be easily accessible and secured by tie-down or safety belts.

            a)   When you are not flying, your survival gear should be stored in a cool, dry place.

        2)   Periodically remove the items in your survival kit and check them for serviceability.

2. **The applicant demonstrates the ability to identify appropriate personal gear to meet physical needs until rescue.**

   a. Determine the type of weather or climate that you could find yourself encountering.

   b. Always bring a pre-packed survival kit that includes, at a minimum, the following:

      1) Food (1,000 calories per day per passenger)
      2) Water (2 pints per day per passenger)
      3) Appropriate clothing (coats for cold climates, light clothes for warm)
      4) Hats and/or face protection depending on possible environments
      5) Medical kit (bandages and pain relievers)
      6) Any prescription drugs prescribed for passengers
      7) Signaling devices (e.g., as simple as a glass mirror or handheld transmitter)
      8) Survival blankets for, at least, every passenger.

   c. If you are flying over water, ensure you have enough life vests for all passengers.

      1) A raft with a cover to prevent sun exposure is also strongly recommended.

3. **The applicant demonstrates the ability to brief the proper use of the fire extinguisher and other survival equipment.**

   a. Explain to the evaluator the urgency of immediate and aggressive extinguishment of an onboard fire. As fires can grow exponentially with time, the risks of exceeding the hazardous concentration levels of extinguishment are considered minimal compared to the risks of an in-flight fire.

   b. Attack the base of the fire at the near edge of the fire and then move the fire extinguisher nozzle with a side-to-side sweeping motion, progressing toward the back of the fire. The optimum firefighting technique differs for each approved extinguisher.

   c. Do not direct the initial discharge at the burning surface at close range, if the burning material might splash and/or splatter.

   d. Keep hand-held fire extinguishers upright.

      1) Hand-held fire extinguishers are designed to be used in the upright position.
      2) Most extinguishers have been designed with a center siphon tube that extends to the bottom of the canister.

         a) Placing a fire extinguisher on its side or upside down prevents the agent from flowing through the tubing, which has been designed to collect the agent from the bottom of the canister.
         b) Laying the extinguisher on its side or turning it upside down to aim at the ceiling may limit the amount of extinguishing agent that is available to be discharged, thereby reducing the extinguisher's firefighting capacity.

   e. Brief the evaluator on the survival kit in your airplane.

   f. Brief the evaluator on how to manually turn on the ELT.

      1) ELTs generally have three switch positions: "ON," "OFF," and "ARMED."

         a) "On" provides continuous signal broadcast.
         b) "Off" means no broadcast is possible and the gravity switch cannot be activated.
         c) "Armed" means the gravity switch will be activated in a crash situation, which turns on the broadcast.
         d) Normally, the ELT is in a rear area of the airplane and is always set on "armed." It is affixed as far aft as possible to avoid possible damage from crash impact.

END OF SKILLS ELEMENT

PART III
SECTION XI:
NIGHT OPERATIONS

Study Unit 53 of Section XI explains the one FAA ACS task (A) of Night Operations. This task includes knowledge, risk management, and skill. Your evaluator is required to test you on this task.

Night flying is considered to be an important phase in your training as a pilot. Proficiency in night flying not only increases utilization of the airplane but also provides important experience in case a prolonged day flight extends into darkness. Many pilots prefer night flying over day flying because the air is usually smoother and generally there is less air traffic with which to contend.

STUDY UNIT FIFTY-THREE
NIGHT PREPARATION

Task	Task A. Night Preparation
References	FAA-H-8083-2, FAA-H-8083-3, FAA-H-8083-25; AIM; POH/AFM
Objective	To determine that the applicant exhibits satisfactory knowledge, risk management, and skills associated with night operations.
Knowledge	The applicant demonstrates understanding of:
PA.XI.A.K1	1. Physiological aspects of night flying as it relates to vision.
PA.XI.A.K2	2. Lighting systems identifying airports, runways, taxiways and obstructions, as well as pilot controlled lighting.
PA.XI.A.K3	3. Airplane equipment requirements for night operations.
PA.XI.A.K4	4. Airplane lighting systems: type, interpretation in flight, when to use each lighting system.
PA.XI.A.K5	5. Personal equipment essential for night flight.
PA.XI.A.K6	6. Night orientation, navigation, and chart reading techniques.
PA.XI.A.K7	7. Safety precautions and emergencies unique to night flying.
PA.XI.A.K8	8. Somatogravic illusion and black hole approach illusion.
PA.XI.A.K9	9. Disorientation that can be experienced in unusual attitudes at night.
PA.XI.A.K10	10. Visual scanning techniques during night operations.
PA.XI.A.K11	11. Hazards of inadvertent IMC.
Risk Management	The applicant demonstrates the ability to identify, assess and mitigate risks, encompassing:
PA.XI.A.R1	1. Collision avoidance, scanning, obstacle and wire strike avoidance.
PA.XI.A.R2	2. Improper planning to avoid terrain.
PA.XI.A.R3	3. Failure to manage Tasks during night operations.
PA.XI.A.R4	4. Failure to maintain situational awareness.
PA.XI.A.R5	5. Environmental considerations at night (e.g., IMC; terrain (roads)).
PA.XI.A.R6	6. Failure to maintain VFR.
PA.XI.A.R7	7. Physiological aspects of night flying.
Skills	N/A
	Note: Not generally evaluated in flight. If the practical test is conducted at night, all ACS tasks are evaluated in that environment, thus there is no need for explicit task elements to exist here.

A. General Information

1. The objective of this task is for you to demonstrate your knowledge, risk management, and skills related to night operations.

2. See *Pilot Handbook* for the following:

   a. In Study Unit 6, "Aeromedical Factors and Aeronautical Decision Making (ADM)"

      1) Subunit 10, "Illusions in Flight," for a discussion of various illusions that can lead to spatial disorientation and landing errors

      2) Subunit 11, "Vision," for a discussion of the physiological aspects of changing light conditions on your vision

   b. In Study Unit 3, "Airports, Air Traffic Control, and Airspace," Subunit 2, "Airport Lighting," for a discussion on various airport and obstruction lighting

53.1 KNOWLEDGE

A.   Task Objectives

1.   **The applicant demonstrates understanding of physiological aspects of night flying as it relates to vision.**

a.   Two types of light-sensitive nerve endings called "cones" and "rods" are located at the back of the eye, or retina, which transmit messages to the brain via the optic nerve.

1)   When entering a dark area, the pupils of the eyes enlarge to receive as much of the available light as possible.

2)   After approximately 5 to 10 min. as the rods become adjusted to the dim light, your eyes will become 100 times more sensitive than they were before you entered the dark area.

a)   The cones stop working altogether in semidarkness.

b)   Since the rods can still function in light of 1/5,000 the intensity at which the cones cease to function, they are used for night vision.

3)   After about 30 min., the rods will be fully adjusted to darkness and about 100,000 times more sensitive to light than they were in the lighted area.

4)   The rods need more time to adjust to darkness than the cones do to bright light. Your eyes become adapted to sunlight in 10 sec., whereas they need 30 min. to fully adjust to a dark night.

b.   Good vision depends on your physical condition. Fatigue, colds, vitamin deficiency, alcohol, stimulants, smoking, or medication can seriously impair your vision.

1)   EXAMPLE: Smoking lowers the sensitivity of the eyes and reduces night vision by approximately 20%.

c.   Various visual scenes encountered during a night flight can create illusions of motion and position. The best way to cope with these illusions is to use and trust your flight instruments. Some of the illusions encountered at night are

1)   False horizon
2)   Autokinesis
3)   Featureless terrain
4)   Runway slopes
5)   Ground lighting

2.   **The applicant demonstrates understanding of lighting systems identifying airports, runways, taxiways and obstructions, as well as pilot controlled lighting.**

a.   Types of airport, runway, and taxiway lighting

1)   Airport rotating beacon
2)   Approach light systems
3)   Visual glide slope indicators (e.g., VASI, PAPI)
4)   Runway end identifier lights
5)   Runway edge lights
6)   In-runway lighting
7)   Taxiway lights

b.   Obstructions are lighted to warn pilots of their presence during nighttime conditions. They may be lighted in any of the following combinations:

1)   Aviation red obstruction lights -- flashing aviation red beacons and steady aviation red lights at night

2)   High-intensity white obstruction lights -- flashing high-intensity white lights during daytime with reduced intensity for twilight and nighttime operation

3)   Dual lighting -- a combination of flashing aviation red beacons and steady aviation red lights at night and flashing high-intensity white lights in daylight

    c.   Pilot control of lighting is available at many airports where there is no operating control tower or FSS. All radio-controlled lighting systems operate on the same frequency, usually the CTAF.

        1)   The control system consists of a three-step control responsive to seven, five, and/or three microphone clicks.

        2)   The Chart Supplement contains descriptions of pilot-controlled lighting at all available airports and their frequencies.

3.   The applicant demonstrates understanding of airplane equipment requirements for night operations.

    a.   In addition to the VFR day equipment requirements discussed in Study Unit 11, the following equipment is required for VFR night operations.

        HINT: Use the mnemonic FLAPS to remember these:

        1)   **F**uses--A set of spare fuses or three spare fuses for each kind required that are accessible to the pilot in flight. This is not applicable if your airplane is equipped with resettable circuit breakers.

        2)   **L**anding light--If operated for hire.

        3)   **A**nticollision lights--Approved aviation red or white anticollision light system on all U.S.-registered civil aircraft.

        4)   **P**osition lights--Red, green, and white navigation lights.

        5)   **S**ource--Of electricity for all electrical and radio equipment.

4.   The applicant demonstrates understanding of airplane lighting systems: type, interpretation in flight, and when to use each lighting system.

    a.   Required lighting for your airplane is found in 14 CFR 91.205(c). Only position lights and an anticollision light system are required.

        1)   Airplane position (navigation) lights are arranged similarly to those of boats and ships.

           a)   A red light is positioned on the left wingtip.

           b)   A green light is on the right wingtip.

           c)   A white light is on the tail.

Navigation Lights
must be displayed from
sunset to sunrise.

        2)   This arrangement provides a means by which you can determine the general direction of movement of other airplanes.

           a)   If both a red and a green light are seen, the other airplane is traveling in a general direction toward you.

           b)   If only a red light is seen, the airplane is traveling from right to left.

           c)   If only a green light is seen, the airplane is traveling from left to right.

           d)   Note that the red and green lights cannot be seen from the rear of the airplane.

3) An anticollision light system may consist of wingtip strobe lights and/or either a red or a white rotating beacon light that is normally located on the vertical stabilizer of most airplanes.

b. While not required for VFR night flight, the following lights are recommended and installed in most airplanes:

1) Landing light, which is useful for taxi, takeoffs, and landings and is a means by which your airplane can be seen by other pilots

2) Individual instrument lights and adequate cockpit illumination

3) Wingtip strobe lights

c. Lighted position lights are required on an aircraft when operating during the period from sunset to sunrise (with the state of Alaska being the exception).

d. A lighted anti-collision lighting system is required at all times when operating an aircraft, unless, at the determination by the pilot-in-command, it would be in the interest of safety to turn them off during certain operating conditions.

5. **The applicant demonstrates understanding of personal equipment essential for night flight.**

a. Before beginning a night flight, you should carefully consider certain personal equipment that should be readily available during the flight.

1) This equipment may not differ greatly from that needed for a day flight, but the importance of its availability when needed at night cannot be over-emphasized.

b. At least one reliable flashlight is recommended as standard equipment on all night flights.

1) A "D" cell size flashlight with a bulb-switching mechanism that can be used to select white or red light is preferable.

a) The white light is used while performing the preflight visual inspection of the airplane, and the red light is used in performing cockpit operations.

b) Since the red light is nonglaring, it will not impair night vision.

2) Some pilots prefer two flashlights, one with a white light for preflight and a penlight type with a red light.

a) The penlight can be suspended by a string from around the neck to ensure that the light is always readily available during flight.

b) CAUTION: If a red light is used for reading a sectional chart, the red features of the chart will not be visible to you.

3) Since red light severely distorts colors and can cause serious difficulty in focusing the eyes on objects inside the cockpit, its use is advisable only when optimum outside night vision capability is necessary.

a) Even so, white cockpit lighting must be available when needed for map reading.

c. Sectional and/or other aeronautical charts are essential for all cross-country flights.

d. To prevent losing essential items in the dark cockpit, you should have a clipboard or mapboard on which charts, navigation logs, and other essentials can be fastened.

1) You may also want to consider a map case to store needed materials.

e. A reliable clock is needed for night flights.

f. All personal equipment should be checked prior to flight to ensure proper functioning.

g. When using portable electronic devices to supplement your paper charts, ensure that they are adequately charged and that you have spare batteries on hand. In addition, make sure that you are familiar with dimming the brightness of your device so as to maintain night adaptation for your eyes.

6. **The applicant demonstrates understanding of night orientation, navigation, and chart reading techniques.**

   a. Although careful planning of any flight is essential for maximum safety and efficiency, night flying demands more attention to all details of preflight preparation and planning.

      1) Preparation for a night flight should include a thorough study of the available weather reports and forecasts, with particular attention given to temperature/dew point spread because of the possibility of formation of ground fog during the night flight.

         a) Plan your cruising altitudes below any forecast cloud layers, because upcoming clouds are much more difficult to see and avoid, especially on moonless or overcast nights.

         b) Any haze can effectively reduce flight visibility to zero at night.

         c) You also need to know the forecast wind direction and speed since drifting cannot be detected as readily at night as during the day.

   b. On night cross-country flights, as on all flights, the proper navigational (sectional) charts should be selected and available.

      1) Avoid red, yellow, or orange course markings as they will tend to disappear under red map lights.

      2) Checkpoints must be selected carefully to ensure being seen at night.

         a) Rotating beacons at airports
         b) Lighted obstructions
         c) Lights of cities
         d) Lights from major highway traffic

      3) The use of radio navigation and radar flight following is highly recommended at night.

      4) Charts should be systematically folded and arranged, and a navigation log carefully filled in prior to every flight to promote cockpit organization.

      5) Accurate awareness of your position and proximity to airports is vital at night.

         a) Suitable emergency landing fields are almost impossible to detect in the dark.

   c. While red cockpit lighting helps preserve your night vision, it can cause you problems, such as improper fuel selection and errors in course plotting or chart reading.

      1) The recommended procedure is toward more complete illumination of the cockpit, with white light used more than red.

         a) You should keep the instrument panel and interior lighting turned up no higher than necessary.

            i) This setting will minimize reflection on your windows and maximize your ability to see dimly lit objects outside.

         b) If a white light is not available and/or it cannot be adjusted, a carefully aimed flashlight can be used for reading charts, checklists, etc.

7. **The applicant demonstrates understanding of safety precautions and emergencies unique to night flying.**

   a. Safety is important in both day and night operations. With your restricted vision at night, you must place additional emphasis on safety during night flight operations.

      1) Night flying demands more attention to all details of preflight preparation and planning.

      2) Proper cockpit management will enhance safety, because you will have all of your equipment and material organized and well arranged.

3) Understand night vision and the limitations it has on your vision.

4) A moonless night with little or no ground lights requires capable instrument flying skills.

b. Perhaps your greatest concern about flying a single-engine airplane at night is complete engine failure, even though adverse weather and poor pilot judgment account for most serious accidents.

1) If the engine fails at night, the first step is to maintain positive control of your airplane. DO NOT PANIC.

a) A normal glide should be established and maintained; turn your airplane toward an airport or away from congested areas.

b) A check should be made to determine the cause of the engine failure, including the position of the following:

i)   Ignition switch
ii)   Fuel selector
iii) Primer/choke (as equipped)

c) If possible, correct the malfunction immediately and restart the engine.

2) Maintain orientation with the wind to avoid a downwind landing.

3) The landing light(s), if equipped, should be checked at altitude and turned on in sufficient time to illuminate the terrain or obstacles along the flight path.

a) If the landing light(s) are unusable and outside references are not available, the airplane should be held in level-landing attitude until the ground is contacted.

4) Most important of all, positive control of your airplane must be maintained at all times.

a) DO NOT allow a stall to occur.

8. **The applicant demonstrates understanding of somatogravic illusion and black hole approach illusion.**

a. The **somatogravic illusion** is caused by a rapid acceleration, such as during takeoff, and can create the illusion of being in a nose-up altitude.

1) The disoriented pilot will push the aircraft into a nose-low, or dive, attitude.

2) A rapid deceleration by a quick reduction of the throttles can have the opposite effect, with the disoriented pilot pulling the aircraft into a nose-up, or stall, attitude.

b. The **black hole approach illusion** (also called a featureless terrain illusion) is caused by an absence of ground features, as when landing over water, darkened areas, and terrain made featureless by snow, and can create the illusion that the aircraft is at a higher altitude than it actually is.

1) The pilot who does not recognize this illusion will fly a lower approach.

9. **The applicant demonstrates understanding of disorientation that can be experienced in unusual attitudes at night.**

a. The limitations of the eye to detect color and detail at night increase the chances of experiencing disorientation in unusual attitudes at night. Although unusual attitude recovery procedures at night are the same as during the day, special care should be taken to confirm instrument rate of movement and indication to avoid further disorientation during the recovery. Use your instrument cross-check procedures with special care to correctly interpret instrument indications before you initiate the recovery.

10. **The applicant demonstrates understanding of visual scanning techniques during night operations.**

   a. During night flight, an object can be seen best by a scanning procedure that uses off-center viewing (i.e., your peripheral vision), by forcing the eyes to view off center.

   1) After some practice, you will find that you can see objects more clearly at night by looking to one side of them rather than directly at them.

   a) Remember that rods do not detect objects while your eyes are moving.

   b. In addition, you should move the eyes more slowly than in daylight, blink the eyes if they become blurred, and concentrate on seeing objects.

11. **The applicant demonstrates understanding of the hazards of inadvertent IMC.**

   a. Continuing VFR into IMC often leads to spatial disorientation or collision with ground/obstacles. It is even more dangerous when the pilot is not instrument rated.

   b. Weather-related accidents, particularly those associated with VFR flight into IMC, continue to be a threat to GA safety because 80% of the VFR-IMC accidents result in a fatality.

   1) Under no circumstances should a VFR night flight be made during poor or marginal weather conditions unless both the pilot and aircraft are certificated and equipped for flight under instrument flight rules (IFR).

   2) Generally, at night it is difficult to see clouds and restrictions to visibility, particularly on dark nights or under overcast. The pilot flying under VFR must exercise caution to avoid flying into clouds or a layer of fog.

   3) Remember that if a descent must be made through fog, smoke, or haze in order to land, the horizontal visibility is considerably less when looking through the restriction than it is when looking straight down through it from above.

   c. Inadvertent IMC (night or day) for a VFR pilot is considered an emergency. Remember not to panic and to "fly the airplane."

   d. For more information on continued flight into IMC, see Study Unit 5, Subunit 4, beginning on page 47.

END OF KNOWLEDGE ELEMENT

53.2 RISK MANAGEMENT

A.   Task Objectives

1.   **The applicant demonstrates the ability to identify, assess, and mitigate risks encompassing collision avoidance, scanning, and obstacle and wire strike avoidance.**

   a.   For information on collision avoidance, scanning, and obstacle avoidance, see Study Unit 7, Subunit 4, beginning on page 66.

   b.   For information on wire strikes, see Study Unit 7, Subunit 6, beginning on page 68.

2.   **The applicant demonstrates the ability to identify, assess, and mitigate risks encompassing improper planning to avoid terrain.**

   a.   For information on terrain avoidance, including controlled flight into terrain (CFIT), see Study Unit 7, Subunit 3, beginning on page 62.

3.   **The applicant demonstrates the ability to identify, assess, and mitigate risks encompassing failure to manage tasks during night operations.**

   a.   For information on task management, see Study Unit 6, Subunit 1, beginning on page 49.

4.   **The applicant demonstrates the ability to identify, assess, and mitigate risks encompassing failure to maintain situational awareness.**

   a.   For information on situational awareness, see Study Unit 7, Subunit 1, beginning on page 57.

5.   **The applicant demonstrates the ability to identify, assess, and mitigate risks encompassing environmental considerations at night [e.g., IMC, terrain (roads)].**

   a.   Never depart at night without a thorough review of your intended flight plan. Courses, distances, and times of each leg should be computed. At night, your attention is needed for aviating, not for navigation planning.

       1)   If possible, use GPS, but VOR would be helpful, too. Avoid flying at night by reference to the ground alone. Terrain and landmarks look very different in the dark, which may make navigation difficult if no electronic or radio navigation aids are used.

   b.   In spite of fewer usable landmarks or checkpoints, night cross-country flights present no particular problem if preplanning is adequate and you continuously monitor position, time estimates, and fuel consumption.

       1)   The light patterns of towns are easily identified, especially when surrounded by dark areas.

           a)   Large metropolitan areas may be of little meaning until you gain more night flying experience.

       2)   Airport rotating beacons, which are installed at various military and civilian airports, are useful checkpoints.

       3)   Busy highways marked by car headlights also make good checkpoints.

       4)   On moonlit nights, especially in dark areas, you will be able to identify some unlit landmarks.

   c.   Crossing large bodies of water on night flights can be potentially hazardous, not only from the standpoint of landing (ditching) in the water, should it become necessary, but also because the horizon may blend in with the water, in which case control of your airplane may become difficult.

       1)   During hazy conditions over open water, the horizon will become obscure, and you may experience a loss of spatial orientation.

2) Even on clear nights, the stars may be reflected on the water surface, appearing as a continuous array of lights and thus making the horizon difficult to identify.

3) Always include instrument references in your scan.

d. Lighted runways, buildings, or other objects may cause illusions when they are seen from different altitudes.

1) At 2,000 ft. AGL, a group of lights on an object may be seen individually, while at 5,000 ft. AGL or higher, the same lights can appear to be one solid light mass.

2) These illusions may become quite acute with altitude changes and, if not overcome, can present problems with respect to approaches to lighted runways.

e. At night, it is normally difficult to see clouds and restrictions to visibility, particularly on dark nights (e.g., no moonlight or under an overcast).

1) If cloud layers are forecast, plan to cruise below the forecast of reported cloud layers. It is difficult to see clouds at the same altitude when cruising at night, so below that level to avoid inadvertently flying into the clouds and creating a problem.

2) You must exercise caution to avoid flying into weather conditions below VFR minimums (e.g., clouds, fog).

3) Normally, the first indication of flying into restricted visibility conditions is the gradual disappearance of lights on the ground.

a) If the lights begin to take on an appearance of being surrounded by a "cotton ball" or glow, you should use extreme caution in attempting to fly farther in that same direction.

4) Remember, if you must make a descent through any fog, smoke, or haze in order to land, visibility is considerably less when you look horizontally through the restriction than it is when you look straight down through it from above.

5) You should never attempt a VFR night flight during poor or marginal weather conditions.

f. To avoid CFIT, planning and preparation are the best defenses. Consider the following:

1) To avoid terrain and obstacles, especially at night or in low visibility, determine safe altitudes in advance by using the altitudes shown on VFR and IFR charts during preflight planning.

2) Use maximum elevation figures (MEFs) and other easily obtainable data to minimize chances of an inflight collision with terrain or obstacles.

3) When planning a nighttime VFR flight, follow IFR practices, such as climbing on a known safe course until well above surrounding terrain. Choose a cruising altitude that provides terrain separation similar to IFR flight 2,000 ft. AGL in mountainous areas and 1,000 ft. AGL in other areas).

4) When receiving radar services, do not depend on air traffic controllers to warn you of terrain hazards. Although controllers will try to warn pilots if they notice a hazardous situation, they may not always be able to recognize that a particular VFR aircraft is dangerously close to terrain.

5) When ATC issues a heading along with an instruction to "maintain VFR," be aware that the heading may not provide adequate terrain clearance. If you have any doubt about your ability to visually avoid terrain and obstacles, advise ATC immediately and take action to reach a safe altitude.

6) For improved night vision, the FAA recommends the use of supplemental oxygen for flights above 5,000 ft.

6.   **The applicant demonstrates the ability to identify, assess, and mitigate risks encompassing failure to maintain VFR.**

   a.   To maintain VFR at night underneath airspace, you must continually be aware of where airspace boundaries are and where you are in reference to them. Frequently check your flight instruments, especially your altimeter, and continually monitor your position using pilotage and navigation instruments to avoid inadvertently entering airspace that you are not cleared to enter.

7.   **The applicant demonstrates the ability to identify, assess, and mitigate risks encompassing physiological aspects of night flying.**

   a.   Spatial disorientation becomes more likely at night, especially when pilots inadvertently lose outside visual references due to flying in a cloud.

   b.   Pilots should adapt their eyes for night flying by avoiding bright white lights for 30 min. prior to flight.

   c.   Due to the eye's physiology, off-center eyesight is better than direct at night. Pilots should scan slowly at night to permit off-center viewing.

   d.   At cabin pressure altitudes above 5,000 ft. MSL, dark adaptation of your vision may be impaired.

   e.   Carbon monoxide from smoking or exhaust fumes, prolonged exposure to bright light, or a deficiency of vitamin A in the diet can impair dark adaptation.

END OF RISK MANAGEMENT ELEMENT

53.3 SKILLS

The following is a general discussion of elements related to night operations that are not specifically included in the Private Pilot ACS. However, these elements are still an important part of your pilot training.

1. **Preflight inspection and required equipment for night flight.**

    a. For information on the equipment required for VFR flight at night, see Subunit 53.1, item A.3.

    b. A thorough preflight inspection of your airplane (both interior and exterior) is necessary, as in any flight.

       1) Since you may do the preflight inspection at night, you must use your flashlight to illuminate the areas you are inspecting. You should take your time and look at each item carefully.

    c. All airplane lights should be turned on and checked (visually) for operation.

       1) Position lights can be checked for loose connections by tapping the light fixture while the light is on.

          a) If the lights blink while being tapped, further investigation (by a qualified mechanic) to find the cause should be initiated.

    d. All personal materials and equipment should be checked to ensure that you have everything and that all equipment is functioning properly.

       1) It is very disconcerting to find, at the time of need, that a flashlight, for example, does not work.

    e. Finally, the parking ramp should be checked prior to entering your airplane. During the day, it is easy to see stepladders, chuckholes, stray wheel chocks, and other obstructions, but at night it is more difficult. A check of the area can prevent taxiing mishaps.

2. **Taxi and before-takeoff procedures.**

    a. Extra caution should be taken at night to ensure that the propeller area is clear.

       1) This can be accomplished by turning on your airplane's rotating beacon (anticollision light) or by flashing other airplane lights to alert any person nearby to remain clear of the propeller.

       2) Also, orally announce "clear prop" and wait a few seconds before engaging the starter.

       3) Think safety.

    b. To avoid excessive drain of electrical current from the battery, keep all unnecessary equipment off until after the engine has been started.

       1) Once the engine has been started, turn on the airplane's position lights.

    c. Due to your restricted vision at night, taxi speeds should be reduced. Never taxi faster than a speed that would allow you to stop within the distance illuminated by your landing light.

       1) Be sure to avoid using wingtip strobes and landing lights in the vicinity of other aircraft.

          a) This vicinity includes the runup area while someone else is landing.
          b) Lights can be distracting and potentially blinding to a pilot.
          c) You would expect others to show courtesy when using lights.

    d.   Use the checklist in your POH/AFM to perform the before-takeoff check.

        1)   During the day, unintended forward movement of your airplane can easily be detected during the runup.

            a)   At night, the airplane may creep forward without being noticed unless you are alert to this possibility.

            b)   Thus, it is important to lock the brakes during the runup and be attentive to any unintentional forward movement.

3.   Takeoff and climb.

    a.   At night, your visual references are limited (and sometimes nonexistent), and you will need to use the flight instruments to a greater degree in controlling the airplane, especially during night takeoffs and departure climbs.

        1)   This does not mean that you will use only the flight instruments but that the flight instruments are used more to cross-check the visual references.

    b.   The cockpit lights (if available) should be adjusted to a minimum brightness that will allow you to read the instruments and switches without hindering your outside vision.

        1)   Low lighting will also eliminate light reflections on the windshield and windows that can obstruct your outside vision.

    c.   Before taxiing onto the active runway for takeoff, you should exercise extreme caution to prevent conflict with other aircraft.

        1)   At controlled airports where ATC issues the clearance for takeoff, it is recommended that you check the final approach course for approaching aircraft.

        2)   At uncontrolled airports, it is recommended that you make a slow 360° turn in the same direction as the flow of air traffic while closely searching for other traffic.

    d.   After ensuring that the final approach and runway are clear of other traffic, you should line up your airplane with the centerline of the runway.

        1)   If the runway has no painted centerline, you should use the runway lighting and align your airplane between and parallel to the two rows of runway edge lights.

        2)   Your landing light and strobe lights (if applicable) should be on as you taxi into this position.

        3)   After the airplane is aligned, the heading indicator should be set to correspond to the known runway direction.

    e.   To begin the takeoff, you should release the brakes and smoothly advance the throttle to takeoff power. As your airplane accelerates, it should be kept moving parallel to the runway edge lights. This is best done by looking at the more distant runway lights rather than those close in and to the side.

        1)   At night, your perception of runway length and width, airplane speed, and flight attitude will vary. You must monitor your flight instruments more closely; e.g., rotation should occur at the proper V_R based on your airspeed indicator, not your bodily senses.

        2)   As the airspeed reaches V_R, the pitch attitude should be adjusted to an attitude that will establish a normal climb by referring to both visual and instrument references (e.g., lights and the attitude indicator).

        3)   Do not attempt to pull the airplane forcibly off the ground. It is best to let it fly off in the liftoff attitude while you are cross-checking the attitude indicator against any outside visual references that may be available.

f.   After becoming airborne, you may have difficulty in determining whether the airplane is getting closer to or farther from the surface because of the darkness of the night.

   1)   By cross-checking your flight instruments, ensure that your airplane continues in a positive climb and does not settle back onto the runway.

      a)   A positive climb rate is indicated by the vertical speed indicator and by a gradual but continual increase in the altimeter indication.

      b)   A climb pitch attitude is indicated on the attitude indicator.

   2)   Check the airspeed to ensure that it is well above a stall and is stabilizing at the appropriate climb speed (e.g., V_Y).

   3)   Use the attitude indicator as well as visual references to ensure that the wings are level, and cross-check with the heading indicator to ensure that you are maintaining the correct heading.

      a)   Normally, no turns should be made until you reach a safe maneuvering altitude.

   4)   Your landing light should be turned off after a climb is well established. This is normally completed during the climb checklist.

      a)   The light may become deceptive if it is reflected by any haze, smoke, or fog that might exist in the takeoff climb.

g.   **Approach and landing procedures.**

   1)   When you arrive at the airport to enter the traffic pattern and land, it is important that you identify the runway lights and other airport lighting as early as possible.

      a)   If you are unfamiliar with the airport layout, sighting of the runway may be difficult until you are very close-in due to other lighting in the area.

      b)   You should fly towards the airport rotating beacon until you identify the runway lights.

      c)   Your landing light should be on to help other pilots and/or ATC to see you.

   2)   To fly a traffic pattern of the proper size and direction when there is little to see but a group of lights, you must positively identify the runway threshold and runway edge lights.

      a)   Confirm that you are entering the pattern for the proper runway by comparing the runway lights to your heading indicator.

      b)   Once this is done, the location of the approach threshold lights should be known at all times throughout the traffic pattern.

   3)   Distance may be deceptive at night due to limited lighting conditions, lack of intervening references on the ground, and your inability to compare the size and location of different ground objects. The estimation of altitude and speed may also be impaired.

      a)   Consequently, you must use your flight instruments more, especially the altimeter and the airspeed indicator.

      b)   Make every effort to execute the approach and landing in the same manner as during the day.

      c)   Constantly cross-check the altimeter, airspeed indicator, and vertical speed indicator against your airplane's position along the base leg and final approach.

4)   After turning onto the final approach and aligning your airplane between the two rows of runway edge lights, you should note and correct for any wind drift.

    a)   Throughout the final approach, power should be used with coordinated pitch changes to provide positive control of your airplane, thus allowing you to accurately adjust airspeed and descent angle.

    b)   A lighted visual approach slope indicator (e.g., VASI or PAPI) should be used if available to help maintain the proper approach angle.

5)   The roundout and touchdown should be made in the same manner as day landings. However, your judgment of height, speed, and sink rate may be impaired by the lack of observable objects in the landing area.

    a)   You may be aided in determining the proper roundout point if you continue a constant approach descent until your airplane's landing light reflects on the runway and the tire marks on the runway or runway expansion joints can be seen clearly.

        i)   At that point, smoothly start the roundout for touchdown and reduce the throttle gradually to idle as your airplane is touching down.

    b)   During landings without the use of a landing light or where tire marks on the runway are not identifiable, the roundout may be started when the runway lights at the far end of the runway first appear to be rising higher than your airplane.

        i)   This demands a smooth and very timely roundout and requires, in effect, that you "feel" for the runway surface, using power and pitch changes as necessary for the airplane to settle softly onto the runway.

END OF SKILLS ELEMENT

PART III
SECTION XII:
POSTFLIGHT PROCEDURES

Study Unit 54 of Section XII explains the one FAA ACS task (A) of Postflight Procedures. This task includes knowledge, risk management, and skill. Your evaluator is required to test you on this task.

STUDY UNIT FIFTY-FOUR
AFTER LANDING, PARKING, AND SECURING

Task	Task A. After Landing, Parking and Securing
References	FAA-H-8083-2, FAA-H-8083-3; POH/AFM
Objective	To determine that the applicant exhibits satisfactory knowledge, risk management, and skills associated with after landing, parking, and securing procedures.
Knowledge	The applicant demonstrates understanding of:
PA.XII.A.K1	1. Positioning aircraft controls for wind.
PA.XII.A.K2	2. Familiarity with airport markings (including hold short lines), signs, and lights.
PA.XII.A.K3	3. Aircraft lighting.
PA.XII.A.K4	4. Towered and non-towered airport operations.
PA.XII.A.K5	5. Visual indicators for wind.
PA.XII.A.K6	6. Airport information resources (Chart Supplements U.S., airport diagrams, and appropriate publications).
PA.XII.A.K7	7. Good cockpit discipline during taxi.
PA.XII.A.K8	8. Appropriate taxi speeds.
PA.XII.A.K9	9. Procedures for appropriate cockpit activities during taxiing including taxi route planning, briefing the location of Hot Spots, and communicating and coordinating with ATC.
PA.XII.A.K10	10. Procedures unique to night operations.
PA.XII.A.K11	11. Hazards of low visibility operations.
PA.XII.A.K12	12. The importance of documenting any in-flight/post-flight discrepancies.
PA.XII.A.K13	13. National Transportation Safety Board (NTSB) accident/incident reporting.
Risk Management	The applicant demonstrates the ability to identify, assess and mitigate risks, encompassing:
PA.XII.A.R1	1. Distractions during aircraft taxi and parking.
PA.XII.A.R2	2. The proximity of other aircraft, vehicles, and people when operating on airport surfaces.
PA.XII.A.R3	3. Spinning propellers.
PA.XII.A.R4	4. Failure to manage Tasks during taxi and parking.
PA.XII.A.R5	5. Confirmation or expectation bias.
PA.XII.A.R6	6. Failure to manage the automation.
PA.XII.A.R7	7. Airport security.
PA.XII.A.R8	8. Failure to maintain directional control after landing or during taxi.
Skills	The applicant demonstrates the ability to:
PA.XII.A.S1	1. Maintain directional control after touchdown while decelerating to an appropriate speed.
PA.XII.A.S2	2. Utilize runway incursion avoidance procedures after landing.
PA.XII.A.S3	3. Park in an appropriate area, considering the safety of nearby persons and property.
PA.XII.A.S4	4. Plan the taxi route to the ramp.
PA.XII.A.S5	5. Follow the appropriate procedure for engine shutdown.
PA.XII.A.S6	6. Complete the after landing checklist after the airplane has stopped.
PA.XII.A.S7	7. Complete the engine shutdown checklist.
PA.XII.A.S8	8. Disembark passengers safely and remain aware of passenger movement while on the ramp area.
PA.XII.A.S9	9. Record aircraft discrepancies and notes for possible service needs before the next flight.
PA.XII.A.S10	10. Conduct an appropriate post flight inspection and secure the aircraft.

A.   General Information

   1.   The objective of this task is for you to demonstrate your knowledge, risk management, and skills related to after landing, parking, and securing procedures.

   2.   A flight is never complete until the airplane is parked, the engine is shut down, and the airplane is secured.

   3.   Some of the content of Subunits 54.1 and 54.2 is abbreviated, based on the assumption that you have thoroughly read and understood Study Unit 21, and the additional common task topics found in Part II. The task objectives and specific references are provided here for your convenience.

54.1 KNOWLEDGE

A.   Task Objectives

   1.   **The applicant demonstrates understanding of positioning aircraft controls for wind.**

      a.   For information on positioning aircraft controls for wind, see Study Unit 21, Subunit 1, item A.1., on page 244.

   2.   **The applicant demonstrates understanding of familiarity with airport markings (including hold short lines), signs, and lights.**

      a.   See Study Unit 3, "Airports, Air Traffic Control, and Airspace," in *Pilot Handbook* for a discussion on airport markings, signs, and lights.

   3.   **The applicant demonstrates understanding of aircraft lighting.**

      a.   For information on aircraft lighting, see Study Unit 21, Subunit 1, item A.3., on page 247.

   4.   **The applicant demonstrates understanding of towered and non-towered airport operations.**

      a.   Towered airports

         1)   After landing, be sure to clear the runway in a timely fashion. Exit at the first available taxiway or on a taxiway as instructed by ATC.

            a)   In the case of ATC instructions to expedite your taxi, only accept them if you feel you can accommodate their request.

            b)   As you exit the runway, be sure to stop only when the aircraft is clear of the runway area (i.e., fully across the hold short markings) and before crossing onto an intersecting taxiway or parallel runway.

         2)   ATC will instruct you to contact ground control for a clearance to taxi.

            a)   You should complete the after-landing checklist before you contact ground control for taxi.

            b)   Once you contact ground control and receive your taxi clearance to the appropriate FBO or location on the field, you should review the intended taxi route before you begin moving.

            c)   Ask for a "progressive taxi" if you are unfamiliar with or unsure of airport procedures.

            d)   Maintain radio contact at all times with ATC until you enter the parking ramp area.

3) FBO ground personnel, or linemen, will often direct you with hand signals to tell you where to taxi and to park your airplane on the ramp.

   a) Some FBOs have their own designated frequency to contact for parking instructions when on their ramp.

   b) At most transient ramps, you should not use your parking brake because the FBO personnel frequently move aircraft.

      i) The normal procedure is to lock the airplane with parking brakes off– wheel chocks or tie-downs secure the airplane.

      ii) Flight controls should be secured per the POH/AFM.

b. Non-towered airports

   1) After landing, clear the runway in a timely fashion.

      a) Exit at the first available taxiway or on a taxiway.

      b) As you exit the runway, be sure to stop only when the aircraft is clear of the runway area (i.e., fully across the hold short markings) and before crossing onto an intersecting taxiway or parallel runway.

         i) After coming to a stop you should make a radio call on the CTAF that you "are clear of runway ____," and complete the after-landing checklist.

         - On a soft field, the after-landing checklist should normally be accomplished only after you have parked your airplane.
         - Some items can be done while taxiing (e.g., turning the carburetor heat OFF if it was used).
         - You should maintain control of the airplane and, on a soft field, come to a complete stop only at the point at which you are parking your airplane.

         ii) Review your intended route of taxi and then make the radio call on the CTAF informing who you are, where you are (e.g., intersection), and where you are intending to taxi to (e.g., name of FBO).

c. Parking

   1) Unless parking in a designated, supervised area, the pilot should select a location and heading that will prevent the propeller or jet blast of other airplanes from striking the airplane broadside.

   2) Whenever possible, the airplane should be parked headed into the existing or forecast wind.

   3) After stopping on the desired heading, the airplane should be allowed to roll straight ahead enough to straighten the nosewheel or tailwheel.

d. Securing

   1) After engine shutdown and deplaning passengers, you should accomplish a postflight inspection.

      a) This includes the general condition of the aircraft.

      b) For a departure, the oil should be checked and fuel added if required.

      c) If the airplane is going to be inactive, it is good operating practice to fill the tanks to the top to prevent water condensation from forming.

   2) When the flight is completed for the day, the aircraft should be hangared or tied down and the flight controls secured.

5. **The applicant demonstrates understanding of visual indicators for wind.**

    a.   For information on visual indicators for wind, see Study Unit 9, Subunit 2, beginning on page 78.

6. **The applicant demonstrates understanding of airport information resources (Chart Supplements U.S., airport diagrams, and appropriate publications).**

    a.   For information on airport information resources, see Study Unit 21, Subunit 1, item A.6., on page 248.

7. **The applicant demonstrates understanding of good cockpit discipline during taxi.**

    a.   For information on good cockpit discipline during taxi, see Study Unit 21, Subunit 1, item A.7., on page 249.

8. **The applicant demonstrates understanding of appropriate taxi speeds.**

    a.   A safe taxi speed is approximately the pace of a brisk walk.

    b.   The primary requirements for safe taxiing are

       1)   Positive control
       2)   The ability to recognize potential hazards in time to avoid them
       3)   The ability to stop or turn where and when desired without undue reliance on the brakes

    c.   Pilots should proceed at a cautious speed on congested or busy ramps.

    d.   Normally, the speed should be at the rate where movement of the airplane is dependent on the throttle. That is, slow enough so when the throttle is closed, the airplane can be stopped promptly.

    e.   When taxiing, it is best to slow down before attempting a turn. Sharp, high-speed turns place undesirable side loads on the landing gear and may result in an uncontrollable swerve or a ground loop.

9. **The applicant demonstrates understanding of procedures for appropriate cockpit activities during taxiing including taxi route planning, briefing the location of Hot Spots, and communicating and coordinating with ATC.**

    a.   For information on appropriate cockpit activities during taxiing, see Study Unit 21, Subunit 1, item A.8., beginning on page 249.

10. **The applicant demonstrates understanding of procedures unique to night operations.**

    a.   For information on procedures unique to night operations, see Study Unit 21, Subunit 1, item A.10., on page 250.

11. **The applicant demonstrates understanding of hazards of low visibility operations.**

    a.   For information on the hazards of low visibility operations, see Study Unit 21, Subunit 1, item A.11., on page 250.

12. **The applicant demonstrates understanding of the importance of documenting any in-flight/post-flight discrepancies.**

    a.   Any discrepancies should be noted, such as gauges or instruments not operating correctly.

    b.   Pilots flying the same aircraft are dependent on you to raise any particular issues with the aircraft so they can be resolved.

       1)   Often instrument or engine failures show signs before complete failure. By alerting the owner/operator of the aircraft, he or she may be able to prevent a future incident.

13. **The applicant demonstrates understanding of National Transportation Safety Board (NTSB) accident/incident reporting.**

    a.   Even when no injuries occur to occupants, an airplane accident resulting in substantial damage must be reported to the nearest NTSB field office immediately.

    b.   The following incidents must also be reported immediately to the NTSB:

        1)   Inability of any required crewmember to perform normal flight duties because of in-flight injury or illness

        2)   In-flight fire

        3)   Flight control system malfunction or failure

        4)   An overdue airplane that is believed to be involved in an accident

        5)   An airplane collision in flight

        6)   Turbine (jet) engine failures

    c.   The operator of an aircraft shall file a report on Board Form 6120.1/2 within 10 days after an accident.

        1)   A report must be filed after 7 days if an overdue aircraft is still missing.

END OF KNOWLEDGE ELEMENT

54.2 RISK MANAGEMENT

A.   Task Objectives

1.   **The applicant demonstrates the ability to identify, assess, and mitigate risks encompassing distractions during aircraft taxi and parking.**

   a.   For information on distractions during aircraft taxi and parking, see Study Unit 21, Subunit 2, item A.1., on page 251.

2.   **The applicant demonstrates the ability to identify, assess, and mitigate risks encompassing the proximity of other aircraft, vehicles, and people when operating on airport surfaces.**

   a.   An awareness of other aircraft that are taking off, landing, or taxiing, and consideration for the right-of-way of others is essential to safety.

   b.   When taxiing, the pilot's eyes should be looking outside the airplane, to the sides, as well as the front.

      1)   The pilot must be aware of the entire area around the airplane to ensure that the airplane will clear all obstructions and other aircraft.

      2)   If at any time there is doubt about the clearance from an object, the pilot should stop the airplane and have someone check the clearance.

      3)   It may be necessary to have the airplane towed or physically moved by a ground crew.

3.   **The applicant demonstrates the ability to identify, assess, and mitigate risks encompassing spinning propellers.**

   a.   It is particularly tragic that propeller to person accidents have included airmen, bystanders, passengers, and children.

   b.   Propeller to person accidents differ from other aircraft accidents in that they usually result in fatal or serious injuries.

      1)   A propeller rotating under power, even at slow idling speed, has sufficient force to inflict serious injury.

      2)   A rotating propeller is extremely dangerous and should be treated with all due caution.

   c.   The propeller is difficult to see when in operation, and the nonprofessional public is often not aware of its danger. Even personnel familiar with the danger of a turning propeller are likely to become complacent.

   d.   Persons directly involved with enplaning or deplaning passengers and aircraft servicing should be instructed as to their specific duties through proper training, with emphasis placed on the dangers of rotating propellers.

   e.   Ramp attendants and passenger handling personnel should be made aware of the proper procedures and methods of directing passengers to and from parked aircraft.

   f.   Treat all propellers as though the ignition switches are "on."

   g.   After an engine run and before the engine is shut down, perform an ignition switch test to detect a faulty ignition switch. Follow the manufacturer's recommendations for the switch test and the procedures to be followed if a faulty switch is found. Applicable airworthiness directive requirements related to ignition switches have been issued to help locate and eliminate faulty switches.

   h.   Boarding or deplaning of passengers with an engine running should only be allowed under close supervision.

   i.   If your propeller strikes anything, you should not continue until an A&P mechanic inspects the propeller and engine.

      1)   You may also have to notify the NTSB, airport manager, or aircraft owner depending on what you hit.

4. **The applicant demonstrates the ability to identify, assess, and mitigate risks encompassing failure to manage tasks during taxi and parking.**

   a. Improper task management can create unnecessary hazards and greatly affect the safety of taxi operations. Good cockpit habits in planning, prioritizing, and sequencing of tasks must be formed early in training to prevent runway incursions and the possibility of a ground collision.

   b. For more information on task management, see Study Unit 6, Subunit 1, beginning on page 49.

5. **The applicant demonstrates the ability to identify, assess, and mitigate risks encompassing confirmation or expectation bias.**

   a. For information on expectation bias, see Study Unit 7, Subunit 5, on page 68.

6. **The applicant demonstrates the ability to identify, assess, and mitigate risks encompassing failure to manage the automation.**

   a. For information on automation management, see Study Unit 6, Subunit 3, beginning on page 51.

7. **The applicant demonstrates the ability to identify, assess, and mitigate risks encompassing airport security.**

   a. The general aviation (GA) community should be concerned with threats posed to general aviation to better learn and understand security awareness.

   b. Actively seeking to learn about security incidents that have occurred at your airport in the past can aid in the prevention of similar incidents occurring in the future.

   c. All possible rule violations and security weaknesses must be analyzed and potentially reported.

      1) General aviation security is designed to preclude

         a) Criminal activity
         b) Terrorist activity
         c) Other illegal activity

   d. Suspicious activity may be defined as activity that creates uneasiness or uncertainty without being criminal or illegal.

   e. Certain activities and/or behaviors in and of themselves may not be suspicious. However, combinations of multiple signs may indicate a higher degree of suspicious activity than individual signs.

   f. Report suspicious circumstances or unusual activity.

      1) Display proper identification, if required at your facility.
      2) Use proper entrances and exits and proper entrance/exit procedures.

   g. There are four primary GA security practices:

      1) Question the individual.
      2) Report the suspicious activity to a supervisor or other facility manager.
      3) Contact local law enforcement.
      4) Contact the General Aviation hotline or Transportation Security Operations Center (TSOC) at (866) GA-SECURE (866-427-3287). The "E" at the end of "SECURE" is correct. It is there for word memory purposes. If you dial 866-427-3287 and 3 (for the last "E"), you will still be connected to TSA.

   h. Most potential security issues will be resolved by questioning individuals and reporting your observations to an FBO employee.

8. **The applicant demonstrates the ability to identify, assess, and mitigate risks encompassing failure to maintain directional control after landing or during taxi.**

    a. The landing process must never be considered complete until the airplane decelerates to the normal taxi speed during the landing roll or has been brought to a complete stop when clear of the landing area.

        1) Many accidents have occurred as a result of pilots abandoning their vigilance and positive control after getting the airplane on the ground.

    b. The pilot must be alert for directional control difficulties immediately upon and after touchdown due to the ground friction on the wheels.

        1) Loss of directional control may lead to an aggravated, uncontrolled, tight turn on the ground (a ground loop) causing the airplane to tip or lean enough for the outside wingtip to contact the ground.

            a) This may even impose a sideward force, which could collapse the landing gear.

    c. Use rudder and ailerons just as you would in the air, but realize that as speed slows, their effectiveness will be reduced.

    d. Use careful application of brakes; maximum brake effectiveness is just short of the point where skidding occurs.

        1) If the brakes are applied so hard that skidding takes place, braking becomes ineffective.

        2) Skidding can be stopped by releasing the brake pressure.

        3) Braking effectiveness is not enhanced by alternately applying and reapplying brake pressure.

        4) Brakes should be applied firmly and smoothly as necessary.

        5) Caution must be exercised when applying brakes to avoid overcontrolling.

    e. Put maximum weight on wheels after touchdown to obtain maximum braking performance and proper touchdown technique to maintain directional control.

    f. Once the airplane has slowed sufficiently and has turned on to the taxiway and stopped, the pilot should retract the flaps and clean up the airplane.

END OF RISK MANAGEMENT ELEMENT

54.3 SKILLS

A. Task Objectives

1. **The applicant demonstrates the ability to maintain directional control after touchdown while decelerating to an appropriate speed.**

    a. Maintain directional control after touchdown while decelerating by doing the following:

        1) Use rudder to control yaw just as you would in the air.

            a) Rudder effectiveness is dependent on airflow over the control surface, which is dependent upon speed.

            b) As speed decreases and the nosewheel has been lowered to the ground, the steerable nose provides more positive directional control.

        2) Use brakes to not only reduce speed on the ground, but also as an aid in directional control when more positive control is required than could be obtained with rudder or nose wheel steering alone.

        3) After touchdown, gently lower the nosewheel to the runway to maintain directional control.

            a) Do not force the nosewheel onto the runway.

                i) Back pressure should be applied to the controls without lifting the nosewheel off the runway.

                    • This will enable the pilot to maintain directional control while keeping weight on the main wheels.

            b) Carefully apply the brakes after the nosewheel is on the ground and directional control is established.

        4) During the ground roll, direction of movement can be changed by carefully applying pressure on one brake or uneven pressures on each brake in the desired direction.

            a) Caution must be exercised when applying brakes to avoid overcontrolling.

        5) Ailerons should be used to keep the wings level during the after-landing roll much the same way they were used in flight.

            a) If a wing starts to rise, aileron control should be applied toward that wing to lower it.

            b) The amount required will depend on speed because as the forward speed of the airplane decreases, the ailerons will become less effective.

        6) After the airplane is on the ground, back-elevator pressure may be gradually relaxed to place normal weight on the nosewheel to aid in better steering.

            a) If available runway permits, the speed of the airplane should be allowed to dissipate in a normal manner.

    b. Make sure the airplane has been slowed to normal taxi speed before turning off the landing runway.

2. **The applicant demonstrates the ability to utilize runway incursion avoidance procedures after landing.**

    a. For information on runway incursion avoidance, see Study Unit 7, Subunit 2, beginning on page 61.

3. **The applicant demonstrates the ability to park in an appropriate area, considering the safety of nearby persons and property.**

   a. Your airplane should be parked on the ramp in a way that facilitates taxiing and parking by other aircraft, and to avoid being struck by other airplanes or their prop/jet wash.

      1) Frequently, airport ramps are marked with painted lines that indicate where and how to park. Airplane tiedown ropes (or chains) also may mark parking spots.

         a) However, these markings do not guarantee adequate spacing from other parked airplanes. You must ensure proper spacing.

      2) Almost always, there are three ropes provided for each airplane: one rope positioned for the middle of each wing and one rope to tie the tail. If the ramp is not paved, each of the tiedown ropes (chains) is usually marked by a tire.

   b. You should chock and/or tie down your airplane so it cannot roll or be blown into another aircraft or other object.

   c. At most transient ramps, you should **not** use your parking brake because the FBO personnel frequently move aircraft.

      1) The normal procedure is to lock the airplane with parking brakes off; wheel chocks or tie-downs secure the airplane.

      2) In many airplanes, leaving the brake on is not recommended because it may cause the hydraulic lines to burst.

4. **The applicant demonstrates the ability to plan the taxi route to the ramp.**

   a. If you are at an uncontrolled field, examine the airport diagram and taxi to your destination by crossing the fewest number of runways.

      1) Crossing runways adds to the risk of having a fatal collision.

5. **The applicant demonstrates the ability to follow the appropriate procedure for engine shutdown.**

   a. Follow the procedures prescribed in your POH/AFM for shutting down the engine and securing the cockpit.

6. **The applicant demonstrates the ability to complete the after landing checklist after the airplane has stopped.**

   a. You should complete the after-landing checklist after the entire aircraft has crossed the hold short line and you have come to a complete stop.

   b. At a controlled airport, ATC will instruct you to contact ground control for a clearance to taxi.

      1) You should contact ground control for taxi after you have completed the after-landing checklist for your airplane.

7. **The applicant demonstrates the ability to complete the engine shutdown checklist.**

   a. Complete the engine shutdown checklist provided in your POH/AFM.

8. **The applicant demonstrates the ability to disembark passengers safely and remain aware of passenger movement while on the ramp area.**

   a. Provide instructions to passengers on how to safely walk from your plane to the FBO.

      1) Escort your passengers to and from the airplane and FBO.

      2) Keep a vigilant eye on your passengers to ensure they are compliant with your directions.

9. **The applicant demonstrates the ability to record aircraft discrepancies and notes for possible service needs before the next flight.**

    a. Note any discrepancy with the aircraft. This includes mechanical, flight characteristics, or avionics.

    b. Inform the owner/operator of the issues during the flight so the aircraft can be repaired.

10. **The applicant demonstrates the ability to conduct an appropriate post flight inspection and secure the aircraft.**

    a. You should inspect the outside of your airplane for any damage that may have occurred during the flight.

    b. You should also inspect the underside of the fuselage to note any excessive oil being blown out of the engine.

    c. Finally, note any malfunctions (discrepancies) in the proper logbooks, and signal to other pilots when an unairworthy condition exists. Always take the airplane out of service if there is an airworthiness problem.

    d. Once the engine has been shut down, you should secure the cockpit by gathering all personal items and ensuring that all trash is removed from the airplane.

    1) Professionalism and courtesy dictate that the airplane be left as it was found.

    e. Hangar storage is the best means of protecting aircraft from the elements, flying debris, vehicles, vandals, etc. Even in hangars, airplanes should be chocked to avoid scrapes and bumps from rolling.

    f. Airplanes stored outside are normally tied down.

    1) Chains or ropes are used to secure the airplane to the ground from three locations on the airplane: usually, the midpoint of each wing and the tail.

    2) Tiedown hooks or eyelets are provided at these locations on most airplanes.

    g. When leaving the airplane tied down for an extended period of time or when expecting windy weather, you should install the control or gust locks that hold the control yoke stationary so the control surfaces cannot bang back and forth in the wind.

    1) On older planes, this is sometimes accomplished by clamping the aileron, elevator, and rudder to adjacent stationary surfaces so they cannot move.

    2) Alternatively, the control yoke (or stick) can be secured tightly with a seatbelt.

    h. Consider filling the fuel tanks to the top to prevent water condensation from forming if the airplane will be inactive for a long period of time.

END OF SKILLS ELEMENT

54.4 COMMON ERRORS

A.   Common Errors during After Landing, Parking, and Securing

    1.   **Hazards resulting from failure to follow recommended procedures**

        a.   The checklist for postflight procedures is as important as those for any other situation. You must follow recommended procedures to prevent creating unsafe situations.

    2.   **Poor planning, improper technique, or faulty judgment in performance of postflight procedures**

        a.   Just because this is the end of a flight, do not rush or slip into bad habits in conducting postflight procedures.

        b.   This task must be approached in the same professional manner as the preflight and flying procedures.

END OF COMMON ERRORS

ABBREVIATIONS AND ACRONYMS IN
PRIVATE PILOT FLIGHT MANEUVERS AND PRACTICAL TEST PREP

14 CFR	Title 14 of the Code of Federal Regulations
A&P	certified mechanic
AATD	advanced aviation training device
AC	advisory circular or convective outlook bulletin
ACS	Airman Certification Standards
AD	airworthiness directive
ADC	air data computer
ADIZ	Air Defense Identification Zone
ADM	aeronautical decision making
AFM	Airplane Flight Manual
AGL	above ground level
AHRS	attitude and heading reference system
AI	attitude indicator
AIM	*Aeronautical Information Manual*
AIRMET	Airmen's Meteorological Information
ALT	altimeter
AME	aviation medical examiner
AOA	angle of attack
ASEL	airplane single-engine land
ASI	airspeed indicator
ASOS	automated surface observing system
ATC	air traffic control
ATD	aviation training device
ATIS	Automatic Terminal Information System
AWC	aviation weather center
AWOS	automated weather observing system
AWSS	automated weather sensor system
AWW	severe weather forecast alert
BATD	Basic Aviation Training Devices
BECMG	becoming
CAS	calibrated airspeed
CAT	clear air turbulence
CDI	course deviation indicator
CFI	certificated flight instructor
CFIT	controlled flight into terrain
CG	center of gravity
CRM	crew resource management
CTAF	Common Traffic Advisory Frequency
CWA	center weather advisory
DF	direction finding
DH	decision height
DME	distance measuring equipment
DOD	department of defense
DP	departure procedure
DUATS	Direct User Access Terminal System
EFD	electronic flight display
EFIS	electronic flight information system
ELSA	experimental light-sport aircraft
ELT	emergency locator transmitter
ETA	estimated time of arrival
ETE	estimated time en route
FA	area forecast
FAA	Federal Aviation Administration
FADEC	full authority digital engine control
FAR	Federal Aviation Regulations
FB	winds and temperatures aloft forecast
FBO	fixed-base operator
FFS	full flight simulator
FIP	forecast icing potential
FL	flight level
FMS	flight management system
fpm	feet per minute
FRZ	flight restricted zone
FSDO	Flight Standards District Office

FSS	flight service station
FSTD	flight simulation training device
FTD	flight training device
GA	general aviation
GAJSC	general aviation joint steering committee
GMT	Greenwich Mean Time
GPH	gallons per hour
GPS	global positioning system
GPWS	Ground Proximity Warning System
HI	heading indicator
HIWAS	hazardous inflight weather advisory service
HSI	horizontal situation indicator
IA	inspection authorization
IAP	instrument approach procedure
IAS	indicated airspeed
ICAO	International Civil Aviation Organization
IFR	instrument flight rules
ILS	instrument landing system
IMC	instrument meteorological conditions
KOEL	kinds of operation equipment list
L/D_{MAX}	best lift/drag
LAA	local airport advisory
LAHSO	land and hold short operations
LLWAS	low-level wind shear alert system
LOC	ILS localizer
LRU	line replaceable unit
MC	magnetic course
MDA	minimum descent altitude
MEF	maximum elevation figure
MEL	minimum equipment list
METAR	aviation routine weather report
MFD	multi-function display
MH	magnetic heading
MOA	military operations areas
MP	manifold pressure
MSA	minimum safe altitude
MSL	mean seal level
MTR	military training routes
MVFR	marginal VFR
NAS	National Airspace System
NAVAID	navigational aid
NEXRAD	next generation radar
NM	nautical miles
NOTAM	notice to airmen
NSA	national security areas
NTSB	National Transportation Safety Board
NWS	National Weather Service
OAT	outside air temperature
OBS	omnibearing selector
PAPI	precision approach path indicator
PFD	primary flight display
PIC	pilot in command
PIM	Pilot's Information Manual
PIREP	pilot weather report
POH	Pilot's Operating Handbook
PROG	short-range surface prognostic
PSK	personal survival kit
RAIM	receiver autonomous integrity monitoring
RNAV	area navigation
ROT	rate of turn
RVR	runway visual range
S.B.	service bulletin
SFRA	special flight rule areas
SIGMET	Significant Meteorological Information

SIGWX	significant weather
SM	statute miles
SODA	statement of demonstrated ability
SRM	single-pilot resource management
SSR	secondary surveillance radar
STC	supplemental type certificate
STOL	short takeoff and landing
SUA	special use airspace
T&SI	turn-and-slip indicator
TAC	terminal area chart
TACAN	tactical air navigation
TAF	terminal aerodrome forecast
TAS	true airspeed
TAWS	Terrain Awareness and Warning System
TC	turn coordinator or true course
TCAS	traffic alert and collision avoidance system
TDWR	terminal doppler weather radar
TFR	temporary flight restriction
TIS	traffic information system
TRSA	terminal radar service areas
TSA	Transportation Security Administration
TSOC	transportation security operations center
UTC	universal coordinated time
V_A	design maneuvering speed
VASI	visual approach slope indicator
$V_{Best\ Glide}$	best glide speed
VDP	visual descent point
V_{FE}	maximum flap extended speed
VFR	visual flight rules
VHF	very high frequency
VHF/DF	VHF direction finder
V_{LE}	maximum landing gear extended speed
V_{LO}	maximum landing gear operating speed
VMC	visual meteorological conditions
V_{ME}	maximum endurance speed
V_{NE}	never-exceed speed
V_{NO}	maximum structural cruising speed
VNR	VFR flight not recommended
VOR	VHF omnidirectional range
VOR/LOC	VOR/localizer
VORTAC	co-located VOR and TACAN
V_R	rotation speed
V_{S1}	stalling speed in a specified configuration
VSI	vertical speed indicator
V_{SO}	stalling speed in the landing configuration
VV	vertical visibility
V_X	best angle of climb speed
V_Y	best rate of climb speed
WA	AIRMET
WAAS	Wide Area Augmentation System
WCA	wind correction angle
WS	SIGMET
WSP	weather system processor
WST	convective SIGMET

AUTHORS' RECOMMENDATIONS

The Experimental Aircraft Association, Inc., is a very successful and effective nonprofit organization that represents and serves those of us interested in flying, in general, and in sport aviation, in particular. We personally invite you to enjoy becoming a member. Visit their website at www.eaa.org.

Types of EAA Memberships:

$40 - Individual (includes subscription to *EAA Sport Aviation* magazine)
$50 - Family (extends all benefits to member's spouse and children under 18, except for an additional EAA magazine subscription)
Free - Student (for those ages 8 to 18 who have completed the EAA Young Eagles program)
$1,295 - Lifetime

Sign up online at www.eaa.org/en/eaa/eaa-membership/types-of-memberships, email membership@eaa.org, or call (800) JOIN-EAA.

The annual EAA Oshkosh AirVenture is an unbelievable aviation spectacular with over 10,000 airplanes at one airport and virtually everything aviation-oriented you can imagine! Plan to spend at least 1 day (not everything can be seen in a day) in Oshkosh (100 miles northwest of Milwaukee). Visit the AirVenture website at www.airventure.org.

The annual Sun 'n Fun EAA Fly-In is also highly recommended. It is held at the Lakeland, FL (KLAL), airport (between Orlando and Tampa). Visit the Sun 'n Fun website at www.sun-n-fun.org.

AIRCRAFT OWNERS AND PILOTS ASSOCIATION

AOPA is the largest, most influential aviation association in the world, with two thirds of all pilots in the United States as members. AOPA's most important contribution to the world's most accessible, safest, least expensive, friendliest, easiest-to-use general aviation environment is their lobbying on our behalf at the federal, state, and local levels. AOPA also provides legal services, advice, and other assistance to the aviation community.

We recommend that you become an AOPA member to get the most out of AOPA's resources. To join, call 1-800-USA-AOPA or visit the AOPA website at www.aopa.org.

LEARN TO FLY – AOPA

AOPA hosts an informational web page on getting started in aviation. "Learn To Fly" contains information for those still dreaming about flying, those who are ready to begin, and those who are already making the journey. At this site, you can see at a glance what your options are, including approximate costs and how long it will take you. You can also learn more about the types of certificates available for new pilots and about additional ratings for current pilots. In addition, you can find information about FAA medical certification, passing knowledge tests, and choosing a flight school and instructor. Visit www.aopa.org/learntofly today!

INDEX